COMPLETE SOLUTION GUIDE

ALGEBRA 2

SPECIAL EDITION FOR CHALK DUST COMPANY

GERRY C. FITCH

CHALK DUST COMPANY

Houghton Mifflin
Custom Publishing

Custom Publishing Editor: Kyle Henderson
Custom Publishing Production Manager: Kathleen McCourt
Sponsoring Editor: Jack Shira
Managing Editor: Cathy Cantin
Senior Associate Editor: Maureen Ross
Associate Editor: Laura Wheel
Assistant Editor: Carolyn Johnson
Supervising Editor: Karen Carter
Project Editor: Patty Bergin
Editorial Assistant: Christine E. Lee
Art Supervisor: Gary Crespo
Marketing Manager: Ros Kane
Senior Manufacturing Coordinator: Sally Culler
Composition and Art: Meridian Creative Group

Cover design: Galen B. Murphy

Printed in the U.S.A.

ISBN: 0-618-10780-0
3-98462

1 2 3 4 5 6 7 8 9 - CCI - 02 01 00

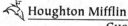 Houghton Mifflin
                     Custom Publishing

222 Berkeley Street • Boston, MA 02116

Address all correspondence and order information to the above address.

Student Solutions Guide for

Intermediate Algebra

Third Edition

Larson/Hostetler

Gerry C. Fitch

Louisiana State University

Houghton Mifflin Company   Boston   New York

Preface

This *Student Solutions Guide* is a supplement to *Intermediate Algebra*, Third Edition by Ron Larson and Robert P. Hostetler. This guide includes solutions for the odd-numbered exercises in the text, including the mid-chapter tests, chapter reviews, chapter tests, and cumulative tests.

These solutions give step-by-step details of each exercise. There are usually several "correct" ways to arrive at a solution to a mathematics problem. Therefore, you should not be concerned if you have approached problems differently than I have. Several accuracy checks have been made to assure that these solutions are correct. Corrections to the solutions or suggestions for improvement are welcome.

Producing this guide has been quite a challenge and a learning experience for me. I would like to thank the editors of Houghton Mifflin Company for allowing me this experience and Larson Texts, Inc. and Meridian Creative Group for their contributions to the production of this guide. And finally, a special word of thanks goes to my husband, Chuck for his support and patience during the writing and proofing of the manuscript.

I hope you will find the *Student Solutions Guide* a helpful supplement as you study algebra.

Gerry C. Fitch
Louisiana State University
Baton Rouge, Louisiana 70803

Part I
Solutions to Integrated Review Exercises

CHAPTER 1   Linear Equations and Inequalities

SECTION 1.1   Linear Equations

1. $5 + x = x + 5$ illustrates the Commutative Property of Addition.

2. $10 \cdot \frac{1}{10} = 1$ illustrates the Multiplicative Inverse Property.

3. $6(x - 2) = 6x - 6 \cdot 2$ illustrates the Distributive Property.

4. $3 + (4 + x) = (3 + 4) + x$ illustrates the Associative Property of Addition.

5. $4 - |-3| = 4 - 3 = 1$

6.
$$-10 - (4 - 18) = -10 - (-14)$$
$$= -10 + 14$$
$$= 4$$

7. $\dfrac{3 - (5 - 20)}{4} = \dfrac{3 - (-15)}{4} = \dfrac{3 + 15}{4} = \dfrac{18}{4} = \dfrac{9}{2}$

8. $\dfrac{|3 - 18|}{3} = \dfrac{|-15|}{3} = \dfrac{15}{3} = 5$

9. $6\left(\dfrac{2}{15}\right) = \dfrac{3 \cdot 2 \cdot 2}{5 \cdot 3} = \dfrac{4}{5}$

10.
$$\frac{7}{12} \div \frac{5}{16} = \frac{7}{12} \cdot \frac{16}{5}$$
$$= \frac{7 \cdot 4 \cdot 4}{4 \cdot 3 \cdot 5}$$
$$= \frac{28}{15}$$

11. Money saved $= \$75(20)(12) = \$18,000$

12. Length of each piece $= \dfrac{135 \text{ feet}}{15} = 9$ feet

SECTION 1.2   Linear Equations and Problem Solving

1. An algebraic expression is a collection of letters (called variables) and real numbers (called constants) combined, using the operations of addition, subtraction, multiplication, and division.

2. The terms of an algebraic expression are those parts separated by addition or subtraction.

3. $a^m \cdot a^n = a^{m+n}$

4. $(ab)^m = a^m b^m$

5. $-360 + 120 = -240$

6. $5(57 - 33) = 5(24) = 120$

7.
$$-\frac{4}{15} \cdot \frac{15}{16} = -\frac{4 \cdot 5 \cdot 3}{5 \cdot 3 \cdot 4 \cdot 4}$$
$$= -\frac{1}{4}$$

8.
$$\frac{3}{8} \div \frac{5}{16} = \frac{3}{8} \cdot \frac{16}{5}$$
$$= \frac{3 \cdot 8 \cdot 2}{8 \cdot 5}$$
$$= \frac{6}{5}$$

9. $(12 - 15)^3 = (-3)^3 = -27$

10. $\left(\frac{5}{8}\right)^2 = \left(\frac{5}{8}\right)\left(\frac{5}{8}\right) = \frac{25}{64}$

11. Perimeter $= x + x + (x + 3) + (3x - 2)$

$\qquad\qquad = (x + x + x + 3x) + (3 - 2)$

$\qquad\qquad = 6x + 1$

12. Perimeter $= (4x + 1) + (2x) + (3x - 1) + x + (x + 2) + (3x)$

$\qquad\qquad = (4x + 2x + 3x + x + x + 3x) + (1 - 1 + 2)$

$\qquad\qquad = 14x + 2$

SECTION 1.3   Business and Scientific Problems

1. The sign of $(-7) + (-3)$ is negative. The rule used is to add two real numbers with like signs, add their absolute values and attach the common sign to the result.

2. The sign of the sum of $-7 + 3$ is negative. The rule used is to add two real numbers with unlike signs, subtract the smaller absolute value from the greater absolute value and attach the sign of the number with the greater absolute value.

3. The sign of $(-6)(-2)$ is positive. The rule used is to multiply two real numbers with like signs, find the product of their absolute values.

4. The sign of the product $6(-2)$ is negative. The rule used is to multiply two real numbers with unlike signs, find the product of their absolute values. The product is negative.

5.
$$2x - 5 = x + 9$$
$$2x - x - 5 = x - x + 9$$
$$x - 5 = 9$$
$$x - 5 + 5 = 9 + 5$$
$$x = 14$$

6.
$$6x + 8 = 8 - 2x$$
$$6x + 2x + 8 = 8 - 2x + 2x$$
$$8x + 8 = 8$$
$$8x + 8 - 8 = 8 - 8$$
$$8x = 0$$
$$\frac{8x}{8} = \frac{0}{8}$$
$$x = 0$$

7.
$$2x + \tfrac{3}{2} = \tfrac{3}{2}$$
$$2x + \tfrac{3}{2} - \tfrac{3}{2} = \tfrac{3}{2} - \tfrac{3}{2}$$
$$2x = 0$$
$$x = 0$$

8.
$$-\frac{x}{10} = 1000$$
$$(-10) \cdot -\frac{x}{10} = 1000(-10)$$
$$x = -10,000$$

9. $-0.35x = 70$
$$\frac{-0.35x}{-0.35} = \frac{70}{-0.35}$$
$$x = -200$$

10. $0.60x = 24$
$$\frac{0.60x}{0.60} = \frac{24}{0.60}$$
$$x = 40$$

11. *Verbal Model:* $\boxed{\begin{array}{c}\text{Length}\\\text{of race}\end{array}} = \boxed{\begin{array}{c}\text{Length of}\\\text{first part}\end{array}} + \boxed{\begin{array}{c}\text{Length of}\\\text{last part}\end{array}}$

Labels: Length of race $= 2.5$

Length of first part $= 1.8$

Length of last part $= x$

Equation: $2.5 = 1.8 + x$

$$2.5 - 1.8 = x$$
$$0.7 \text{ mile} = x$$

12. *Verbal Model:* | Total soybeans | = | Soybeans in January | + | Soybeans in February | + | Soybeans in March |

Equation:

$x = 34\frac{1}{3} + 18\frac{1}{5} + 25\frac{5}{6}$

$x = 34\frac{10}{30} + 18\frac{6}{30} + 25\frac{25}{30}$

$x = (34 + 18 + 25) + \left(\frac{10}{30} + \frac{6}{30} + \frac{25}{30}\right)$

$x = 77\frac{41}{30} = 78\frac{11}{30}$ tons

SECTION 1.4   Linear Inequalities

1. $3yx = 3xy$ illustrates the Commutative Property of Multiplication.

2. $3xy - 3xy = 0$ illustrates the Additive Inverse Property.

3. $6(x - 2) = 6x - 6 \cdot 2$ illustrates the Distributive Property.

4. $3x + 0 = 3x$ illustrates the Additive Identity Property.

5. $x^2 - y^2, x = 4, y = 3$

$4^2 - 3^2 = 16 - 9 = 7$

6. $4s + st, s = 3, t = -4$

$4(3) + 3(-4) = 12 + -12 = 0$

7. $\dfrac{x}{x^2 + y^2}, x = 0, y = 3$

$\dfrac{0}{0^2 + 3^2} = \dfrac{0}{9} = 0$

8. $\dfrac{z^2 + 2}{x^2 - 1}, x = 2, z = -1$

$\dfrac{(-1)^2 + 2}{2^2 - 1} = \dfrac{1 + 2}{4 - 1} = \dfrac{3}{3} = 1$

9. $\dfrac{a}{1 - r}, a = 2, r = \dfrac{1}{2}$

$\dfrac{2}{1 - \frac{1}{2}} = \dfrac{2}{\frac{1}{2}} = 4$

10. $2l + 2w, l = 3, w = 1.5$

$2(3) + 2(1.5) = 6 + 3 = 9$

11. $A = \frac{1}{2}(b_1 + b_2)h$

$A = \frac{1}{2}(7 + 4)3.6$

$A = 19.8$ square meters

12. $A = \frac{1}{2}(b_1 + b_2)h$

$A = \frac{1}{2}(16 + 10)8$

$A = 104$ square feet

SECTION 1.5   Absolute Value Equations and Inequalities

1. If n is an integer, $2n$ is an even integer and $2n + 1$ is an odd integer.

2. $-2x^4$ and $(-2x)^4$ are not equal. By order of operations $-2x^4 = -2x^4$ and $(-2x)^4 = 16x^4$.

3. $\dfrac{35}{14} = \dfrac{7 \cdot 5}{7 \cdot 2} = \dfrac{5}{2}$

Divide the numerator and denominator by 7 to put the fraction in simplified form.

4. $\dfrac{4}{5} \div \dfrac{z}{3} = \dfrac{4}{5} \cdot \dfrac{3}{z} = \dfrac{12}{5z}$

To divide fractions, multiply by the reciprocal of the divisor.

5. $-3.2 < 2$ because -3.2 is to the left of 2 on the number line.

6. $-3.2 > -4.1$ because -3.2 is to the right of -4.1 on the number line.

7. $-\frac{3}{4} > -5$ because $-\frac{3}{4}$ is to the right of -5 on the number line.

8. $-\frac{1}{5} > -\frac{1}{3}$ because $-\frac{1}{5}\left(-\frac{3}{15}\right)$ is to the right of $-\frac{1}{3}\left(-\frac{5}{15}\right)$ on the number line.

9. $\pi > -3$ because π is to the right of -3 on the number line.

10. $6 < \frac{13}{2}$ because 6 is to the left of $\frac{13}{2}\left(6\frac{1}{2}\right)$ on the number line.

11. *Verbal Model:* $\boxed{\text{Difference}} = \boxed{\begin{array}{c}\text{Actual}\\\text{expense}\end{array}} - \boxed{\begin{array}{c}\text{Budgeted}\\\text{amount}\end{array}}$

Equation: $x = 163{,}356 - 162{,}700$

$x = \$656$ which is more than $500.

12. *Verbal Model:* $\boxed{\text{Difference}} = \boxed{\begin{array}{c}\text{Actual}\\\text{expense}\end{array}} - \boxed{\begin{array}{c}\text{Budgeted}\\\text{amount}\end{array}}$

Equation: $x = |42{,}335 - 42{,}640|$

$x = |-305| = \$305$ which is less than $500.

CHAPTER 2   Graphs and Functions

SECTION 2.1   The Rectangular Coordinate System

1. $3x = 7$ is a linear equation because it can be written in the form $ax + b = 0$. Since $x^2 + 3x = 2$ cannot be written in the form $ax + b = 0$, it is not a linear equation.

2. To check $x = 3$ is a solution of the equation $5x - 4 = 11$ substitute 3 for x in the equation. If the result is true, $x = 3$ is a solution.

3. $6x(2x^2) = (6 \cdot 2) \cdot (x \cdot x^2) = 12x^3$

4. $3t^2 \cdot t^4 = 3t^{2+4} = 3t^6$

5. $-(-3x^2)^3(2x^4) = (-1)(-3)^3(2)(x^2)^3(x^4)$
$$= (-1)(-27)(2)(x^6)(x^4)$$
$$= 54x^{10}$$

6. $(4x^3y^2)(-2xy^3) = (4)(-2)(x^3)(x)(y^2)(y^3)$
$$= -8x^4y^5$$

7. $4 - 3(2x + 1) = 4 - 6x - 3 = 1 - 6x$

8. $5(x + 2) - 4(2x - 3) = 5x + 10 - 8x + 12$
$$= -3x + 22$$

9. $24\left(\dfrac{y}{3} + \dfrac{y}{6}\right) = 8y + 4y = 12y$

10. $0.12x + 0.05(2000 - 2x) = 0.12x + 100 - 0.1x$
$$= 0.02x + 100$$

11. Your rate $= \frac{1}{4}$ job per hour

Friend's rate $= \frac{1}{5}$ job per hour

Verbal model: $\boxed{\begin{array}{c}\text{Work}\\\text{done}\end{array}} = \boxed{\begin{array}{c}\text{Work done}\\\text{by you}\end{array}} + \boxed{\begin{array}{c}\text{Work done}\\\text{by friend}\end{array}}$

Labels: Work done $= 1$

Your rate $= \dfrac{1}{4}$

Friend's rate $= \dfrac{1}{5}$

Time $= t$

—CONTINUED—

11. —CONTINUED—

Equation:

$$1 = \frac{1}{4}t + \frac{1}{5}t$$

$$1 = \left(\frac{1}{4} + \frac{1}{5}\right)t$$

$$1 = \left(\frac{9}{20}\right)t$$

$$\frac{1}{\frac{9}{20}} = t$$

$$\frac{20}{9} = t \approx 2.2 \text{ hours}$$

12. *Verbal model:*

$$\boxed{\text{Distance}} = \boxed{\text{Rate}} \cdot \boxed{\text{Time}}$$

Labels: Distance = 200 miles at 50 mph

200 miles at 42 mph

400 miles at x mph

Rate = 50, 42, x

$$\text{Time} = \frac{200}{50} + \frac{200}{42} \text{ or } \frac{400}{x}$$

Equation:

$$\frac{200}{50} + \frac{200}{42} = \frac{400}{x}$$

$$4 + \frac{100}{21} = \frac{400}{x}$$

$$\frac{184}{21} = \frac{400}{x}$$

$$x = \frac{21(400)}{184} \approx 45.65 \text{ mph}$$

SECTION 2.2   Graphs of Equations

1. If $t - 3 > 7$ and c is an algebraic expression, then
$t - 3 + c > 7 + c$.

2. If $t - 3 < 7$ and $c < 0$, then $(t - 3)c > 7c$.

3. Multiplicative Inverse Property:

$$y\left(\frac{1}{y}\right) = 1$$

4. $u + v = v + u$ illustrates the Commutative Property of Addition.

5. $2x + 3 \geq 5$

$2x + 3 - 3 \geq 5 - 3$

$2x \geq 2$

$\dfrac{2x}{2} \geq \dfrac{2}{2}$

$x \geq 1$

6. $5 - 3x > 14$

$5 - 5 - 3x > 14 - 5$

$-3x > 9$

$\dfrac{-3x}{-3} < \dfrac{9}{-3}$

$x < -3$

7. $-4 < 10x + 1 < 6$

$-4 - 1 < 10x + 1 - 1 < 6 - 1$

$-5 < 10x < 5$

$\dfrac{-5}{10} < \dfrac{10x}{10} < \dfrac{5}{10}$

$\dfrac{-1}{2} < x < \dfrac{1}{2}$

8. $-2 \leq 1 - 2x \leq 2$

$-2 - 1 \leq 1 - 1 - 2x \leq 2 - 1$

$-3 \leq -2x \leq 1$

$\dfrac{-3}{-2} \geq \dfrac{-2x}{-2} \geq \dfrac{1}{-2}$

$\dfrac{3}{2} \geq x \geq \dfrac{-1}{2}$

$\dfrac{-1}{2} \leq x \leq \dfrac{3}{2}$

9. $-3 \leq -\dfrac{x}{2} \leq 3$

$2 \cdot -3 \leq 2 \cdot -\dfrac{x}{2} \leq 3 \cdot 2$

$-6 \leq -x \leq 6$

$\dfrac{-6}{-1} \geq \dfrac{-x}{-1} \geq \dfrac{6}{-1}$

$6 \geq x \geq -6$

$-6 \leq x \leq 6$

10. $-5 < x - 25 < 5$

$-5 + 25 < x - 25 + 25 < 5 + 25$

$20 < x < 30$

11. *Verbal model:*

$$\boxed{\begin{array}{c}\text{Compared}\\\text{number}\end{array}} = \boxed{\text{Percent}} \cdot \boxed{\begin{array}{c}\text{Base}\\\text{number}\end{array}}$$

Labels: Compared number $= a$

Percent $= p$

Base number $= b$

Equation: $a = pb$

$32{,}500 = 1.12b$

$\dfrac{32{,}500}{1.12} = b$

$\$29{,}018 \approx b$

12. *Verbal model:*

$$\boxed{\begin{array}{c}\text{Compared}\\\text{number}\end{array}} = \boxed{\text{Percent}} \cdot \boxed{\begin{array}{c}\text{Base}\\\text{number}\end{array}}$$

Labels:

Compared number $= a$

Percent $= p$

Base number $= b$

Equation:

$a = pb$

$a = (0.035)(3100)$

$a = \$108.50$

SECTION 2.3   Slope and Graphs of Linear Equations

1. Two equations having the same set of solutions are called equivalent.

2. $12x - 5 = 13$

$\qquad 12x = 13 + 5$

3. $x + \dfrac{x}{2} = 4$

$2\left(x + \dfrac{x}{2}\right) = (4)2$

$2x + x = 8$

$3x = 8$

$\dfrac{3x}{3} = \dfrac{8}{3}$

$x = \dfrac{8}{3}$

4. $\dfrac{1}{3}x + 1 = 10$

$3\left(\dfrac{1}{3}x + 1\right) = (10)3$

$x + 3 = 30$

$x = 27$

5. $-4(x - 5) = 0$

$-4x + 20 = 0$

$-4x = -20$

$\dfrac{-4x}{-4} = \dfrac{-20}{-4}$

$x = 5$

6. $\dfrac{3}{8}x + \dfrac{3}{4} = 2$

$8\left(\dfrac{3}{8}x + \dfrac{3}{4}\right) = (2)8$

$3x + 6 = 16$

$3x = 10$

$x = \dfrac{10}{3}$

7. $8(x - 14) = 32$

$8x - 112 = 32$

$8x = 144$

$\dfrac{8x}{8} = \dfrac{144}{8}$

$x = 18$

8. $12(3 - x) = 5 - 7(2x + 1)$

$36 - 12x = 5 - 14x - 7$

$36 - 12x = -14x - 2$

$36 + 2x = -2$

$2x = -38$

$x = -19$

9. $-(2x + 8) + \dfrac{1}{3}(6x + 5) = 0$

$\quad\quad -2x - 8 + 2x + \dfrac{5}{3} = 0$

$\quad\quad\quad\quad \dfrac{-24}{3} + \dfrac{5}{3} = 0$

$\quad\quad\quad\quad\quad \dfrac{-19}{3} \neq 0$

No solution

10. $(1 + r)500 = 550$

$\quad\quad 1 + r = \dfrac{550}{500}$

$\quad\quad 1 + r = 1.1$

$\quad\quad\quad\; r = 1.1 - 1$

$\quad\quad\quad\; r = 0.1$

11. *Verbal model:*

$$\boxed{\begin{array}{c}\text{Total} \\ \text{cost}\end{array}} = \boxed{\begin{array}{c}\text{Cost of} \\ \text{first minute}\end{array}} + 0.45\boxed{\begin{array}{c}\text{Number of} \\ \text{additional} \\ \text{minutes}\end{array}}$$

Labels:

Total cost = \$11

Cost of first minute = \$1.10

Number of additional minutes = x

Inequality:

$11 \geq 1.10 + 0.45t > 1.10$

$9.9 \geq 0.45t > 0$

$22 \geq t > 0$

$0 < t \leq 22$

$0 < t \leq 23$ (with first minute)

12. $0.65m + 4500 < 20{,}000$

$\quad\quad 0.65m < 15{,}500$

$\quad\quad\quad\;\; m < 23{,}846$

SECTION 2.4 Equations of Lines

1. The ratio of the real number a to the real number b is $\dfrac{a}{b}$.

2. $\dfrac{4}{5} = \dfrac{12}{u}$ is a proportion.

3. *Verbal model:*

$$\boxed{\begin{array}{c}\text{Compared} \\ \text{number}\end{array}} = \boxed{\text{Percent}} \cdot \boxed{\text{Base number}}$$

Labels:

Compared number = a

Percent = p

Base number = b

Equation:

$a = p \cdot b$

$a = 0.075 \cdot 25$

$a = 1.875$

4. *Verbal model:* $\boxed{\text{Compared number}} = \boxed{\text{Percent}} \cdot \boxed{\text{Base number}}$

Labels: Compared number $= a$

Percent $= p$

Base number $= b$

Equation: $a = pb$

$a = 1.50(6000)$

$a = 9000$

5. *Verbal model:* $\boxed{\text{Compared number}} = \boxed{\text{Percent}} \cdot \boxed{\text{Base number}}$

Labels: Compared number $= a$

Percent $= p$

Base number $= b$

Equation: $a = p \cdot b$

$225 = p \cdot 150$

$\frac{225}{150} = p$

$1.5 = p$

$150\% = p$

6. *Verbal model:* $\boxed{\text{Compared number}} = \boxed{\text{Percent}} \cdot \boxed{\text{Base number}}$

Labels: Compared number $= a$

Percent $= p$

Base number $= b$

Equation: $a = pb$

$93 = p \cdot 600$

$\frac{93}{600} = p$

$0.155 = p$

$15.5\% = p$

7. *Verbal model:* $\boxed{\begin{array}{c}\text{Compared}\\\text{number}\end{array}} = \boxed{\text{Percent}} \cdot \boxed{\text{Base number}}$

Labels: Compared number $= a$

Percent $= p$

Base number $= b$

Equation: $a = p \cdot b$

$160 = p \cdot 240$

$\frac{160}{240} = p$

$0.66\frac{2}{3} = p$

$66\frac{2}{3}\% = p$

8. *Verbal model:* $\boxed{\begin{array}{c}\text{Compared}\\\text{number}\end{array}} = \boxed{\text{Percent}} \cdot \boxed{\text{Base number}}$

Labels: Compared number $= a$

Percent $= p$

Base number $= b$

Equation: $a = pb$

$42 = 0.12b$

$\frac{42}{0.12} = b$

$350 = b$

9. *Verbal model:* $\boxed{\begin{array}{c}\text{Compared}\\\text{number}\end{array}} = \boxed{\text{Percent}} \cdot \boxed{\text{Base number}}$

Labels: Compared number $= a$

Percent $= p$

Base number $= b$

Equation: $a = pb$

$400 = 0.005b$

$\frac{400}{0.005} = b$

$80,000 = b$

10. *Verbal model:* $\boxed{\begin{array}{c}\text{Compared}\\\text{number}\end{array}} = \boxed{\text{Percent}} \cdot \boxed{\text{Base number}}$

Labels: Compared number $= a$

Percent $= p$

Base number $= b$

Equation: $a = pb$

$132 = 0.48b$

$\frac{132}{0.48} = b$

$275 = b$

11. *Verbal model:*

$$\boxed{\dfrac{\text{Cement}}{\text{Sand}}} = \boxed{\dfrac{\text{Cement}}{\text{Sand}}}$$

Proportion:

$$\frac{1}{4} = \frac{90 - x}{x}$$

$$4(90 - x) = x$$

$$360 - 4x = x$$

$$360 = 5x$$

$$72 = x \text{ pounds}$$

12. $96 - 32t = 0$

$$96 = 32t$$

$$\frac{96}{32} = t$$

$$3 = t \text{ seconds}$$

SECTION 2.5 Relations and Functions

1. If $a < b$ and $b < c$, then $a < c$ by the Transitive Property.

2. $9x = 36$

$$9x = \tfrac{1}{9}(36)$$

$$x = 4$$

3. "y is no more than 45" translates into $y \le 45$.

4. "x is at least 15" can be expressed in inequality notation as $x \ge 15$.

5. $6y - 3x + 3x - 10y = (6y - 10y) + (-3x + 3x)$

$$= -4y$$

6. $8(x - 2) - 3(x - 2) = 8x - 16 - 3x + 6$

$$= 5x - 10$$

$$= 5(x - 2)$$

7. $\frac{2}{3}t - \frac{5}{8} + \frac{5}{6}t = \left(\frac{2}{3} + \frac{5}{6}\right)t - \frac{5}{8}$

$$= \left(\frac{4}{6} + \frac{5}{6}\right)t - \frac{5}{8}$$

$$= \frac{9}{6}t - \frac{5}{8}$$

$$= \frac{3}{2}t - \frac{5}{8}$$

8. $\frac{3}{8}x - \frac{1}{12}x + 8 = \left(\frac{3}{8} - \frac{1}{12}\right)x + 8$

$$= \left(\frac{9}{24} - \frac{2}{24}\right)x + 8$$

$$= \frac{7}{24}x + 8$$

9. $3x^2 - 5x + 3 + 28x - 33x^2 = (3x^2 - 33x^2) + (-5x + 28x) + 3$

$$= -30x^2 + 23x + 3$$

10. $4x^3 - 3x^2y + 4xy^2 + 15x^2y + y^3 = 4x^3 + (-3 + 15)(x^2y) + 4xy^2 + y^3$

$$= 4x^3 + 12x^2y + 4xy^2 + y^3$$

11. *Verbal model:*

$$\boxed{\frac{\text{Cups flour}}{\text{Batches cookies}}} = \boxed{\frac{\text{Cups flour}}{\text{Batches cookies}}}$$

Proportion:

$$\frac{2\frac{1}{2}}{1} = \frac{x}{3\frac{1}{2}}$$

$$x = 2\frac{1}{2} \cdot 3\frac{1}{2}$$

$$x = \frac{5}{2} \cdot \frac{7}{2}$$

$$x = \frac{35}{4} = 8\frac{3}{4} \text{ cups}$$

12. *Verbal model:*

$$\boxed{\frac{\text{Gasoline}}{\text{Oil}}} = \boxed{\frac{\text{Gasoline}}{\text{Oil}}}$$

Proportion:

$$\frac{32}{1} = \frac{x}{\frac{1}{2}}$$

$$x = 32 \cdot \frac{1}{2}$$

$$x = 16 \text{ pints or 4 gallons}$$

SECTION 2.6   Graphs of Functions

1. $8x \cdot \dfrac{1}{8x} = 1$ illustrates the Multiplicative Inverse Property.

2. $3x + 0 = 3x$ illustrates the Additive Identity Property.

3. $-4(x + 10) = -4 \cdot x + (-4)(10)$ illustrates the Distributive Property

4. $5 + (-3 + x) = (5 - 3) + x$ illustrates the Associative Property of Addition.

5. $5x^4(x^2) = 5x^{4+2} = 5x^6$

6. $3(x + 1)^2(x + 1)^3 = 3(x + 1)^{2+3} = 3(x + 1)^5$

7. $(-4t^3) = (-4)^3(t)^3 = -64t^3$

8. $-(-2x)^4 = -(-2)^4 x^4 = -(+16)x^4 = -16x^4$

9. $(u^2v)^4 = (u^2)^4 v^4 = u^8 v^4$

10. $(3a^2b)^2(2b^3) = 3^2(a^2)^2 b^2(2)(b^3)$

$$= (9 \cdot 2)(a^4)(b^{2+3})$$

$$= 18a^4 b^5$$

11. *Verbal model:*   Discount $=$ Discount rate $\cdot$ List price

Labels: Discount $= x$

Discount rate $= 20\%$

List price $= \$239.95$

Equation: $x = 0.20(239.95)$

$x = \$47.99$

Verbal model: Total cost $=$ List price $+$ Shipping

Labels: Total cost $= x$

List price $= \$188.95$

Shipping $= \$4.32$

Equation: $x = 188.95 + 4.32$

$x = \$193.27$

Verbal model: Sale price $=$ List price $-$ Discount

Labels: Sale price $= x$

List price $= \$239.95$

Discount $= \$47.99$

Equation: $x = 239.95 - 47.99$

$x = \$191.96$

The department store price is a better bargain.

12. *Verbal model:*   Compared number $=$ Percent $\cdot$ Base number

Labels: Compared number $= a$

Percent $= p$

Base number $= b$

Equation: $a = pb$

$a = 1.30(739)$

$a = \$960.70$

CHAPTER 3   Polynomials and Factoring

SECTION 3.1   Adding and Subtracting Polynomials

1. If the product of two real numbers is -96 and one of the factors is 12, the other factor is negative.

2. The sum of the digits of $576 = 5 + 7 + 6 = 18$. 576 is divisible by 9 and 3.

3. -6^2 is positive is a false statement. $-6^2 = -1 \cdot 6^2 = -1 \cdot 36 = -36$

4. $(-6)^2$ is positive is a true statement. $(-6)^2 = (-6)(-6) = 36$

5.
$$2x - 12 \geq 0$$
$$2x - 12 + 12 \geq 12$$
$$2x \geq 12$$
$$\frac{2x}{2} \geq \frac{12}{2}$$
$$x \geq 6$$

6.
$$7 - 3x < 4 - x$$
$$7 - 3x + x < 4 - x + x$$
$$7 - 2x < 4$$
$$7 - 7 - 2x < 4 - 7$$
$$-2x < -3$$
$$\frac{-2x}{2} > \frac{-3}{-2}$$
$$x > \frac{3}{2}$$

7.
$$-2 < 4 - 2x < 10$$
$$-2 - 4 < 4 - 4 - 2x < 10 - 4$$
$$-6 < -2x < 6$$
$$\frac{-6}{-2} > \frac{-2x}{-2} > \frac{6}{-2}$$
$$3 > x > -3$$
$$-3 < x < 3$$

8.
$$4 \leq x + 5 < 8$$
$$4 - 5 \leq x + 5 - 5 < 8 - 5$$
$$-1 \leq x < 3$$

9. $|x - 3| < 2$
$$-2 < x - 3 < 2$$
$$-2 + 3 < x - 3 + 3 < 2 + 3$$
$$1 < x < 5$$

10. $|x - 5| > 3$

$$x - 5 > 3 \qquad \text{or} \qquad x - 5 < -3$$
$$x - 5 + 5 > 3 + 5 \qquad\qquad x - 5 + 5 < -3 + 5$$
$$x > 8 \qquad \text{or} \qquad x < 2$$

11. *Verbal model:*

$$\boxed{\frac{\text{Tax}}{\text{Assessed Value}}} = \boxed{\frac{\text{Tax}}{\text{Assessed Value}}}$$

Proportion:

$$\frac{2400}{145,000} = \frac{x}{90,000}$$

$$x = \frac{(2400)(90,000)}{145,000}$$

$$x = \$1489.66$$

12. *Verbal model:* $\boxed{\dfrac{\text{Gallons}}{\text{Miles}}} = \boxed{\dfrac{\text{Gallons}}{\text{Miles}}}$

Proportion: $\dfrac{7}{200} = \dfrac{x}{325}$

$$x = \dfrac{7.325}{200}$$

$$x = 11.375 \text{ gallons or } 11\dfrac{3}{8} \text{ gallons}$$

SECTION 3.2   Multiplying Polynomials

1. The point $(-2, 3)$ is 2 units to the left of the y-axis and 3 units above the x-axis.

2. Point 3 units from x-axis and 4 units from y-axis $(4, 3), (-4, 3), (-4, -3), (4, -3)$

3. $y = \dfrac{3}{5}x + 4$

$(15, \quad)$

$y = \dfrac{3}{5}(15) + 4$

$y = 9 + 4$

$y = 13$

4. $y = 3 - \dfrac{5}{9}x$

$(12, \quad)$

$y = 3 - \dfrac{5}{9}(12)$

$y = 3 - \dfrac{20}{3}$

$y = \dfrac{9}{3} - \dfrac{20}{3}$

$y = -\dfrac{11}{3}$

5. $y = 5.5 - 0.95x$

$(\quad, -1)$

$-1 = 5.5 - 0.95x$

$-6.5 = -0.95x$

$\dfrac{-6.5}{-0.95} = x$

$6.84 \approx x$

6. $y = 3 + 0.2x$

$(\quad, 4.4)$

$4.4 = 3 + 0.2x$

$1.4 = 0.2x$

$\dfrac{1.4}{0.2} = x$

$7 = x$

7. $f(x) = \dfrac{1}{3}x^2$

(a) $f(6) = \dfrac{1}{3}(6)^2 = \dfrac{1}{3} \cdot 36 = 12$

(b) $f\left(\dfrac{3}{4}\right) = \dfrac{1}{3}\left(\dfrac{3}{4}\right)^2 = \dfrac{1}{3} \cdot \dfrac{9}{16}$

$\quad = \dfrac{3}{16}$

8. $f(x) = 3 - 2x$

(a) $f(5) = 3 - 2(5)$

$\quad = 3 - 10$

$\quad = -7$

(b) $f(x + 3) - f(3) = 3 - 2(x + 3) - [3 - 2(3)]$

$\quad = 3 - 2x - 6 - 3 + 6$

$\quad = -2x$

9. $g(x) = \dfrac{x}{x + 10}$

    (a) $g(5) = \dfrac{5}{5 + 10} = \dfrac{5}{15} = \dfrac{1}{3}$

    (b) $g(c - 6) = \dfrac{c - 6}{(c - 6) + 10} = \dfrac{c - 6}{c + 4}$

10. $h(x) = \sqrt{x - 4}$

    (a) $h(16) = \sqrt{16 - 4}$

           $= \sqrt{12}$

           $= \sqrt{4 \cdot 3}$

           $= 2\sqrt{3}$

    (b) $h(t + 3) = \sqrt{t + 3 - 4}$

              $= \sqrt{t - 1}$

11. $g(x) = 7 - \dfrac{3}{2}x$

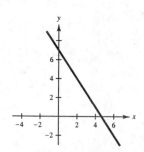

12. $h(x) = |3 - x|$

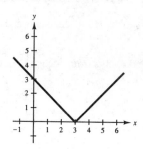

SECTION 3.3   Factoring Polynomials

1. A function f from a set A to a set B is a rule of correspondence that assigns to each element x in the set A exactly one element y in the set B.

2. The set A (see Exercise 1) is called the domain (or set of inputs) of the function f, and the set B (see Exercise 1) contains the range (or set of outputs) of the function f.

3. y is not a function of x.

Answers will vary.

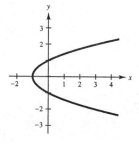

$x = y^2 - 1$

4. y is a function of x.

Answers will vary.

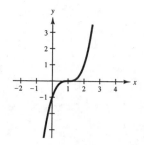

5. $y = 6 - \dfrac{2}{3}x$

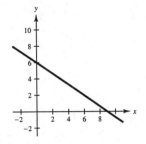

Function

6. $y = \dfrac{5}{2}x - 4$

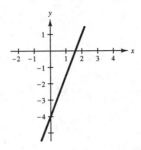

Function

7. $2y - 4x + 3 = 0$

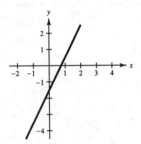

Function

8. $3x + 2y + 12 = 0$

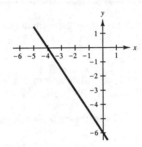

Function

9. $|y| - x = 0$

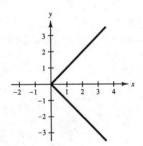

Not a function

10. $|y| = 2 - x$

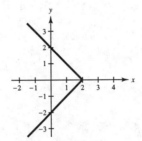

Not a function

11.

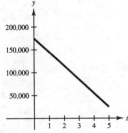

12. (a)*Verbal model:* $\boxed{\text{Area}} = \boxed{\text{Length}} \cdot \boxed{\text{Width}}$

   Function: $A(x) = x \cdot (250 - x)$

(b)

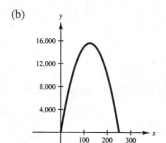

SECTION 3.4   Factoring Trinomials

1. A function can have only one value of y corresponding to $x = 0$.

2. Leading coefficient of $6t^3 + 3t^2 + 5t - 4$ is 6.

3. The set of all real numbers x whose distance from 0 is less than 5 can be represented by $|x| < 5$.

4. The set of all real numbers x whose distance from 6 is more than 3 is represented by $|x - 6| > 3$.

5. $(-3, 2), (5, -4)$

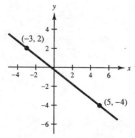

$$m = \frac{-4 - 2}{5 - (-3)} = \frac{-6}{8} = \frac{-3}{4}$$

6. $(2, 8), (7, -3)$

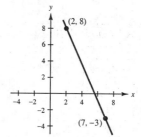

$$m = \frac{-3 - 8}{7 - 2} = \frac{-11}{5}$$

7. $\left(\dfrac{5}{2}, \dfrac{7}{2}\right), \left(\dfrac{7}{3}, -2\right)$

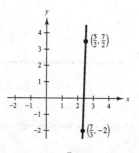

$$m = \frac{-2 - \dfrac{7}{2}}{\dfrac{7}{3} - \dfrac{5}{2}} \cdot \frac{6}{6} = \frac{-12 - 21}{14 - 15} = \frac{-33}{-1} = 33$$

8. $\left(-\dfrac{9}{4}, -\dfrac{1}{4}\right), \left(-3, \dfrac{9}{2}\right)$

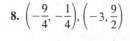

$$m = \frac{\dfrac{9}{2} - \left(-\dfrac{1}{4}\right)}{-3 - \left(\dfrac{-9}{4}\right)} \cdot \frac{4}{4} = \frac{18 + 1}{-12 + 9} = \frac{19}{-3} = -\frac{19}{3}$$

9. $(6, 4), (6, -3)$

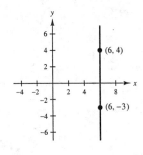

$$m = \frac{-3 - 4}{6 - 6} = \frac{-7}{0}$$

m is undefined

10. $(-4, 5), (7, 5)$

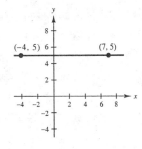

$$m = \frac{5 - 5}{7 - (-4)} = \frac{0}{11} = 0$$

11. *Verbal model:*   ☐ Interest ☐ = ☐ Principal ☐ · ☐ Rate ☐ · ☐ Time ☐

Equation: $i = 12{,}000 \cdot 0.12 \cdot \frac{1}{2}$

$i = \$720$

Verbal model: ☐ Payment ☐ = ☐ Principal ☐ + ☐ Interest ☐

Equation: $x = 12{,}000 + 720$

$x = \$12{,}720$

12. *Verbal model:*   ☐ Distance ☐ = ☐ Rate ☐ · ☐ Time ☐

☐ Time ☐ = $\dfrac{\text{Distance}}{\text{Rate}}$

Equation: $\dfrac{100}{54} + \dfrac{100}{45} = \dfrac{200}{x}$

$500x + 600x = 54000$

$1100x = 54000$

$x = \dfrac{54000}{1100}$

$x \approx 49.1 \text{ mph}$

SECTION 3.5   Solving Polynomial Equations

1. $3uv - 3uv = 0$ illustrates the Additive Inverse Property.

2. $5z \cdot 1 = 5z$ illustrates the Multiplicative Identity Property.

3. $2s(1 - s) = 2s - 2s^2$ illustrates the Distributive Property.

4. $(3x)y = 3(xy)$ illustrates the Associative Property of Multiplication.

5. $4 - \dfrac{1}{2}x = 6$

$4 - 4 - \dfrac{1}{2}x = 6 - 4$

$-\dfrac{1}{2}x = 2$

$(-2)\left(-\dfrac{1}{2}x\right) = (2)(-2)$

$x = -4$

6. $500 - 0.75x = 235$

$500 - 500 - 0.75x = 235 - 500$

$-0.75x = -265$

$\dfrac{-0.75x}{-0.75} = \dfrac{-265}{-0.75}$

$x \approx 353.33$

7. $4(x - 3) - (4x + 5) = 0$

$4x - 12 - 4x - 5 = 0$

$-17 \neq 0$

No solution

8. $12(3 - x) = 5 - 7(2x + 1)$

$36 - 12x = 5 - 14x - 7$

$36 - 12x = -2 - 14x$

$36 - 12x + 14x = -2 - 14x + 14x$

$36 + 2x = -2$

$36 - 36 + 2x = -2 - 36$

$2x = -38$

$\dfrac{2x}{2} = -\dfrac{38}{2}$

$x = -19$

9. $\dfrac{12 + x}{4} = 13$

$4\left(\dfrac{12 + x}{4}\right) = (13)4$

$12 + x = 52$

$12 - 12 + x = 52 - 12$

$x = 40$

10. $8(t - 24) = 0$

$t - 24 = 0$

$t = 24$

11. (a) $P = R - C$

$P = \left(16x - \dfrac{1}{4}x^2\right) - (12 + 8x)$

$= 16x - \dfrac{1}{4}x^2 - 12 - 8x$

$= -\dfrac{1}{4}x^2 + 8x - 12$

(b)

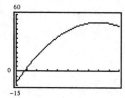

Keystrokes:

[Y=] [(−)] 1 [÷] 4 [X,T,θ] [x²] [+] 8 [X,T,θ] [−] 12 [GRAPH]

(c) $P(16) = -\dfrac{1}{4}(16)^2 + 8(16) - 12$

$= -\dfrac{1}{4}(256) + 128 - 12$

$= -64 + 128 - 12$

$= 52$

12. $-16t^2 + 576 = 0$

$-16t^2 + 576 - 576 = 0 - 576$

$-16t^2 = -576$

$\dfrac{-16t^2}{-16} = \dfrac{-576}{-16}$

$t^2 = 36$

$t = 6$ seconds

CHAPTER 4 Rational Expressions, Equations, and Functions

SECTION 4.1 Integer Exponents and Scientific Notation

1. The graph of an equation is the set of solution points of the equation on a rectangular coordinate system.

2. The point-plotting method for graphing an equation begins by creating a table of solution points of the equation. Plot these points on a rectangular coordinate system, and connect the points with a smooth curve or line.

3. $g(x) = \sqrt{x - 2}$

   $g(2) = \sqrt{2 - 2} = \sqrt{0} = 0$ $(2, 0)$

   $g(6) = \sqrt{6 - 2} = \sqrt{4} = 2$ $(6, 2)$

4. To find the x-intercept, let $y = 0$ and solve the equation for x. To find the y-intercept, let $x = 0$ and solve the equation for y.

5. $(7x^2)(2x^3) = 14x^{2+3} = 14x^5$

6. $(y^2z^3)(z^2)^4 = (y^2z^3)(z^8) = y^2z^{3+8} = y^2z^{11}$

7. $\dfrac{a^4b^2}{ab^2} = a^{4-1}b^{2-2} = a^3b^0 = a^3$

8. $(x + 2)^4 \div (x + 2)^3 = (x + 2)^{4-3} = (x + 2)^1 = x + 2$

9. $f(x) = 5 - 2x$

   Keystrokes:

   $\boxed{Y=}$ 5 $\boxed{-}$ 2 $\boxed{X,T,\theta}$ $\boxed{GRAPH}$

   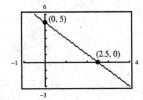

10. $h(x) = \frac{1}{2}x + |x|$

    Keystrokes:

    $\boxed{Y=}$ $\boxed{(}$ 1 $\boxed{\div}$ 2 $\boxed{)}$ $\boxed{X,T,\theta}$ $\boxed{+}$ $\boxed{ABS}$ $\boxed{X,T,\theta}$ $\boxed{GRAPH}$

    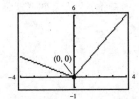

11. $g(x) = x^2 - 4x$

    Keystrokes:

    $\boxed{Y=}$ $\boxed{X,T,\theta}$ $\boxed{x^2}$ $\boxed{-}$ 4 $\boxed{X,T,\theta}$ $\boxed{GRAPH}$

    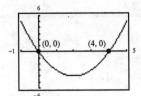

12. $f(x) = 2\sqrt{x + 1}$

    Keystrokes:

    $\boxed{Y=}$ 2 $\boxed{\sqrt{}}$ $\boxed{(}$ $\boxed{X,T,\theta}$ $\boxed{+}$ 1 $\boxed{)}$ $\boxed{GRAPH}$

    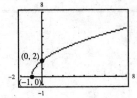

SECTION 4.2   Rational Expressions and Functions

1. Slope $= m = \dfrac{y_2 - y_1}{x_2 - x_1}$

2. (a) $m > 0$ (b) $m < 0$
(c) $m = 0$ (d) m is undefined.

3. $2(x + 5) - 3 - (2x - 3) = 2x + 10 - 2x$
$= 10$

4. $3(y + 4) + 5 - (3y + 5) = 3y + 12 + 5 - 3y - 5$
$= 12$

5. $4 - 2[3 + 4(x + 1)] = 4 - 2[3 + 4x + 4]$
$= 4 - 2[7 + 4x]$
$= 4 - 14 - 8x$
$= -10 - 8x$

6. $5x + x[3 - 2(x - 3)] = 5x + x[3 - 2x + 6]$
$= 5x + x[9 - 2x]$
$= 5x + 9x - 2x^2$
$= -2x^2 + 14x$

7. $\left(\dfrac{5}{x^2}\right)^2 = \dfrac{25}{x^4}$

8. $-\dfrac{(2u^2v)^2}{-3uv^2} = -\dfrac{4u^4v^2}{-3uv^2} = \dfrac{4u^3}{3}$

9. *Verbal*
Model: $\boxed{\text{Gallons solution 1}} \cdot 30\% + \boxed{\text{Gallons solution 2}} \cdot 60\% = \boxed{\text{Total gallons}} \cdot 40\%$

Labels: Gallons solution 1 $= x$
Gallons solution 2 $= 20 - x$
Total gallons $= 20$

Equation: $0.30x + 0.60(20 - x) = 20(0.40)$
$0.30x + 12 - 0.60x = 8$
$-0.30x = -4$
$x = 13\frac{1}{3}$ gallons at 30%
$20 - x = 6\frac{2}{3}$ gallons at 60%

10. *Verbal*
Model: $\boxed{\text{Original price}} \cdot 75\% = \boxed{\text{Sale price}}$

Labels: Original price $= x$
Sale price $= \$375$

Equation: $x \cdot 0.75 = 375$
$x = \$500$

SECTION 4.3   Multiplying and Dividing Rational Expressions

1. $9t^2 - 4 = (3t - 2)(3t + 2)$

2. $4x^2 - 12x + 9 = (2x - 3)^2$

3. $8x^3 + 64 = (2x + 4)(4x^2 - 8x + 16)$

4. $3x^2 + 13x - 10 = (3x - 2)(x + 5)$

5. $5x - 20x^2 = 5x(1 - 4x)$

6. $64 - (x - 6)^2 = [8 - (x - 6)][8 + (x - 6)]$
$= (8 - x + 6)(8 + x - 6)$
$= (14 - x)(2 + x)$

7. $15x^2 - 16x - 15 = (5x + 3)(3x - 5)$

8. $16t^2 + 8t + 1 = (4t + 1)^2$

9. $y^3 - 64 = (y - 4)(y^2 + 4y + 16)$

10. $8x^3 + 1 = (2x + 1)(4x^2 - 2x + 1)$

11.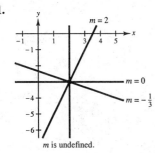

m is undefined.

12.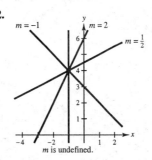

m is undefined.

SECTION 4.4   Adding and Subtracting Rational Expressions

1. (a) $5y - 3x - 4 = 0$

$$5y = 3x + 4$$

$$y = \tfrac{3}{5}x + \tfrac{4}{5}$$

   (b) $5y - 3x - 4 = 0$

$$5y = 3x + 4$$

$$y = \tfrac{3}{5}x + \tfrac{4}{5}$$

$$y - y_1 = \tfrac{3}{5}(x - x_1) + \tfrac{4}{5} \quad \text{Let } x_1 = 1.$$

$$y - y_1 = \tfrac{3}{5}(x - 1) + \tfrac{4}{5}$$

$$y - \tfrac{7}{5} = \tfrac{3}{5}(x - 1) \qquad y_1 = \tfrac{7}{5}$$

   (Many answers)

2. If $m > 0$, the line rises from left to right.

If $m < 0$, the line falls from left to right.

3. $-6x(10 - 7x) = -60x + 42x^2$

$$= 42x^2 - 60x$$

4. $(2 - y)(3 + 2y) = 6 + 4y - 3y - 2y^2$

$$= 6 + y - 2y^2$$

5. $(11 - x)(11 + x) = 121 - x^2$

6. $(4 - 5z)(4 + 5z) = 16 + 20z - 20z - 25z^2$

$$= 16 - 25z^2$$

7. $(x + 1)^2 = (x + 1)(x + 1)$

$$= x^2 + 2x + 1$$

8. $t(t^2 + 1) - t(t^2 - 1) = t^3 + t - t^3 + t$

$$= 2t$$

9. $(x - 2)(x^2 + 2x + 4) = x^3 + 2x^2 + 4x - 2x^2 - 4x - 8$

$$= x^3 - 8$$

10. $t(t - 4)(2t + 3) = t(2t^2 + 3t - 8t - 12)$

$$= t(2t^2 - 5t - 12)$$

$$= 2t^3 - 5t^2 - 12t$$

11. Perimeter = Sum of all sides

$$= 7(x) + (x + 3) + (2x) + (2x + 3)$$

$$= 12x + 6$$

Area = Area rectangle 1 + Area rectangle 2 + Area rectangle 3

$$= (x \cdot x) + (x + 3)(3x) + (x \cdot x)$$

$$= x^2 + 3x^2 + 9x + x^2$$

$$= 5x^2 + 9x$$

12. Perimeter = Sum of all sides

$$= 3x + 4x + 5x$$

$$= 12x$$

Area = $\frac{1}{2} \cdot$ Base $\cdot$ Height

$$= \frac{1}{2} \cdot 3x \cdot 4x$$

$$= 6x^2$$

SECTION 4.5   Dividing Polynomials

1. $\dfrac{120y}{90} = \dfrac{30 \cdot 4y}{30 \cdot 3} = \dfrac{4y}{3}$ Divide the numerator and the denominator by 30.

2. $(2n + 1)(2n + 3) = 4n^2 + 6n + 2n + 3 = 4n^2 + 8n + 3$

3. $(2n + 1) + (2n + 3) = 4n + 4$

4. $2n(2n + 2) = 4n^2 + 4n$

5.
$$3(2 - x) = 5x$$
$$6 - 3x = 5x$$
$$6 - 3x + 3x = 5x + 3x$$
$$6 = 8x$$
$$\frac{6}{8} = \frac{8x}{8}$$
$$\frac{3}{4} = x$$

6.
$$125 - 50x = 0$$
$$125 - 125 - 50x = 0 - 125$$
$$-50x = -125$$
$$\frac{-50x}{-50} = \frac{-125}{-50}$$
$$x = \frac{5}{2}$$

7.
$$8y^2 - 50 = 0$$
$$2(4y^2 - 25) = 0$$
$$2(2y - 5)(2y + 5) = 0$$
$$2y - 5 = 0 \qquad 2y + 5 = 0$$
$$y = \tfrac{5}{2} \qquad\qquad y = -\tfrac{5}{2}$$

8. $t^2 - 8t = 0$
$$t(t - 8) = 0$$
$$t = 0 \qquad t - 8 = 0$$
$$t = 8$$

9. $x^2 + x - 42 = 0$

$(x + 7)(x - 6) = 0$

$x + 7 = 0 \quad x - 6 = 0$

$x = -7 \qquad x = 6$

10. $x(10 - x) = 25$

$10x - x^2 = 25$

$-x^2 + 10x - 25 = 0$

$x^2 - 10x + 25 = 0$

$(x - 5)^2 = 0$

$x - 5 = 0$

$x = 5$

11. *Verbal model:* $\boxed{\text{Salary}} = \boxed{\text{Salary}} + \boxed{\text{Commission}}$

Labels: Monthly wage $= y$

Salary $= 1500$

Commission $= 0.12x$

Function: $y = 1500 + 0.12x$

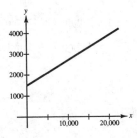

12. *Verbal model:* $\boxed{\begin{array}{c}\text{Total} \\ \text{enrollment}\end{array}} = \boxed{\begin{array}{c}\text{Enrollment} \\ \text{per year}\end{array}} + 3500$

Labels: Total enrollment $= n$

Enrollment per year $= 60t$

Function: $n = 60t + 3500$

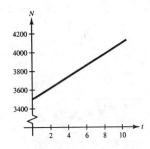

SECTION 4.6   Solving Rational Equations

1. $(-2, y)$ can be located in quadrants II or III.

2. $(x, 3)$ can be located in quadrants I or II.

3. Points whose y-coordinates are 0 are located on the x-axis.

4. $(9, -6)$

5. $7 - 3x > 4 - x$

$-2x > -3$

$x < \frac{3}{2}$

6. $2(x + 6) - 20 < 2$

$2x + 12 - 20 < 2$

$2x - 8 < 2$

$2x < 10$

$x < 5$

7. $|x - 3| < 2$

$-2 < x - 3 < 2$

$1 < x < 5$

8. $|x - 5| > 3$

$x - 5 > 3 \quad \text{or} \quad x - 5 < -3$

$x > 8 \quad \text{or} \qquad x < 2$

9. $\left|\frac{1}{4}x - 1\right| \geq 3$

$\frac{1}{4}x - 1 \geq 3$ or $\frac{1}{4}x - 1 \leq -3$

$\frac{1}{4}x \geq 4$ $\frac{1}{4}x \leq -2$

$x \geq 16$ or $x \leq -8$

10. $\left|2 - \frac{1}{3}x\right| \leq 10$

$-10 \leq 2 - \frac{1}{3}x \leq 10$

$-12 \leq -\frac{1}{3}x \leq 8$

$36 \geq x \geq -24$

$-24 \leq x \leq 36$

11.

Labels: Distance $= d$

1st jogger's rate $= 6$; 1st jogger's time $= x + \frac{5}{60}$

2nd jogger's rate $= 8$; 2nd jogger's time $= x$

Equation: $d = 6\left(x + \frac{1}{12}\right)$

$d = 8x$

$6\left(x + \frac{1}{12}\right) = 8x$

$6x + \frac{1}{2} = 8x$

$\frac{1}{2} = 2x$

$\frac{1}{4} = x$ hours, or 15 minutes

$d = 8\left(\frac{1}{4} \text{ hour}\right) = 2$ miles

12. *Verbal Model:* $\boxed{\begin{array}{c}\text{Amount} \\ \text{at 7.5\%}\end{array}} + \boxed{\begin{array}{c}\text{Amount} \\ \text{at 9\%}\end{array}} = 24{,}000$

$7.5\% \cdot \boxed{\begin{array}{c}\text{Amount} \\ \text{at 7.5\%}\end{array}} + 9\% \cdot \boxed{\begin{array}{c}\text{Amount} \\ \text{at 9\%}\end{array}} = 1935$

Labels: Amount at 7.5% $= x$

Amount at 9% $= y$

System:

$x + y = 24{,}000$

$0.075x + 0.09y = 1935$

$y = 24{,}000 - x$

$0.075x + 0.09(24{,}000 - x) = 1935$

$0.075x + 2160 - 0.09x = 1935$

$-0.015x = -225$

$x = \$15{,}000$ at 7.5%

$y = \$9000$ at 9%

CHAPTER 5   Radicals and Complex Numbers

SECTION 5.1   Radicals and Rational Exponents

1. $a^m \cdot a^n = a^{m+n}$

2. $(ab)^m = a^m b^m$

3. $(a^m)^n = a^{mn}$

4. $\dfrac{a^m}{a^n} = a^{m-n}$, if $m > n$

5. $3x + y = 4$

$$y = -3x + 4$$

6. $2x + 3y = 2$

$$3y = -2x + 2$$

$$y = -\frac{2}{3}x + \frac{2}{3}$$

7. $x^2 + 3y = 4$

$$3y = 4 - x^2$$

$$y = \frac{4 - x^2}{3} = \frac{1}{3}(4 - x^2)$$

8. $x^2 + y - 4 = 0$

$$y = -x^2 + 4$$

9. $2\sqrt{x} - 3y = 15$

$$-3y = -2\sqrt{x} + 15$$

$$y = \frac{2}{3}\sqrt{x} - 5$$

10. $6|x| - 5y + 10 = 0$

$$-5y = -6|x| - 10$$

$$y = \frac{6}{5}|x| + 2$$

11. *Verbal Model:* $\boxed{\begin{array}{c}\text{Rate}\\\text{person 1}\end{array}} + \boxed{\begin{array}{c}\text{Rate}\\\text{person 2}\end{array}} = \boxed{\begin{array}{c}\text{Rate}\\\text{together}\end{array}}$

Labels: Your time = 4 hours

Friend's time = 6 hours

Time together = x hours

Equation: $\dfrac{1}{4} + \dfrac{1}{6} = \dfrac{1}{x}$

$$12x\left(\frac{1}{4} + \frac{1}{6}\right) = \left(\frac{1}{x}\right)12x$$

$$3x + 2x = 12$$

$$5x = 12$$

$$x = \frac{12}{5} \text{ hours}$$

12. *Verbal Model:* $\boxed{\begin{array}{c}\text{Total}\\\text{time}\end{array}} = \boxed{\text{Time 1}} + \boxed{\text{Time 2}}$

$\boxed{\text{Rate}} = \dfrac{\boxed{\text{Distance}}}{\boxed{\text{Time}}}$

Labels: Time 1 = $\dfrac{90}{54}$

Time 2 = $\dfrac{90}{42}$

Equation: Rate = $\dfrac{180}{\frac{90}{54} + \frac{90}{42}}$

Rate = 47.25 mph

SECTION 5.2   Simplifying Radical Expressions

1. Graph $x - y = -3$ with a dotted line since the inequality is $>$. Test one point in each half-plane formed by the line. Shade the half-plane that satisfies the inequality.

2. $3x + 4y \le 4$ and $3x + 4y < 4$

The first inequality includes the points on the line $3x + 4y = 4$ and the second does not.

3. $-x^3 + 3x^2 - x + 3 = -x^2(x - 3) - 1(x - 3)$

$$= (x - 3)(-x^2 - 1)$$

$$= -(x - 3)(x^2 + 1)$$

4. $4t^2 - 169 = (2t - 13)(2t + 13)$

5. $x^2 - 3x + 2 = (x - 2)(x - 1)$

6. $2x^2 + 5x - 7 = (2x + 7)(x - 1)$

7. $11x^2 + 6x - 5 = (11x - 5)(x + 1)$

8. $4x^2 - 28x + 49 = (2x - 7)(2x - 7)$

$$= (2x - 7)^2$$

9. *Verbal Model:*

$$\boxed{\begin{array}{c}\text{Adult}\\\text{tickets}\end{array}} + \boxed{\begin{array}{c}\text{Student}\\\text{tickets}\end{array}} = 1200$$

$$\boxed{\begin{array}{c}\text{Price adult}\\\text{tickets}\end{array}} \cdot \boxed{\begin{array}{c}\text{Adult}\\\text{tickets}\end{array}} + \boxed{\begin{array}{c}\text{Price student}\\\text{tickets}\end{array}} \cdot \boxed{\begin{array}{c}\text{Student}\\\text{tickets}\end{array}} = 21,120$$

Labels: Adult tickets $= x$

Student tickets $= y$

System: $x + y = 1200$

$20x + 12.50y = 21,120$

Solve by substitution:

$$y = 1200 - x$$

$$20x + 12.50(1200 - x) = 21,120$$

$$20x + 15,000 - 12.50x = 21,120$$

$$7.5x = 6120$$

$$x = 816 \text{ adults}$$

$$y = 1200 - 816 = 384 \text{ students}$$

10. *Verbal Model:*

$$\boxed{\dfrac{\text{Number defective units 1}}{\text{Total number units 1}}} = \boxed{\dfrac{\text{Number defective units 2}}{\text{Total number units 2}}}$$

Labels: Number defective units (2) $= x$

Equation: $\dfrac{2}{75} = \dfrac{x}{10,000}$

$$x = \dfrac{2(10,000)}{75}$$

$$x \approx 267 \text{ units}$$

SECTION 5.3   Multiplying and Dividing Radical Expressions

1. $x^2 + bx + c = (x + m)(x + n)$

$mn = c$

2. $x^2 + bx + c = (x + m)(x + n)$

If $c > 0$, the signs of m and n must be the same.

3. If $c < 0$, the signs of m and n must be different.

4. If m and n have like signs, then $m + n = b$.

5. $(-1, -2), (3, 6)$

$m = \dfrac{y_2 - y_1}{x_2 - x_1} = \dfrac{6 - (-2)}{3 - (-1)} = \dfrac{6 + 2}{3 + 1} = \dfrac{8}{4} = 2$

$y - y_1 = m(x - x_1)$

$y - 6 = 2(x - 3)$

$y - 6 = 2x - 6$

$y = 2x$

$0 = 2x - y$

6. $(1, 5), (6, 0)$

$m = \dfrac{y_2 - y_1}{x_2 - x_1} = \dfrac{0 - 5}{6 - 1} = \dfrac{-5}{5} = -1$

$y - y_1 = m(x - x_1)$

$y - 0 = -1(x - 6)$

$y = -x + 6$

$x + y - 6 = 0$

7. $(6, 3), (10, 3)$

$m = \dfrac{y_2 - y_1}{x_2 - x_1} = \dfrac{3 - 3}{10 - 6} = \dfrac{0}{4} = 0$

$y - y_1 = m(x - x_1)$

$y - 3 = 0(x - 10)$

$y - 3 = 0$

8. $(4, -2), (4, 5)$

$m = \dfrac{y_2 - y_1}{x_2 - x_1} = \dfrac{5 - (-2)}{4 - 4} = \dfrac{7}{0} =$ undefined

$x = 4$

$x - 4 = 0$

9. $\left(\dfrac{4}{3}, 8\right), (5, 6)$

$m = \dfrac{y_2 - y_1}{x_2 - x_1} = \dfrac{6 - 8}{5 - \frac{4}{3}} = \dfrac{-2}{\frac{11}{3}} = -\dfrac{6}{11}$

$y - y_1 = m(x - x_1)$

$y - 6 = -\dfrac{6}{11}(x - 5)$

$11y - 66 = -6x + 30$

$0 = 6x + 11y - 96$

10. $(7, 4), (10, 1)$

$m = \dfrac{y_2 - y_1}{x_2 - x_1} = \dfrac{1 - 4}{10 - 7} = \dfrac{-3}{3} = -1$

$y - y_1 = m(x - x_1)$

$y - 1 = -1(x - 10)$

$y - 1 = -x + 10$

$x + y - 11 = 0$

11. *Verbal Model:* $\boxed{\text{Distance}} = \boxed{\text{Rate}} \cdot \boxed{\text{Time}}$

$\dfrac{\boxed{\text{Distance}}}{\boxed{\text{Rate}}} = \boxed{\text{Time}}$

Labels: Time $= t$

Distance $= 360$

Rate $= r$

Equation: $\dfrac{360}{r} = t$

12. *Verbal Model:* $\boxed{\text{Perimeter}} = 2 \cdot \boxed{\text{Length}} + 2 \cdot \boxed{\text{Width}}$

Labels: Perimeter $= P$

Length $= L$

Width $= \dfrac{L}{3}$

Equation: $P = 2L + 2\left(\dfrac{L}{3}\right)$

$P = \dfrac{8}{3}L$

SECTION 5.4   Solving Radical Equations

1. $f(x) = \dfrac{4}{(x + 2)(x - 3)}$

The function is undefined when the denominator is zero.
Set the denominator equal to zero and solve for x.

$(x + 2)(x - 3) = 0$

$x + 2 = 0 \qquad x - 3 = 0$

$x = -2 \qquad x = 3$

The domain is all real numbers x such that $x \neq -2$ and $x \neq 3$.

2. $\dfrac{2x^2 + 5x - 3}{x^2 - 9} = \dfrac{2x - 1}{x - 3}, \quad x \neq -3$

$\dfrac{2(-3)^2 + 5(-3) - 3}{(-3)^2 - 9} = \dfrac{2(-3) - 1}{-3 - 3}$

$\dfrac{18 - 15 - 3}{9 - 9} = \dfrac{-7}{-6}$

$\dfrac{0}{0} = \dfrac{7}{6}$

Undefined

3. $(-3x^2y^3)^2 \cdot (4xy^2) = 9x^4y^6 \cdot 4xy^2 = 36x^5y^8$

4. $(x^2 - 3xy)^0 = 1$

5. $\dfrac{64r^2s^4}{16rs^2} = 4r^{2-1}s^{4-2} = 4rs^2$

6. $\left(\dfrac{3x}{4y^3}\right)^2 = \left(\dfrac{3x}{4y^3}\right)\left(\dfrac{3x}{4y^3}\right) = \dfrac{9x^2}{16y^6}$

7. $\dfrac{x+13}{x^3(3-x)} \cdot \dfrac{x(x-3)}{5} = \dfrac{x+13}{x^3(3-x)} \cdot \dfrac{-x(3-x)}{5}$

$\qquad = \dfrac{-(x+13)}{5x^2}$

8. $\dfrac{x+2}{5x+15} \cdot \dfrac{x-2}{5(x-3)} = \dfrac{(x+2)(x-2)}{5(x+3)5(x-3)}$

$\qquad = \dfrac{x^2-4}{25(x^2-9)}$

9. $\dfrac{2x}{x-5} - \dfrac{5}{5-x} = \dfrac{2x}{x-5} + \dfrac{5}{x-5} = \dfrac{2x+5}{x-5}$

10. $\dfrac{3}{x-1} - 5 = \dfrac{3}{x-1} - 5\left(\dfrac{x-1}{x-1}\right)$

$\qquad = \dfrac{3}{x-1} - \dfrac{5(x-1)}{x-1}$

$\qquad = \dfrac{3-5x+5}{x-1}$

$\qquad = \dfrac{8-5x}{x-1}$

$\qquad = -\dfrac{5x-8}{x-1}$

11. $y = 2x - 3$

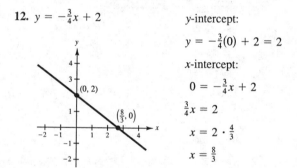

y-intercept:

$y = 2(0) - 3$

$y = -3$

x-intercept:

$0 = 2x - 3$

$3 = 2x$

$\dfrac{3}{2} = x$

12. $y = -\dfrac{3}{4}x + 2$

y-intercept:

$y = -\dfrac{3}{4}(0) + 2 = 2$

x-intercept:

$0 = -\dfrac{3}{4}x + 2$

$\dfrac{3}{4}x = 2$

$x = 2 \cdot \dfrac{4}{3}$

$x = \dfrac{8}{3}$

SECTION 5.5 Complex Numbers

1. $\dfrac{3t}{5} \cdot \dfrac{8t^2}{15} = \dfrac{(3t)(8t^2)}{(5)(15)} = \dfrac{24t^3}{75}$

Multiply numerators. Multiply denominators.

2. $\dfrac{3t}{5} \div \dfrac{8t^2}{15} = \dfrac{3t}{5} \cdot \dfrac{15}{8t^2} = \dfrac{(3t)(15)}{(5)(8t^2)} = \dfrac{9}{8t}$

Multiply by the reciprocal of the divisor.

3. $\dfrac{3t}{5} + \dfrac{8t^2}{15} = \dfrac{9t}{15} + \dfrac{8t^2}{15} = \dfrac{9t + 8t^2}{15}$

Change each fraction into an equivalent fraction with the lowest common denominator as the denominator. Add the numerators and put over the lowest common denominator.

4. $\dfrac{t-5}{5-t} = \dfrac{t-5}{-1(t-5)} = -1$

5. $\dfrac{x^2}{2x+3} \div \dfrac{5x}{2x+3} = \dfrac{x^2}{2x+3} \cdot \dfrac{2x+3}{5x}$

$\qquad = \dfrac{x^2(2x+3)}{(2x+3)5x}$

$\qquad = \dfrac{x}{5}$

6. $\dfrac{x-y}{5x} \div \dfrac{x^2-y^2}{x^2} = \dfrac{x-y}{5x} \cdot \dfrac{x^2}{(x-y)(x+y)}$

$\qquad = \dfrac{(x-y)x^2}{5x(x-y)(x+y)}$

$\qquad = \dfrac{x}{5(x+y)}$

7. $\dfrac{\dfrac{9}{x}}{\left(\dfrac{6}{x}+2\right)} \cdot \dfrac{x}{x} = \dfrac{9}{6+2x}$

8. $\dfrac{\left(1+\dfrac{2}{x}\right)}{\left(x-\dfrac{4}{x}\right)} \cdot \dfrac{x}{x} = \dfrac{x+2}{x^2-4} = \dfrac{x+2}{(x-2)(x+2)} = \dfrac{1}{x-2}$

9. $\dfrac{\dfrac{4}{x^2-9}+\dfrac{2}{x-2}}{\dfrac{1}{x+3}+\dfrac{1}{x-3}} \cdot \dfrac{(x-3)(x+3)(x-2)}{(x-3)(x+3)(x-2)} = \dfrac{4(x-2)+2(x^2-9)}{(x-3)(x-2)+(x+3)(x-2)}$

$\qquad = \dfrac{4x-8+2x^2-18}{x^2-5x+6+x^2+x-6}$

$\qquad = \dfrac{2x^2+4x-26}{2x^2-4x}$

$\qquad = \dfrac{2(x^2+2x-13)}{2x(x-2)}$

$\qquad = \dfrac{x^2+2x-13}{x(x-2)}$

10. $\dfrac{\left(\dfrac{1}{x+1}+\dfrac{1}{2}\right)}{\left(\dfrac{3}{2x^2+4x+2}\right)} = \dfrac{\left(\dfrac{1}{x+1}+\dfrac{1}{2}\right)}{\left(\dfrac{3}{2(x^2+2x+1)}\right)} \cdot \dfrac{2(x+1)^2}{2(x+2)^2}$

$\qquad = \dfrac{2(x+1)+(x+1)^2}{3}$

$\qquad = \dfrac{2x+2+x^2+2x+1}{3}$

$\qquad = \dfrac{x^2+4x+3}{3}$

$\qquad = \dfrac{(x+1)(x+3)}{3}$

11. $\dfrac{\dfrac{4x}{3}-\dfrac{x}{2}}{3} \cdot \dfrac{6}{6} = \dfrac{8x-3x}{18} = \dfrac{5x}{18}$

1st number: $\dfrac{x}{2}+\dfrac{5x}{18} = \dfrac{9x}{18}+\dfrac{5x}{18} = \dfrac{14x}{18} = \dfrac{7x}{9}$

2nd number: $\dfrac{14x}{18}+\dfrac{5x}{18} = \dfrac{19x}{18}$

12. $\dfrac{1}{\left(\dfrac{1}{c_1}+\dfrac{1}{c_2}\right)} = \dfrac{1}{\dfrac{1}{c_1}+\dfrac{1}{c_2}} \cdot \dfrac{c_1 c_2}{c_1 c_2} = \dfrac{c_1 c_2}{c_2+c_1}$

CHAPTER 6 Quadratic Equations and Inequalities

SECTION 6.1 Factoring and Extracting Square Roots

1. The leading coefficient is -3 because $-3t^3$ is the term of highest degree.

2. $(y^2 - 2)(y^3 + 7) = y^5 + 7y^2 - 2y^3 - 14$

Degree: 5 (the highest power)

3.

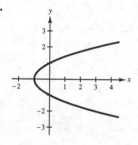

For some values of x there correspond two values of y.

4.

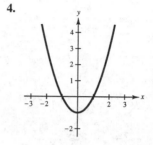

For each value of x there corresponds exactly one value of y.

5. $(x^3 \cdot x^{-2})^{-3} = (x^{3+(-2)})^{-3} = (x^1)^{-3} = x^{-3} = \dfrac{1}{x^3}$

6. $(5x^{-4}y^5)(-3x^2y^{-1}) = -15x^{-4+2}y^{5+(-1)}$

$$= -15x^{-2}y^4 = \dfrac{-15y^4}{x^2}$$

7. $\left(\dfrac{2x}{3y}\right)^{-2} = \left(\dfrac{3y}{2x}\right)^2 = \dfrac{9y^2}{4x^2}$

8. $\left(\dfrac{7u^{-4}}{3v^{-2}}\right)\left(\dfrac{14u}{6v^2}\right)^{-1} = \left(\dfrac{7u^{-4}}{3v^{-2}}\right)\left(\dfrac{6v^2}{14u}\right)$

$$= \dfrac{42u^{-4-1}v^{2-(-2)}}{42} = u^{-5}v^4 = \dfrac{v^4}{u^5}$$

9. $\dfrac{6u^2v^{-3}}{27uv^3} = \dfrac{2u^{2-1}v^{-3-3}}{9} = \dfrac{2u^1v^{-6}}{9} = \dfrac{2u}{9v^6}$

10. $\dfrac{-14r^4s^2}{-98rs^2} = \dfrac{1r^{4-1}s^{2-2}}{7} = \dfrac{r^3s^0}{7} = \dfrac{r^3}{7}$

11. $N = \dfrac{k}{\sqrt{t+1}}$

$300 = \dfrac{k}{\sqrt{0+1}}$

$300 = k$

$N = \dfrac{300}{\sqrt{8+1}}$

$N = 100$ prey

12. $t = \dfrac{k}{r}$

$2 = \dfrac{k}{58}$

$116 = k$

$t = \dfrac{116}{72}$

$t = \dfrac{29}{18} \approx 1.6$ hours

k measures the distance traveled in t hours at r miles per hour.

SECTION 6.2   Completing the Square

1. $(ab)^4 = a^4 b^4$

2. $(a^r)^8 = a^{r \cdot 8} = a^{8r}$

3. $\left(\dfrac{a}{b}\right)^{-r} = \left(\dfrac{b}{a}\right)^r = \dfrac{b^r}{a^r}, \ a \neq 0, b \neq 0$

4. $a^{-r} = \dfrac{1}{a^r}, \ a \neq 0$

5.
$$\dfrac{4}{x} - \dfrac{2}{3} = 0$$
$$(3x)\left(\dfrac{4}{x} - \dfrac{2}{3}\right) = (0)(3x)$$
$$12 - 2x = 0$$
$$-2x = -12$$
$$x = 6$$

6. $2x - 3[1 + (4 - x)] = 0$
$$2x - 3[1 + 4 - x] = 0$$
$$2x - 3[5 - x] = 0$$
$$2x - 15 + 3x = 0$$
$$5x = 15$$
$$x = 3$$

7. $3x^2 - 13x - 10 = 0$
$$(3x + 2)(x - 5) = 0$$
$$3x + 2 = 0 \qquad x - 5 = 0$$
$$x = -\tfrac{2}{3} \qquad\quad x = 5$$

8.
$$x(x - 3) = 40$$
$$x^2 - 3x - 40 = 0$$
$$(x - 8)(x + 5) = 0$$
$$x - 8 = 0 \qquad x + 5 = 0$$
$$x = 8 \qquad\quad x = -5$$

9. $g(x) = \tfrac{2}{3}x - 5$

y-intercept:

$g(0) = \tfrac{2}{3}(0) - 5 = -5$

x-intercept:

$0 = \tfrac{2}{3}x - 5$

$0 = 2x - 15$

$15 = 2x$

$\tfrac{15}{2} = x$

$7.5 = x$

10. $h(x) = 5 - \sqrt{x}$

y-intercept:

$h(0) = 5 - \sqrt{0} = 5$

x-intercept:

$0 = 5 - \sqrt{x}$

$\sqrt{x} = 5$

$x = 5^2 = 25$

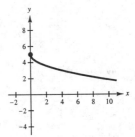

11. $f(x) = \dfrac{4}{x + 2}$

y-intercept:

$f(0) = \dfrac{4}{0 + 2} = 2$

x-intercept:

$0 = \dfrac{4}{x + 2}$

$0 = 4$, none

Vertical asymptote: $x + 2 = 0$
$$x = -2$$

Horizontal asymptote: $y = 0$ since the degree of the numerator is less than the degree of the denominator.

12. $f(x) = 2x + |x - 1|$

y-intercept:

$f(0) = 2(0) + |0 - 1| = 1$

x-intercept:

$0 = 2x + |x - 1|$

$-2x = |x - 1|$

$-2x = x - 1 \qquad\qquad -2x = -x + 1$

$-3x = -1 \qquad\qquad\quad -x = 1$

$x = \tfrac{1}{3} \qquad\qquad\qquad x = -1$

Check:

$-2\left(\tfrac{1}{3}\right) \overset{?}{=} \left|\tfrac{1}{3} - 1\right|$

$-\tfrac{2}{3} \neq \tfrac{2}{3}$

Check:

$-2(-1) = |-1 - 1|$

$2 = |-2|$

$2 = 2$

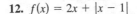

SECTION 6.3   The Quadratic Formula

1. Multiplication Property: $\sqrt{ab} = \sqrt{a}\sqrt{b}$

2. Division Property: $\sqrt{\dfrac{a}{b}} = \dfrac{\sqrt{a}}{\sqrt{b}}, \quad b \neq 0$

3. $\sqrt{72}$ is not in simplest form. A factor (36) of 72 is a perfect square.

$$\sqrt{72} = \sqrt{36 \cdot 2} = 6\sqrt{2}$$

4. $10/\sqrt{5}$ is not in simplest form. There is a radical in the denominator which needs to be rationalized.

$$\frac{10}{\sqrt{5}} = \frac{10}{\sqrt{5}} \cdot \frac{\sqrt{5}}{\sqrt{5}} = \frac{10\sqrt{5}}{5} = 2\sqrt{5}$$

5. $\sqrt{128} + 3\sqrt{50} = \sqrt{64 \cdot 2} + 3\sqrt{25 \cdot 2}$

$$= 8\sqrt{2} + 15\sqrt{2}$$
$$= 23\sqrt{2}$$

6. $3\sqrt{5}\sqrt{500} = 3\sqrt{5 \cdot 500} = 3\sqrt{2500} = 3 \cdot 50 = 150$

7. $\left(3 + \sqrt{2}\right)\left(3 - \sqrt{2}\right) = 3^2 - \left(\sqrt{2}\right)^2 = 9 - 2 = 7$

8. $\left(3 + \sqrt{2}\right)^2 = 3^2 + 2(3)\sqrt{2} + \left(\sqrt{2}\right)^2$

$$= 9 + 6\sqrt{2} + 2$$
$$= 11 + 6\sqrt{2}$$

9. $\dfrac{8}{\sqrt{10}} = \dfrac{8}{\sqrt{10}} \cdot \dfrac{\sqrt{10}}{\sqrt{10}} = \dfrac{8\sqrt{10}}{10} = \dfrac{4\sqrt{10}}{5}$

10. $\dfrac{5}{\sqrt{12} - 2} = \dfrac{5}{\sqrt{12} - 2} \cdot \dfrac{\sqrt{12} + 2}{\sqrt{12} + 2}$

$$= \frac{5\left(\sqrt{12} + 2\right)}{\left(\sqrt{12}\right)^2 - 2^2}$$

$$= \frac{5\left(\sqrt{12} + 2\right)}{12 - 4}$$

$$= \frac{5\left(2\sqrt{3} + 2\right)}{8}$$

$$= \frac{10\left(\sqrt{3} + 1\right)}{8}$$

$$= \frac{5\left(\sqrt{3} + 1\right)}{4}$$

11. *Verbal Model:* $\boxed{\text{Perimeter}} = 2 \cdot \boxed{\text{Length}} + 2 \cdot \boxed{\text{Width}}$

$$50 = 2l + 2w$$
$$25 = l + w$$
$$25 - w = l$$

Common Formula: $a^2 + b^2 = c^2$

Equation:
$$(25 - w)^2 + w^2 = \left(5\sqrt{13}\right)^2$$
$$625 - 50w + w^2 + w^2 = (25)(13)$$
$$2w^2 - 50w + 300 = 0$$
$$w^2 - 25w + 150 = 0$$
$$(w - 10)(w - 15) = 0$$
$$w = 10 \qquad\qquad w = 15$$
$$25 - w = 15 \qquad 25 - w = 10$$

10 inches $\times$ 15 inches

12.
$$p = 75 - \sqrt{1.2(x - 10)}$$
$$59.90 = 75 - \sqrt{1.2(x - 10)}$$
$$-15.10 = -\sqrt{1.2(x - 10)}$$
$$(-15.10)^2 = \left(-\sqrt{1.2(x - 10)}\right)^2$$
$$228.01 = 1.2(x - 10)$$
$$190.00 \approx x - 10$$
$$200 \text{ units} \approx x$$

SECTION 6.4   Applications of Quadratic Equations

1. $m = \dfrac{y_2 - y_1}{x_2 - x_1}$

2. (a) Slope-intercept form: $y = mx + b$

(b) Point-slope form: $y - y_1 = m(x - x_1)$

(c) General form: $Ax + By + C = 0$

(d) Horizontal line: $y - b = 0$

3. $(0, 0), (4, -2)$

$$m = \frac{-2 - 0}{4 - 0} = \frac{-2}{4} = \frac{-1}{2}$$

$$y = -\frac{1}{2}x$$

$$2y = -x$$

$$x + 2y = 0$$

4. $(0, 0), (100, 75)$

$$m = \frac{75 - 0}{100 - 0} = \frac{75}{100} = \frac{3}{4}$$

$$y - 0 = \frac{3}{4}(x - 0)$$

$$y = \frac{3}{4}x$$

$$4y = 3x$$

$$0 = 3x - 4y$$

5. $(-1, -2), (3, 6)$

$$m = \frac{6 - (-2)}{3 - (-1)} = \frac{6 + 2}{3 + 1} = \frac{8}{4} = 2$$

$$y - 6 = 2(x - 3)$$

$$y - 6 = 2x - 6$$

$$0 = 2x - y$$

6. $(1, 5), (6, 0)$

$$m = \frac{0 - 5}{6 - 1} = \frac{-5}{5} = -1$$

$$y - 0 = -1(x - 6)$$

$$y = -x + 6$$

$$x + y - 6 = 0$$

7. $\left(\dfrac{3}{2}, 8\right), \left(\dfrac{11}{2}, \dfrac{5}{2}\right)$

$$m = \frac{\frac{5}{2} - 8}{\frac{11}{2} - \frac{3}{2}} \cdot \frac{2}{2} = \frac{5 - 16}{11 - 3} = \frac{-11}{8}$$

$$y - 8 = \frac{-11}{8}\left(x - \frac{3}{2}\right)$$

$$y - 8 = \frac{-11}{8}x + \frac{33}{16}$$

$$16y - 128 = -22x + 33$$

$$22x + 16y - 161 = 0$$

8. $(0, 2), (7.3, 15.4)$

$$m = \frac{15.4 - 2}{7.3 - 0} = \frac{13.4}{7.3} = \frac{134}{73}$$

$$y - 2 = \frac{134}{73}(x - 0)$$

$$y - 2 = \frac{134}{73}x$$

$$73y - 146 = 134x$$

$$0 = 134x - 73y + 146$$

9. $(0, 8), (5, 8)$

$$m = \frac{8 - 8}{5 - 0} = \frac{0}{5} = 0$$

$$y - 8 = 0(x - 0)$$

$$y - 8 = 0$$

10. $(-3, 2), (-3, 5)$

$$m = \frac{5 - 2}{(-3) - (-3)} = \frac{3}{0} = \text{undefined}$$

$$x = -3$$

$$x + 3 = 0$$

11. *Verbal Model:* $\boxed{\begin{array}{c}\text{Cost per person}\\ \text{current group}\end{array}} - \boxed{\begin{array}{c}\text{Cost per person}\\ \text{new group}\end{array}} = 6250$

Labels: Number current group $= x$

Number new group $= x + 2$

Equation:

$$\frac{250{,}000}{x} - \frac{250{,}000}{x + 2} = 6250$$

$$x(x + 2)\left(\frac{250{,}000}{x} - \frac{250{,}000}{x + 2}\right) = (6250)x(x + 2)$$

$$250{,}000(x + 2) - 250{,}000x = 6250(x^2 + 2x)$$

$$250{,}000x + 500{,}000 - 250{,}000x = 6250x^2 + 12{,}500x$$

$$0 = 6250x^2 + 12{,}500x - 500{,}000$$

$$0 = x^2 + 2x - 80$$

$$0 = (x + 10)(x - 8)$$

$$x = -10 \qquad x = 8 \text{ people}$$

$$\text{Reject}$$

12. *Verbal Model:* $\boxed{\begin{array}{c}\text{Time}\\ \text{upstream}\end{array}} + \boxed{\begin{array}{c}\text{Time}\\ \text{downstream}\end{array}} = \boxed{\begin{array}{c}\text{Total}\\ \text{time}\end{array}}$

Labels: Speed of the current $= x$

Equation:

$$\frac{35}{18 - x} + \frac{35}{18 + x} = 4$$

$$(18 - x)(18 + x)\left(\frac{35}{18 - x} + \frac{35}{18 + x}\right) = (4)(18 - x)(18 + x)$$

$$35(18 + x) + 35(18 - x) = 4(324 - x^2)$$

$$630 + 35x + 630 - 35x = 1296 - 4x^2$$

$$4x^2 - 36 = 0$$

$$4(x^2 - 9) = 0$$

$$x^2 = 9$$

$$x = \pm 3$$

Reject -3

$x = 3$ miles per hour

SECTION 6.5   Quadratic and Rational Inequalities

1. 36.82×10^8 is not written in scientific notation. The number must be between 1 and 10 such as 3.682×10^9.

2. $(n_1 \times 10^2)(n_2 \times 10^4) = n_1 \cdot n_2 \cdot 10^{2+4}$

$$= n_1 \cdot n_2 \cdot 10^6$$

$$1 \le n_1 < 10 \quad \text{and} \quad 1 \le n_2 < 10$$

$$[1 \cdot 1 \le n_1 \cdot n_2 < 10 \cdot 10]10^6$$

$$10^6 \le (n_1 \times 10^2)(n_2 \times 10^4) < 10^8$$

3. $6u^2v - 192v^2 = 6v(u^2 - 32v)$

4. $5x^{2/3} - 10x^{1/3} = 5x^{1/3}(x^{1/3} - 2)$

5. $x(x - 10) - 4(x - 10) = (x - 4)(x - 10)$

6. $x^3 + 3x^2 - 4x - 12 = (x^3 + 3x^2) + (-4x - 12)$

$$= x^2(x + 3) - 4(x + 3)$$

$$= (x + 3)(x^2 - 4)$$

$$= (x + 3)(x - 2)(x + 2)$$

7. $16x^2 - 121 = (4x - 11)(4x + 11)$

8. $4x^3 - 12x^2 + 16x = 4x(x^2 - 3x + 4)$

9. Area = Length · Width

$$A = \frac{3}{2}h \cdot h$$

$$= \frac{3}{2}h^2$$

10. Area $= \frac{1}{2} \cdot$ Base · Height

$$= \frac{1}{2} \cdot b \cdot \frac{2}{3}b$$

$$= \frac{1}{3}b^2$$

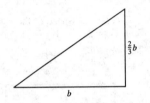

11. Divide figure into 5 congruent squares, each with side length x.

Area $= 5 \cdot$ Area of square

$$= 5 \cdot x^2$$

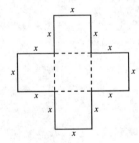

12. Area = Area of rectangle + Area of triangle

$$= x \cdot (x + 6) + \frac{1}{2} \cdot x \cdot 4$$

$$= x^2 + 6x + 2x$$

$$= x^2 + 8x$$

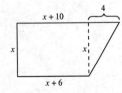

CHAPTER 7   Linear Models and Graphs of Nonlinear Models

SECTION 7.1   Variation

1.
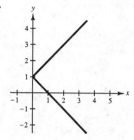
For some x there corresponds more than one value of y.

2.
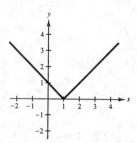
For each x there corresponds exactly one value of y.

3. $f(x) = x^2 - 4x + 9$
    Domain: $(-\infty, \infty)$

4. $h(x) = \dfrac{x - 1}{x^2(x^2 + 1)}$
    Domain: $x^2(x^2 + 1) \neq 0$
    $\qquad x^2 \neq 0 \qquad x^2 + 1 \neq 0$
    $\qquad\qquad x \neq 0$
    $\qquad (-\infty, 0) \cup (0, \infty)$

5. $f(x) = 2x^3 - 3x^2 - 18x + 27$
    $\qquad = (2x - 3)(x + 3)(x - 3)$

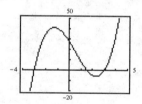

Yes, graphs are the same.

6. $(2x - 3)(x + 3)(x - 3) = (2x - 3)(x^2 - 9)$
    $\qquad\qquad\qquad\qquad = 2x^3 - 18x - 3x^2 + 27$
    $\qquad\qquad\qquad\qquad = 2x^3 - 3x^2 - 18x + 27$

7. $\dfrac{2x^3 - 3x^2 - 18x + 27}{2x - 3}$

$$
\begin{array}{r}
x^2 \qquad\quad - 9 \\
2x - 3 \,\overline{\smash{)}\, 2x^3 - 3x^2 - 18x + 27} \\
\underline{2x^3 - 3x^2} \qquad\qquad\quad \\
-18x + 27 \\
\underline{-18x + 27} \\
0
\end{array}
$$

$x^2 - 9 = (x - 3)(x + 3)$

8. $\dfrac{2x^3 - 3x^2 - 18x + 27}{x^2 - 9} = x^2 - 9 \,\overline{\smash{)}\, 2x^3 - 3x^2 - 18x + 27}$

$$
\begin{array}{r}
2x - 3 \qquad\qquad\qquad\quad \\
x^2 - 9 \,\overline{\smash{)}\, 2x^3 - 3x^2 - 18x + 27} \\
\underline{2x^3 \qquad\quad - 18x} \qquad\quad \\
-3x^2 \qquad\quad + 27 \\
\underline{-3x^2 \qquad\quad + 27} \\
0
\end{array}
$$

9. $f(x) = x^2 - 3$

$$\frac{f(2+h) - f(2)}{h} = \frac{(2+h)^2 - 3 - (2^2 - 3)}{h}$$

$$= \frac{4 + 4h + h^2 - 3 - 4 + 3}{h}$$

$$= \frac{4h + h^2}{h}$$

$$= \frac{h(4+h)}{h}$$

$$= 4 + h$$

10. $f(x) = \dfrac{3}{x+5}$

$$\frac{f(2+h) - f(2)}{h} = \frac{\dfrac{3}{(2+h)+5} - \dfrac{3}{2+5}}{h}$$

$$= \frac{\dfrac{3}{7+h} - \dfrac{3}{7}}{h} \cdot \frac{7(7+h)}{7(7+h)}$$

$$= \frac{21 - 3(7+h)}{7h(7+h)}$$

$$= \frac{21 - 21 - 3h}{7h(7+h)}$$

$$= \frac{-3h}{7h(7+h)}$$

$$= \frac{-3}{7(7+h)}$$

SECTION 7.2   Graphs of Linear Inequalities

1. $\sqrt[4]{6x}$ index $= 4$, radicand $= 6x$

2. $a^{\frac{1}{n}}$ in radical form is $\sqrt[n]{a}$.

3.
$$7 - 3x > 4 - x$$
$$7 - 3x + x > 4 - x + x$$
$$7 - 2x > 4$$
$$7 - 2x - 7 > 4 - 7$$
$$-2x > -3$$
$$\frac{-2x}{-2} < \frac{-3}{-2}$$
$$x < \frac{3}{2}$$

4.
$$2(x+6) - 20 < 2$$
$$2x + 12 - 20 < 2$$
$$2x - 8 < 2$$
$$2x - 8 + 8 < 2 + 8$$
$$2x < 10$$
$$\frac{2x}{2} < \frac{10}{2}$$
$$x < 5$$

5.
$$\frac{x}{6} + \frac{x}{4} < 1$$
$$12\left(\frac{x}{6} + \frac{x}{4}\right) < (1)12$$
$$2x + 3x < 12$$
$$5x < 12$$
$$\frac{5x}{5} < \frac{12}{5}$$
$$x < \frac{12}{5}$$

6.
$$\frac{5-x}{2} \geq 8$$
$$2\left(\frac{5-x}{2}\right) \geq (8)2$$
$$5 - x \geq 16$$
$$5 - 5 - x \geq 16 - 5$$
$$-x \geq 11$$
$$\frac{-x}{-1} \leq \frac{11}{-1}$$
$$x \leq -11$$

7.
$$|x - 3| < 2$$
$$-2 < x - 3 < 2$$
$$-2 + 3 < x - 3 + 3 < 2 + 3$$
$$1 < x < 5$$

8. $|x - 5| > 3$

$$x - 5 < -3 \qquad \text{or} \qquad x - 5 > 3$$

$$x - 5 + 5 < -3 + 5 \qquad x - 5 + 5 > 3 + 5$$

$$x < 2 \qquad \text{or} \qquad x > 8$$

9. $g(x) = x^5 - 2$

Keystrokes:

$\boxed{Y=}$ $\boxed{X,T,\theta}$ $\boxed{\wedge}$ 5 $\boxed{-}$ 2 $\boxed{GRAPH}$

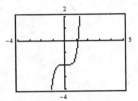

Vertical shift 2 units downward

10. $g(x) = (x - 2)^5$

Keystrokes:

$\boxed{Y=}$ $\boxed{(}$ $\boxed{X,T,\theta}$ $\boxed{-}$ 2 $\boxed{)}$ $\boxed{\wedge}$ 5 $\boxed{GRAPH}$

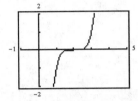

Horizontal shift 2 units to the right

11. $g(x) = -x^5$

Keystrokes:

$\boxed{Y=}$ $\boxed{(-)}$ $\boxed{X,T,\theta}$ $\boxed{\wedge}$ 5 $\boxed{GRAPH}$

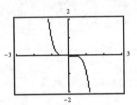

Reflection in the x-axis

12. $g(x) = (-x)^5$

Keystrokes:

$\boxed{Y=}$ $\boxed{(}$ $\boxed{(-)}$ $\boxed{X,T,\theta}$ $\boxed{)}$ $\boxed{\wedge}$ 5 $\boxed{GRAPH}$

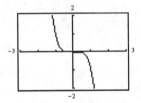

Reflection in the y-axis

SECTION 7.3 Graphs of Quadratic Functions

1. $(x + b)^2 = x^2 + 2bx + b^2$

(Recall $(x + b)^2 = (x + b)(x + b)$ then multiply by FOIL.)

2. $x^2 + 5x + \frac{25}{4}$

To complete the square, take one-half of b and square it.

$\left(\frac{1}{2}b\right)^2$

3. $(4x + 3y) - 3(5x + y) = 4x + 3y - 15x - 3y$

$$= -11x$$

4. $(-15u + 4v) + 5(3u - 9v) = -15u + 4v + 15u - 45v$

$$= -41v$$

5. $2x^2 + (2x - 3)^2 + 12x = 2x^2 + 4x^2 - 12x + 9 + 12x$

$$= 6x^2 + 9$$

6. $y^2 - (y + 2)^2 + 4y = y^2 - (y^2 + 4y + 4) + 4y$

$$= y^2 - y^2 - 4y - 4 + 4y$$

$$= -4$$

7. $\sqrt{24x^2y^3} = \sqrt{4 \cdot 6 \cdot x^2 \cdot y^2 \cdot y}$

$\qquad = 2|x|y\sqrt{6y}$

8. $\sqrt[3]{9} \cdot \sqrt[3]{15} = \sqrt[3]{9 \cdot 15}$

$\qquad = \sqrt[3]{3^3 \cdot 5}$

$\qquad = 3\sqrt[3]{5}$

9. $(12a^{-4}b^6)^{1/2} = \sqrt{\dfrac{12b^6}{a^4}} = \sqrt{\dfrac{4 \cdot 3 \cdot b^6}{a^4}} = \dfrac{2b^3}{a^2}\sqrt{3}$

10. $(16^{1/3})^{3/4} = 16^{1/3 \cdot 3/4} = 16^{1/4} = \sqrt[4]{16} = 2$

11. $h = -16t^2 + s_0$

$\qquad s_0 = 80 \qquad h = 0$

$\qquad 0 = -16t^2 + 80$

$\qquad 16t^2 = 80$

$\qquad t^2 = 5$

$\qquad t = \pm\sqrt{5}$

$\qquad$ Reject $-\sqrt{5}$

$\qquad t = \sqrt{5} \approx 2.24$ seconds

12. $h = -16t^2 + s_0$

$\qquad s_0 = 150 \qquad h = 0$

$\qquad 0 = -16t^2 + 150$

$\qquad 16t^2 = 150$

$\qquad t^2 = \dfrac{150}{16}$

$\qquad t = \pm\sqrt{\dfrac{150}{16}}$

$\qquad$ Reject $-\sqrt{\dfrac{150}{16}}$

$\qquad t = \dfrac{\sqrt{25 \cdot 6}}{4} = \dfrac{5\sqrt{6}}{4} \approx 3.06$ seconds

SECTION 7.4   Conic Sections

1. $(3t + 1) - (3t + 1) = 0$ illustrates the Additive Inverse Property.

2. $3x(x - 2) = 3x^2 - 6x$ illustrates the Distributive Property.

3. $2(3y) = (2 \cdot 3)y$ illustrates the Associative Property of Multiplication.

4. $-3 + x = x - 3$ illustrates the Commutative Property of Addition.

5. $(x^2 \cdot x^3)^4 = (x^{2+3})^4 = (x^5)^4 = x^{20}$

6. $4^{-2} \cdot x^2 = \dfrac{x^2}{4^2} = \dfrac{x^2}{16}$

7. $\dfrac{15y^{-3}}{10y^2} = \dfrac{5 \cdot 3y^{-3-2}}{5 \cdot 2} = \dfrac{3}{2}y^{-5} = \dfrac{3}{2y^5}$

8. $\left(\dfrac{3x^2}{2y}\right)^{-2} = \left(\dfrac{2y}{3x^2}\right)^2 = \dfrac{4y^2}{9x^4}$

9. $\dfrac{3x^2y^3}{18x^{-1}y^2} = \dfrac{3x^{2-(-1)}y^{3-2}}{6 \cdot 3} = \dfrac{1x^3y^1}{6} = \dfrac{x^3y}{6}$

10. $(x^2 + 1)^0 = 1$

11. *Verbal model:*

$$\boxed{\dfrac{\text{Total cost}}{\begin{array}{c}\text{Original}\\\text{number}\\\text{of persons}\end{array}}} - \boxed{\dfrac{\text{Total cost}}{\begin{array}{c}\text{Original}\\\text{number of}\\\text{persons now}\end{array}}} = 8$$

Labels: Original number of persons $= x$

Number of persons now $= x + 3$

Equation:

$$\frac{288}{x} - \frac{288}{x+3} = 8$$

$$288(x+3) - 288x = 8x(x+3)$$

$$288x + 864 - 288x = 8x^2 + 24x$$

$$0 = 8x^2 + 24x - 864$$

$$0 = x^2 + 3x - 108$$

$$0 = (x+12)(x-9)$$

$x = -12$ $x = 9$ people

discard $x + 3 = 12$ people

12. *Verbal model:*

$$\boxed{\dfrac{\text{Total cost}}{\begin{array}{c}\text{Original}\\\text{number}\\\text{of persons}\end{array}}} - \boxed{\dfrac{\text{Total cost}}{\begin{array}{c}\text{Original}\\\text{number of}\\\text{persons now}\end{array}}} = 1500$$

Labels: Original number of persons $= x$

Number of persons now $= x + 3$

Equation:

$$\frac{135{,}000}{x} - \frac{135{,}000}{x+3} = 1500$$

$$135{,}000(x+3) - 135{,}000x = 1500x(x+3)$$

$$135{,}000x + 405{,}000 - 135{,}000x = 1500x^2 + 4500x$$

$$0 = 1500x^2 + 4500x - 405{,}000$$

$$0 = x^2 + 3x - 270$$

$$0 = (x-15)(x+18)$$

$x = 15$ $x = -18$

$x + 3 = 18$ discard

SECTION 7.5   Graphs of Rational Functions

1. Leading coefficient in $7x^2 + 3x - 4$ is 7. It is the coefficient of the ax^2-term.

2. Degree is 5.

$$(x^4 + 3)(x - 4) = x^5 - 4x^4 + 3x - 12$$

3. Many answers

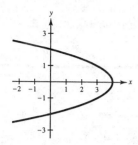

For some x there corresponds more than one value of y.

5. $-2x^5(5x^3) = -10x^8$

7. $(2x - 15)^2 = (2x - 15)(2x - 15)$
$$= 4x^2 - 60x + 225$$

9. $[(x + 1) - y][(x + 1) + y] = (x + 1)^2 - y^2$
$$= x^2 + 2x + 1 - y^2$$
$$= x^2 - y^2 + 2x + 1$$

11. *Verbal Model:* $\boxed{\text{Area}} = \dfrac{1}{2} \cdot \boxed{\text{Base}} \cdot \boxed{\text{Height}}$

Labels: Area $= A = 80$
Base $= x$
Height $= x - 12$

Equation: $A = \dfrac{1}{2} \cdot x \cdot (x - 12)$

$$80 = \dfrac{1}{2}x^2 - 6x$$

$$0 = x^2 - 12x - 160$$

$$0 = (x - 20)(x + 8)$$

$$x = 20 \text{ meters} \quad x = -8$$

$x - 12 = 8$ meters

Base $= 20$ meters

Height $= 8$ meters

4. Many answers

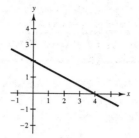

For each x there corresponds exactly one value of y.

6. $3x(5 - 2x) = 15x - 6x^2$

8. $(3x + 2)(7x - 10) = 21x^2 + 14x - 30x - 20$
$$= 21x^2 - 16x - 20$$

10. $(x + 3)(x^2 - 3x + 9) = x^3 - 3x^2 + 9x + 3x^2 - 9x + 27$
$$= x^3 + 27$$

12. *Verbal Model:* $\boxed{\begin{array}{c}\text{Surface}\\\text{area}\end{array}} = \boxed{\begin{array}{c}\text{Area of}\\\text{bottom}\end{array}} + 4 \cdot \boxed{\begin{array}{c}\text{Area of}\\\text{one side}\end{array}}$

Labels: Surface area $= 825$
Area of bottom $= x \cdot x$
Area of one side $= 10 \cdot x$

Equation: $825 = x \cdot x + 4(10 \cdot x)$

$$825 = x^2 + 40x$$

$$0 = x^2 + 40x - 825$$

$$0 = (x + 55)(x - 15)$$

$$x + 55 = 0 \qquad x - 15 = 0$$

$$x = -55 \qquad x = 15 \text{ inches}$$

15 inches $\times$ 15 inches

CHAPTER 8   Systems of Equations

SECTION 8.1   Systems of Equations

1. Answers vary.

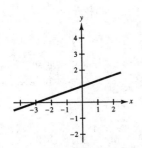

2. Answers vary.

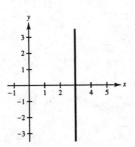

3. $\frac{3}{2}$

$$m_1 \cdot m_2 = -1$$

$$-\frac{2}{3} \cdot \frac{3}{2} = -1$$

4. The line with $m = -3$ is steeper because this line's slope is the greater absolute value.

5. $y - 3(4y - 2) = 1$

$$y - 12y + 6 = 1$$

$$-11y = -5$$

$$y = \frac{5}{11}$$

6. $x + 6(3 - 2x) = 4$

$$x + 18 - 12x = 4$$

$$-11x = -14$$

$$x = \frac{14}{11}$$

7. $\frac{1}{2}x + \frac{1}{5}x = 15$

$$5x + 2x = 150$$

$$7x = 150$$

$$x = \frac{150}{7}$$

8. $\frac{1}{10}(x - 4) = 6$

$$x - 4 = 60$$

$$x = 64$$

9. $3x + 4y - 5 = 0$

$$4y = -3x + 5$$

$$y = -\frac{3}{4}x + \frac{5}{4}$$

10. $-2x - 3y + 6 = 0$

$$-3y = 2x - 6$$

$$y = \frac{2}{-3}x + 2$$

11. $y = -3x + 2$

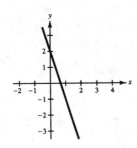

12. $4x - 2y = -4$

$$-2y = -4x - 4$$

$$y = 2x + 2$$

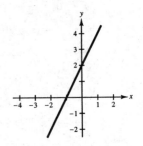

13. $3x + 2y = 8$

$2y = -3x + 8$

$y = -\frac{3}{2}x + 4$

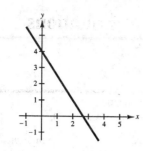

14. $x + 3 = 0$

$x = -3$

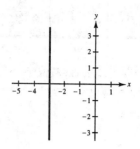

SECTION 8.2   Linear Systems in Two Variables

1. $2(x + y) = 2x + 2y$

Distributive Property

2. $x - 4 = 7$

$x - 4 + 4 = 7 + 4$

$x = 11$

Addition Property of Equality

3. $1 < 2x + 5 < 9$

$-4 < 2x < 4$

$-2 < x < 2$

4. $0 \le \dfrac{x - 4}{2} < 6$

$0 \le x - 4 < 12$

$4 \le x < 16$

5. $|6x| > 12$

$6x > 12$ or $6x < -12$

$x > 2$ $x < -2$

6. $|1 - 2x| < 5$

$-5 < 1 - 2x < 5$

$-6 < -2x < 4$

$3 > x > -2$

$-2 < x < 3$

7. $4x - 12 < 0$

$4x < 12$

$x < 3$

8. $4x + 4 \ge 9$

$4x \ge 5$

$x \ge \frac{5}{4}$

9. *Verbal Model:* $\boxed{\text{Total cost}} = \boxed{\text{Number of miles}} \cdot \boxed{\text{Cost per mile}} + \boxed{\text{Initial cost}}$

$C = 0.45m + 6200$

Equation: $C < 15,000$

$0.45m + 6200 < 15,000$

$0.45m < 8800$

$m < \dfrac{8800}{0.45}$

$m\,19,555.56$

10. *Verbal Model:* $\boxed{\text{Payment Plan 1}} = 2500$

$\boxed{\text{Payment Plan 2}} = 4\% \cdot \boxed{\text{Gross sales}} + 1500$

$\boxed{\text{Payment Plan 2}} > \boxed{\text{Payment Plan 1}}$

Labels: Gross sales $= x$

Equation: $0.04x + 1500 > 2500$

$0.04x > 1000$

$x > \$25,000$

SECTION 8.3 Linear Systems in Three Variables

1. No, $2x + 8 = 7$ has only one solution.

$$2x + 8 = 7$$
$$2x = -1$$
$$x = -\frac{1}{2}$$

2. $\dfrac{t}{6} + \dfrac{5}{8} = \dfrac{7}{4}$

Multiply both sides of the equation by the lowest common denominator, 24.

3. $4x^2(x^3)^2 = 4x^2 \cdot x^6 = 4x^8$

4. $(2x^2y)^3(xy^3)^4 = 8x^6y^3 \cdot x^4y^{12}$
$$= 8x^{10}y^{15}$$

5. $\dfrac{8x^{-4}}{2x^7} = 4x^{-4-(7)} = 4x^{-11} = \dfrac{4}{x^{11}}$

6. $\left(\dfrac{t^4}{3}\right)^{-1} = \dfrac{3}{t^4}$

7. $|2x - 4| = 6$

$2x - 4 = 6 \quad$ or $\quad 2x - 4 = -6$
$\quad 2x = 10 \qquad\qquad 2x = -2$
$\qquad x = 5 \qquad\qquad\quad x = -1$

8. $\frac{1}{4}(5 - 2x) = 9x - 7x$
$$\tfrac{1}{4}(5 - 2x) = 2x$$
$$5 - 2x = 8x$$
$$5 = 10x$$
$$\tfrac{5}{10} = x$$
$$\tfrac{1}{2} = x$$

9. *Verbal Model:* $\boxed{\text{Distance}} = \boxed{\text{Rate}} \cdot \boxed{\text{Time}}$

$$d = 15t$$

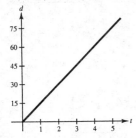

10. *Verbal Model:* $\boxed{\text{Volume}} = (\text{side})^3$

Labels: $\quad$ Volume $= V$

$\qquad\qquad$ Side $= s$

Equation: $\quad V = s^3$

11. Area $= \pi \cdot (\text{radius})^2 \qquad$ Circumference $= 2 \cdot \pi \cdot \text{radius}$

$$A = \pi r^2 \qquad\qquad\qquad C = 2\pi r$$

$$A = \pi\left(\dfrac{C}{2\pi}\right)^2 \qquad\qquad \dfrac{C}{2\pi} = r$$

$$A = \pi \cdot \dfrac{C^2}{4\pi^2}$$

$$A = \dfrac{C^2}{4\pi}$$

SECTION 8.4   Matrices and Linear Systems

1. $2ab - 2ab = 0$

Additive Inverse Property

2. $8t \cdot 1 = 8t$

Multiplicative Identity Property

3. $b + 3a = 3a + b$

Commutative Property of Addition

4. $3(2x) = (3 \cdot 2)x$

Associative Property of Multiplication

5. $(-3, 2), \left(-\frac{3}{2}, -2\right)$

$$m = \frac{y_2 - y_1}{x_2 - x_1}$$

$$= \frac{-2 - 2}{-\frac{3}{2} - (-3)}$$

$$= \frac{-4}{-\frac{3}{2} + 3}$$

$$= \frac{-4}{\frac{3}{2}}$$

$$= -4 \cdot \frac{2}{3} = -\frac{8}{3}$$

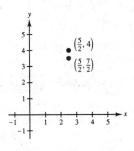

6. $(0, -6), (8, 0)$

$$m = \frac{y_2 - y_1}{x_2 - x_1}$$

$$= \frac{0 - (-6)}{8 - 0}$$

$$= \frac{6}{8}$$

$$= \frac{3}{4}$$

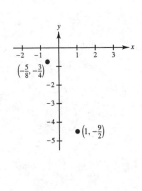

7. $\left(\frac{5}{2}, \frac{7}{2}\right), \left(\frac{5}{2}, 4\right)$

$$m = \frac{y_2 - y_1}{x_2 - x_1}$$

$$= \frac{4 - \frac{7}{2}}{\frac{5}{2} - \frac{5}{2}}$$

$$= \frac{\frac{1}{2}}{0} = \text{undefined}$$

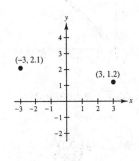

8. $\left(-\frac{5}{8}, -\frac{3}{4}\right), \left(1, -\frac{9}{2}\right)$

$$m = \frac{y_2 - y_1}{x_2 - x_1}$$

$$= \frac{-\frac{9}{2} - \left(-\frac{3}{4}\right)}{1 - \left(-\frac{5}{8}\right)}$$

$$= \frac{-\frac{18}{4} + \frac{3}{4}}{\frac{8}{8} + \frac{5}{8}} = \frac{-\frac{15}{4}}{\frac{13}{8}}$$

$$= -\frac{15}{4} \cdot \frac{8}{13}$$

$$= -\frac{30}{13}$$

9. $(3, 1.2), (-3, 2.1)$

$$m = \frac{y_2 - y_1}{x_2 - x_1}$$

$$= \frac{2.1 - 1.2}{-3 - 3}$$

$$= \frac{0.9}{-6}$$

$$= -0.15$$

10. $(12, 8), (6, 8)$

$m = \dfrac{y_2 - y_1}{x_2 - x_1}$

$= \dfrac{8 - 8}{12 - 6}$

$= \dfrac{0}{6}$

$= 0$

11. *Verbal Model:*

$\boxed{\begin{array}{c}\text{Current}\\\text{number}\\\text{members}\end{array}} = \boxed{\begin{array}{c}\text{Number}\\\text{members}\\\text{before drive}\end{array}} + 10\% \cdot \boxed{\begin{array}{c}\text{Number}\\\text{members}\\\text{before drive}\end{array}}$

Labels: Number members before drive $= x$

Equation: $8415 = x + 0.10x$

$8415 = 1.10x$

$7650 = x$

12. *Verbal Model:*

$\boxed{\begin{array}{c}\text{Amount}\\\text{increase}\end{array}} = 4\% \cdot \boxed{\text{Price}}$

Labels: Amount increase $= x$

Price $= \$23,500$

Equation: $x = 0.04(23,500)$

$x = \$940$

SECTION 8.5   Determinants and Linear Systems

1. $(px + m)(qx + n) = ax^2 + bx + c$

$pqx^2 + pnx + mqx + mn$

$(pq)x^2 + (pn + mq)x + mn$

So $a = pq$.

2. $(px + m)(qx + n) = ax^2 + bx + c$

$pqx^2 + pnx + mqx + mn$

$(pq)x^2 + (pn + mq)x + mn$

So $b = pn + mq$.

3. $(px + m)(qx + n) = ax^2 + bx + c$

$pqx^2 + pnx + mqx + mn$

$(pq)x^2 + (pn + mq)x + mn$

So $c = mn$.

4. If $a = 1$ then $p = 1$ and $q = 1$ or $p = -1$ and $q = -1$.

5. $3x^2 + 9x - 12 = 0$

$3(x^2 + 3x - 4) = 0$

$3(x + 4)(x - 1) = 0$

$x = -4 \quad x = 1$

6. $x^2 - x - 6 = 0$

$(x - 3)(x + 2) = 0$

$x = 3 \quad x = -2$

7. $4x^2 - 20x + 25 = 0$

$(2x - 5)(2x - 5) = 0$

$x = \frac{5}{2} \quad x = \frac{5}{2}$

8. $x^2 - 16 = 0$

$(x - 4)(x + 4) = 0$

$x = 4 \qquad x = -4$

9. $x^3 + 64 = 0$

$(x + 4)(x^2 - 4x + 16) = 0$

$x = -4 \qquad x^2 - 4x + 16 = 0$

Not real

10. $3x^3 - 6x^2 + 4x - 8 = 0$

$3x^2(x - 2) + 4(x - 2) = 0$

$(x - 2)(3x^2 + 4) = 0$

$x = 2 \qquad 3x^2 + 4 = 0$

Not real

11. *Verbal Model:* $\boxed{\text{Distance}} = \boxed{\text{Rate}} \cdot \boxed{\text{Time}}$

Equation $320 = r \cdot t$

$\dfrac{320}{r} = t$

12. *Verbal Model:* $\text{Perimeter} = \boxed{\begin{array}{c}\text{Length}\\ \text{side 1}\end{array}} + \boxed{\begin{array}{c}\text{Length}\\ \text{side 2}\end{array}} + \boxed{\begin{array}{c}\text{Length}\\ \text{side 3}\end{array}}$

Equation: $P = (x + 1) + \left(\dfrac{1}{2}x + 5\right) + (3x + 1)$

$= \left(x + \dfrac{1}{2}x + 3x\right) + (1 + 5 + 1)$

$= \dfrac{9}{2}x + 7$

CHAPTER 9   Exponential and Logarithmic Functions

SECTION 9.1   Exponential Functions

1. Graph the line $x + y = 5$. Test one point in each of the half-planes formed by this line. If the point satisfies the inequality, shade the entire half-plane to denote that every point in the region satisfies the inequality.

2. $3x - 5y \le 15$ and $3x - 5y < 15$

The difference between the two graphs is that the first contains the boundary (because of the equal sign) and the second does not.

3. $y > x - 2$

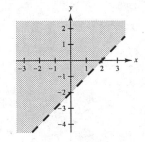

Test point: $(0, 0)$

$0 > 0 - 2$

True

4. $y \le 5 - \dfrac{3}{2}x$

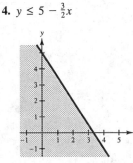

Test point: $(0, 0)$

$0 \le 5 - 0$

True

5. $y < \dfrac{2}{3}x - 1$

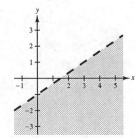

Test point: $(3, -1)$

$-1 < \dfrac{2}{3}(3) - 1$

$-1 < 1$

True

Test point: $(0, 0)$

$0 < 0 - 1$

False

6. $x > 6 - y$

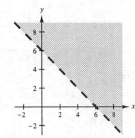

Test point: $(0, 0)$

$0 > 6 - 0$

False

7. $y \leq -2$

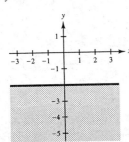

Test point: $(0, -4)$

$-4 \leq -2$

True

8. $x > 7$

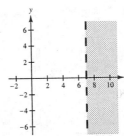

Test point: $(8, 0)$

$8 > 7$

True

9. $2x + 3y \geq 6$

$3y \geq -2x + 6$

$y \geq -\frac{2}{3}x + 2$

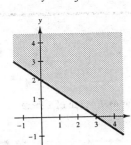

Test point: $(3, 2)$

$2 \geq -\frac{2}{3}(3) + 2$

$2 \geq 0$

True

10. $5x - 2y < 5$

$-2y < 5 - 5x$

$y > \frac{5}{2}x - \frac{5}{2}$

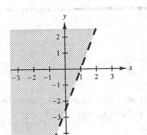

Test point: $(0, 0)$

$0 > 0 - \frac{5}{2}$

True

11.

Verbal Model:

| Rate for person 1 | + | Rate for person 2 | = | Rate together |

Labels:

Rate for person 1 $= \dfrac{1}{x}$

Rate for person 2 $= \dfrac{1}{x + 3}$

Rate together $= \dfrac{1}{10}$

Equation:

$$\frac{1}{x} + \frac{1}{x + 3} = \frac{1}{10}$$

$$10x(x + 3)\left(\frac{1}{x} + \frac{1}{x + 3}\right) = \left(\frac{1}{10}\right)10x(x + 3)$$

$$10(x + 3) + 10x = x(x + 3)$$

$$10x + 30 + 10x = x^2 + 3x$$

$$0 = x^2 - 17x - 30$$

$$x = \frac{-(-17) \pm \sqrt{(-17)^2 - 4(1)(-30)}}{2(1)}$$

$$x = \frac{17 \pm \sqrt{289 + 120}}{2}$$

$$x = \frac{17 \pm \sqrt{409}}{2}$$

$$x \approx 18.6 \text{ and } -1.61 \text{ (reject)}$$

$$x + 3 \approx 21.6$$

12. *Formula:* $c^2 = a^2 + b^2$

    Labels: $c = $ hypotenuse

             $a = 60$ feet

             $b = 30$ feet

   Equation: $c^2 = 60^2 + 30^2$

              $c^2 = 3600 + 900$

              $c^2 = 4500$

               $c = \sqrt{4500} = \sqrt{900 \cdot 5} = 30\sqrt{5}$

               $c \approx 67.1$ feet

SECTION 9.2   Inverse Functions

1. $x - y^2 = 0$

    $x = y^2$

  $\pm\sqrt{x} = y$

y is not a function of x because for some values of x there correspond two values of y. For example, $(4, 2)$ and $(4, -2)$ are solution points.

2. $|x| - 2y = 4$

    $-2y = -|x| + 4$

      $y = \frac{1}{2}|x| - 2$

y is a function of x because for each value of x there corresponds exactly one value of y.

3. $f(x) = \sqrt{4 - x^2}$, $g(x) = \dfrac{6}{\sqrt{4 - x^2}}$

The domain of f is $[-2, 2]$. The domain of g is $(-2, 2)$. g is undefined at $x = \pm 2$.

4. $h(x) = 8 - \sqrt{x}$ over $\{0, 4, 9, 16\}$

Range: $\{4, 5, 6, 8\}$

$h(0) = 8 - \sqrt{0} = 8$

$h(4) = 8 - \sqrt{4} = 6$

$h(9) = 8 - \sqrt{9} = 5$

$h(16) = 8 - \sqrt{16} = 4$

5. $-(5x^2 - 1) + (3x^2 - 5) = -5x^2 + 1 + 3x^2 - 5$

                          $= -2x^2 - 4$

6. $(-2x)(-5x)(3x + 4) = 10x^2(3x + 4)$

                     $= 30x^3 + 40x^2$

7. $(u - 4v)(u + 4v) = u^2 - 16v^2$ (multiply by FOIL)

8. $(3a - 2b)^2 = (3a - 2b)(3a - 2b)$

             $= 9a^2 - 6ab - 6ab + 4b^2$

             $= 9a^2 - 12ab + 4b^2$

9. $(t - 2)^3 = (t - 2)^2(t - 2)$

          $= (t^2 - 4t + 4)(t - 2)$

          $= t^3 - 4t^2 + 4t - 2t^2 + 8t - 8$

          $= t^3 - 6t^2 + 12t - 8$

10. $\dfrac{6x^3 - 3x^2}{12x} = \dfrac{6x^3}{12x} - \dfrac{3x^2}{12x}$

              $= \dfrac{x^2}{2} - \dfrac{x}{4}$

11. $v = \sqrt{2gh}$

$80 = \sqrt{2(32)h}$

$80 = \sqrt{64h}$

$80^2 = 64h$

$\dfrac{80^2}{64} = h = 100$ feet

12.   *Verbal Model:*

Total cost	=	First minute cost	+	Additional minute cost

Labels: Total cost = 5.15

First minute cost = 0.95

Additional minute cost = 0.35x

Equation: $5.15 = 0.95 + 0.35x$

$4.20 = 0.35x$

$12 = x$

13 minutes

SECTION 9.3   Logarithmic Functions

1. $g(x) = (x - 4)^2$

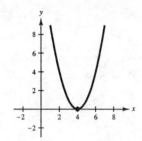

Horizontal shift 4 units right

2. $h(x) = -x^2$

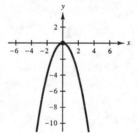

Reflection in the x-axis

3. $j(x) = x^2 + 1$

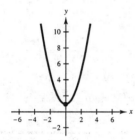

Vertical shift 1 unit up

4. $k(x) = (x + 3)^2 - 5$

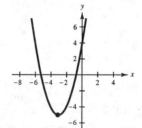

Horizontal shift 3 units left

Vertical shift 5 units down

5. $2x^3 - 6x = 2x(x^2 - 3)$

6. $16 - (y + 2)^2 = [4 - (y + 2)][4 + (y + 2)]$

$= (4 - y - 2)(4 + y + 2)$

$= (2 - y)(6 + y)$

7. $t^2 + 10t + 25 = (t + 5)(t + 5)$

$= (t + 5)^2$

8. $5 - u + 5u^2 - u^3 = 1(5 - u) + u^2(5 - u)$

$= (5 - u)(1 + u^2)$

9. $y = 3 - \frac{1}{2}x$

Intercepts:

$y = 3 - \frac{1}{2}(0) = 3$, $(0, 3)$

$0 = 3 - \frac{1}{2}x$

$\frac{1}{2}x = 3$

$x = 6$, $(6, 0)$

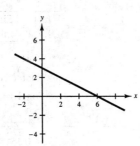

10. $3x - 4y = 6$

Intercepts:

$3(0) - 4y = 6$

$y = -\frac{3}{2}$

$3x - 4(0) = 6$

$3x = 6$

$x = 2$

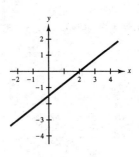

11. $y = x^2 - 6x + 5$

Intercepts: Vertex:

$y = 5$, $(0, 5)$ $y = (x^2 - 6x + 9) + 5 - 9$

$0 = x^2 - 6x + 5$ $= (x - 3)^2 - 4$

$0 = (x - 1)(x - 5)$ $(3, -4)$

$x = 1 \qquad x = 5$

$(1, 0), (5, 0)$

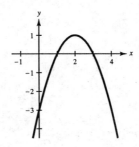

12. $y = -(x - 2)^2 + 1$

Intercepts: Vertex:

$y = -(0 - 2)^2 + 1 = -3$, $(0, -3)$ $(2, 1)$

$0 = -(x - 2)^2 + 1$

$(x - 2)^2 = 1$

$x - 2 = \pm 1$

$x = 2 \pm 1$

$x = 3, 1$

$(3, 0), (1, 0)$

SECTION 9.4   Properties of Logarithms

1. Multiplication Property: $\sqrt[n]{u}\,\sqrt[n]{v} = \sqrt[n]{uv}$

2. Division Property: $\dfrac{\sqrt[n]{u}}{\sqrt[n]{v}} = \sqrt[n]{\dfrac{u}{v}}$

3. $\sqrt{2x}$ and $\sqrt[3]{2x}$ cannot be added because the indices are different.

4. $1/\sqrt{2x}$ is not in simplest form. The radical in the denominator must be rationalized.

$$\frac{1}{\sqrt{2x}} = \frac{1}{\sqrt{2x}} \cdot \frac{\sqrt{2x}}{\sqrt{2x}} = \frac{\sqrt{2x}}{2x}$$

5. $25\sqrt{3x} - 3\sqrt{12x} = 25\sqrt{3x} - 3 \cdot 2\sqrt{3x}$

$= 25\sqrt{3x} - 6\sqrt{3x}$

$= (25 - 6)\sqrt{3x}$

$= 19\sqrt{3x}$

6. $\left(\sqrt{x} + 3\right)\left(\sqrt{x} - 3\right) = x - 9$ (multiply by FOIL)

7. $\sqrt{u}\left(\sqrt{20} - \sqrt{5}\right) = \sqrt{20u} - \sqrt{5u}$

$\qquad = 2\sqrt{5u} - \sqrt{5u}$

$\qquad = (2 - 1)\sqrt{5u}$

$\qquad = \sqrt{5u}$

8. $\left(2\sqrt{t} + 3\right)^2 = \left(2\sqrt{t} + 3\right)\left(2\sqrt{t} + 3\right)$

$\qquad = 4t + 6\sqrt{t} + 6\sqrt{t} + 9$

$\qquad = 4t + 12\sqrt{t} + 9$

9. $\dfrac{50x}{\sqrt{2}} = \dfrac{50x}{\sqrt{2}} \cdot \dfrac{\sqrt{2}}{\sqrt{2}}$

$\qquad = \dfrac{50x\sqrt{2}}{2}$

$\qquad = 25x\sqrt{2}$

10. $\dfrac{12}{\sqrt{t+2} + \sqrt{t}} = \dfrac{12}{\sqrt{t+2} + \sqrt{t}} \cdot \dfrac{\sqrt{t+2} - \sqrt{t}}{\sqrt{t+2} - \sqrt{t}}$

$\qquad = \dfrac{12\left(\sqrt{t+2} - \sqrt{t}\right)}{t + 2 - t}$

$\qquad = \dfrac{12\left(\sqrt{t+2} - \sqrt{t}\right)}{2}$

$\qquad = 6\left(\sqrt{t+2} - \sqrt{t}\right)$

11. $\qquad p = 30 - \sqrt{0.5(x - 1)}$

$\quad 26.76 = 30 - \sqrt{0.5(x - 1)}$

$\quad -3.24 = -\sqrt{0.5(x - 1)}$

$\quad\; 3.24 = \sqrt{0.5(x - 1)}$

$\quad 3.24^2 = 0.5(x - 1)$

$10.4976 = 0.5x - 0.5$

$10.9976 = 0.5x$

$21.9952 = x$

$22 \text{ units} \approx x$

12. *Verbal Model:* $\boxed{\begin{array}{c}\text{Sale}\\\text{price}\end{array}} = \boxed{\begin{array}{c}\text{List}\\\text{price}\end{array}} \cdot \boxed{100\% - \text{Discount rate}}$

Labels: Sale price $= 1955$

List price $= x$

$100\% - \text{Discount rate} = 100\% - 15\%$

$\qquad\qquad\qquad\qquad\qquad = 85\%$

Equation: $1955 = x \cdot 0.85$

$\$2300 = x$

SECTION 9.5 Solving Exponential and Logarithmic Equations

1. $7x - 2y = 8$

$\;\; x + \;\; y = 4$

It is not possible for this system to have exactly two solutions. A system of linear equations has no solutions, one solution, or an infinite number of solutions.

2. $\;\; 8x - 4y = 5$

$-2x + \;\; y = 1$

This system has no solution because the equations represent parallel lines and have no point of intersection.

3. $\quad \frac{2}{3}x + \frac{2}{3} = 4x - 6$

$3\left(\frac{2}{3}x + \frac{2}{3}\right) = (4x - 6)3$

$\quad 2x + 2 = 12x - 18$

$\qquad\;\; 20 = 10x$

$\qquad\;\;\; 2 = x$

4. $x^2 - 10x + 17 = 0$

$\qquad x^2 - 10x = -17$

$x^2 - 10x + 25 = -17 + 25$

$\qquad (x - 5)^2 = 8$

$\qquad\;\; x - 5 = \pm\sqrt{8}$

$\qquad\qquad x = 5 \pm 2\sqrt{2}$

(can use quadratic formula also)

5. $\dfrac{5}{2x} - \dfrac{4}{x} = 3$

$2x\left(\dfrac{5}{2x} - \dfrac{4}{x}\right) = (3)2x$

$5 - 8 = 6x$

$-3 = 6x$

$-\dfrac{3}{6} = x$

$-\dfrac{1}{2} = x$

6. $\dfrac{1}{x} + \dfrac{2}{x - 5} = 0$

$x(x - 5)\left(\dfrac{1}{x} + \dfrac{2}{x - 5}\right) = (0)x(x - 5)$

$(x - 5) + 2x = 0$

$3x = 5$

$x = \dfrac{5}{3}$

7. $|x - 4| = 3$

$x - 4 = 3$ or $x - 4 = -3$

$x = 7$ $x = 1$

8. $\sqrt{x + 2} = 7$ **Check:**

$\left(\sqrt{x + 2}\right)^2 = 7^2$ $\sqrt{47 + 2} \overset{?}{=} 7$

$x + 2 = 49$ $\sqrt{49} \overset{?}{=} 7$

$x = 47$ $7 = 7$

9. *Verbal Model:* $\boxed{\text{Distance}} = \boxed{\text{Rate}} \cdot \boxed{\text{Time}}$

Function: $d = 73 \cdot t$

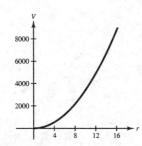

10. $V = \pi r^2 h$

$V = \pi(5)^2 h$

$V = 25\pi h$

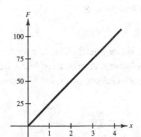

11. $V = \pi r^2 h$

$V = \pi r^2(10)$

$V = 10\pi r^2$

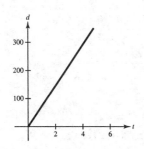

12. $F = kx$

$100 = k(4)$

$25 = k$

$F = 25x$

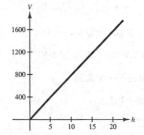

SECTION 9.6   Applications

1. $y = kx^2$

Direct variation as *n*th power

2. $y = \dfrac{k}{x}$

Inverse variation

3. $z = kxy$

Joint variation

4. $z = \dfrac{kx}{y}$

Joint variation

5. $x - y = 0$

$x + 2y = 9$

$x - y = 0$

$\underline{-x - 2y = -9}$

$ -3y = -9$

$ y = 3$

$x - 3 = 0$

$ x = 3$

$(3, 3)$

6. $2x + 5y = 15$

$3x + 6y = 20$

$3(2x + 5y = 15)3$

$-2(3x + 6y = 20) - 2$

$6x + 15y = 45$

$\underline{-6x - 12y = -40}$

$ 3y = 5$

$ y = \frac{5}{3}$

$2x + 5\left(\frac{5}{3}\right) = 15$

$2x = 15 - \frac{25}{3}$

$2x = \frac{45}{3} - \frac{25}{3}$

$2x = \frac{20}{3}$

$x = \frac{20}{3} \cdot \frac{1}{2}$

$x = \frac{10}{3}$

$\left(\frac{10}{3}, \frac{5}{3}\right)$

7. $y = x^2$

$-3x + 2y = 2$

$-3x + 2x^2 = 2$

$2x^2 - 3x - 2 = 0$

$(2x + 1)(x - 2) = 0$

$x = -\frac{1}{2} \qquad x = 2$

$y = \left(-\frac{1}{2}\right)^2 \qquad y = 2^2$

$y = \frac{1}{4} \qquad\quad y = 4$

$\left(-\frac{1}{2}, \frac{1}{4}\right) \qquad (2, 4)$

8. $x - y^3 = 0$

$x - 2y^2 = 0$

$x - y^3 = 0$

$\underline{-x + 2y^2 = 0}$

$2y^2 - y^3 = 0$

$y^2(2 - y) = 0$

$y = 0 \qquad\qquad y = 2$

$x - 0 = 0 \qquad\quad x - 2^3 = 0$

$x = 0 \qquad\qquad x = 8$

$(0, 0) \qquad\qquad\qquad (8, 2)$

9. $x - y = -1$

$x + 2y - 2z = 3$

$3x - y + 2z = 3$

$x - y = -1$

$3y - 2z = 4$

$2y + 2z = 6$

$x - y = -1$

$3y - 2z = 4$

$5y = 10$

$y = 2$

$x - 2 = -1$

$x = 1$

$1 + 2(2) - 2z = 3$

$-2z = -2$

$z = 1$

$(1, 2, 1)$

10. $2x + y - 2z = 1$

$x - z = 1$

$3x + 3y + z = 12$

$R_1 \leftrightarrow R_2$

$x - z = 1$

$2x + y - 2z = 1$

$3x + 3y + z = 12$

$-2R_1 + R_2 \qquad -3R_1 + R_3$

$x - z = 1$

$y = -1$

$3y + 4z = 9$

$3(-1) + 4z = 9$

$4z = 12$

$z = 3$

$x - 3 = 1$

$x = 4$

$(4, -1, 3)$

11. (a) Graph opens down because $a < 0$.

(b) $0 = -x^2 + 4x$

$0 = -x(x - 4)$

$-x = 0 \qquad x - 4 = 0$

$x = 0 \qquad\quad x = 4$

$(0, 0) \qquad\quad (4, 0)$

(c) $x = \dfrac{-b}{2a}$

$x = \dfrac{-4}{2(-1)} = 2$

$y = -2^2 + 4(2) = -4 + 8 = 4$

$(2, 4)$

12. *Keystrokes:*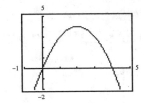

CHAPTER 10   Sequences, Series, and Probability

SECTION 10.1   Sequences and Series

1. Multiplicative Property of Equality

$-7x = 35$

$-\frac{1}{7} \cdot -7x = 35 \cdot -\frac{1}{7}$

$x = -5$

(Multiply both sides of the equation by the reciprocal of the coefficient of the variable.)

2. Additive Property of Equality

$7x + 63 = 35$

$7x + 63 - 63 = 35 - 63$

$7x = -28$

(Add the opposite of 63 on both sides of the equation.)

3. $t = -3$ is a solution of the equation $t^2 + 4t + 3 = 0$ if the equation is true when -3 is substituted for t.

4. $\dfrac{3}{x} - \dfrac{1}{x + 1} = 10$

The first step in solving this equation is to multiply both sides of the equation by the lowest common denominator $x(x + 1)$.

5. $(x + 10)^{-2} = \dfrac{1}{(x + 10)^2}$

6. $\dfrac{18(x - 3)^5}{(x - 3)^2} = 18(x - 3)^{5-2}$

$= 18(x - 3)^3$

7. $(a^2)^{-4} = a^{-8} = \dfrac{1}{a^8}$

8. $(8x^3)^{1/3} = 8^{1/3}x^{3 \cdot 1/3} = 2x$

9. $\sqrt{128x^3} = \sqrt{64 \cdot 2 \cdot x^2 \cdot x}$

$= 8x\sqrt{2x}$

10. $\dfrac{5}{\sqrt{x} - 2} = \dfrac{5}{\sqrt{x} - 2} \cdot \dfrac{\sqrt{x} + 2}{\sqrt{x} + 2}$

$= \dfrac{5(\sqrt{x} + 2)}{(\sqrt{x})^2 - 2^2}$

$= \dfrac{5(\sqrt{x} + 2)}{x - 4}$

11. (a) *Verbal Model:*   Area = Length · Width

   Equation: $f(x) = (2x - 3) \cdot x$

   (b) *Keystrokes:*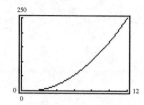

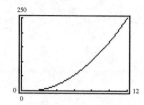

   (c) Let $y_2 = 200$ and find the intersection of the two graphs. $x \approx 10.8$

12. (a) *Verbal Model:*   Area = $\frac{1}{2}$ · Base · Height

   Equation: $f(x) = \frac{1}{2} \cdot x \cdot (x - 4)$

   (b) *Keystrokes:*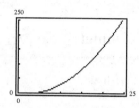

   (c) Let $y_2 = 200$ and find the intersection of the two graphs. $x \approx 22.1$

SECTION 10.2   Arithmetic Sequences

1. An algebraic expression is a collection of letters (called variables) and real numbers (called constants) combined with the operations of addition, subtraction, multiplication, and division.

2. The terms of an algebraic expression are those parts separated by addition or subtraction.

3. A trinomial of degree 3 is any polynomial with 3 terms and whose highest exponent on a variable is 3, such as $2x^3 - 3x^2 + 2$.

4. A monomial of degree 4 is any polynomial with only one term and the highest exponent on the variable is 4, such as $7x^4$.

5. $f(x) = x^3 - 2x$
   Domain: $(-\infty, \infty)$

6. $g(x) = \sqrt[3]{x}$
   Domain: $(-\infty, \infty)$

7. $h(x) = \sqrt{16 - x^2}$
   Domain: $[-4, 4]$
      $16 - x^2 \geq 0$
   $(4 - x)(4 + x) \geq 0$
   Test intervals: Negative: $(-\infty, -4]$
                Positive: $[-4, 4]$
                Negative: $[4, \infty)$
                Positive: $[-4, 4]$

8. $A(x) = \dfrac{3}{36 - x^2}$
   Domain: $(-\infty, -6) \cup (-6, 6) \cup (6, \infty)$
      $36 - x^2 \neq 0$
   $(6 - x)(6 + x) \neq 0$
   $6 - x \neq 0 \qquad 6 + x \neq 0$
   $\quad 6 \neq x \qquad\quad x \neq -6$

9. $g(t) = \ln(t - 2)$
   Domain: $(2, \infty)$
   $t - 2 > 0$
      $t > 2$

10. $f(s) = 630e^{-0.2s}$
   Domain: $(-\infty, \infty)$

11. *Formula:* $A = P\left(1 + \dfrac{r}{n}\right)^{nt}$

$A = 10{,}000\left(1 + \dfrac{0.075}{365}\right)^{365(15)}$

$A \approx \$30{,}798.61$

12. *Formula:* $A = P\left(1 + \dfrac{r}{n}\right)^{nt}$

$A = 4000\left(1 + \dfrac{0.06}{12}\right)^{12(5)}$

$A = \$5395.40$

SECTION 10.3   Geometric Sequences and Series

1. The point is 6 units to the left of the y-axis and 4 units above the x-axis.

2.

3. The graph of f is the set of ordered pairs $(x, f(x))$, where x is in the domain of f.

4. $f(x) = 2\sqrt{x + 4}$

x-intercept: Let $y = 0$ and solve for x.

$0 = 2\sqrt{x + 4}$

$0 = \sqrt{x + 4}$

$0 = \left(\sqrt{x + 4}\right)^2$

$0 = x + 4$

$-4 = x$

$(-4, 0)$

y-intercept: Let $x = 0$ and solve for y.

$y = 2\sqrt{0 + 4}$

$= 2\sqrt{4}$

$= 2 \cdot 2$

$y = 4$

$(0, 4)$

5. $3x - 5 > 0$

$3x > 5$

$x > \frac{5}{3}$

6. $\frac{3}{2}y + 11 < 20$

$\frac{3}{2}y < 9$

$y < 9 \cdot \frac{2}{3}$

$y < 6$

7. $100 < 2x + 30 < 150$

$70 < 2x < 120$

$35 < x < 60$

8. $-5 < -\dfrac{x}{6} < 2$

$-30 < -x < 12$

$30 > x > -12$

$-12 < x < 30$

9. $2x^2 - 7x + 5 > 0$

$(2x - 5)(x - 1) > 0$

Critical numbers: $x = 1, \dfrac{5}{2}$

Positive: $(-\infty, 1)$

Negative: $\left(1, \dfrac{5}{2}\right)$

Positive: $\left(\dfrac{5}{2}, \infty\right)$

Solution: $(-\infty, 1) \cup \left(\dfrac{5}{2}, \infty\right)$

10. $2x - \dfrac{5}{x} > 3$

$2x - \dfrac{5}{x} - 3 > 0$

$\dfrac{2x^2 - 5 - 3x}{x} > 0$

$\dfrac{(2x - 5)(x + 1)}{x} > 0$

Critical numbers: $x = -1, 0, \dfrac{5}{2}$

Test intervals:

Negative: $(-\infty, -1) \cup \left(0, \dfrac{5}{2}\right)$

Positive: $(-1, 0) \cup \left(\dfrac{5}{2}, \infty\right)$

Solution: $(-1, 0) \cup \left(\dfrac{5}{2}, \infty\right)$

11. *Formula:* $a^2 + b^2 = c^2$

Equation: $a^2 + a^2 = 19^2$

$2a^2 = 361$

$a^2 = 180.5$

$a = \sqrt{180.5}$

$a \approx 13.4$ inches

12. *Formula:* $a^2 + b^2 = c^2$

Equation: $25^2 + 40^2 = c^2$

$625 + 1600 = c^2$

$2225 = c^2$

$47.2 \approx c$

SECTION 10.4   The Binomial Theorem

1. It is not possible to find the determinant of this matrix because it is not square.

2. The three elementary row operations are:

(1) interchange two rows.

(2) multiply a row by a nonzero constant.

(3) add a multiple of one row to another row.

3. This matrix is in row-echelon form.

4. $\det A = \begin{vmatrix} 10 & 25 \\ 6 & -5 \end{vmatrix} = 10(-5) - 6(25)$

$= -50 - 150$

$= -200$

5. $\det A = \begin{vmatrix} 3 & 7 \\ -2 & 6 \end{vmatrix} = 3(6) - (-2)(7)$

$= 18 + 14$

$= 32$

6. $\det A = \begin{vmatrix} 3 & -2 & 1 \\ 0 & 5 & 3 \\ 6 & 1 & 1 \end{vmatrix}$

$= 0 + 5\begin{vmatrix} 3 & 1 \\ 6 & 1 \end{vmatrix} - 3\begin{vmatrix} 3 & -2 \\ 6 & 1 \end{vmatrix}$ (using second row)

$= 5(-3) - 3(15)$

$= -15 - 45$

$= -60$

7. $\det A = \begin{vmatrix} 4 & 3 & 5 \\ 3 & 2 & -2 \\ 5 & -2 & 0 \end{vmatrix}$

$= 5 \begin{vmatrix} 3 & 5 \\ 2 & -2 \end{vmatrix} - (-2) \begin{vmatrix} 4 & 5 \\ 3 & -2 \end{vmatrix} + 0$ (using third row)

$= 5(-16) + 2(-23)$

$= -80 - 46$

$= -126$

8. $(x_1, y_1) = (-5, 8), (x_2, y_2) = (10, 0), (x_3, y_3) = (3, -4)$

$\begin{vmatrix} x_1 & y_1 & 1 \\ x_2 & y_2 & 1 \\ x_3 & y_3 & 1 \end{vmatrix} = \begin{vmatrix} -5 & 8 & 1 \\ 10 & 0 & 1 \\ 3 & -4 & 1 \end{vmatrix}$

$\qquad = -10 \begin{vmatrix} 8 & 1 \\ -4 & 1 \end{vmatrix} + 0 - 1 \begin{vmatrix} -5 & 8 \\ 3 & -4 \end{vmatrix}$ (using second row)

$\qquad = -10(12) - 1(-4)$

$\qquad = -120 + 4$

$\qquad = -116$

Area $= -\frac{1}{2}(-116) = 58$

9. $2 = a(0)^2 + b(0) + c \Longrightarrow 2 = \qquad\qquad + c$

$8 = a(10)^2 + b(10) + c \Longrightarrow 8 = 100a + 10b + c$

$0 = a(20)^2 + b(20) + c \Longrightarrow 0 = 400a + 20b + c$

$\begin{bmatrix} 0 & 0 & 1 & : & 2 \\ 100 & 10 & 1 & : & 8 \\ 400 & 20 & 1 & : & 0 \end{bmatrix}$

$D = \begin{vmatrix} 0 & 0 & 1 \\ 100 & 10 & 1 \\ 400 & 20 & 1 \end{vmatrix} = 1 \begin{vmatrix} 100 & 10 \\ 400 & 20 \end{vmatrix} = (1)(-2000) = -2000$

$a = \dfrac{\begin{vmatrix} 2 & 0 & 1 \\ 8 & 10 & 1 \\ 0 & 20 & 1 \end{vmatrix}}{-2000} = \dfrac{2 \begin{vmatrix} 10 & 1 \\ 20 & 1 \end{vmatrix} - 0 + 1 \begin{vmatrix} 8 & 10 \\ 0 & 20 \end{vmatrix}}{-2000} = \dfrac{2(-10) + 160}{-2000} = \dfrac{140}{-2000} = -0.07$

$b = \dfrac{\begin{vmatrix} 0 & 2 & 1 \\ 100 & 8 & 1 \\ 400 & 0 & 1 \end{vmatrix}}{-2000} = \dfrac{0 - 2 \begin{vmatrix} 100 & 1 \\ 400 & 1 \end{vmatrix} + 1 \begin{vmatrix} 100 & 8 \\ 400 & 0 \end{vmatrix}}{-2000} = \dfrac{(-2)(-300) - 3200}{-2000} = \dfrac{-2600}{-2000} = 1.3$

$c = \dfrac{\begin{vmatrix} 0 & 0 & 2 \\ 100 & 10 & 8 \\ 400 & 20 & 0 \end{vmatrix}}{-2000} = \dfrac{0 + 0 + 2 \begin{vmatrix} 100 & 10 \\ 400 & 20 \end{vmatrix}}{-2000} = \dfrac{2(-2000)}{-2000} = 2$

$y = -0.07x^2 + 1.3x + 2$

10. $(x_1, y_1) = (2, -1), (x_2, y_2) = (4, 7)$

$$\begin{vmatrix} x & y & 1 \\ 2 & -1 & 1 \\ 4 & 7 & 1 \end{vmatrix} = 0$$

$$x \begin{vmatrix} -1 & 1 \\ 7 & 1 \end{vmatrix} - y \begin{vmatrix} 2 & 1 \\ 4 & 1 \end{vmatrix} + 1 \begin{vmatrix} 2 & -1 \\ 4 & 7 \end{vmatrix} = 0 \qquad \text{(using first row)}$$

$$x(-8) - y(-2) + 1(18) = 0$$

$$-8x + 2y + 18 = 0 \qquad \text{(divide by } -2)$$

$$4x - y - 9 = 0 \text{ or}$$

$$y = 4x - 9$$

SECTION 10.5   Counting Principles

1. $g(x) = 2(5^x)$ is exponential since it has a constant base and a variable exponent.

2. $e^2 \cdot e^{-x^2} = e^{2+(-x^2)} = e^{2-x^2}$ using the law of exponents
$$a^m \cdot a^n = a^{m+n}$$

3. $\log_4 64 = 3$ in exponential form is $4^3 = 64$.

4. $\log_3 \frac{1}{81} = -4$ in exponential form is $3^{-4} = \frac{1}{81}$.

5. $\ln 1 = 0$ in exponential form is $e^0 = 1$.

6. $\ln 5 \approx 1.6094 \ldots$ in exponential form is $e^{1.6094\cdots} \approx 5$.

7.
$$3^x = 50$$
$$\log_3 3^x = \log_3 50$$
$$x = \frac{\log 50}{\log 3}$$
$$x \approx 3.56$$

8.
$$e^{x/2} = 8$$
$$\ln e^{x/2} = \ln 8$$
$$\frac{x}{2} = \ln 8$$
$$x = 2 \ln 8$$
$$x \approx 4.16$$

9. $\log_2(x - 5) = 6$
$$x - 5 = 2^6$$
$$x = 69$$

10. $\ln(x + 3) = 10$
$$x + 3 = e^{10}$$
$$x = e^{10} - 3$$
$$x \approx 22{,}023.47$$

11. (a) *Keystrokes:* [Y=] 22,000 [(] 0.8 [)] [^] [X,T,θ] [GRAPH]

(b) Let $y_2 = 15{,}000$ and find the intersection. $t = 1.7$

12. $y = Ce^{kt}$ $y = 10e^{kt}$ $y = 10e^{-0.00012097t}$

$10 = Ce^{k(0)}$ $5 = 10e^{k(5730)}$ $y = 10e^{-0.00012097(3000)}$

$10 = C$ $\dfrac{1}{2} = e^{5730k}$ $y \approx 6.96$ grams

$$\ln \dfrac{1}{2} = \ln e^{5730k}$$

$$\ln \dfrac{1}{2} = 5730k$$

$$\dfrac{\ln \frac{1}{2}}{5730} = k$$

$$-0.00012097 \approx k$$

SECTION 10.6   Probability

1. $\log_a 1 = 0$

2. $\log_a a = 1$

3. $\log_a a^x = x$

4. $\log_a(uv) = \log_a u + \log_a v$

5. $\log_a \dfrac{u}{v} = \log_a u - \log_a v$

6. $\log_a u^n = n \log_a u$

7. $\log_2(x^2 y) = \log_2 x^2 + \log_2 y = 2 \log_2 x + \log_2 y$

8. $\log_2 \sqrt{x^2 + 1} = \log_2 (x^2 + 1)^{1/2} = \frac{1}{2} \log_2 (x^2 + 1)$

9. $\ln \dfrac{7}{x-3} = \ln 7 - \ln(x - 3)$

10. $\ln\left(\dfrac{u+2}{u-2}\right)^2 = 2 \ln\left(\dfrac{u+2}{u-2}\right) = 2[\ln(u + 2) - \ln(u - 2)]$

11. (a) *Keystrokes:*

y_1 Y= 10,000 ÷ (1 + 4 eˣ ((−) X,T,θ ÷

3)) GRAPH

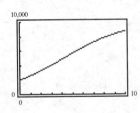

(b) Let $y_2 = 5000$ and find the intersection of the two graphs. $x \approx 4$ years.

(c) Trace along the graph. The maximum level of annual sales is 10,000.

12. $A = Pe^{rt}$

$A = 1000e^{0.055(1)}$

$A = \$1056.54$

Effective yield $= \dfrac{56.54}{1000} = 0.0565 = 5.65\%$

Part II
Solutions to Odd-Numbered Exercises

C H A P T E R   P
Prerequisites: Fundamentals of Algebra

CHAPTER P
Prerequisites: Fundamentals of Algebra

Section P.1   The Real Number System
Solutions to Odd-Numbered Exercises

1. $\left\{-10, -\sqrt{5}, -\frac{2}{3}, -\frac{1}{4}, 0, \frac{5}{8}, 1, \sqrt{3}, 4, 2\pi, 6\right\}$

    (a) Natural numbers: $\{1, 4, 6\}$

    (b) Integers: $\{-10, 0, 1, 4, 6\}$

    (c) Rational numbers: $\left\{-10, -\frac{2}{3}, -\frac{1}{4}, 0, \frac{5}{8}, 1, 4, 6\right\}$

    (d) Irrational numbers: $\left\{-\sqrt{5}, \sqrt{3}, 2\pi\right\}$

3. $\left\{-3.5, -\sqrt{4}, -\frac{1}{2}, -0.\overline{3}, 0, 3, \sqrt{5}, 3\pi, 25.2\right\}$

    (a) Natural numbers: $\{3\}$

    (b) Integers: $\left\{-\sqrt{4}, 0, 3\right\}$

    (c) Rational numbers: $\left\{-3.5, -\sqrt{4}, -\frac{1}{2}, -0.\overline{3}, 0, 3, 25.2\right\}$

    (d) Irrational numbers: $\left\{\sqrt{5}, 3\pi\right\}$

5. $\{-5, -4, -3, -2, -1, 0, 1, 2, 3\}$

7. $\{1, 3, 5, 7, 9\}$

9. (a) The point representing the real number 3 lies between 2 and 4.

    (b) The point representing the real number $\frac{5}{2}$ lies between 2 and 3.

    (c) The point representing the real number $-\frac{7}{2}$ lies between -4 and -3.

    (d) The point representing the real number -5.2 lies between -6 and -5.

11. $a = -1, b = 3$

    $-1 < 3$

13. $a = -\frac{9}{2}, b = -2$

    $-\frac{9}{2} < -2$

15. $2 < 5$ because 2 is to the left of 5 on the number line.

17. $10 > 4$ because 10 is the right of 4 on the number line.

19. $-7 < -2$ because -7 is to the left of -2 on the number line.

21. $-5 < -2$ because -5 is to the left of -2 on the number line.

23. $\frac{1}{3} > \frac{1}{4}$ because $\frac{1}{3}$ is to the right of $\frac{1}{4}$ on the number line.

25. $-\frac{5}{8} < \frac{1}{2}$ because $-\frac{5}{8}$ is to the left of $\frac{1}{2}$ on the number line.

27. $-\frac{2}{3} > -\frac{10}{3}$ because $-\frac{2}{3}$ is to the right of $-\frac{10}{3}$ on the number line.

29. $2.75 < \pi$ because 2.75 is to the left of π on the number line.

31. Distance $= 10 - 4 = 6$

33. Distance $= 7 - (-12) = 7 + 12 = 19$

35. Distance $= 18 - (-32) = 18 + 32 = 50$

37. Distance $= 0 - (-8) = 0 + 8 = 8$

39. Distance $= 35 - 0 = 35$

41. Distance $= (-6) - (-9) = (-6) + 9 = 3$

43. $|10| = 10$

45. $|-225| = 225$

47. $-|-85| = -85$

49. $-|16| = -16$

51. $-\left|-\frac{3}{4}\right| = -\frac{3}{4}$

53. $-|3.5| = -3.5$

55. $|-\pi| = \pi$

57. $|-6| > |2|$ since $6 > 2$.

59. $|47| > |-27|$ since $47 > 27$.

61. $-|-16.8| = -|16.8|$ since $-16.8 = -16.8$.

63. $\left|-\frac{3}{4}\right| > -\left|\frac{4}{5}\right|$ since $\frac{3}{4} > -\frac{4}{5}$.

65. Opposite: -34
Absolute value: 34

67. Opposite: 160
Absolute value: 160

69. Opposite: $\frac{3}{11}$
Absolute value: $\frac{3}{11}$

71. Opposite: $-\frac{5}{4}$
Absolute value: $\frac{5}{4}$

73. Opposite: -4.7
Absolute value: 4.7

75. $|7| = 7$

77. $|-5| = 5$

79. $\left|-\frac{3}{5}\right| = \frac{3}{5}$

81. Opposite of $\frac{5}{3}$ is $-\frac{5}{3}$.

83. Opposite of -4.25 is 4.25.

85. Opposite of 0.7 is -0.7.

87. $x < 0$

89. $x \geq 0$

91. $2 < z \leq 10$

93. $p < \$225$

95. True

97. False. $\frac{2}{3}$ is not an integer.

99. False. $|3 + (-2)| = 1 \neq 5 = |3| + |-2|$

101. The set of integers includes the natural numbers, zero, and the negative integers.

103. Yes, the nonnegative real numbers include 0.

105. Place them on the real number line. The number on the right is greater.

Section P.2   Operations with Real Numbers

1. $13 + 32 = 45$

3. $-13 + 32 = +(32 - 13) = 19$

5. $13 + (-32) = -(32 - 13) = -19$

7. $-7 - 15 = -7 + (-15)$
$\qquad = -(7 + 15) = -22$

9. $-13 + (-8) = -(13 + 8) = -21$

11. $4 - 16 + (-8) = 4 + (-16) + (-8)$
$\qquad = -(16 - 4) + (-8)$
$\qquad = -12 + (-8)$
$\qquad = -(12 + 8)$
$\qquad = -20$

13. $5.8 - 6.2 + 1.1 = 5.8 + (-6.2) + 1.1$
$\qquad = -(6.2 - 5.8) + 1.1$
$\qquad = -0.4 + 1.1$
$\qquad = +(1.1 - 0.4)$
$\qquad = 0.7$

15. $\dfrac{3}{8} + \dfrac{7}{8} = \dfrac{3 + 7}{8}$
$\qquad = \dfrac{10}{8}$
$\qquad = \dfrac{5}{4}$

17. $\dfrac{3}{4} - \dfrac{1}{4} = \dfrac{3 - 1}{4}$
$\qquad = \dfrac{2}{4} = \dfrac{1}{2}$

19. $\dfrac{3}{5} + \left(-\dfrac{1}{2}\right) = \dfrac{3(2)}{5(2)} - \dfrac{1(5)}{2(5)}$
$\qquad = \dfrac{6}{10} - \dfrac{5}{10}$
$\qquad = \dfrac{6 - 5}{10}$
$\qquad = \dfrac{1}{10}$

21. $\dfrac{5}{8} + \dfrac{1}{4} - \dfrac{5}{6} = \dfrac{5(3)}{8(3)} + \dfrac{1(6)}{4(6)} - \dfrac{5(4)}{6(4)}$
$\qquad = \dfrac{15}{24} + \dfrac{6}{24} - \dfrac{20}{24}$
$\qquad = \dfrac{15 + 6 - 20}{24}$
$\qquad = \dfrac{1}{24}$

23. $5\dfrac{3}{4} + 7\dfrac{3}{8} = \dfrac{23}{4} + \dfrac{59}{8}$
$\qquad = \dfrac{23(2)}{4(2)} + \dfrac{59(1)}{8(1)}$
$\qquad = \dfrac{46 + 59}{8}$
$\qquad = \dfrac{105}{8} \text{ or } 13\dfrac{1}{8}$

25. $85 - |-25| = 85 - 25 = 60$

27. $-(-11.325) + |34.625| = 11.325 + 34.625$
$\qquad = 45.95$

29. $-|-15.667| - 12.333 = -15.667 - 12.333$
$\qquad = -15.667 + (-12.333)$
$\qquad = -28.000$
$\qquad = -28$

31. $4(5) = 5 + 5 + 5 + 5$

33. $3(-4) = (-4) + (-4) + (-4)$

35. $\frac{1}{4} + \frac{1}{4} + \frac{1}{4} + \frac{1}{4} + \frac{1}{4} + \frac{1}{4} = 6\left(\frac{1}{4}\right)$

37. $(-15) + (-15) + (-15) + (-15) = 4(-15)$

39. $5(-6) = -30$

41. $(-8)(-6) = 48$

43. $-6(12) = -72$

45. $\left(-\frac{5}{8}\right)\left(-\frac{4}{5}\right) = \frac{1}{2}$

47. $-\dfrac{3}{2}\left(\dfrac{8}{5}\right) = \dfrac{-24}{10} = \dfrac{-12}{5}$

49. $\dfrac{1}{2}\left(\dfrac{1}{6}\right) = \dfrac{1}{12}$

51. $\dfrac{-9}{8}\left(\dfrac{16}{27}\right)\left(\dfrac{1}{2}\right) = \dfrac{-9 \cdot \cancel{2} \cdot \cancel{8} \cdot 1}{\cancel{8} \cdot \cancel{9} \cdot 3 \cdot \cancel{2}}$

$\qquad\qquad\qquad\qquad = -\dfrac{1}{3}$

53. $\dfrac{-18}{-3} = 6$

55. $\dfrac{-48}{16} = -3$

57. $63 \div (-7) = \dfrac{63}{-7} = -9$

59. $-\dfrac{4}{5} \div \dfrac{8}{25} = -\dfrac{4}{5} \cdot \dfrac{25}{8} = -\dfrac{5}{2}$

61. $\left(\dfrac{-1}{3}\right) \div \left(\dfrac{-5}{6}\right) = \left(\dfrac{-1}{3} \div \dfrac{-5}{6}\right) = \left(\dfrac{-1}{3} \cdot \dfrac{-6}{5}\right) = \dfrac{2}{5}$

63. $5\dfrac{3}{4} \div 2\dfrac{1}{8} = \dfrac{23}{4} \div \dfrac{17}{8}$

$\qquad\qquad = \dfrac{23}{4} \cdot \dfrac{8}{17}$

$\qquad\qquad = \dfrac{46}{17}$

65. $4\dfrac{1}{8} \div 3\dfrac{3}{2} = \dfrac{33}{8} \div \dfrac{9}{2}$

$\qquad\qquad = \dfrac{33}{8} \cdot \dfrac{2}{9}$

$\qquad\qquad = \dfrac{11}{12}$

67. $4^3 = (4)(4)(4)$

69. $\left(\dfrac{-3}{4}\right)^4 = \left(\dfrac{-3}{4}\right)\left(\dfrac{-3}{4}\right)\left(\dfrac{-3}{4}\right)\left(\dfrac{-3}{4}\right)$

71. $(-0.8)^6 = (-0.8)(-0.8)(-0.8)(-0.8)(-0.8)(-0.8)$

73. $(-7) \times (-7) \times (-7) = (-7)^3$

75. $(-5)(-5)(-5)(-5) = (-5)^4$

77. $-(7 \times 7 \times 7) = -7^3$

79. $(-2)^4 = (-2)(-2)(-2)(-2)$

$\qquad\qquad = 16$

81. $(-2)^3 = (-2)(-2)(-2)$

$\qquad\qquad = -8$

83. $-4^3 = -(4)(4)(4)$

$\qquad\quad = -64$

85. $\left(\dfrac{4}{5}\right)^3 = \left(\dfrac{4}{5}\right)\left(\dfrac{4}{5}\right)\left(\dfrac{4}{5}\right)$

$\qquad\quad = \dfrac{64}{125}$

87. $-\left(-\dfrac{1}{2}\right)^5 = -\left(-\dfrac{1}{2}\right)\left(-\dfrac{1}{2}\right)\left(-\dfrac{1}{2}\right)\left(-\dfrac{1}{2}\right)\left(-\dfrac{1}{2}\right)$

$\qquad\qquad = -\left(-\dfrac{1}{32}\right)$

$\qquad\qquad = \dfrac{1}{32}$

89. $(0.3)^3 = (0.3)(0.3)(0.3)$

$\qquad\qquad = 0.027$

91. $5(-0.4)^3 = 5(-0.4)(-0.4)(-0.4)$

$\qquad\qquad = 5(-0.064)$

$\qquad\qquad = -0.32$

93. $16 - 6 - 10 = (16 - 6) - 10$

$\qquad\qquad\quad = 10 - 10$

$\qquad\qquad\quad = 0$

95. $24 - 5 \cdot 2^2 = 24 - 5 \cdot 4$

$\qquad\qquad\quad = 24 - (5 \cdot 4)$

$\qquad\qquad\quad = 24 - 20$

$\qquad\qquad\quad = 4$

97. $28 \div 4 + 3 \cdot 5 = (28 \div 4) + (3 \cdot 5)$

$\qquad\qquad\qquad = 7 + 15$

$\qquad\qquad\qquad = 22$

99. $14 - 2(8 - 4) = 14 - 2(4)$

$\qquad\qquad\qquad = 14 - 8$

$\qquad\qquad\qquad = 6$

101. $45 + 3(16 \div 4) = 45 + 3(4)$

$\qquad\qquad\qquad = 45 + 12$

$\qquad\qquad\qquad = 57$

103. $2 + [8 - (14 \div 2)] = 2 + [8 - 7]$
$$= 2 + 1$$
$$= 3$$

105. $5^2 - 2[9 - (18 - 8)] = 25 - 2[9 - 10]$
$$= 25 - 2[-1]$$
$$= 25 + 2$$
$$= 27$$

107. $5^3 + |-14 + 4| = 125 + |-10|$
$$= 125 + 10$$
$$= 135$$

109. $\dfrac{8 + 7}{12 - 15} = \dfrac{15}{-3} = -5$

111. $\dfrac{4^2 - 5}{11} - 7 = \dfrac{16 - 5}{11} - 7$
$$= \dfrac{11}{11} - 7$$
$$= 1 - 7$$
$$= -6$$

113. $\dfrac{6 \cdot 2^2 - 12}{3^2 + 3} = \dfrac{6 \cdot 4 - 12}{9 + 3}$
$$= \dfrac{24 - 12}{12}$$
$$= \dfrac{12}{12}$$
$$= 1$$

115. $5.6[13 - 2.5(-6.3)] = 5.6[13 + 15.75]$
$$= 5.6[28.75]$$
$$= 161$$

117. $5^6 - 3(400) = 15,625 - 1200 = 14,425$

119. $\dfrac{500}{(1.055)^{20}} = \dfrac{500}{2.9177575} = 171.36448 \approx 171.36$

121. $\dfrac{1}{4} + \dfrac{2}{9} + \dfrac{1}{10} + x + \dfrac{1}{3} = 1$

Thus:

$$x = 1 - \left(\dfrac{1}{4} + \dfrac{2}{9} + \dfrac{1}{10} + \dfrac{1}{3} \right)$$

$$= 1 - \left(\dfrac{45}{180} + \dfrac{40}{180} + \dfrac{18}{180} + \dfrac{60}{180} \right) = 1 - \left(\dfrac{45 + 40 + 18 + 60}{180} \right) = 1 - \dfrac{163}{180} = \dfrac{180}{180} - \dfrac{163}{180} = \dfrac{17}{180}.$$

123. $\$2618.68 + \$1236.45 - \$25.62 - \$455.00 - \$125.00 - \$715.95 = \$2533.56$

125. (a)

Day	Daily Gain or Loss
Tuesday	+5
Wednesday	+8
Thursday	−5
Friday	+16

(b) $(+5) + (+8) + (-5) + (+16) = +24 =$ the sum of the daily gains and losses. The sum of the daily gains and losses is equal to the difference of the value of the stock on Friday and the value of the stock on Monday. This sum could be determined from the graph by $\$524$ (value on Friday) $- \$500$ (value on Monday) $= \$24$.

127. (a) $\$50(12)(18) = \$10,800$

(b) $50\left[\left(1 + \dfrac{0.09}{12}\right)^{216} - 1\right]\left(1 + \dfrac{12}{0.09}\right) \approx 27,018.71558 \approx 27,018.72$

The fund would have $\$27,018.72$.

(c) $27,018.72 - 10,800 = \$16,218.72$

129. $l = 5m,\ w = 3m$

$A = lw$

$A = 5 \cdot 3 = 15$ square meters

131. $b = 8\ cm,\ h = 5\ cm$

$A = \frac{1}{2}bh$

$A = \frac{1}{2}(8)(5) = 20$ square inches

133. $V = l \cdot w \cdot h = 14" \cdot 18" \cdot 42" = 10,584\ \text{in}^3 \div 1728\ \text{in}^3 = 6.125\ \text{ft}^3$

135. (a) $20 \times 3 + 18 = 20 \times 21 = 420$

Student incorrectly added the 3 and the 18 instead of multiplying the 20 and the 3 first. Order of operations must be followed.

$20 \times 3 + 18 = 60 + 18 = 78$

(b) UPC of 07673720012 9

1. $(0 + 6 + 3 + 2 + 0 + 2) \times 3 = 39$

2. $7 + 7 + 7 + 0 + 1 = 22$

3. $39 + 22 = 61$

4. Next highest multiple of $10 = 70$
$70 - 61 = 9$ which is the check digit
Yes, it checks.

(c) UPC of 04180048700 3

1. $(0 + 1 + 0 + 4 + 7 + 0) \times 3 = 36$

2. $4 + 8 + 0 + 8 + 0 = 20$

3. $36 + 20 = 56$

4. Next highest multiple of $10 = 60$
$60 - 56 = 4$ which is not the check digit
No, it does not check.

137. True. A rational number is an integer divided by an integer. The reciprocal of such a number is still an integer divided by an integer, and thus, a rational number.

139. False. If a negative number is raised to an odd power, the result will be negative.

141. Yes. For example, $(-3) + (-4) = -7$

$$-7 < -3 \text{ and } -7 < -4$$

143. If the numbers have like signs, the product or quotient is positive.

If the numbers have unlike signs, the product or quotient is negative.

145. Evaluate additions and subtractions from left to right.

$$6 - 5 - 2 = (6 - 5) - 2 \qquad \text{not} \qquad 6 - (5 - 2)$$
$$= 1 - 2 \qquad\qquad\qquad 6 - 3$$
$$= -1 \qquad\qquad\qquad\quad 3$$

147. Only common factors (not terms) of the numerator and denominator can be canceled.

149. The squaring of the four must be performed before multiplying by the three by order of operations.

$$3 \cdot 4^2 = 3 \cdot 16$$
$$= 48$$

Section P.3   Properties of Real Numbers

1. $3 + (-5) = -5 + 3$
Commutative Property of Addition

3. $25 - 25 = 0$
Additive Inverse Property

5. $6(-10) = -10(6)$
Commutative Property of
Multiplication

7. $7 \cdot 1 = 7$
Multiplicative Identity Property

9. $25 + 35 = 35 + 25$
Commutative Property of Addition

11. $3 + (12 - 9) = (3 + 12) - 9$
Associative Property of Addition

13. $(8 - 5)(10) = 8 \cdot 10 - 5 \cdot 10$
Distributive Property

15. $(10 + 8) + 3 = 10 + (8 + 3)$
Associative Property of Addition

17. $5(2a) = (5 \cdot 2)a$
Associative Property of
Multiplication

19. $1 \cdot (5t) = 5t$
Multiplicative Identity Property

21. $3x + 0 = 3x$
Additive Identity Property

23. $4 + (3 - x) = (4 + 3) - x$
Associative Property of Addition

25. $3(6 + b) = 3 \cdot 6 + 3 \cdot b$
Distributive Property

27. $6(x + 3) = 6 \cdot x + 6 \cdot 3$
Distributive Property

29. $3(6y) = (3 \cdot 6)y$

31. $15(-3) = (-3)15$

33. $5(6 + z) = 5 \cdot 6 + 5 \cdot z$

35. $25 + (-x) = (-x) + 25$

37. $(x + 8) \cdot 1 = (x + 8)$

39. (a) Additive Inverse: -10
(b) Multiplicative Inverse: $\frac{1}{10}$

41. (a) Additive Inverse: 16
(b) Multiplicative Inverse: $-\frac{1}{16}$

43. (a) Additive Inverse: $-6z$
(b) Multiplicative Inverse: $\frac{1}{6z}$

45. (a) Additive Inverse: $-(x + 1)$ or $-x - 1$
(b) Multiplicative Inverse: $\frac{1}{x + 1}$

47. $(x + 5) - 3 = x + (5 - 3)$

49. $32 + (4 + y) = (32 + 4) + y$

51. $3(4 \cdot 5) = (3 \cdot 4)5$

53. $6(2y) = (6 \cdot 2) \cdot y = 12y$

55. $20(2 + 5) = 20 \cdot 2 + 20 \cdot 5$

57. $5(3x - 4) = 5 \cdot 3x - 5 \cdot 4$ or $5 \cdot 3x + 5 \cdot -4$

59. $(x + 6)(-2) = x \cdot (-2) + 6 \cdot (-2)$

61. $-6(2y - 5) = -6(2y) + (-6)(-5)$

63. $3(x + 5) = 3x + 15$

65. $-2(x + 8) = -2x - 16$

67. $ac = bc, c \neq 0$ Original equation

$\frac{1}{c}(ac) = \frac{1}{c}(bc)$ Multiplication Property of Equality

$\frac{1}{c}(ca) = \frac{1}{c}(cb)$ Commutative Property of Multiplication

$\left(\frac{1}{c} \cdot c\right)a = \left(\frac{1}{c} \cdot c\right)b$ Associative Property of Multiplication

$1 \cdot a = 1 \cdot b$ Multiplicative Inverse Property

$a = b$ Multiplicative Identity Property

69.

$x + 5 = 3$	Original Equation
$(x + 5) + (-5) = 3 + (-5)$	Addition Property of Equality
$x + (5 + (-5)) = 3 - 5$	Associative Property of Addition
$x + 0 = -2$	Additive Inverse Property
$x = -2$	Additive Identity Property

71.

$2x - 5 = 6$	Original equation
$(2x - 5) + 5 = 6 + 5$	Addition Property of Equality
$2x + (-5 + 5) = 11$	Associative Property of Addition
$2x + 0 = 11$	Additive Inverse Property
$2x = 11$	Additive Identity Property
$\frac{1}{2}(2x) = \frac{1}{2}(11)$	Multiplication Property of Equality
$\left(\frac{1}{2} \cdot 2\right)x = \frac{11}{2}$	Associative Property of Multiplication
$1 \cdot x = \frac{11}{2}$	Multiplicative Inverse Property
$x = \frac{11}{2}$	Multiplicative Identity Property

73. $16(1.75) = 16\left(2 - \frac{1}{4}\right) = 16(2) - 16\left(\frac{1}{4}\right)$
$$= 32 - 4$$
$$= 28$$

75. $7(62) = 7(60 + 2)$
$$= 7(60) + 7(2)$$
$$= 420 + 14$$
$$= 434$$

77. $9(6.98) = 9(7 - 0.02)$
$$= 9(7) - 9(0.02)$$
$$= 63 - 0.18$$
$$= 62.82$$

79. $a(b + c) = ab + ac$, Distributive Property

81. Use the graph to approximate the dividend paid in 1995. According to the graph, the dividend paid in 1995 was approximately \$0.60.

83. Dividend per share $= 0.08t + 0.21$

2000 dividend per share $= 0.08(10) + 0.21 = \$1.01$

85. Given two real numbers a and b, the sum a plus b is the same as the sum b plus a.

87. The multiplicative inverse of a real number $a(a \neq 0)$ is the number $\frac{1}{a}$. The product of a number and its multiplicative inverse is the multiplicative identity 1. For example, $8 \cdot \frac{1}{8} = 1$.

89. $0 \cdot a = 0$ is the Multiplicative Property of zero.

91. let $a = 1$ & $b = 2$

$\quad a \odot b \neq b \odot a$

$\quad 1 \odot 2 \neq 2 \odot 1$

$\quad 2 \cdot 1 + 2 \neq 2 \cdot 2 + 1$

$\quad\quad\quad 4 \neq 5$

So, the Commutative Property is not true.

let $a = 1, b = 2, c = 3$

$\quad a \odot (b \odot c) \neq (a \odot b) \odot c$

$\quad 1 \odot (2 \odot 3) \neq (1 \odot 2) \odot 3$

$\quad 2 \cdot 1 + (2 \cdot 2 + 3) \neq (2 \cdot 1 + 2) \odot 3$

$\quad\quad 2 + 7 \neq 4 \odot 3$

$\quad\quad\quad 9 \neq 2 \cdot 4 + 3$

$\quad\quad\quad 9 \neq 8 + 3$

$\quad\quad\quad 9 \neq 11$

So, the Associative Property is not true.

Mid-Chapter Quiz for Chapter P

1. $-4.5 > -6$

2. $\frac{3}{4} < \frac{3}{2}$

3. $|-3.2| = 3.2$

4. $-|5.75| = -5.75$

5. $|-15 - 7| = |-22| = 22$

6. $|(-10.5) - (-6.75)| = |-10.5 + 6.75|$
$= |-3.75| = 3.75$

7. $32 + (-18) = 14$

8. $-10 - 12 = (-10) + (-12) = -(10 + 12) = -22$

9. $\frac{3}{4} + \frac{7}{4} = \frac{3 + 7}{4} = \frac{10}{4} = \frac{5}{2}$

10. $2\frac{2}{3} - \frac{1}{6} = \frac{4}{6} - \frac{1}{6}$
$= \frac{4 - 1}{6} = \frac{3}{6} = \frac{1}{2}$

11. $(-12)(-4) = 48$

12. $\left(-\frac{4}{5}\right)\left(\frac{15}{32}\right) = \frac{(-4)(15)}{(5)(32)}$
$= \frac{\overset{-1}{\cancel{(-4)}}\overset{3}{\cancel{(15)}}}{\underset{1}{\cancel{(5)}}\underset{8}{\cancel{(32)}}} = -\frac{3}{8}$

13. $\frac{7}{12} \div \frac{5}{6} = \frac{7}{12} \cdot \frac{6}{5}$
$= \frac{(7)(6)}{(12)(5)} = \frac{(7)\overset{1}{\cancel{(6)}}}{\underset{2}{\cancel{(12)}}(5)} = \frac{7}{10}$

14. $\left(-\frac{3}{2}\right)^3 = \left(-\frac{3}{2}\right)\left(-\frac{3}{2}\right)\left(-\frac{3}{2}\right)$
$= \frac{(-3)(-3)(-3)}{(2)(2)(2)} = -\frac{27}{8}$

15. $3 - 2^2 + 25 \div 5 = 3 - 4 + 25 \div 5$
$= 3 - 4 + 5$
$= -1 + 5$
$= 4$

16. $\frac{18 - 2(3 + 4)}{6^2 - (12 \cdot 2 + 10)} = \frac{18 - 2(7)}{36 - (24 + 10)}$
$= \frac{18 - 14}{36 - (34)}$
$= \frac{4}{2}$
$= 2$

17. (a) $8(u - 5) = 8 \cdot u - 8 \cdot 5$ Distributive Property

(b) $10x - 10x = 0$ Additive Inverse Property

18. (a) $(7 + y) - z = 7 + (y - z)$ Associative Property of Addition

(b) $2x \cdot 1 = 2x$ Multiplicative Identity Property

19. $1522.76 - 328.37 - 65.99 - 50.00 + 413.88 = \$1492.28$

20. $(\$30)(2)(12)(5) = \$3600$

21.
$$1 = \tfrac{1}{3} + \tfrac{1}{4} + \tfrac{1}{8} + x$$
$$1 - \tfrac{1}{3} - \tfrac{1}{4} - \tfrac{1}{8} = x$$
$$\tfrac{24}{24} - \tfrac{8}{24} - \tfrac{6}{24} - \tfrac{3}{24} = x$$
$$\tfrac{7}{24} = x$$

The sum of the parts of a circle is equal to 1.

Section P.4   Algebraic Expressions

1. Terms: $10x$, 5

3. Terms: $-3y^2$, $2y$, -8

5. Terms: $4x^2$, $-3y^2$, $-5x$, $2y$

7. Terms: x^2, $-2.5x$, $-\dfrac{1}{x}$

9. The coefficient of $5y^3$ is 5.

11. The coefficient of $-\dfrac{3}{4}t^2$ is $-\dfrac{3}{4}$.

13. $4 - 3x = -3x + 4$ illustrates the Commutative Property of Addition

15. $-5(2x) = (-5 \cdot 2)x$ illustrates the Associative Property of Multiplication

17. $5(x + 6) = 5x + 30$

19. $6x + 6 = 6(x + 1)$

21. $x^3 \cdot x^4 = x \cdot x \cdot x \cdot x \cdot x \cdot x \cdot x$

23. $z^2 \cdot z^5 = z \cdot z \cdot z \cdot z \cdot z \cdot z \cdot z$

25. $(-5x)(-5x)(-5x)(-5x) = (-5x)^4$

27. $(x \cdot x \cdot x)(y \cdot y \cdot y) = x^3 y^3$

29. $-2^3 \cdot 2^4 = -2^{3+4}$
$$= -2^7$$

31. $x^5 \cdot x^7 \cdot x = x^{5+7+1} = x^{13}$

33. $3^3 y^4 \cdot y^2 = 3^3 y^{4+2} = 27y^6$

35. $(-4x)^2 = (-4)^2 \cdot x^2 = 16x^2$

37. $-4(2x)^2 = -4(4x^2)$
$$= -16x^2$$

39. $(-5z^2)^3 = (-5z^2)(-5z^2)(-5z^2)$
$$= (-5 \cdot -5 \cdot -5)(z^{2+2+2})$$
$$= -125z^6$$

41. $(2xy)(3x^2y^3) = (2 \cdot 3) \cdot (x \cdot x^2) \cdot (y \cdot y^3)$
$$= 6 \cdot (x^{1+2}) \cdot (y^{1+3})$$
$$= 6x^3 y^4$$

43. $(5y^2)(-y^4)(2y^3) = (5 \cdot -1 \cdot 2)(y^{2+4+3})$
$$= -10y^9$$

45. $-5z^4(-5z)^4 = -5z^4(625z^4)$
$$= (-5 \cdot 625)(z^{4+4})$$
$$= -3125z^8$$

47. $(-2a^2)^3(-8a) = (-8a^6)(-8a)$

$\qquad\qquad = (-8 \cdot -8)(a^{6+1})$

$\qquad\qquad = 64a^7$

49. $(3uv)^2(-6u^3v) = (3^2u^2v^2)(-6u^3v)$

$\qquad\qquad = (3^2 \cdot -6) \cdot (u^2 \cdot u^3) \cdot (v^2 \cdot v)$

$\qquad\qquad = (9 \cdot -6) \cdot (u^{2+3}) \cdot (v^{2+1})$

$\qquad\qquad = -54u^5v^3$

51. $(x^n)^4 = x^{n \cdot 4} = x^{4n}$

53. $x^{n+1} \cdot x^3 = x^{n+1+3} = x^{n+4}$

55. $3x + 4x = (3 + 4)x = 7x$

57. $9y - 5y + 4y = (9 - 5 + 4)y = 8y$

59. $3x - 2y + 5x + 20y = (3x + 5x) + (-2y + 20y)$

$\qquad\qquad = (3 + 5)x + (-2 + 20)y$

$\qquad\qquad = 8x + 18y$

61. $7x^2 - 2x - x^2 = 7x^2 - x^2 - 2x$

$\qquad\qquad = (7 - 1)x^2 - 2x$

$\qquad\qquad = 6x^2 - 2x$

63. $-3z^4 + 6z - z + 8 + z^4 = -3z^4 + z^4 + 6z - z + 8$

$\qquad\qquad = (-3 + 1)z^4 + (6 - 1)z + 8$

$\qquad\qquad = -2z^4 + 5z + 8$

65. $2uv + 5u^2v^2 - uv - (uv)^2 = (2uv - uv) + (5u^2v^2 - u^2v^2)$

$\qquad\qquad = (2 - 1)uv + (5 - 1)u^2v^2$

$\qquad\qquad = uv + 4u^2v^2$

67. $4(2x^2 + x - 3) = 8x^2 + 4x - 12$

69. $-3(6y^2 - y - 2) = -18y^2 + 3y + 6$

71. $10(x - 3) + 2x - 5 = 10x - 30 + 2x - 5$

$\qquad\qquad = (10x + 2x) + (-30 - 5)$

$\qquad\qquad = (10 + 2)x + (-30 - 5)$

$\qquad\qquad = 12x - 35$

73. $-3(3y - 1) + 2(y - 5) = -9y + 3 + 2y - 10$

$\qquad\qquad = -9y + 2y + 3 - 10$

$\qquad\qquad = (-9 + 2)y - 7$

$\qquad\qquad = -7y - 7$

75. $-3(y^2 - 2) + y^2(y + 3) = -3y^2 + 6 + y^3 + 3y^2$

$\qquad\qquad = (-3 + 3)y^2 + 6 + y^3$

$\qquad\qquad = 6 + y^3$

77. $y^2(y + 1) + y(y^2 + 1) = y^3 + y^2 + y^3 + y$

$\qquad\qquad = (y^3 + y^3) + (y^2) + (y)$

$\qquad\qquad = 2y^3 + y^2 + y$

79. $3[2x - 4(x - 8)] = 3[2x - 4x + 32]$

$\qquad\qquad = 3[-2x + 32]$

$\qquad\qquad = -6x + 96$

81. $8x + 3x[10 - 4(3 - x)] = 8x + 3x[10 - 12 + 4x]$

$\qquad\qquad = 8x + 3x[-2 + 4x]$

$\qquad\qquad = 8x - 6x + 12x^2$

$\qquad\qquad = 2x + 12x^2$

83. $2[3(b - 5) - (b^2 + b + 3)] = 2[3b - 15 - b^2 - b - 3]$

$\qquad\qquad = 6b - 30 - 2b^2 - 2b - 6$

$\qquad\qquad = (-2b^2) + (6b - 2b) + (-30 - 6)$

$\qquad\qquad = -2b^2 + 4b - 36$

85. $2x(5x^2) - 4x^3(x + 15) = 10x^3 - 4x^4 - 60x^3$

$$= -(10 - 60)x^3 - 4x^4$$

$$= -4x^4 - 50x^3$$

87. (a) Substitution: $5 - 3\left(\frac{2}{3}\right)$

Value of expression: 3

(b) Substitution: $5 - 3(5)$

Value of expression: -10

89. (a) Substitution: $10 - 4(-1)^2$

Value of expression: $10 - 4 = 6$

(b) Substitution: $10 - 4\left(\frac{1}{2}\right)^2$

Value of expression: $10 - 4\left(\frac{1}{4}\right) = 10 - 1 = 9$

91. (a) Substitution: $\dfrac{0}{0^2 + 1}$

Value of expression: 0

(b) Substitution: $\dfrac{3}{3^2 + 1}$

Value of expression: $\dfrac{3}{10}$

93. (a) Substitution: $3(1) + 2(5)$

Value of expression: 13

(b) Substitution: $3(-6) + 2(-9)$

Value of expression: -36

95. (a) Substitution: $2^2 - (2)(-1) + (-1)^2 = 4 - (-2) + 1$

$$= 7$$

Value of expression: 7

(b) Substitution: $(-3)^2 - (-3)(-2) + (-2)^2 = 9 - 6 + 4$

$$= 7$$

Value of expression: 7

97. (a) Substitution: $|5 - 2| = |3| = 3$

Value of expression: 3

(b) Substitution: $|-2 - (-2)| = |-2 + 2| = |0| = 0$

Value of expression: 0

99. (a) Substitution: $40\left(5\frac{1}{4}\right)$

Value of expression: 210

(b) Substitution: $35(4)$

Value of expression: 140

101. $A = \frac{1}{2}b(b - 3)$

$A = \frac{1}{2}(15)(15 - 3)$

$= \frac{1}{2}(15)(12)$

$= 90$

103. $A = lw$

$A = (2x + 3)x$

$A = 2x^2 + 3x$

105. Graphically, the sales in 1995 is approximately $2800 million.

Let $t = 5$.

Sales $= 193.89(5) + 1830.89$

$= 969.45 + 1830.89$

$= \$2800.34$

107. Graphically, the median sale price in 1995 is approximately $134 thousand.

Let $t = 5$.

Sale price $= 5.9(5) + 106.0$

$= 29.5 + 106.0$

$= \$135.5$ thousand

109.

$$\boxed{\text{Total area}} = 2 \cdot \boxed{\begin{array}{c}\text{Area of} \\ \text{trapezoid}\end{array}} + 2 \cdot \boxed{\begin{array}{c}\text{Area of} \\ \text{triangle}\end{array}}$$

$$\text{Area} = \left[\frac{1}{2} \cdot h(b_1 + b_2)\right] + 2\left[\frac{1}{2} \cdot b \cdot h\right]$$

$$\text{Area} = 12(60 + 40) + 20 \cdot 12$$

$$= 12(100) + 240$$

$$= 1200 + 240$$

$$= 1440 \text{ square feet}$$

111. (d) $(0 + 3 + 1 + 2 + 6 + 7)3 + (4 + 8 + 9 + 3 + a)$

  (e) $81 + a$, the next-highest multiple of 10 will be 90.

  $90 - (81 + a) = 4 \qquad 9 - a = 4 \qquad a = 5$

  $90 - 81 - a = 4 \qquad\quad -a = -5 \qquad$ No. The work shows the only possible answer.

113. To combine like terms add (or subtract) their respective coefficients and attach the common variable factor. Example: $5x^4 - 3x^4 = (5 - 3)x^4 = 2x^4$

115. The Distributive Property is used to simplify $5x + 3x$ as follows: $5x + 3x = (5 + 3)x = 8x$.

117. It is not possible to evaluate $\dfrac{x + 2}{y - 3}$ when $x = 5$ and $y = 3$ because $\dfrac{7}{0}$ is undefined.

Section P.5 Constructing Algebraic Expressions

1. The sum of 8 and a number n is translated into the algebraic expression $8 + n$.

3. The sum of 12 and twice a number n is translated into the algebraic expression $12 + 2n$.

5. Six less than a number n is translated into the algebraic expression $n - 6$.

7. Four times a number n minus 3 is translated into the algebraic expression $4n - 3$.

9. One-third of a number n is translated into the algebraic expression $\frac{1}{3}n$.

11. The quotient of a number x and 6 is translated into the algebraic expression $\frac{x}{6}$.

13. Eight times the ratio of N and 5 is translated into the algebraic expression $8 \cdot \frac{N}{5}$.

15. The number c is quadrupled and the product is increased by 10 is translated into the algebraic expression $4c + 10$.

17. Thirty percent of the list price L is translated into the algebraic expression $0.30L$.

19. The sum of a number and 5 divided by 10 is translated into the algebraic expression $\frac{n + 5}{10}$.

21. The absolute value of the difference between a number and 5 is translated into the algebraic expression $|n - 5|$.

23. The product of three and the square of a number decreased by 4 is translated into the algebraic expression $3x^2 - 4$.

25. A verbal description of $t - 2$ is a number decreased by 2.

27. A verbal description of $y + 50$ is the sum of a number and 50.

29. A verbal description of $3x + 2$ is the sum of three times a number and two.

31. A verbal description of $\frac{z}{2}$ is the ratio of a number to two.

33. A verbal description of $\frac{4}{5}x$ is four-fifths of a number.

35. A verbal description of $8(x - 5)$ is eight times the difference of a number and five.

37. A verbal description of $\frac{x + 10}{3}$ is the sum of a number and ten, divided by three.

39. A verbal description of $x(x + 7)$ is some number times the sum of the same number and seven.

41. *Verbal Description:* The amount of money (in dollars) represented by n quarters

Label: n = number of quarters

Algebraic Description: $0.25n$ = amount of money (in dollars)

43. *Verbal Description:* The amount of money (in dollars) represented by m dimes

Label: m = number of dimes

Algebraic Description: $\frac{m}{10}$

45. *Verbal Description:* The amount of money (in cents) represented by m nickels and n dimes

Label: m = number of dimes

n = number of dimes

Algebraic Description: $5m + 10n$

47. *Verbal Description:* The distance traveled in t hours at an average speed of 55 miles per hour

Label: t = number of hours

Algebraic Description: $55t$

49. *Verbal Description:* The time to travel 100 miles at an average speed of r miles per hour

Label: r = average speed

Algebraic Description: $\frac{100}{r}$

51. *Verbal Description:* The amount of antifreeze in a cooling system containing y gallons of coolant that is 45% antifreeze

Label: y = number of gallons

Algebraic Description: $0.45y$

53. *Verbal Description:* The amount of wage tax due for a taxable income of I dollars that is taxed at the rate of 1.25%

Label: I = number of dollars

Algebraic Description: $0.0125I$

55. *Verbal Description:*   The sale price of a coat that has a list price of L dollars if the sale is a "20% off" sale

    Label: L = number of dollars

    Algebraic Description: $0.80L$

57. *Verbal Description:*   The total hourly wage for an employee when the base pay is $8.25 per hour plus 60 cents for each of q units producted per hour

    Label: q = number of units produced

    Algebraic Description: $8.25 + 0.60q$

59. *Verbal Description:*   The sum of a number n and three times the number

    Label: n = the number

                  $3n$ = three times the number

    Algebraic Description: $n + 3n = 4n$

61. *Verbal Description:*   The sum of two consecutive odd integers, the first of which is $2n + 1$.

    Labels: $2n + 1$ = first odd integer

             $2n + 3$ = second odd integer

    Algebraic Description: $(2n + 1) + (2n + 3) = 4n + 4$

63. *Verbal Description:*   The product of two consecutive even integers, divided by 4

    Labels: $2n$ = first even integer

             $2n + 2$ = second even integer

    Algebraic Description: $\dfrac{2n(2n + 2)}{4} = \dfrac{4n(n + 1)}{4}$

                                 $= n(n + 1)$

65. Area = side $\cdot$ side

         $= s \cdot s$

         $= s^2$

67. Area $= \frac{1}{2}$(base)(height)

       $= \frac{1}{2}(b)(0.75b)$

       $= 0.375b^2$

69. Perimeter $= 2(2w) + 2(w) = 4w + 2w = 6w$

     Area $= 2w \cdot w = 2w^2$

71. Perimeter $= 3 + 2x + 6 + x + 3 + x = 4x + 12$

    Area $= (x \cdot 3) + (3 \cdot 2x) = 3x + 6x = 9x$

73. $l \cdot (l - 6)$ = area of billiard table

    The unit of measure for the area is feet^2 or square feet.

75.

n	0	1	2	3	4	5
$5n - 3$	-3	2	7	12	17	22
Differences		5	5	5	5	5

77. The third row difference for the algebraic expression $an + b$ would be a.

79. The phrase *reduced by* implies subtraction.

81. $4x$ is the equivalent to (a) x multiplied by 4 and (c) the product of x and 4.

83. Using a specific case may make it easier to see the form of the expression for the general case.

Review Exercises for Chapter P

1. $-5 < 3$

3. $-\frac{8}{5} < -\frac{2}{5}$

5. $d = |9 - (-2)|$
$= |11|$
$= 11$

7. $d = |-13.5 - (-6.2)|$
$= |-13.5 + 6.2|$
$= |-7.3|$
$= 7.3$

9. $|-5| = 5$

11. $-|-7.2| = -7.2$

13. $15 + (-4) = 11$

15. $340 - 115 + 5 = 230$

17. $-63.5 + 21.7 = -41.8$

19. $\frac{4}{21} + \frac{7}{21} = \frac{11}{21}$

21. $-\frac{5}{6} + 1 = -\frac{5}{6} + \frac{6}{6} = \frac{1}{6}$

23. $8\frac{3}{4} - 6\frac{5}{8} = \frac{35}{4} - \frac{53}{8} = \frac{70}{8} - \frac{53}{8} = \frac{17}{8}$

25. $-7 \cdot 4 = -28$

27. $120(-5)(7) = -4200$

29. $\frac{3}{8} \cdot \frac{-2}{15} = \frac{-6}{120} = \frac{-1}{20}$

31. $\frac{-56}{-4} = 14$

33. $-\frac{7}{15} \div -\frac{7}{30} = -\frac{7}{15} \cdot \frac{30}{-7} = 2$

35. $(-6)^3 = (-6)(-6)(-6) = -216$

37. $-4^2 = -1 \cdot 4 \cdot 4 = -16$

39. $-\left(-\frac{1}{2}\right) = -1 \cdot \left(-\frac{1}{2}\right)\left(-\frac{1}{2}\right)\left(-\frac{1}{2}\right) = \frac{1}{8}$

41. $120 - (5^2 \cdot 4) = 120 - (25 \cdot 4)$
$= 120 - 100$
$= 20$

43. $8 + 3[6^2 - 2(7 - 4)] = 8 + 3[36 - 2(3)]$
$= 8 + 3[36 - 6]$
$= 8 + 3[30]$
$= 8 + 90$
$= 98$

45. Additive Inverse Property justifies $13 - 13 = 0$.

47. Distributive Property justifies $7(9 + 3) = 7 \cdot 9 + 7 \cdot 3$.

49. Associative Property of Addition justifies
$5 + (4 - y) = (5 + 4) - y$.

51. $(u - v)(2) = 2(u - v)$ illustrates the Commutative
Property of Multiplication.

53. $8(x - y) = 8 \cdot x - 8 \cdot y$ illustrates the Distributive
Property.

55. $-(-u + 3v) = u - 3v$

57. $-y(3y - 10) = -3y^2 + 10y$

59. $x^2 \cdot x^3 \cdot x = x^{2+3+1} = x^6$

61. $(xy)(-3x^2y^3) = -3 \cdot x^{1+2} \cdot y^{1+3}$
$= -3x^3y^4$

63. $(5ab)(25a^3) = 125a^4b$

65. $7x - 2x = (7 - 2)x$

   $\qquad = 5x$

67. $3u - 2v + 7v - 3u = (3u - 3u) + (-2v + 7v)$

   $\qquad\qquad\qquad\qquad = 5v$

69. $5(x - 4) + 10 = 5x - 20 + 10$

   $\qquad\qquad\quad = 5x - 10$

71. $3x - (y - 2x) = 3x - y + 2x$

   $\qquad\qquad\qquad = 5x - y$

73. $3[b + 5(b - a)] = 3[b + 5b - 5a]$

   $\qquad\qquad\qquad = 3b + 15b - 15a$

   $\qquad\qquad\qquad = 18b - 15a$

75. (a) $x = 3$

   Substitute: $3^2 - 2(3) - 3$

   Value of expression: 0

   (b) $x = 0$

   Substitute: $(0)^2 - 2(0) - 3$

   Value of expression: -3

77. $200 - 3n$

79. $n^2 + 49$

81. The sum of twice a number and seven

83. The difference of a number and five, all divided by four

85. $0.18I =$ tax on I dollars at 18%

87. $l \cdot (l - 5) =$ area of rectangle with length l and width $(l - 5)$

89. Combined expenditures $= 12.1 + 10.8 + 38.6 + 9.2 + 40.3 = \$111.0$

91. Difference between the airports with the greatest and smallest passenger volumes

   $= 30.8 - 15.2$

   $= 15.6$ million

93. Airports from greatest to smallest volume:

   1. Atlanta/Hartsfield   30.8

   2. Chicago/O'Hare   30.5

   3. Dallas/Ft. Worth   26.6

   4. Los Angeles   22.7

   5. Denver   15.2

   6. San Francisco   15.2

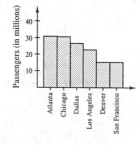

Chapter Test for Chapter P

1. (a) $-\frac{5}{2} > -|-3|$

   (b) $-\frac{2}{3} > -\frac{3}{2}$

2. $d = |-6.2 - 5.7| = 11.9$

3. $-14 + 9 - 15 = (-14 + 9) - 15$

                       $= -5 - 15$

                       $= -20$

4. $\frac{2}{3} + \left(-\frac{7}{6}\right) = \frac{4}{6} + \left(-\frac{7}{6}\right) = -\frac{3}{6} = -\frac{1}{2}$

5. $-2(225 - 150) = -2(75) = -150$

6. $(-3)(4)(-5) = (-12)(-5)$

                       $= 60$

7. $\left(-\frac{7}{16}\right)\left(-\frac{8}{21}\right) = \frac{1}{6}$

8 $\frac{5}{18} \div \frac{15}{8} = \frac{5}{18} \cdot \frac{8}{15} = \frac{4}{27}$

9. $\left(-\frac{3}{5}\right)^3 = \frac{-27}{125}$

10. $\frac{4^2 - 6}{5} + 13 = \frac{16 - 6}{5} + 13$

                         $= \frac{10}{5} + 13$

                         $= 2 + 13$

                         $= 15$

11. (a) $(-3 \cdot 5) \cdot 6 = -3(5 \cdot 6)$ demonstrates the Associative Property of Multiplication.

   (b) $3y \cdot \dfrac{1}{3y} = 1$ demonstrates the Multiplicative Inverse Property.

12. $5(2x - 3) = 5(2x) - 5(3)$

13. $(3x^2 y)(-xy)^2 = (3x^2 y)(x^2 y^2) = 3x^4 y^3$

14. $3x^2 - 2x - 5x^2 + 7x - 1 = -2x^2 + 5x - 1$

15. $a(5a - 4) - 2(2a^2 - 2a) = 5a^2 - 4a - 4a^2 + 4a$

                               $= a^2$

16. $4t - [3t - (10t + 7)] = 4t - [3t - 10t - 7]$

                             $= 4t - [-7t - 7]$

                             $= 4t + 7t + 7$

                             $= 11t + 7$

17. Evaluating an expression means to substitute numerical values for each of the variables in the expression and then to simplify according to the rules for order of operations.

   (a) $x = -1 \Longrightarrow 4 - (-1 + 1)^2$

                   $4 - (0)^2$

                      4

   (b) $x = 3 \Longrightarrow 4 - (3 + 1)^2$

                   $4 - (4)^2$

                   $4 - 16$

                  -12

18. "The product of a number n and 5 is decreased by 8" is translated into the algebraic expression $5n - 8$.

19. Perimeter $= 2(l) + 2(0.6l) = 2l + 1.2l = 3.2l$

  Area $= l(0.6l) = 0.6l^2$

20. *Verbal Description:*   The sum of two consecutive even integers, the first of which is $2n$.

  Labels: $2n = $ first even integer

  $2n + 2 = $ second even integer

  Algebraic Description: $2n + (2n + 2) = 4n + 2$

21. *Verbal model:* $9 \cdot$ | Length of each piece | $=$ | Total length |

  Equation: $9 \cdot n = 144$

  $n = 16$ feet

22. *Verbal model:* | Volume of 1 cord | $=$ | Length | $\cdot$ | Width | $\cdot$ | Height |

  Equation: $V = 4 \cdot 4 \cdot 8$

  $V = 128$ cubic feet

  Verbal model: | Volume of 5 cords | $= 5 \cdot$ | Volume of 1 cord |

  Equation: $V = 5 \cdot 128$

  $= 640$ cubic feet

CHAPTER 1
Linear Equations and Inequalities

CHAPTER 1
Linear Equations and Inequalities

Section 1.1   Linear Equations
Solutions to Odd-Numbered Exercises

1. (a) $\quad x = 0$

$3(0) - 7 \overset{?}{=} 2$

$-7 \neq 2$

No

(b) $\quad x = 3$

$3(3) - 7 \overset{?}{=} 2$

$9 - 7 = 2$

$2 = 2$

Yes

3. (a) $\quad x = 4$

$4 + 8 \overset{?}{=} 3(4)$

$12 = 12$

Yes

(b) $\quad x = -4$

$-4 + 8 \overset{?}{=} 3(-4)$

$4 \neq -12$

No

5. (a) $\quad x = -11$

$3(-11) + 3 \overset{?}{=} 2(-11 - 4)$

$-33 + 3 = 2(-15)$

$-30 = -30$

Yes

(b) $\quad x = 5$

$3(5) + 3 \overset{?}{=} 2(5 - 4)$

$15 + 3 = 2(1)$

$18 \neq 2$

No

7. (a) $\quad x = -4$

$\frac{1}{4}(-4) \overset{?}{=} 3$

$-1 \neq 3$

No

(b) $\quad x = 12$

$\frac{1}{4}(12) \overset{?}{=} 3$

$3 = 3$

Yes

9.

$3(x - 1) = 3x$	Original equation
$3x - 3 = 3x$	Distributive Property
$3x - 3 - 3x = 3x - 3x$	Subtract $3x$ from both sides.
$-3 = 0$	Simplify.

No solution since $-3 \neq 0$.

11.

$5(x + 3) = 2x + 3(x + 5)$	Original equation
$5x + 15 = 2x + 3x + 15$	Distributive Property
$5x + 15 = 5x + 15$	Combine like terms.

Identity since both sides equal.

13. $3x + 4 = 10$ is linear since variable has exponent 1.

15. $\frac{4}{x} - 3 = 5$ is not linear since variable has exponent -1 not 1.

17.

$3x + 15 = 0$	Original equation
$3x + 15 - 15 = 0 - 15$	Subtract 15 from both sides.
$3x = -15$	Combine like terms.
$\dfrac{3x}{3} = \dfrac{-15}{3}$	Divide both sides by 3.
$x = -5$	Simplify.

19. $-2x + 5 = 12$ Original equation

     $-2x + 5 - 5 = 12 - 5$ Subtract 5 from both sides.

           $-2x = 7$ Combine like terms.

           $\dfrac{-2x}{-2} = \dfrac{7}{-2}$ Divide both sides by -2.

           $x = -\dfrac{7}{2}$ Simplify.

21. $x - 3 = 0$ **Check:** $3 - 3 \overset{?}{=} 0$

     $x - 3 + 3 = 0 + 3$ $0 = 0$

         $x = 3$

23. $3x = 12$ **Check:** $3(4) \overset{?}{=} 12$

     $\dfrac{3x}{3} = \dfrac{12}{3}$ $12 = 12$

     $x = 4$

25. $-6y = 4.2$ **Check:** $-6(-0.7) \overset{?}{=} 4.2$

     $\dfrac{-6y}{-6} = \dfrac{4.2}{-6}$ $4.2 = 4.2$

     $y = -0.7$

27. $6x + 4 = 0$ **Check:**

   $6x + 4 - 4 = 0 - 4$ $6\left(-\dfrac{2}{3}\right) + 4 \overset{?}{=} 0$

         $6x = -4$ $-4 + 4 \overset{?}{=} 0$

         $\dfrac{6x}{6} = \dfrac{-4}{6}$ $0 = 0$

           $x = -\dfrac{4}{6}$

           $x = -\dfrac{2}{3}$

29. $-2u + 5 = 7$ **Check:**

   $-2u + 5 - 5 = 7 - 5$ $-2(-1) + 5 \overset{?}{=} 7$

         $-2u = 2$ $2 + 5 \overset{?}{=} 7$

         $\dfrac{-2u}{-2} = \dfrac{2}{-2}$ $7 = 7$

           $u = -1$

31. $4x - 7 = -11$ **Check:**

   $4x - 7 + 7 = -11 + 7$ $4(-1) - 7 \overset{?}{=} -11$

         $4x = -4$ $-4 - 7 \overset{?}{=} -11$

         $\dfrac{4x}{4} = \dfrac{-4}{4}$ $-11 = -11$

           $x = -1$

33. $23x - 4 = 42$ **Check:**

   $23x - 4 + 4 = 42 + 4$ $23(2) - 4 \overset{?}{=} 42$

         $23x = 46$ $46 - 4 \overset{?}{=} 42$

         $\dfrac{23x}{23} = \dfrac{46}{23}$ $42 = 42$

           $x = 2$

35. $3t + 8 = -2$ **Check:**

   $3t + 8 - 8 = -2 - 8$ $3\left(-\dfrac{10}{3}\right) + 8 \overset{?}{=} -2$

         $3t = -10$ $-10 + 8 \overset{?}{=} -2$

         $\dfrac{3t}{3} = \dfrac{-10}{3}$ $-2 = -2$

           $t = -\dfrac{10}{3}$

37. $8 - 5t = 20 + t$ **Check:**

$8 - 5t + 5t = 20 + t + 5t$ $8 - 5(-2) \stackrel{?}{=} 20 + (-2)$

$8 = 20 + 6t$ $8 + 10 \stackrel{?}{=} 18$

$8 - 20 = 20 + 6t - 20$ $18 = 18$

$-12 = 6t$

$\dfrac{-12}{6} = \dfrac{6t}{6}$

$-2 = t$

39. $4x - 5 = 2x - 1$ **Check:**

$4x - 2x - 5 = 2x - 2x - 1$ $4(2) - 5 \stackrel{?}{=} 2(2) - 1$

$2x - 5 = -1$ $8 - 5 \stackrel{?}{=} 4 - 1$

$2x - 5 + 5 = -1 + 5$ $3 = 3$

$2x = 4$

$\dfrac{2x}{2} = \dfrac{4}{2}$

$x = 2$

41. $7 - 8x = 13x$ **Check:**

$7 - 8x + 8x = 13x + 8x$ $7 - 8\left(\dfrac{1}{3}\right) \stackrel{?}{=} 13\left(\dfrac{1}{3}\right)$

$7 = 21x$ $7 - \dfrac{8}{3} \stackrel{?}{=} \dfrac{13}{3}$

$\dfrac{7}{21} = \dfrac{21x}{21}$ $\dfrac{21}{3} - \dfrac{8}{3} \stackrel{?}{=} \dfrac{13}{3}$

$\dfrac{1}{3} = x$ $\dfrac{13}{3} = \dfrac{13}{3}$

43. $4y - 3 = 4y$

$4y - 3 + 3 = 4y + 3$

$4y = 4y + 3$

$4y - 4y = 4y + 3 - 4y$

$0 = 3$

$0 \neq 3$

No solution

45. $-8t = -16t$ **Check:**

$-8t + 16t = -16t + 16t$ $-8(0) \stackrel{?}{=} -16(0)$

$8t = 0$ $0 = 0$

$\dfrac{8t}{8} = \dfrac{0}{8}$

$t = 0$

47. $-9y - 4 = -9y$

$-9y + 9y - 4 = -9y + 9y$

$-4 = 0$

$-4 \neq 0$

No solution

49. $8(x - 8) = 24$ **Check:**

$8x - 64 = 24$ $8(11 - 8) \stackrel{?}{=} 24$

$8x - 64 + 64 = 24 + 64$ $8(3) \stackrel{?}{=} 24$

$8x = 88$ $24 = 24$

$\dfrac{8x}{8} = \dfrac{88}{8}$

$x = 11$

51. $-4(t + 2) = 0$ **Check:**

$-4t - 8 = 0$ $-4[(-2) + 2] \stackrel{?}{=} 0$

$-4t - 8 + 8 = 0 + 8$ $-4[0] \stackrel{?}{=} 0$

$-4t = 8$ $0 = 0$

$\dfrac{-4t}{-4} = \dfrac{8}{-4}$

$t = -2$

53.
$$3(x - 4) = 7x + 6$$
$$3x - 12 = 7x + 6$$
$$3x - 7x - 12 = 7x - 7x + 6$$
$$-4x - 12 = 6$$
$$-4x - 12 + 12 = 6 + 12$$
$$-4x = 18$$
$$\frac{-4x}{-4} = \frac{18}{-4}$$
$$x = -\frac{9}{2}$$

Check:
$$3\left(-\frac{9}{2} - 4\right) \overset{?}{=} 7\left(-\frac{9}{2}\right) + 6$$
$$3\left(-\frac{9}{2} - \frac{8}{2}\right) \overset{?}{=} -\frac{63}{2} + \frac{12}{2}$$
$$3\left(-\frac{17}{2}\right) \overset{?}{=} -\frac{51}{2}$$
$$-\frac{51}{2} = -\frac{51}{2}$$

55.
$$8x - 3(x - 2) = 12$$
$$8x - 3x + 6 = 12$$
$$5x + 6 = 12$$
$$5x + 6 - 6 = 12 - 6$$
$$5x = 6$$
$$\frac{5x}{5} = \frac{6}{5}$$
$$x = \frac{6}{5}$$

Check:
$$8\left(\frac{6}{5}\right) - 3\left(\frac{6}{5} - 2\right) \overset{?}{=} 12$$
$$\frac{48}{5} - 3\left(\frac{6}{5} - \frac{10}{5}\right) \overset{?}{=} 12$$
$$\frac{48}{5} - 3\left(-\frac{4}{5}\right) \overset{?}{=} 12$$
$$\frac{48}{5} + \frac{12}{5} \overset{?}{=} 12$$
$$\frac{60}{5} \overset{?}{=} 12$$
$$12 = 12$$

57.
$$5 - (2y - 4) = 15$$
$$5 - 2y + 4 = 15$$
$$-2y + 9 = 15$$
$$-2y + 9 - 9 = 15 - 9$$
$$-2y = 6$$
$$\frac{-2y}{-2} = \frac{6}{-2}$$
$$y = -3$$

Check:
$$5 - [2(-3) - 4] \overset{?}{=} 15$$
$$5 - [-6 - 4] \overset{?}{=} 15$$
$$5 - [-10] \overset{?}{=} 15$$
$$5 + 10 \overset{?}{=} 15$$
$$15 = 15$$

59.
$$12(x + 3) = 7(x + 3)$$
$$12x + 36 = 7x + 21$$
$$12x + 36 - 7x = 7x + 21 - 7x$$
$$5x + 36 = 21$$
$$5x + 36 - 36 = 21 - 36$$
$$5x = -15$$
$$\frac{5x}{5} = \frac{-15}{5}$$
$$x = -3$$

Check:
$$12[(-3) + 3] \overset{?}{=} 7[(-3) + 3]$$
$$12[0] \overset{?}{=} 7[0]$$
$$0 = 0$$

61.
$$2(x + 7) - 9 = 5(x - 4)$$
$$2x + 14 - 9 = 5x - 20$$
$$2x + 5 = 5x - 20$$
$$2x + 5 - 2x = 5x - 20 - 2x$$
$$5 = 3x - 20$$
$$5 + 20 = 3x - 20 + 20$$
$$25 = 3x$$
$$\frac{25}{3} = \frac{3x}{3}$$
$$\frac{25}{3} = x$$

Check:
$$2\left(\frac{25}{3} + 7\right) - 9 \overset{?}{=} 5\left(\frac{25}{3} - 4\right)$$
$$2\left(\frac{25}{3} + \frac{21}{3}\right) - 9 \overset{?}{=} 5\left(\frac{25}{3} - \frac{12}{3}\right)$$
$$2\left(\frac{46}{3}\right) - 9 \overset{?}{=} 5\left(\frac{13}{3}\right)$$
$$\frac{92}{3} - \frac{27}{3} \overset{?}{=} \frac{65}{3}$$
$$\frac{65}{3} = \frac{65}{3}$$

63. $\dfrac{u}{5} = 10$ **Check:**

$5\left(\dfrac{u}{5}\right) = (10)5$ $\dfrac{50}{5} \overset{?}{=} 10$

$u = 50$ $10 = 10$

65. $t - \dfrac{2}{5} = \dfrac{3}{2}$ **Check:**

$10\left(t - \dfrac{2}{5}\right) = \left(\dfrac{3}{2}\right)10$ $\dfrac{19}{10} - \dfrac{2}{5} \overset{?}{=} \dfrac{3}{2}$

$10t - 4 = 15$ $\dfrac{19}{10} - \dfrac{4}{10} \overset{?}{=} \dfrac{15}{10}$

$10t - 4 + 4 = 15 + 4$ $\dfrac{15}{10} = \dfrac{15}{10}$

$10t = 19$

$\dfrac{10t}{10} = \dfrac{19}{10}$

$t = \dfrac{19}{10}$

67. $\dfrac{t}{5} - \dfrac{t}{2} = 1$ **Check:**

$10\left(\dfrac{t}{5} - \dfrac{t}{2}\right) = (1)10$ $\dfrac{-\frac{10}{3}}{5} - \dfrac{-\frac{10}{3}}{2} \overset{?}{=} 1$

$2t - 5t = 10$ $\dfrac{10}{-15} + \dfrac{10}{6} \overset{?}{=} 1$

$-3t = 10$ $-\dfrac{2}{3} + \dfrac{5}{3} \overset{?}{=} 1$

$\dfrac{-3t}{-3} = \dfrac{10}{-3}$ $\dfrac{3}{3} \overset{?}{=} 1$

$t = \dfrac{10}{-3}$ $1 = 1$

69. $\dfrac{8x}{5} - \dfrac{x}{4} = -3$ **Check:**

$20\left(\dfrac{8x}{5} - \dfrac{x}{4}\right) = (-3)20$ $\dfrac{8}{5}\left(-\dfrac{20}{9}\right) - \dfrac{1}{4}\left(-\dfrac{20}{9}\right) \overset{?}{=} -3$

$4(8x) - 5x = -60$ $-\dfrac{32}{9} + \dfrac{5}{9} \overset{?}{=} -3$

$32x - 5x = -60$ $-\dfrac{27}{9} \overset{?}{=} -3$

$27x = -60$ $-3 = -3$

$\dfrac{27x}{27} = \dfrac{-60}{27}$

$x = -\dfrac{20}{9}$

71. $\dfrac{1}{3}x + 1 = \dfrac{1}{12}x - 4$ **Check:**

$12\left(\dfrac{1}{3}x + 1\right) = \left(\dfrac{1}{12}x - 4\right)12$ $\dfrac{1}{3}(-20) + 1 \overset{?}{=} \dfrac{1}{12}(-20) - 4$

$4x + 12 = x - 48$ $\dfrac{-20}{3} + \dfrac{3}{3} \overset{?}{=} \dfrac{-20}{12} - 4$

$4x + 12 - x = x - 48 - x$ $\dfrac{-17}{3} \overset{?}{=} \dfrac{-5}{3} - \dfrac{12}{3}$

$3x + 12 = -48$ $-\dfrac{17}{3} = -\dfrac{17}{3}$

$3x + 12 - 12 = -48 - 12$

$3x = -60$

$\dfrac{3x}{3} = \dfrac{-60}{3}$

$x = -20$

73.
$$\frac{25 - 4u}{3} = \frac{5u + 12}{4} + 6$$

$$12\left(\frac{25 - 4u}{3}\right) = \left(\frac{5u + 12}{4} + 6\right)12$$

$$4(25 - 4u) = 3(5u + 12) + 72$$

$$100 - 16u = 15u + 36 + 72$$

$$100 - 16u = 15u + 108$$

$$100 - 16u + 16u = 15u + 108 + 16u$$

$$100 = 31u + 108$$

$$100 - 108 = 31u + 108 - 108$$

$$-8 = 31u$$

$$\frac{-8}{31} = \frac{31u}{31}$$

$$-\frac{8}{31} = u$$

Check:

$$\frac{25 - 4\left(-\frac{8}{31}\right)}{3} \stackrel{?}{=} \frac{5\left(-\frac{8}{31}\right) + 12}{4} + 6$$

$$\frac{25 + \frac{32}{31}}{3} \stackrel{?}{=} \frac{-\frac{40}{31} + 12}{4} + 6$$

$$\frac{25}{3} + \frac{32}{93} \stackrel{?}{=} \frac{-10}{31} + 3 + 6$$

$$\frac{775}{93} + \frac{32}{93} \stackrel{?}{=} \frac{-10}{31} + \frac{93}{31} + \frac{186}{31}$$

$$\frac{807}{93} \stackrel{?}{=} \frac{269}{31}$$

$$\frac{269}{31} = \frac{269}{31}$$

75.
$$0.3x + 1.5 = 8.4$$

$$10(0.3x + 1.5) = (8.4)10$$

$$3x + 15 = 84$$

$$3x + 15 - 15 = 84 - 15$$

$$3x = 69$$

$$\frac{3x}{3} = \frac{69}{3}$$

$$x = 23$$

Check:

$$0.3(23) + 1.5 \stackrel{?}{=} 8.4$$

$$6.9 + 1.5 \stackrel{?}{=} 8.4$$

$$8.4 = 8.4$$

77.
$$1.2(x - 3) = 10.8$$

$$1.2x - 3.6 = 10.8$$

$$10(1.2x - 3.6) = (10.8)10$$

$$12x - 36 = 108$$

$$12x - 36 + 36 = 108 + 36$$

$$12x = 144$$

$$\frac{12x}{12} = \frac{144}{12}$$

$$x = 12$$

Check:

$$1.2(12 - 3) \stackrel{?}{=} 10.8$$

$$1.2(9) \stackrel{?}{=} 10.8$$

$$10.8 = 10.8$$

79.
$$\frac{2}{3}(2x - 4) = \frac{1}{2}(x + 3) - 4$$

$$6\left[\frac{2}{3}(2x - 4)\right] = \left[\frac{1}{2}(x + 3) - 4\right]6$$

$$4(2x - 4) = 3(x + 3) - 24$$

$$8x - 16 = 3x + 9 - 24$$

$$8x - 16 = 3x - 15$$

$$8x - 3x - 16 = 3x - 3x - 15$$

$$5x - 16 = -15$$

$$5x - 16 + 16 = -15 + 16$$

$$5x = 1$$

$$\frac{5x}{5} = \frac{1}{5}$$

$$x = \frac{1}{5}$$

Check:

$$\frac{2}{3}\left[2\left(\frac{1}{5}\right) - 4\right] \stackrel{?}{=} \frac{1}{2}\left(\frac{1}{5} + 3\right) - 4$$

$$\frac{2}{3}\left(\frac{2}{5} - \frac{20}{5}\right) \stackrel{?}{=} \frac{1}{2}\left(\frac{1}{5} + \frac{15}{5}\right) - 4$$

$$\frac{2}{3}\left(-\frac{18}{5}\right) \stackrel{?}{=} \frac{1}{2}\left(\frac{16}{5}\right) - 4$$

$$-\frac{12}{5} \stackrel{?}{=} \frac{8}{5} - \frac{20}{5}$$

$$-\frac{12}{5} = -\frac{12}{5}$$

81. Verbal Model:

$$\boxed{\text{First integer}} + \boxed{\text{Second integer}} = 251$$

Labels: $n = $ first integer

$n + 1 = $ second integer

Equation: $n + (n + 1) = 251$

$2n + 1 = 251$

$2n + 1 - 1 = 251 - 1$

$2n = 250$

$\dfrac{2n}{2} = \dfrac{250}{2}$

$n = 125$

$n + 1 = 126$

83. Verbal Model:

$$\boxed{\text{First even integer}} + \boxed{\text{Second even integer}} = 166$$

Labels: $n = $ first even integer

$n + 2 = $ second even integer

Equation: $n + (n + 2) = 166$

$2n + 2 = 166$

$2n + 2 - 2 = 166 - 2$

$2n = 164$

$\dfrac{2n}{2} = \dfrac{164}{2}$

$n = 82$

$n + 2 = 84$

85. Verbal Model:

$$162 + 32 \cdot \boxed{\text{Number of hours}} = 210$$

Label: $n = $ number of hours for the repair

Equation: $162 + 32n = 210$

$162 - 162 + 32n = 210 - 162$

$32n = 48$

$\dfrac{32n}{32} = \dfrac{48}{32}$

$n = \dfrac{3}{2}$

The repairs took 1.5 hours to complete.

87. The fountain reaches its maximum height when the velocity of the stream of water is zero.

$0 = 48 - 32t$

$0 + 32t = 48 - 32t + 32t$

$32t = 48$

$\dfrac{32t}{32} = \dfrac{48}{32}$

$t = \dfrac{3}{2}$ seconds $= 1.5$ seconds

89. $\dfrac{t}{10} + \dfrac{t}{15} = 1$

$\dfrac{3t}{30} + \dfrac{2t}{30} = 1$

$\dfrac{5t}{30} = 1$

$\dfrac{t}{6} = 1$

$6\left(\dfrac{t}{6}\right) = 6(1)$

$t = 6$ hours

91. (a)

t	1	1.5	2	3	4	5
Width	300	240	200	150	120	100
Length	300	360	400	450	480	500
Area	90,000	86,400	80,000	67,500	57,600	50,000

—CONTINUED—

91. (a) —CONTINUED—

If $t = 1$: $1200 = 2w + 2w$

$1200 = 4w$

$300 = w$

$300 = l$

If $t = 3$: $1200 = 2w + 2(3w)$

$1200 = 8w$

$150 = w$

$450 = l$

If $t = 1.5$: $1200 = 2w + 2(1.5w)$

$1200 = 5w$

$240 = w$

$360 = l$

If $t = 4$: $1200 = 2w + 2(4w)$

$1200 = 10w$

$120 = w$

$480 = l$

If $t = 2$: $1200 = 2w + 2(2w)$

$1200 = 6w$

$200 = w$

$400 = l$

If $t = 5$: $1200 = 2w + 2(5w)$

$1200 = 12w$

$100 = w$

$500 = l$

(b) Since the length is t times the width and the perimeter is fixed, as t gets larger, the length gets larger and the area gets smaller. The maximum area occurs when the length and width are equal.

93.

$$5500 = 207t + 4962$$

$$5500 - 4962 = 207t + 4962 - 4962$$

$$538 = 207t$$

$$\frac{538}{207} = \frac{207t}{207}$$

$$2.6 \approx t$$

From the graph, 1993 is the year in which expenditures reached $5500.

95. A conditional equation is an equation whose solution set is not the entire set of real numbers. An identity is an equation whose solution set is all real numbers.

97. Evaluating an expression means finding its value when its variables are replaced by real numbers. Solving an equation means finding all values of the variable for which the equation is true.

99. Equivalent equations have the same solution set. For example, $3x + 4 = 10$ and $3x - 6 = 0$ are equivalent.

101. False. Multiplying both sides of an equation by zero does not yield an equivalent equation.

Section 1.2   Linear Equations and Problem Solving

1. *Verbal Model:* $\boxed{\text{Number}} + \boxed{30} = \boxed{82}$

Label: Number $= x$

Equation: $x + 30 = 82$

$x + 30 - 30 = 82 - 30$

$x = 52$

3. *Verbal Model:* $\boxed{\begin{array}{c}\text{Annual}\\\text{salary}\end{array}} = 26 \cdot \boxed{\begin{array}{c}\text{Amount of}\\\text{each paycheck}\end{array}} + \boxed{\text{Bonus}}$

Labels: Annual salary $= 30{,}500$

Amount of each paycheck $= x$

Bonus $= 2300$

Equation: $30{,}500 = 26x + 2300$

$30{,}500 - 2300 = 26x + 2300 - 2300$

$28{,}200 = 26x$

$\dfrac{28{,}200}{26} = \dfrac{26x}{26}$

$\$1084.62 = x$

5. Percent: 30%

Parts out of 100: 30

Decimal: 0.30

Fraction: $\frac{30}{100} = \frac{3}{10}$

7. Percent: 7.5%

Parts out of 100: 7.5

Decimal: 0.075

Fraction: $\frac{75}{1000} = \frac{3}{40}$

9. Percent: 12.5%

Parts out of 100: 12.5

Decimal: 0.125

Fraction: $\frac{1}{8}$

11. *Verbal Model:* $\boxed{\text{Compared number}} = \boxed{\text{Percent}} \cdot \boxed{\text{Base number}}$

Labels: Compared number = a
Percent = p
Base number = b

Equation: $a = p \cdot b$

$a = (0.35)(250)$

$a = 87.5$

13. *Verbal Model:* $\boxed{\text{Compared number}} = \boxed{\text{Percent}} \cdot \boxed{\text{Base number}}$

Labels: Compared number = a
Percent = p
Base number = b

Equation: $a = p \cdot b$

$a = (0.085)(816)$

$a = 69.36$

15. *Verbal Model:* $\boxed{\text{Compared number}} = \boxed{\text{Percent}} \cdot \boxed{\text{Base number}}$

Labels: Compared number = a
Percent = p
Base number = b

Equation: $a = p \cdot b$

$a = (0.004)(150{,}000)$

$a = 600$

17. *Verbal Model:* $\boxed{\text{Compared number}} = \boxed{\text{Percent}} \cdot \boxed{\text{Base number}}$

Labels: Compared number = a
Percent = p
Base number = b

Equation: $a = p \cdot b$

$84 = (0.24)(b)$

$\frac{84}{0.24} = b$

$350 = b$

19. *Verbal Model:* $\boxed{\text{Compared number}} = \boxed{\text{Percent}} \cdot \boxed{\text{Base number}}$

Labels: Compared number = a
Percent = p
Base number = b

Equation: $a = p \cdot b$

$42 = (0.105)(b)$

$\frac{42}{0.105} = b$

$400 = b$

21. *Verbal Model:* $\boxed{\text{Compared number}} = \boxed{\text{Percent}} \cdot \boxed{\text{Base number}}$

Labels: Compared number = a
Percent = p
Base number = b

Equation: $a = p \cdot b$

$96 = (0.008)(b)$

$\frac{96}{0.008} = b$

$12{,}000 = b$

23. *Verbal Model:* $\boxed{\text{Compared number}} = \boxed{\text{Percent}} \cdot \boxed{\text{Base number}}$

Labels: Compared number $= a$

Percent $= p$

Base number $= b$

Equation: $\quad a = p \cdot b$

$\qquad 1650 = (p)(5000)$

$\qquad \dfrac{1650}{5000} = p$

$\qquad 33\tfrac{1}{3}\% = p$

25. *Verbal Model:* $\boxed{\text{Compared number}} = \boxed{\text{Percent}} \cdot \boxed{\text{Base number}}$

Labels: Compared number $= a$

Percent $= p$

Base number $= b$

Equation: $\quad a = p \cdot b$

$\qquad 2100 = (p)(1200)$

$\qquad \dfrac{2100}{1200} = p$

$\qquad 175\% = p$

27. $\dfrac{120 \text{ meters}}{180 \text{ meters}} = \dfrac{12}{18} = \dfrac{2}{3}$

29. $\dfrac{36 \text{ inches}}{48 \text{ inches}} = \dfrac{36}{48} = \dfrac{3}{4}$

31. $\dfrac{40 \text{ milliliters}}{1 \text{ liter}} = \dfrac{0.04 \text{ liter}}{1}$

$\qquad = \dfrac{4}{100} = \dfrac{1}{25}$

33. $\dfrac{5 \text{ pounds}}{24 \text{ ounces}} = \dfrac{80 \text{ ounces}}{24 \text{ ounces}} = \dfrac{10}{3}$

35. $\dfrac{x}{6} = \dfrac{2}{3}$

$\quad x = 6 \cdot \dfrac{2}{3}$

$\quad x = 4$

37. $\dfrac{t}{4} = \dfrac{3}{2}$

$\quad t = 4 \cdot \dfrac{3}{2}$

$\quad t = 6$

39. $\dfrac{5}{4} = \dfrac{t}{6}$

$\quad t = \dfrac{5}{4} \cdot 6$

$\quad t = \dfrac{15}{2} = 7\tfrac{1}{2} = 7.5$

41. $\dfrac{y}{6} = \dfrac{y-2}{4}$

$\quad 4y = 6(y-2)$

$\quad 4y = 6y - 12$

$\quad 12 = 2y$

$\quad\; 6 = y$

43. $\dfrac{y+1}{10} = \dfrac{y-1}{6}$

$\quad 6(y+1) = 10(y-1)$

$\quad 6y + 6 = 10y - 10$

$\qquad\; 16 = 4y$

$\qquad\;\; 4 = y$

45. *Verbal Model:* $\boxed{\text{Freshmen}} = \boxed{\text{Percent}} \cdot \boxed{\text{Total enrollment}}$

Labels: Freshmen $= a$

Percent $= p$

Total enrollment $= b$

Equation: $a = p \cdot b$

$\qquad a = (0.38)(3000)$

$\qquad a = 1140$

47. *Verbal Model:* $\boxed{\text{Students failing test}} = \boxed{\text{Percent}} \cdot \boxed{\text{Total students}}$

Labels: Students failing test $= a$

Percent $= p$

Total students $= b$

Equation: $a = p \cdot b$

$\qquad a = (1 - 0.95)(40)$

$\qquad a = (0.05)(40)$

$\qquad a = 2$

49. *Verbal Model:* $\boxed{\text{Number laid off}} = \boxed{\text{Percent}} \cdot \boxed{\text{Number of employees}}$

Labels: Number laid off $= a$

Percent $= p$

Number of employees $= b$

Equation: $a = p \cdot b$

$25 = (p)(160)$

$\dfrac{25}{160} = p$

$15.625\% = p$

51. *Verbal Model:* $\boxed{\text{Tip}} = \boxed{\text{Percent}} \cdot \boxed{\text{Cost of meal}}$

Labels: Tip $= a$

Percent $= p$

Cost of meal $= b$

Equation: $10 - 8.45 = p \cdot 8.45$

$1.55 = p \cdot 8.45$

$\dfrac{1.55}{8.45} = \dfrac{p \cdot 8.45}{8.45}$

$0.18 \approx p$

$18\% \approx p$

53. *Verbal Model:* $\boxed{\text{Commission}} = \boxed{\text{Percent}} \cdot \boxed{\text{Price of home}}$

Labels: Commission $= a$

Percent $= p$

Price of home $= b$

Equation: $12{,}250 = p \cdot 175{,}000$

$\dfrac{12{,}250}{175{,}000} = \dfrac{p \cdot 175{,}000}{175{,}000}$

$0.07 = p$

$7\% = p$

55. *Verbal Model:* $\boxed{\text{Defective parts}} = \boxed{\text{Percent}} \cdot \boxed{\text{Total parts}}$

Labels: Defective parts $= a$

Percent $= p$

Total parts $= b$

Equation: $a = p \cdot b$

$3 = (0.015)(b)$

$\dfrac{3}{0.015} = b$

$200 = b$ total parts

57. (a) *Verbal Model:* $\boxed{\text{Area of larger floor}} = \boxed{\text{Percent}} \cdot \boxed{\text{Area of smaller floor}}$

Labels: Area of larger floor $= a$

Percent $= p$

Area of smaller floor $= b$

Equation: $a = p \cdot b$

$320 = (p)(180)$

$\dfrac{320}{180} = \dfrac{p(180)}{180}$

$1.7778 \approx p$

$177.78\% \approx p$

(b) *Verbal Model:* $\boxed{\text{Area of smaller floor}} = \boxed{\text{Percent}} \cdot \boxed{\text{Area of larger floor}}$

Labels: Area of smaller floor $= a$

Percent $= p$

Area of larger floor $= b$

Equation: $a = p \cdot b$

$180 = (p)(320)$

$\dfrac{180}{320} = \dfrac{p(320)}{320}$

$0.5625 \approx p$

$56.25\% \approx p$

59. *Verbal Model:* | County's population | = | Percent | · | Total population |

Labels: County's population $= a$

Percent $= p$

Total population $= b$

Equation: $a = p \cdot b$

Monroe:

$457{,}500 = p(1{,}483{,}700)$

$\dfrac{457{,}500}{1{,}483{,}700} = p$

$0.3084 \approx p$

$30.84\% \approx p$

Spring:

$258{,}700 = p(1{,}483{,}700)$

$\dfrac{258{,}700}{1{,}483{,}700} = p$

$0.1744 \approx p$

$17.44\% \approx p$

Washington:

$89{,}100 = p(1{,}483{,}700)$

$\dfrac{89{,}100}{1{,}483{,}700} = p$

$0.0601 \approx p$

$6.01\% \approx p$

West:

$189{,}400 = p(1{,}483{,}700)$

$\dfrac{189{,}400}{1{,}483{,}700} = p$

$0.1277 \approx p$

$12.77\% \approx p$

Howard:

$167{,}700 = p(1{,}483{,}700)$

$\dfrac{167{,}700}{1{,}483{,}700} = p$

$0.1130 \approx p$

$11.30\% \approx p$

Clark:

$321{,}300 = p(1{,}483{,}700)$

$\dfrac{321{,}300}{1{,}483{,}700} = p$

$0.2166 \approx p$

$21.66\% \approx p$

61. Using the bar graph, the decrease in the per capita consumption of beef from 1980 to 1995 is approximately 8 pounds. The approximate percent decrease is:

Verbal Model: | Amount of decrease | = | Percent | · | Beef consumption in 1980 |

Labels: Amount of decrease $= a$

Percent $= p$

Beef consumption in 1980 $= b$

Equation: $a = p \cdot b$

$8 = p \cdot 70$

$\frac{8}{70} = p \approx 11\%$

63. *Verbal Model:* | Total number of pounds of pork consumed | = | Number of pounds of pork consumed per capita | · | Number of persons |

Equation: $x = 47 \cdot 250{,}000{,}000$

$x \approx 11{,}750$ million pounds

65. $\dfrac{\text{Tax}}{\text{Pay}} = \dfrac{12.50}{625} = \dfrac{125}{6250} = \dfrac{1}{50}$

67. $\dfrac{\text{Expanded volume}}{\text{Compressed volume}} = \dfrac{425 \text{ cu cm}}{20 \text{ cu cm}} = \dfrac{85}{4}$

69. $\dfrac{\text{Area 1}}{\text{Area 2}} = \dfrac{\pi(4)^2}{\pi(6)^2} = \dfrac{16\pi}{36\pi} = \dfrac{4}{9}$

71. $\dfrac{\text{Total price}}{\text{Total units}} = \dfrac{0.95}{20} = \dfrac{90}{2000} = \$0.0475$ per ounce

73. $\dfrac{\text{Total price}}{\text{Total units}} = \dfrac{1.69}{20} = \dfrac{169}{2000} = \$0.0845$ per ounce

75. (a) Unit price $= \dfrac{2.32}{14.5} = \$0.16$ per ounce

 (b) Unit price $= \dfrac{0.99}{5.5} = \$0.18$ per ounce

 The $14\frac{1}{2}$-ounce bag is a better buy.

77. (a) Unit price $= \dfrac{1.69}{4} = \$0.4225$ per ounce

 (b) Unit price $= \dfrac{2.39}{6} = \$0.3983$ per ounce

 The 6-ounce tube is a better buy.

79. Proportion: $\dfrac{x}{7} = \dfrac{4}{5.5}$

 $x = 7 \cdot \dfrac{4}{5.5}$

 $x = 5\frac{1}{11}$

81. Proportion: $\dfrac{x}{6} = \dfrac{2}{4}$

 $x = 6 \cdot \dfrac{2}{4}$

 $x = 3$

83. Proportion: $\dfrac{h}{86} = \dfrac{6}{11}$

 $h = \dfrac{6 \cdot 86}{11}$

 $h = \dfrac{516}{11}$

 $h \approx 46.9$ feet

85. Proportion: $\dfrac{5}{105} = \dfrac{x}{360}$

 $x = \dfrac{5 \cdot 360}{105}$

 $x = \dfrac{1800}{105}$

 $x \approx 17.1$ gallons

87. *Verbal Model:* $\boxed{\dfrac{\text{Tax}}{\text{Assessed value}}} = \boxed{\dfrac{\text{Tax}}{\text{Assessed value}}}$

 Proportion: $\dfrac{x}{160,000} = \dfrac{1650}{110,000}$

 $x = 160,000 \cdot \dfrac{1650}{110,000}$

 $x = \$2400$ taxes

89. *Verbal Model:* $\boxed{\dfrac{\text{Defective units}}{\text{Total units}}} = \boxed{\dfrac{\text{Defective units}}{\text{Total units}}}$

 Proportion: $\dfrac{x}{200,000} = \dfrac{1}{75}$

 $x = 200,000 \cdot \dfrac{1}{75}$

 $x = 2667$ defective units

91. Percent means parts out of 100.

93. No, $\frac{1}{2}\% \neq 50\%$.

 $0.5\% = 0.005$

 $50\% = 0.5$

95. No. It is necessary to know one of the following: the total number of students in the class, the number of boys in the class, or the number of girls in the class.

97. Mathematical modeling is using mathematics to solve problems that occur in real-life situations. For examples review the real-life problems in the exercise set.

Section 1.3   Business and Scientific Problems

1. *Verbal Model:* $\boxed{\text{Selling price}} = \boxed{\text{Cost}} + \boxed{\text{Markup}}$

Labels: Selling price = 64.33
Cost = 45.97
Markup = x

Equation: $64.33 = 45.97 + x$
$x = 64.33 - 45.97$
$x = \$18.36$

Verbal Model: $\boxed{\text{Markup}} = \boxed{\text{Markup rate}} \cdot \boxed{\text{Cost}}$

Labels: Markup = 18.36
Markup rate = x
Cost = 45.97

Equation: $18.36 = x \cdot 45.97$
$\dfrac{18.36}{45.97} = x$
$40\% = x$

3. *Verbal Model:* $\boxed{\text{Selling price}} = \boxed{\text{Cost}} + \boxed{\text{Markup}}$

Labels: Selling price = 250.80
Cost = x
Markup = 98.80

Equation: $250.80 = x + 98.80$
$250.80 - 98.80 = x$
$\$152.00 = x$

Verbal Model: $\boxed{\text{Markup}} = \boxed{\text{Markup rate}} \cdot \boxed{\text{Cost}}$

Labels: Markup = 98.80
Markup rate = x
Cost = 152.00

Equation: $98.80 = x \cdot 152.00$
$\dfrac{98.80}{152.00} = x$
$65\% = x$

5. *Verbal Model:* $\boxed{\text{Selling price}} = \boxed{\text{Cost}} + \boxed{\text{Markup}}$

Labels: Selling price = 26,922.50
Cost = x
Markup = 4672.50

Equation: $26{,}922.50 = x + 4672.50$
$26{,}922.50 - 4672.50 = x$
$\$22{,}250.00 = x$

Verbal Model: $\boxed{\text{Markup}} = \boxed{\text{Markup rate}} \cdot \boxed{\text{Cost}}$

Labels: Markup = 4672.50
Markup rate = x
Cost = 22,250.00

Equation: $4672.50 = x \cdot 22{,}250.00$
$\dfrac{4672.50}{22{,}250.00} = x$
$21\% = x$

7. *Verbal Model:* $\boxed{\text{Markup}} = \boxed{\text{Markup rate}} \cdot \boxed{\text{Cost}}$

Labels: Markup = x
Markup rate = 85.2%
Cost = 225.00

Equation: $x = 85.2\% \cdot 225.00$
$x = \$191.70$

Verbal Model: $\boxed{\text{Selling price}} = \boxed{\text{Cost}} + \boxed{\text{Markup}}$

Labels: Selling price = x
Cost = 225.00
Markup = 191.70

Equation: $x = 225.00 + 191.70$
$x = \$416.70$

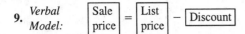

9. *Verbal Model:*   Sale price $=$ List price $-$ Discount

Labels: Sale price $= 25.74$
List price $= 49.95$
Discount $= x$

Equation: $25.74 = 49.95 - x$

$x = 49.95 - 25.74$

$x = \$24.21$

Verbal Model: Discount $=$ Discount rate $\cdot$ List price

Labels: Discount $= 24.21$
Discount rate $= x$
List price $= 49.95$

Equation: $24.21 = x \cdot 49.95$

$\dfrac{24.21}{49.95} = x$

$48.5\% \approx x$

11. *Verbal Model:*   Sale price $=$ List price $-$ Discount

Labels: Sale price $= x$
List price $= 300.00$
Discount $= 189.00$

Equation: $x = 300.00 - 189.00$

$x = \$111.00$

Verbal Model: Discount $=$ Discount rate $\cdot$ List price

Labels: Discount $= 189.00$
Discount rate $= x$
List price $= 300.00$

Equation: $189.00 = x \cdot 300.00$

$\dfrac{189.00}{300.00} = x$

$63\% = x$

13. *Verbal Model:*   Discount $=$ Discount rate $\cdot$ List price

Labels: Discount $= x$
Discount rate $= 65\%$
List price $= 95.00$

Equation: $x = 65\% \cdot 95.00$

$x = \$61.75$

Verbal Model: Sale price $=$ List price $-$ Discount

Labels: Sale price $= x$
List price $= 95.00$
Discount $= 61.75$

Equation: $x = 95.00 - 61.75$

$x = \$33.25$

15. *Verbal Model:*   Sale price $=$ List price $-$ Discount

Labels: Sale price $= 893.10$
List price $= x$
Discount $= 251.90$

Equation: $893.10 = x - 251.90$

$893.10 + 251.90 = x$

$\$1145.00 = x$

Verbal Model: Discount $=$ Discount rate $\cdot$ List price

Labels: Discount $= 251.90$
Discount rate $= x$
List price $= 1145.00$

Equation: $251.90 = x \cdot 1145.00$

$\dfrac{251.90}{1145.005} = x$

$22\% = x$

17. *Verbal Model:* $\boxed{\text{Selling price}} = \boxed{\text{Cost}} + \boxed{\text{Markup}}$

Labels: Selling price = 85

Cost = 62.95

Markup = x

Equation: $85 = 62.95 + x$

$x = 85 - 62.95$

$x = \$22.05$

19. *Verbal Model:* $\boxed{\text{Selling price}} = \boxed{\text{Cost}} + \boxed{\text{Markup}}$

Labels: Selling price = 25

Cost = 15

Markup = x

Equation: $25 = 15 + x$

$10 = x$

Verbal Model: $\boxed{\text{Markup}} = \boxed{\text{Markup rate}} \cdot \boxed{\text{Cost}}$

Labels: Markup = 10

Markup rate = x

Cost = 15

Equation: $10 = x \cdot 15$

$\frac{10}{15} = x$

$66\frac{2}{3}\% = x$

21. *Verbal Model:* $\boxed{\text{Sale price}} = \boxed{\text{List price}} - \boxed{\text{Discount}}$

Labels: Sale price = 50

List price = 75

Discount = x

Equation: $50 = 75 - x$

$x = 75 - 50$

$x = \$25$

23. *Verbal Model:* $\boxed{\text{Sale price}} = \boxed{\text{List price}} - \boxed{\text{Discount}}$

Labels: Sale price = 16

List price = 20

Discount = x

Equation: $16 = 20 - x$

$x = 20 - 16$

$x = \$4$

Verbal Model: $\boxed{\text{Discount}} = \boxed{\text{Discount rate}} \cdot \boxed{\text{List price}}$

Labels: Discount = 4

Discount rate = x

List price = 20

Equation: $4 = x \cdot 20$

$\frac{4}{20} = x$

$20\% = x$

25. *Verbal Model:* $\boxed{\text{Total cost}} = \boxed{\text{Cost of first minute}} + \boxed{\text{Cost of additional minutes}}$

Labels: Total cost = 5.15

Cost of first minute = 0.75

Cost of additional minutes = $0.55x$

Equation: $5.15 = 0.75 + 0.55x$

$4.40 = 0.55x$

$8 = x$

Length of call = 9 minutes

—CONTINUED—

25. —CONTINUED—

Verbal Model: $\boxed{\text{Discount}} = \boxed{\text{Discount rate}} \cdot \boxed{\text{List price}}$

Labels:
Discount = x
Discount rate = 60%
List price = 5.15

Equation:
$x = 60\% \cdot 5.15$
$x = \$3.09$

Verbal Model: $\boxed{\text{Selling price}} = \boxed{\text{List price}} - \boxed{\text{Discount}}$

Labels:
Selling price = x
List price = 5.15
Discount = 3.09

Equation:
$x = 5.15 - 3.09$
$x = \$2.06$

27. *Verbal Model:* $\boxed{\text{Cost}} + \boxed{\text{Markup}} = \boxed{\text{Selling price}}$

Labels:
Cost = x
Markup = $0.10x$
Selling price = 59.565
(Each tire costs \$19.855, so three tires cost \$59.565.)

Equation:
$x + 0.10x = 59.565$
$1.10x = 59.565$
$x = \$54.15$

29. *Verbal Model:* $\boxed{\text{Sales tax}} = \boxed{\text{Sales tax rate}} \cdot \boxed{\text{Cost}}$

Labels:
Sales tax = x
Sales tax rate = 6%
Cost = 4450

Equation:
$x = 6\% \cdot 4450$
$x = \$267$

Verbal Model: $\boxed{\text{Total bill}} = \boxed{\text{Cost}} + \boxed{\text{Sales tax}}$

Labels:
Total bill = x
Cost = 4450
Sales tax = 267

Equation:
$x = 4450 + 267$
$x = \$4717$

Verbal Model: $\boxed{\text{Amount financed}} = \boxed{\text{Total bill}} - \boxed{\text{Down payment}}$

Labels:
Amount financed = x
Total bill = 4717
Down payment = 1000

Equation:
$x = 4717 - 1000$
$x = \$3717$

31. *Verbal Model:* $\boxed{\text{Total bill}} = \boxed{\text{Bill for parts}} + \boxed{\text{Bill for labor}}$

Labels:
Total bill = 216.37
Bill for parts = 136.37
Bill for labor = $32x$
Number of hours of labor = x

Equation:
$216.37 = 136.37 + 32x$
$80 = 32x$
$\frac{80}{32} = x$
$2.5 \text{ hours} = x$

33. *Verbal Model:* $\boxed{\text{Total bill}} = \boxed{\text{Bill for parts}} + \boxed{\text{Bill for labor}}$

Labels:
Total bill = 380
Bill for parts = 275
Bill for labor = $35x$
Number of hours of labor = x

Equation:
$380 = 1275 + 35x$
$105 = 35x$
$\frac{105}{35} = x$
$3 \text{ hours} = x$

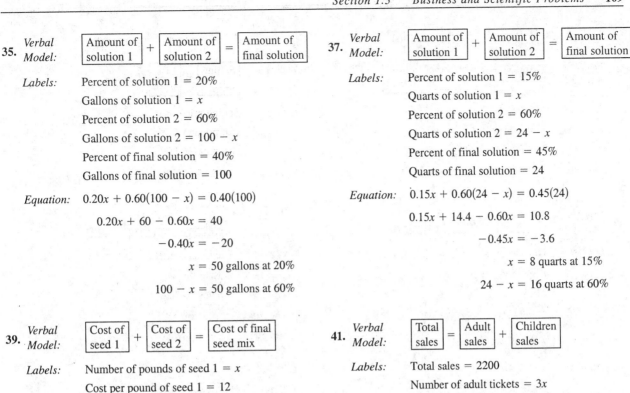

35. *Verbal Model:* $\boxed{\begin{array}{c}\text{Amount of}\\\text{solution 1}\end{array}} + \boxed{\begin{array}{c}\text{Amount of}\\\text{solution 2}\end{array}} = \boxed{\begin{array}{c}\text{Amount of}\\\text{final solution}\end{array}}$

Labels: Percent of solution 1 = 20%

Gallons of solution 1 = x

Percent of solution 2 = 60%

Gallons of solution 2 = $100 - x$

Percent of final solution = 40%

Gallons of final solution = 100

Equation: $0.20x + 0.60(100 - x) = 0.40(100)$

$0.20x + 60 - 0.60x = 40$

$-0.40x = -20$

$x = 50$ gallons at 20%

$100 - x = 50$ gallons at 60%

37. *Verbal Model:* $\boxed{\begin{array}{c}\text{Amount of}\\\text{solution 1}\end{array}} + \boxed{\begin{array}{c}\text{Amount of}\\\text{solution 2}\end{array}} = \boxed{\begin{array}{c}\text{Amount of}\\\text{final solution}\end{array}}$

Labels: Percent of solution 1 = 15%

Quarts of solution 1 = x

Percent of solution 2 = 60%

Quarts of solution 2 = $24 - x$

Percent of final solution = 45%

Quarts of final solution = 24

Equation: $0.15x + 0.60(24 - x) = 0.45(24)$

$0.15x + 14.4 - 0.60x = 10.8$

$-0.45x = -3.6$

$x = 8$ quarts at 15%

$24 - x = 16$ quarts at 60%

39. *Verbal Model:* $\boxed{\begin{array}{c}\text{Cost of}\\\text{seed 1}\end{array}} + \boxed{\begin{array}{c}\text{Cost of}\\\text{seed 2}\end{array}} = \boxed{\begin{array}{c}\text{Cost of final}\\\text{seed mix}\end{array}}$

Labels: Number of pounds of seed 1 = x

Cost per pound of seed 1 = 12

Number of pounds of seed 2 = $100 - x$

Cost per pound of seed 2 = 20

Number of pounds of final seed mix = 100

Cost per pound of final seed mix = 14

Equation: $12x + 20(100 - x) = 14(100)$

$12x + 2000 - 20x = 1400$

$-8x = -600$

$x = 75$ pounds at \$12 per pound

$100 - x = 25$ pounds at \$20 per pound

41. *Verbal Model:* $\boxed{\begin{array}{c}\text{Total}\\\text{sales}\end{array}} = \boxed{\begin{array}{c}\text{Adult}\\\text{sales}\end{array}} + \boxed{\begin{array}{c}\text{Children}\\\text{sales}\end{array}}$

Labels: Total sales = 2200

Number of adult tickets = $3x$

Price of adult tickets = 6

Number of children tickets = x

Price of children tickets = 4

Equation: $2200 = 6(3x) + 4x$

$2200 = 18x + 4x$

$2200 = 22x$

100 children tickets = x

43. *Verbal Model:* $\boxed{\begin{array}{c}\text{Original}\\\text{antifreeze}\\\text{solution}\end{array}} - \boxed{\begin{array}{c}\text{Some}\\\text{antifreeze}\\\text{solution}\end{array}} + \boxed{\begin{array}{c}\text{Pure}\\\text{antifreeze}\end{array}} = \boxed{\begin{array}{c}\text{Final}\\\text{antifreeze}\\\text{solution}\end{array}}$

Labels: Number of gallons of original antifreeze = 5

Percent of antifreeze in original mix = 40%

Number of gallons antifreeze withdrawn = x

Number of gallons of pure antifreeze = x

Percent of pure antifreeze = 100%

Number of gallons of final solution = 5

Percent of antifreeze in final solution = 50%

Equation: $0.40(5) - 0.40x + 1.00x = 0.50(5)$

$2 - 0.40x + 1.00x = 2.5$

$0.60x = 0.5$

$x = \frac{5}{6}$ gallon

45. *Verbal Model:* $\boxed{\text{Distance}} = \boxed{\text{Rate}} \cdot \boxed{\text{Time}}$

Labels: Distance = d

Rate = 650

Time = 3.5

Equation: $d = 650 \cdot 3.5$

$d = 2275$ miles

47. *Verbal Model:* $\boxed{\text{Distance}} = \boxed{\text{Rate}} \cdot \boxed{\text{Time}}$

Labels: Distance = 1000

Rate = 110

Time = t

Equation: $1000 = 110 \cdot t$

$\frac{1000}{110} = t$

$\frac{100}{11}$ hour = t

49. *Verbal Model:* $\boxed{\text{Distance}} = \boxed{\text{Rate}} \cdot \boxed{\text{Time}}$

Labels: Distance = 1000

Rate = r

Time = $\frac{3}{2}$

Equation: $1000 = r \cdot \frac{3}{2}$

$\frac{1000}{3/2} = r$

$\frac{2000}{3}$ ft/sec = r

51. *Verbal Model:* $\boxed{\text{Distance}} = \boxed{\text{Rate}} \cdot \boxed{\text{Time}}$

Labels: Distance = 30

Rate = 12

Time = x

Equation: $30 = 12x$

$\frac{30}{12} = x$

2.5 hours = x

53. *Verbal Model:* $\boxed{\text{Distance}} = \boxed{\text{Rate}} \cdot \boxed{\text{Time}}$

Labels: Distance = x

Rates = 480 and 600

Time = $\frac{4}{3}$

Equation: $x = 480\left(\frac{4}{3}\right) + 600\left(\frac{4}{3}\right)$

$x = 1440$ miles

55. *Verbal Model:* $\boxed{\text{Distance}} = \boxed{\text{Rate}} \cdot \boxed{\text{Time}}$

Labels: Distance = 5000

Rate = 17,000

Time = t

Equation: $5000 = 17{,}000 \cdot t$

$\frac{5000}{17{,}000} = t$

$\frac{5}{17}$ hour = t

17.65 minutes $\approx t$

57. *Verbal Model:* $\boxed{\text{Distance}} = \boxed{\text{Rate}} \cdot \boxed{\text{Time}}$

Labels: Distance = 317

Rate for first part of trip = 58

Time for first part of trip = x

Rate for second part of trip = 52

Time for second part of trip = $5\frac{3}{4} - x$

Equation: $58x = 58 \cdot x$ (1st part of trip)

$52\left(5\frac{3}{4} - x\right) = 52 \cdot \left(5\frac{3}{4} - x\right)$ (2nd part of trip)

$317 = 58x + 52\left(5\frac{3}{4} - x\right)$

$317 = 58x + 299 - 52x$

$18 = 6x$

3 hours = x (1st part of trip at 58 mph)

$2\frac{3}{4}$ hours = $5\frac{3}{4} - x$ (2nd part of trip at 52 mph)

59. (a) Printer's rate = 8 pages per minute

(b) Shop's rate = 30 units in 8 hours

$= \frac{30}{8}$ units per hour

$= \frac{15}{4}$ units per hour

61. (a) Your rate $= \frac{1}{3}$ job per hour

Friend's rate $= \frac{1}{4}$ job per hour

(b) *Verbal Model:* $\boxed{\begin{array}{c}\text{Work}\\\text{done}\end{array}} = \boxed{\begin{array}{c}\text{Work done}\\\text{by you}\end{array}} + \boxed{\begin{array}{c}\text{Work done}\\\text{by friend}\end{array}}$

Labels: Work done $= 1$

Your rate $= \frac{1}{3}$

Your time $= t$

Friend's rate $= \frac{1}{4}$

Friend's time $= t$

Equation: $1 = \left(\frac{1}{3}\right)(t) + \left(\frac{1}{4}\right)(t)$

$1 = \left(\frac{1}{3} + \frac{1}{4}\right)t$

$1 = \left(\frac{7}{12}\right)t$

$\dfrac{1}{7/12} = t$

$1\frac{5}{7}$ hours $= \dfrac{12}{7}$ hours $= t$

63. $E = IR$

$\dfrac{E}{I} = R$

65. $S = L - rL$

$S = L(1 - r)$

$\dfrac{S}{1 - r} = L$

67. $h = 48t + \dfrac{1}{2}at^2$

$h - 48t = \dfrac{1}{2}at^2$

$2(h - 48t) = at^2$

$2h - 96t = at^2$

$\dfrac{2h - 96t}{t^2} = a$

69. *Common formula:* $V = lwh$

Equation: $V = 3 \cdot 4 \cdot 2$

$V = 24$ cubic units

71. *Common formula:* $V = \pi r^2 h$

Equation: $V = \pi\left(3\frac{1}{2}\right)^2 12$

$V = 147\pi$

$V \approx 461.8$ cubic centimeters

73. *Verbal Model:* Perimeter $= 2\boxed{\text{Width}} + 2\boxed{\text{Height}}$

Labels: Perimeter $= 3$

Height $= x$

Width $= 0.62x$

Equation: $3 = 2(0.62x) + 2(x)$

$3 = 1.24x + 2x$

$3 = 3.24x$

0.926 feet $\approx x$

75. *Verbal Model:* $\boxed{\text{Perimeter}} = \boxed{\text{Side}} + \boxed{\text{Side}} + \boxed{\text{Side}}$

Equation: $129 = x + x + x$

$129 = 3x$

$43 = x$

$x = 43$ centimeters

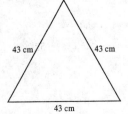

77. *Verbal Model:* $\boxed{\text{Interest}} = \boxed{\text{Principal}} \cdot \boxed{\text{Rate}} \cdot \boxed{\text{Time}}$

Labels: Interest $= I$
Principal $= 5000$
Rate $= 9.5\%$
Time $= 6$

Equation: $I = (5000)(0.095)(6)$
$I = \$2850$

79. *Verbal Model:* $\boxed{\text{Interest}} = \boxed{\text{Principal}} \cdot \boxed{\text{Rate}} \cdot \boxed{\text{Time}}$

Labels: Interest $= 500$
Principal $= P$
Rate $= 7\%$
Time $= 2$

Equation: $500 = (P)(0.07)(2)$
$500 = P(0.14)$
$\dfrac{500}{0.14} = P$
$\$3571.43 \approx P$

81. *Verbal Model:* $\boxed{\text{Interest}} = \boxed{\text{Principal}} \cdot \boxed{\text{Rate}} \cdot \boxed{\text{Time}}$

Labels: Interest $= 3500$
Principal at $10\% = x$
Principal at $8\% = 40{,}000 - x$
Time $= 1$

Equation: $3500 = 0.10x + 0.08(40{,}000 - x)$
$3500 = 0.10x + 3200 - 0.08x$
$300 = 0.02x$
$\dfrac{300}{0.02} = x$
$\$15{,}000 = x$

83. (a) $y = 9.24 + 0.307t, \ 0 \le t \le 7$

From the graph, 1993 was the year when the average hourly wage was $10.15.

$10.15 = 9.24 + 0.307t$
$0.91 = 0.307t$
$2.9641 \approx t$
$3 \approx t$

Yes, the result would be the same, 1993.

(b) The average annual hourly raise for bus drivers during this 8-year period is $0.307. Determine the average hourly wage for each year using the model. The difference between each two consecutive years is $0.307.

85. The bus drivers' average salaries were increasing at a greater annual rate at $0.307 compared to $0.209 for the cafeteria workers.

87. Markup is the difference between the cost a retailer pays for a product and the price at which the retailer sells the product. Markup rate is the percent increase of the markup.

89. If it takes you t hours to complete a task, you can complete $1/t$ of the task in 1 hour.

91. No, it quadruples. The area of a square of side s is s^2. If the length of the sides is $2s$, the area is $(2s)^2 = 4s^2$.

Mid-Chapter Quiz for Chapter 1

1. $4x + 3 = 11$
$4x + 3 - 3 = 11 - 3$
$4x = 8$
$\dfrac{4x}{4} = \dfrac{8}{4}$
$x = 2$

Check:
$4(2) + 3 \overset{?}{=} 11$
$8 + 3 \overset{?}{=} 11$
$11 = 11$

2. $-3(z - 2) = 0$
$\dfrac{-3(z - 2)}{-3} = \dfrac{0}{-3}$
$z - 2 = 0$
$z - 2 + 2 = 0 + 2$
$z = 2$

Check:
$-3(2 - 2) \overset{?}{=} 0$
$-3(0) \overset{?}{=} 0$
$0 = 0$

3. $2(y + 3) = 18 - 4y$

$2y + 6 = 18 - 4y$

$2y + 4y + 6 = 18 - 4y + 4y$

$6y + 6 - 6 = 18 - 6$

$6y = 12$

$\dfrac{6y}{6} = \dfrac{12}{6}$

$y = 2$

Check:

$2(2 + 3) \overset{?}{=} 18 - 4(2)$

$2(5) \overset{?}{=} 18 - 8$

$10 = 10$

4. $5t + 7 = 7(t + 1) - 2t$

$5t + 7 = 7t + 7 - 2t$

$5t + 7 = 5t + 7$

Identity

5. $\dfrac{1}{4}x + 6 = \dfrac{3}{2}x - 1$

$4\left(\dfrac{1}{4}x + 6\right) = 4\left(\dfrac{3}{2}x - 1\right)$

$x + 24 = 6x - 4$

$x - x + 24 = 6x - 4 - x$

$24 = 5x - 4$

$24 + 4 = 5x - 4 + 4$

$28 = 5x$

$\dfrac{28}{5} = \dfrac{5x}{5}$

$\dfrac{28}{5} = x$

Check:

$\dfrac{1}{4}\left(\dfrac{28}{5}\right) + 6 \overset{?}{=} \dfrac{3}{2}\left(\dfrac{28}{5}\right) - 1$

$\dfrac{7}{5} + \dfrac{30}{5} \overset{?}{=} \dfrac{42}{5} - \dfrac{5}{5}$

$\dfrac{37}{5} = \dfrac{37}{5}$

6. $\dfrac{u}{4} + \dfrac{u}{3} = 1$

$12\left(\dfrac{u}{4} + \dfrac{u}{3}\right) = 12(1)$

$3u + 4u = 12$

$7u = 12$

$\dfrac{7u}{7} = \dfrac{12}{7}$

$u = \dfrac{12}{7}$

Check:

$\dfrac{\frac{12}{7}}{4} + \dfrac{\frac{12}{7}}{3} \overset{?}{=} 1$

$\dfrac{3}{7} + \dfrac{4}{7} \overset{?}{=} 1$

$\dfrac{7}{7} \overset{?}{=} 1$

$1 = 1$

7. $\dfrac{4 - x}{5} + 5 = \dfrac{5}{2}$

$10\left(\dfrac{4 - x}{5} + 5\right) = 10\left(\dfrac{5}{2}\right)$

$2(4 - x) + 50 = 25$

$8 - 2x + 50 = 25$

$-2x + 58 = 25$

$-2x + 58 - 58 = 25 - 58$

$-2x = -33$

$\dfrac{-2x}{-2} = \dfrac{-33}{-2}$

$x = \dfrac{33}{2}$

Check:

$\dfrac{4 - \frac{33}{2}}{5} + 5 \overset{?}{=} \dfrac{5}{2}$

$\dfrac{\frac{8}{2} - \frac{33}{2}}{5} + 5 \overset{?}{=} \dfrac{5}{2}$

$-\dfrac{25}{2} \cdot \dfrac{1}{5} + 5 \overset{?}{=} \dfrac{5}{2}$

$-\dfrac{5}{2} + \dfrac{10}{2} \overset{?}{=} \dfrac{5}{2}$

$\dfrac{5}{2} = \dfrac{5}{2}$

8. $0.2x + 0.3 = 1.5$

$10(0.2x + 0.3) = 10(1.5)$

$2x + 3 = 15$

$2x + 3 - 3 = 15 - 3$

$2x = 12$

$\dfrac{2x}{2} = \dfrac{12}{2}$

$x = 6$

Check:

$0.2(6) + 0.3 \overset{?}{=} 1.5$

$1.2 + 0.3 \overset{?}{=} 1.5$

$1.5 = 1.5$

9.
$$3x + \frac{11}{12} = \frac{5}{16}$$

$$3x + \frac{11}{12} - \frac{11}{12} = \frac{5}{16} - \frac{11}{12}$$

$$3x = \frac{15}{48} - \frac{44}{48}$$

$$3x = -\frac{29}{48}$$

$$\frac{3x}{3} = -\frac{29}{48} \div 3$$

$$x = -\frac{29}{48} \cdot \frac{1}{3}$$

$$x = -\frac{29}{144} \approx -0.20$$

10.
$$0.42x + 6 = 5.25x - 0.80$$

$$0.42x + 6 - 5.25x = 5.25x - 0.80 - 5.25x$$

$$-4.83x + 6 = -0.80$$

$$-4.83x + 6 - 6 = -0.80 - 6$$

$$-4.83x = -6.80$$

$$\frac{-4.83x}{-4.83} = \frac{-6.80}{-4.83}$$

$$x \approx 1.41$$

11. 0.45 is 45 hundredths so $0.45 = \frac{45}{100}$ which reduces to $\frac{9}{20}$ and since percent means hundredths, $0.45 = 45\%$.

12. *Verbal Model:* $\boxed{\text{Compared number}} = \boxed{\text{Percent}} \cdot \boxed{\text{Base number}}$

Labels: Compared number $= a$

Percent $= p$

Base number $= b$

Equation: $a = p \cdot b$

$$500 = (2.50)(b)$$

$$\frac{500}{2.50} = b$$

$$200 = b$$

13. $\frac{\text{Total price}}{\text{Total units}} = \frac{2.35}{12} = \frac{235}{1200} \approx \$0.1958 \text{ per ounce}$

14. *Verbal Model:* $\boxed{\dfrac{\text{Defective units}}{\text{Total units}}} = \boxed{\dfrac{\text{Defective units}}{\text{Total units}}}$

Proportion: $\frac{x}{600,000} = \frac{1}{300}$

$$x = 600,000 \cdot \frac{1}{300}$$

$$x = 2000 \text{ defective units}$$

15. Store computer:

Verbal Model: $\boxed{\text{Discount}} = \boxed{\text{Discount rate}} \cdot \boxed{\text{List price}}$

Labels: Discount $= x$

Discount rate $= 0.25$

List price $= 1750$

Equation: $x = (0.25)(1750)$

$$x = \$437.50$$

Verbal Model: $\boxed{\text{Selling price}} = \boxed{\text{List price}} - \boxed{\text{Discount}}$

Labels: Selling price $= x$

List price $= 1750$

Discount $= 437.50$

Equation: $x = 1750 - 437.50$

$$x = \$1312.50$$

—CONTINUED—

15. —CONTINUED—

Mail-order catalog computer

Verbal Model: $\boxed{\text{Selling price}} = \boxed{\text{List price}} + \boxed{\text{Shipping}}$

Labels: Selling price $= x$

List price $= 1250$

Shipping $= 24.95$

Equation: $x = 1250 + 24.95$

$x = \$1274.95$

The mail-order catalog computer is the better buy.

16. *Verbal Model:* $\boxed{\text{Total wages}} = \boxed{\text{Regular wages}} + \boxed{\text{Overtime wages}}$

Labels: Total wages $= 616$

Regular wages $= 40(12.25)$

Overtime wages $= x(18)$

Number of hours $= x$

Equation: $616 = 40(12.25) + x(18)$

$616 = 490 + 18x$

$126 = 18x$

$7 \text{ hours} = x$

17. *Verbal Model:* $\boxed{\text{Amount of solution 1}} + \boxed{\text{Amount of solution 2}} = \boxed{\text{Amount of final solution}}$

Labels: Percent of solution 1 $= 25\%$

Gallons of solution 1 $= x$

Percent of solution 2 $= 50\%$

Gallons of solution 2 $= 50 - x$

Percent of final solution $= 30\%$

Gallons of final solution $= 50$

Equation: $0.25x + 0.50(50 - x) = 0.30(50)$

$0.25x + 25 - 0.50x = 15$

$25 - 0.25x = 15$

$-0.25x = -10$

$x = 40 \text{ gallons at } 25\%$

$50 - x = 10 \text{ gallons at } 50\%$

18. *Verbal Model:* $\boxed{\text{Distance}} = \boxed{\text{Rate}} \cdot \boxed{\text{Time}}$

Labels: Distance $= 500$

Rate of first part $= 62$

Time for first part $= x$

Rate of second part $= 46$

Time for second part $= 6 - x$

Equation: $300 = 62x + 46(6 - x)$

$300 = 62x + 276 - 46x$

$24 = 16x$

$1.5 \text{ hours} = x \text{ (first part of trip at 62 mph)}$

$4.5 \text{ hours} = 6 - x \text{ (second part of trip at 46 mph)}$

19. *Verbal Model:*   Work done = Portion done by first person + Portion done by second person

Labels: Work done = 1

Rate of first person = $\frac{1}{6}$

Rate of second person = $\frac{1}{8}$

Time for both = t

Equation: $1 = \left(\frac{1}{6}\right)(t) + \left(\frac{1}{8}\right)(t)$

$1 = \left(\frac{1}{6} + \frac{1}{8}\right)(t)$

$1 = \left(\frac{14}{48}\right)(t)$

$3.43 \text{ hours} \approx \frac{24}{7} = \frac{48}{14} = t$

20. Perimeter of square I = 20   Perimeter of square II = 32

$4s = 20$ $4s = 32$

$s = 5$ $s = 8$

Length of side of square III = 5 + 8   Area = s^2

$= 13$ $= 13^2$

$= 169 \text{ square inches}$

Section 1.4   Linear Inequalities

1. (a) $7(3) - 10 > 0$

$21 - 10 > 0$

$11 > 0$

Yes

(b) $7(-2) - 10 > 0$

$-14 - 10 > 0$

$-24 > 0$

No

(c) $7\left(\frac{5}{2}\right) - 10 > 0$

$\frac{35}{2} - 10 > 0$

$\frac{35}{2} - \frac{20}{2} > 0$

$\frac{15}{2} > 0$

Yes

(d) $7\left(\frac{1}{2}\right) - 10 > 0$

$\frac{7}{2} - 10 > 0$

$\frac{7}{2} - \frac{20}{2} > 0$

$-\frac{13}{2} > 0$

No

3. (a) $0 < \dfrac{10 + 5}{6} < 2$

$0 < \dfrac{15}{6} < 2$

$0 < 2\dfrac{3}{6} < 2$

No

(b) $0 < \dfrac{4 + 5}{6} < 2$

$0 < \dfrac{9}{6} < 2$

$0 < 1\dfrac{3}{6} < 2$

Yes

(c) $0 < \dfrac{0 + 5}{6} < 2$

$0 < \dfrac{5}{6} < 2$

Yes

(d) $0 < \dfrac{-6 + 5}{6} < 2$

$0 < \dfrac{-1}{6} < 2$

No

5. Matches graph (d).

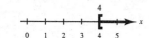

7. Matches graph (a).

9. Matches graph (f).

11. Matches graph (a).

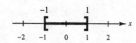

13. Matches graph (d).

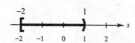

15. $x \le 2$

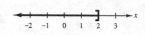

17. $x > 3.5$

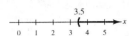

19. $-5 < x \le 3$

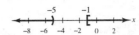

21. $4 > x \ge 1$

23. $\frac{3}{2} \ge x > 0$

25. $x < -5$ or $x \ge -1$

27. $x \le 3$ or $x > 7$

29. $5 - \frac{1}{3}x > 8$

$-3\left(5 - \frac{1}{3}x\right) < (8) - 3$

$-15 + x < -24$

31. $x - 4 \ge 0$

$x - 4 + 4 \ge 0 + 4$

$x \ge 4$

33. $x + 7 \le 9$

$x + 7 - 7 \le 9 - 7$

$x \le 2$

35. $2x < 8$

$\dfrac{2x}{2} < \dfrac{8}{2}$

$x < 4$

37. $-9x \ge 36$

$\dfrac{-9x}{-9} \le \dfrac{36}{-9}$

$x \le -4$

39. $-\dfrac{3}{4}x < -6$

$-\dfrac{4}{3} \cdot -\dfrac{3}{4}x > -6 \cdot -\dfrac{4}{3}$

$x > 8$

41. $5 - x \le -2$

$5 - x - 5 \le -2 - 5$

$-x \le -7$

$-1 \cdot x \ge -7 \cdot -1$

$x \ge 7$

43. $2x - 5 > 9$

$2x - 5 + 5 > 9 + 5$

$2x > 14$

$\dfrac{2x}{2} > \dfrac{14}{2}$

$x > 7$

45. $5 - 3x < 7$

$5 - 3x - 5 < 7 - 5$

$-3x < 2$

$\dfrac{-3x}{-3} > \dfrac{2}{-3}$

$x > -\dfrac{2}{3}$

47. $3x - 11 > -x + 7$

$3x - 11 + x > -x + 7 + x$

$4x - 11 > 7$

$4x - 11 + 11 > 7 + 11$

$4x > 18$

$\dfrac{4x}{4} > \dfrac{18}{4}$

$x > \dfrac{9}{2}$

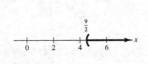

49. $-3x + 7 < 8x - 13$

$-3x - 8x + 7 < 8x - 8x - 13$

$-11x + 7 < -13$

$-11x + 7 - 7 < -13 - 7$

$-11x < -20$

$\dfrac{-11x}{-11} > \dfrac{-20}{-11}$

$x > \dfrac{20}{11}$

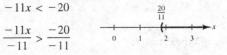

51. $\dfrac{x}{4} > 2 - \dfrac{x}{2}$

$4\left(\dfrac{x}{4}\right) > \left(2 - \dfrac{x}{2}\right)4$

$x > 8 - 2x$

$x + 2x > 8 - 2 + 2x$

$3x > 8$

$\dfrac{3x}{3} > \dfrac{8}{3}$

$x > \dfrac{8}{3}$

53. $\dfrac{x - 4}{3} + 3 \le \dfrac{x}{8}$

$24\left(\dfrac{x - 4}{3} + 3\right) \le \left(\dfrac{x}{8}\right)24$

$8(x - 4) + 72 \le 3x$

$8x - 32 + 72 \le 3x$

$8x + 40 \le 3x$

$8x - 3x + 40 \le 3x - 3x$

$5x + 40 \le 0$

$5x + 40 - 40 \le 0 - 40$

$5x \le -40$

$\dfrac{5x}{5} \le -\dfrac{40}{5}$

$x \le -8$

55. $\dfrac{3x}{5} - 4 < \dfrac{2x}{3} - 3$

$15\left(\dfrac{3x}{5} - 4\right) < \left(\dfrac{2x}{3} - 3\right)15$

$9x - 60 < 10x - 45$

$9x - 10x - 60 < 10x - 45 - 10x$

$-x - 60 < -45$

$-x - 60 + 60 < -45 + 60$

$-x < 15$

$x > -15$

57. $0 < 2x - 5 < 9$

$0 + 5 < 2x - 5 + 5 < 9 + 5$

$5 < 2x < 14$

$\dfrac{5}{2} < \dfrac{2x}{2} < \dfrac{14}{2}$

$\dfrac{5}{2} < x < 7$

59. $8 < 6 - 2x \le 12$

$8 - 6 < 6 - 6 - 2x \le 12 - 6$

$2 < -2x \le 6$

$\dfrac{2}{-2} > \dfrac{-2x}{-2} \ge \dfrac{6}{-2}$

$-1 > x \ge -3$

$-3 \le x < -1$

61. $-1 < -\dfrac{x}{6} < 1$

$(-6)(-1) > (-6)\left(-\dfrac{x}{6}\right) > (-6)(1)$

$6 > x > -6$

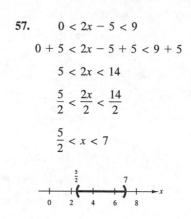

63. $-3 < \dfrac{2x - 3}{2} < 3$

$-6 < 2x - 3 < 6$

$-6 + 3 < 2x - 3 + 3 < 6 + 3$

$-3 < 2x < 9$

$\dfrac{-3}{2} < \dfrac{2x}{2} < \dfrac{9}{2}$

$-\dfrac{3}{2} < x < \dfrac{9}{2}$

65. $1 > \dfrac{x - 4}{-3} > -2$

$-3 < x - 4 < 6$

$-3 + 4 < x - 4 + 4 < 6 + 4$

$1 < x < 10$

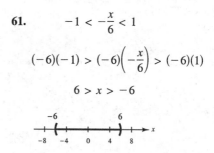

67. $2x - 4 \leq 4$ and $2x + 8 > 6$

$2x - 4 + 4 \leq 4 + 4$ and $2x + 8 - 8 > 6 - 8$

$2x \leq 8$ and $2x > -2$

$\dfrac{2x}{2} \leq \dfrac{8}{2}$ and $\dfrac{2x}{2} > \dfrac{-2}{2}$

$x \leq 4$ and $x > -1$

$-1 < x \leq 4$

69. $7 + 4x < -5 + x$ and $2x + 10 \leq -2$

$7 + 4x - x < -5 + x - x$ and $2x + 10 - 10 \leq -2 - 10$

$7 + 3x < -5$ and $2x \leq -12$

$7 - 7 + 3x < -5 - 7$ and $\dfrac{2x}{2} \leq \dfrac{-12}{2}$

$3x < -12$ and $x \leq -6$

$\dfrac{3x}{3} < \dfrac{-12}{3}$

$x < -4$ and $x \leq -6$

$\boxed{x \leq -6}$

71. $6 - \dfrac{x}{2} > 1$ or $\dfrac{5}{4}x - 6 \geq 4$

$6 - 6 - \dfrac{x}{2} > 1 - 6$ or $\dfrac{5}{4}x - 6 + 6 \geq 4 + 6$

$-\dfrac{x}{2} > -5$ or $\dfrac{5}{4}x \geq 10$

$-2\left(-\dfrac{x}{2}\right) < (-5)(-2)$ or $\dfrac{4}{5}\left(\dfrac{5}{4}x\right) \geq (10)$

$x < 10$ or $x \geq 8$

$-\infty < x < \infty$

73. $7x + 11 < 3 + 4x$ or $\dfrac{5}{2}x - 1 \geq 9 - \dfrac{3}{2}x$

$7x - 4x + 11 < 3 + 4x - 4x$ or $\dfrac{5}{2}x + \dfrac{3}{2}x - 1 \geq 9 - \dfrac{3}{2}x + \dfrac{3}{2}x$

$3x + 11 < 3$ or $4x - 1 \geq 9$

$3x + 11 - 11 < 3 - 11$ or $4x - 1 + 1 \geq 9 + 1$

$3x < -8$ or $4x \geq 10$

$\dfrac{3x}{3} < -\dfrac{8}{3}$ or $\dfrac{4x}{4} \geq \dfrac{10}{4}$

$x < -\dfrac{8}{3}$ or $x \geq \dfrac{5}{2}$

75. $-3(y + 10) \geq 4(y + 10)$

$-3y - 30 \geq 4y + 40$

$3y - 3y - 30 \geq 3y + 4y + 40$

$-30 \geq 7y + 40$

$-40 - 30 \geq 7y + 40 - 40$

$-70 \geq 7y$

$-10 \geq y$

77. $-4 \leq 2 - 3(x + 2) < 11$

$-4 \leq 2 - 3x - 6 < 11$

$-4 \leq 4 - 3x < 11$

$-4 + 4 \leq -4 - 3x + 4 < 11 + 4$

$0 \leq -3x < 15$

$\dfrac{0}{-3} \geq \dfrac{-3x}{-3} > \dfrac{15}{-3}$

$0 \geq x > -5$

79. $x < -3$ or $x \geq 2$

$\{x \mid x < -3\} \cup \{x \mid x \geq 2\}$

81. $-5 \leq x < 4$

$\{x \mid x \geq -5\} \cap \{x \mid x < 4\}$

83. $x \leq -2.5$ or $x \geq -0.5$

$\{x \mid x \leq -2.5\} \cup \{x \mid x \geq -0.5\}$

85. $\{x \mid x \geq -7\} \cap \{x \mid x < 0\}$

87. $\{x \mid x < -5\} \cup \{x \mid x > 3\}$

89. $\left\{x \mid x > -\frac{9}{2}\right\} \cap \left\{x \mid x \leq -\frac{3}{2}\right\}$

91. "x is nonnegative" using inequality notation is $x \geq 0$.

93. "z is at least 2" using inequality notation is $z \geq 2$.

95. "n is at least 10, but no more than 16" using inequality notation is $10 \leq n \leq 16$.

97. A verbal description of $x \geq \frac{5}{2}$ is x is at least $\frac{5}{2}$.

99. A verbal description of $3 \leq y < 5$ is y is at least 3 and less than 5.

101. A verbal description of $0 < z \leq \pi$ is z is greater than 0 and no more than π.

103. *Verbal Model:* $\boxed{\text{Transportation costs}} + \boxed{\text{Other costs}} \leq \boxed{\text{Total money for trip}}$

Labels: Transportation costs = 1900

Other costs = C

Total money = 4500

Inequality: $1900 + C \leq 4500$

$1900 + C - 1900 \leq 4500 - 1900$

$C \leq 2600$

105. *Verbal Model:* $\boxed{\text{Temp in Miami}} > \boxed{\text{Temp in Washington}} > \boxed{\text{Temp in New York}}$

The average temperature in Miami, therefore, is greater than ($>$) the average temperature in New York.

107. *Verbal Model:* $\boxed{\text{Operating cost}} < \boxed{\$12{,}000}$

Label: Operating cost $= 0.35m + 2900$

Inequality: $0.35m + 2900 < 12{,}000$

$0.35m + 2900 - 2900 < 12{,}000 - 2900$

$0.35m < 9100$

$\dfrac{0.35m}{0.35} < \dfrac{9100}{0.35}$

$m < 26{,}000$ miles

109. *Verbal Model:* $\boxed{\text{Revenue}} > \boxed{\text{Cost}}$

Labels: Revenue $= 89.95x$

Cost $= 61x + 875$

Inequality: $89.95x > 61x + 875$

$89.95x - 61x > 61x + 875 - 61x$

$28.95x > 875$

$\dfrac{28.95x}{28.95} > \dfrac{875}{28.95}$

$x > 30.224525$

$x \geq 31$

111. *Verbal Model:* $\boxed{\begin{array}{c}\text{Cost of}\\\text{first minute}\end{array}} + \boxed{\begin{array}{c}\text{Cost of additional}\\\text{minutes}\end{array}} \leq \boxed{\$5.00}$

Label: Number of additional minutes $= x$

Inequality: $\$0.96 + \$0.75 \leq \$5.00$

$$0.96 + 0.75x - 0.96 \leq 5.00 - 0.96$$

$$0.75x \leq 4.04$$

$$\frac{0.75x}{0.75} \leq \frac{4.04}{0.75}$$

$$x \leq 5.386667$$

Since x represents the additional minutes after the first minute, the call must be less than 6.38 minutes. If a portion of a minute is billed as a full minute, then the call must be less than or equal to 6 minutes.

113. *Verbal Model:* $36 \leq \boxed{\text{Perimeter}} \leq 64$

Label: Perimeter $= 2x + 32$

Inequality: $36 \leq 2x + 32 \leq 64$

$$36 - 32 \leq 2x + 32 - 32 \leq 64 - 32$$

$$4 \leq 2x \leq 32$$

$$\frac{4}{2} \leq \frac{2x}{2} \leq \frac{32}{2}$$

$$2 \leq x \leq 16$$

115. $12 \leq 4n \leq 30$

$$\frac{12}{4} \leq \frac{4n}{4} \leq \frac{30}{4}$$

$$3 \leq n \leq \frac{15}{2}$$

117. *Verbal Model:* $\boxed{\text{Second plan}} > \boxed{\text{First plan}}$

Labels: First payment plan: \$12.50 per hour

Second payment plan: $\$8 + \$0.75n$ per hour where n represents the number of units produced.

Inequality: $8 + 0.75n > 12.5$

$$0.75n > 4.5$$

$$n > 6$$

If more than 6 units are produced per hour, the second payment plan yields the greater hourly wage.

119. *Verbal Model:* $\boxed{\begin{array}{c}\text{Air pollutant}\\\text{emission}\end{array}} > 6$

Label: Air pollutant emission $= 5.890 - 0.276t$

Inequality: $5.890 - 0.276t > 6$

$$5.890 - 5.890 - 0.276t > 6 - 5.890$$

$$-0.276t > 0.11$$

$$\frac{-0.276t}{-0.276} < \frac{0.11}{-0.276}$$

$$t < -0.399$$

$t = -1 \rightarrow$ year 1989

$t = -2 \rightarrow$ year 1988

$t = -3 \rightarrow$ year 1987

121. (f) $C = 31.20 + 11.91x \leq 50$

$$11.91x \leq 18.8$$

$$x \leq \frac{18.8}{11.91}$$

$$x \leq 1.58$$

At most, you can purchase one premium movie channel.

(g) $C = 34.19 + 3.95x \leq 50$

$$3.95x \leq 15.81$$

$$x \leq 4.00$$

At most, you can purchase four pay-per-view movies.

123. Yes, dividing both sides of an inequality by 5 is the same as multiplying both sides by $\frac{1}{5}$.

$$5x = 15 \qquad\qquad 5x = 15$$

$$\frac{5x}{5} = \frac{15}{5} \qquad \frac{1}{5} \cdot 5x = 15 \cdot \frac{1}{5}$$

$$x = 3 \qquad\qquad x = 3$$

125. The multiplication and division properties differ. The inequality symbol is reversed if both sides of the inequality are multiplied or divided by a negative real number.

127. If $-5 \le t < 8$, then $(-1)(-5) \ge (-1)(t) > (-1)(8)$ and $5 \ge -t > -8$ or $-8 < -t \le 5$.

Section 1.5   Absolute Value Equations and Inequalities

1. $|4x + 5| = 10,\ x = -3$

$|4(-3) + 5| \overset{?}{=} 10$

$|-12 + 5| \overset{?}{=} 10$

$|-7| \overset{?}{=} 10$

$7 \ne 10$

No

3. $|6 - 2w| = 2,\ w = 4$

$|6 - 2(4)| \overset{?}{=} 2$

$|6 - 8| \overset{?}{=} 2$

$|-2| \overset{?}{=} 2$

$2 = 2$

Yes

5. $x - 10 = 17$ or $x - 10 = -17$

7. $4x + 1 = \frac{1}{2}$ or $4x + 1 = -\frac{1}{2}$

9. $|x| = 4$

$x = 4$ or $x = -4$

11. $|t| = -45$

No solution

13. $|h| = 0$

$h = 0$

15. $|5x| = 15$

$5x = 15$ or $5x = -15$

$x = 3 \qquad\quad x = -3$

17. $|x - 16| = 5$

$x - 16 = 5$ or $x - 16 = -5$

$x = 21 \qquad\qquad x = 11$

19. $|2s + 3| = 25$

$2s + 3 = 25$ or $2s + 3 = -25$

$2s = 22 \qquad\quad 2s = -28$

$s = 11 \qquad\quad s = -14$

21. $|32 - 3y| = 16$

$32 - 3y = 16$ or $32 - 3y = -16$

$-3y = -16 \qquad\quad -3y = -48$

$y = \frac{16}{3} \qquad\qquad y = 16$

23. $|3x + 4| = -16$

No solution

25. $|4 - 3x| = 0$

$4 - 3x = 0$

$-3x = -4$

$x = \frac{4}{3}$

27. $\left|\frac{2}{3}x + 4\right| = 9$

$\frac{2}{3}x + 4 = 9$ or $\frac{2}{3}x + 4 = -9$

$\frac{2}{3}x = 5 \qquad\quad \frac{2}{3}x = -13$

$2x = 15 \qquad\quad 2x = -39$

$x = \frac{15}{2} \qquad\quad x = -\frac{39}{2}$

29. $|0.32x - 2| = 4$

$0.32x - 2 = 4$ or $0.32x - 2 = -4$

$0.32x = 6 \qquad\qquad 0.32x = -2$

$x = \frac{6}{0.32} \qquad\qquad x = \frac{-2}{0.32}$

$x = 18.75 \qquad\qquad x = -6.25$

31. $|5x - 3| + 8 = 22$

$\quad |5x - 3| = 14$

$\quad 5x - 3 = 14 \quad \text{or} \quad 5x - 3 = -14$

$\quad\quad 5x = 17 \quad\quad\quad 5x = -11$

$\quad\quad\quad x = \frac{17}{5} \quad\quad\quad\quad x = -\frac{11}{5}$

33. $|3x + 9| - 12 = -8$

$\quad |3x + 9| = 4$

$\quad 3x + 9 = 4 \quad \text{or} \quad 3x + 9 = -4$

$\quad\quad 3x = -5 \quad\quad\quad 3x = -13$

$\quad\quad\quad x = -\frac{5}{3} \quad\quad\quad\quad x = -\frac{13}{3}$

35. $-2|7 - 4x| = -16$

$\quad |7 - 4x| = 8$

$\quad 7 - 4x = 8 \quad \text{or} \quad 7 - 4x = -8$

$\quad\quad -4x = 1 \quad\quad\quad -4x = -15$

$\quad\quad\quad x = -\frac{1}{4} \quad\quad\quad\quad x = \frac{15}{4}$

37. $3|2x - 5| + 4 = 7$

$\quad 3|2x - 5| = 3$

$\quad |2x - 5| = 1$

$\quad 2x - 5 = 1 \quad \text{or} \quad 2x - 5 = -1$

$\quad\quad 2x = 6 \quad\quad\quad 2x = 4$

$\quad\quad\quad x = 3 \quad\quad\quad\quad x = 2$

39. $|x + 8| = |2x + 1|$

$\quad x + 8 = 2x + 1 \quad \text{or} \quad x + 8 = -(2x + 1)$

$\quad\quad 8 = x + 1 \quad\quad\quad x + 8 = -2x - 1$

$\quad\quad 7 = x \quad\quad\quad\quad 3x + 8 = -1$

$\quad\quad\quad\quad\quad\quad\quad\quad\quad 3x = -9$

$\quad\quad\quad\quad\quad\quad\quad\quad\quad\quad x = -3$

41. $|x + 2| = |3x - 1|$

$\quad x + 2 = 3x - 1 \quad \text{or} \quad x + 2 = -(3x - 1)$

$\quad\quad 3 = 2x \quad\quad\quad\quad x + 2 = -3x + 1$

$\quad\quad \frac{3}{2} = x \quad\quad\quad\quad\quad 4x = -1$

$\quad\quad\quad\quad\quad\quad\quad\quad\quad\quad x = -\frac{1}{4}$

43. $|45 - 4x| = |32 - 3x|$

$\quad 45 - 4x = 32 - 3x \quad \text{or} \quad 45 - 4x = -(32 - 3x)$

$\quad\quad 45 = 32 + x \quad\quad\quad 45 - 4x = -32 + 3x$

$\quad\quad 13 = x \quad\quad\quad\quad\quad 45 = -32 + 7x$

$\quad\quad\quad\quad\quad\quad\quad\quad\quad 77 = 7x$

$\quad\quad\quad\quad\quad\quad\quad\quad\quad 11 = x$

45. $|4x - 10| = 2|2x + 3|$

$\quad 4x - 10 = 2(2x + 3) \quad \text{or} \quad 4x - 10 = -2(2x + 3)$

$\quad\quad 4x - 10 = 4x + 6 \quad\quad\quad 4x - 10 = -4x - 6$

$\quad\quad\quad -10 = 6 \quad\quad\quad\quad\quad 8x - 10 = -6$

$\quad\quad\quad \text{No solution} \quad\quad\quad\quad 8x = 4$

$\quad\quad\quad\quad\quad\quad\quad\quad\quad\quad x = \frac{4}{8} = \frac{1}{2}$

47. $|x - 5| = 3$

49. (a) $x = 2$

$\quad |2| < 3$

$\quad 2 < 3$

$\quad \text{Yes}$

(b) $x = -4$

$\quad |-4| < 3$

$\quad 4 < 3$

$\quad \text{No}$

(c) $x = 4$

$\quad |4| < 3$

$\quad 4 < 3$

$\quad \text{No}$

(d) $x = -1$

$\quad |-1| < 3$

$\quad 1 < 3$

$\quad \text{Yes}$

51. (a) $x = 9$

$\quad |9 - 7| \geq 3$

$\quad |2| \geq 3$

$\quad 2 \geq 3$

$\quad \text{No}$

(b) $x = -4$

$\quad |-4 - 7| \geq 3$

$\quad |-11| \geq 3$

$\quad 11 \geq 3$

$\quad \text{Yes}$

(c) $x = 11$

$\quad |11 - 7| \geq 3$

$\quad |4| \geq 3$

$\quad 4 \geq 3$

$\quad \text{Yes}$

(d) $x = 6$

$\quad |6 - 7| \geq 3$

$\quad |-1| \geq 3$

$\quad 1 \geq 3$

$\quad \text{No}$

53. $|y + 5| < 3$

$-3 < y + 5 < 3$

55. $|7 - 2h| \geq 9$

$7 - 2h \geq 9$ or $7 - 2h \leq -9$

57. "All x greater than -2 *and* less than 5."

59. "All x less than or equal to 4 *or* greater than 7."

61. $|y| < 4$

$-4 < y < 4$

63. $|x| \geq 6$

$x \geq 6$ or $x \leq -6$

65. $|2x| < 14$

$-14 < 2x < 14$

$-7 < x < 7$

67. $\left|\dfrac{y}{3}\right| \leq 3$

$-3 \leq \dfrac{y}{3} \leq 3$

$-9 \leq y \leq 9$

69. $|y - 2| \leq 4$

$-4 \leq y - 2 \leq 4$

$-2 \leq y \leq 6$

71. $|x + 6| > 10$

$x + 6 > 10$ or $x + 6 < -10$

$\quad\; x > 4 \qquad\qquad x < -16$

73. $|2x - 1| \leq 7$

$-7 \leq 2x - 1 \leq 7$

$-6 \leq 2x \leq 8$

$-3 \leq x \leq 4$

75. $|6t + 15| \geq 30$

$6t + 15 \leq -30$ or $6t + 15 \geq 30$

$6t \leq -45 \qquad\qquad 6t \geq 15$

$t \leq -\dfrac{45}{6} \qquad\qquad t \geq \dfrac{15}{6}$

$t \leq -\dfrac{15}{2} \qquad\qquad t \geq \dfrac{5}{2}$

77. $|2 - 5x| > -8$

$-\infty < x < \infty$

Absolute value is always positive.

79. $|3x + 10| < -1$

No solution

Absolute value is never negative.

81. $\dfrac{|x + 2|}{10} \leq 8$

$|x + 2| \leq 80$

$-80 \leq x + 2 \leq 80$

$-82 \leq x \leq 78$

83. $\dfrac{|y - 16|}{4} < 30$

$|y - 16| < 120$

$-120 < y - 16 < 120$

$-104 < y < 136$

85. $\left|\dfrac{z}{10} - 3\right| > 8$

$\dfrac{z}{10} - 3 < -8$ or $\dfrac{z}{10} - 3 > 8$

$\dfrac{z}{10} < -5 \qquad\qquad \dfrac{z}{10} > 11$

$z < -50 \qquad\qquad z > 110$

87. $|0.2x - 3| < 4$

$-4 < 0.2x - 3 < 4$

$-1 < 0.2x < 7$

$\dfrac{-1}{0.2} < x < \dfrac{7}{0.2}$

$-5 < x < 35$

89. $\left|6 - \dfrac{3}{5}x\right| \leq 0.4$

$-0.4 \leq 6 - \dfrac{3}{5}x \leq 0.4$

$-2 \leq 30 - 3x \leq 2$

$-32 \leq -3x \leq -28$

$\dfrac{32}{3} \geq x \geq \dfrac{28}{3}$

$\dfrac{28}{3} \leq x \leq \dfrac{32}{3}$

91. $-2|3x + 6| < 4$

$|3x + 6| > -2$

$-\infty < x < \infty$

Absolute value is always positive.

93. $\left|9 - \dfrac{x}{2}\right| - 7 \leq 4$

$\left|9 - \dfrac{x}{2}\right| \leq 11$

$-11 \leq 9 - \dfrac{x}{2} \leq 11$

$-20 \leq -\dfrac{x}{2} \leq 2$

$40 \geq x \geq -4$

$-4 \leq x \leq 40$

95. $|3x + 2| < 4$

Keystrokes: $\boxed{Y=}$ $\boxed{ABS}$ $\boxed{(}$ 3 $\boxed{X,T,\theta}$ $\boxed{+}$ 2 $\boxed{)}$ $\boxed{<}$ 4 $\boxed{GRAPH}$

$-2 < x < \frac{2}{3}$

97. $|2x + 3| > 9$

Keystrokes: $\boxed{Y=}$ $\boxed{ABS}$ $\boxed{(}$ 2 $\boxed{X,T,\theta}$ $\boxed{+}$ 3 $\boxed{)}$ $\boxed{>}$ 9 $\boxed{GRAPH}$

$x < -6$ or $x > 3$

99. $|x - 5| + 3 \le 5$

Keystrokes: $\boxed{Y=}$ $\boxed{ABS}$ $\boxed{(}$ $\boxed{X,T,\theta}$ $\boxed{-}$ 5 $\boxed{)}$ $\boxed{+}$ 3 $\boxed{\le}$ 5 $\boxed{GRAPH}$

$3 \le x \le 7$

101. Matches graph (d).

$|x - 4| \le 4$

$-4 \le x - 4 \le 4$

$0 \le x \le 8$

103. Matches graph (b).

$\frac{1}{2}|x - 4| > 4$

$|x - 4| > 8$

$x - 4 > 8$ or $x - 4 < -8$

$x > 12$ $x < -4$

105. $[-2, 2]$

$|x| \le 2$

107. $(16, 22)$

$16 < x < 22$

$-3 < x - 19 < 3$

$|x - 19| < 3$

109. $|x| < 3$

111. $|x - 5| > 6$

113. $|t - 72| < 10$

$-10 < t - 72 < 10$

$62 < t < 82$

115. (a) $|s - x| \le \frac{3}{16}$

(b) $\left|5\frac{1}{8} - x\right| \le \frac{3}{16}$

$-\frac{3}{16} \le 5\frac{1}{8} - x \le \frac{3}{16}$

$-\frac{3}{16} \le \frac{41}{8} - x \le \frac{3}{16}$

$-\frac{85}{16} \le -x \le -\frac{79}{16}$

$\frac{85}{16} \ge x \ge \frac{79}{16}$

117. The absolute value of a real number measures the distance of the real number from zero.

119. The solutions of $|x| = a$ are $x = a$ and $x = -a$. For example, to solve $|x - 3| = 5$:

$x - 3 = 5$ or $x - 3 = -5$

$x = 8$ $x = -2$

121. The graph of $|x - 4| < 1$ can be described as all real numbers less than one unit from 4.

123. $|x - 3| \le 3$ since

$-3 \le x - 3 \le 3$

$0 \le x \le 6.$

Review Exercises for Chapter 1

1. (a) $45 - 7(3) = 3$

$45 - 21 = 3$

$24 = 3$

Not a solution

(b) $45 - 7(6) = 3$

$45 - 42 = 3$

$3 = 3$

Solution

3. (a) $\dfrac{\frac{35}{12}}{7} + \dfrac{\frac{35}{12}}{5} = 1$

$\dfrac{5}{12} + \dfrac{7}{12} = 1$

$\dfrac{12}{12} = 1$

$1 = 1$

Solution

(b) $\dfrac{-\frac{2}{35}}{7} + \dfrac{-\frac{2}{35}}{5} = 1$

$-\dfrac{2}{245} + -\dfrac{2}{175} = 1$

$-\dfrac{10}{1225} + -\dfrac{14}{1225} = 1$

$-\dfrac{24}{1225} = 1$

Not a solution

---

5. $x + 2 = 5$

$x + 2 - 2 = 5 - 2$

$x = 3$

Check:

$3 + 2 \overset{?}{=} 5$

$5 = 5$

7. $-3x = 36$

$\dfrac{-3x}{-3} = \dfrac{36}{-3}$

$x = -12$

Check:

$-3(-12) \overset{?}{=} 36$

$36 = 36$

---

9. $-\dfrac{1}{8}x = 3$

$(-8)\left(-\dfrac{1}{8}x\right) = (3)(-8)$

$x = -24$

Check:

$-\dfrac{1}{8}(-24) \overset{?}{=} 3$

$3 = 3$

11. $5x + 4 = 19$

$5x + 4 - 4 = 19 - 4$

$5x = 15$

$\dfrac{5x}{5} = \dfrac{15}{5}$

$x = 3$

Check:

$5(3) + 4 \overset{?}{=} 19$

$15 + 4 \overset{?}{=} 19$

$19 = 19$

---

13. $17 - 7x = 3$

$17 - 7x - 17 = 3 - 17$

$-7x = -14$

$\dfrac{-7x}{-7} = \dfrac{-14}{-7}$

$x = 2$

Check:

$17 - 7(2) \overset{?}{=} 3$

$17 - 14 \overset{?}{=} 3$

$3 = 3$

15. $7x - 5 = 3x + 11$

$7x - 3x - 5 = 3x - 3x + 11$

$4x - 5 = 11$

$4x - 5 + 5 = 11 + 5$

$4x = 16$

$\dfrac{4x}{4} = \dfrac{16}{4}$

$x = 4$

Check:

$7(4) - 5 \overset{?}{=} 3(4) + 11$

$28 - 5 \overset{?}{=} 12 + 11$

$23 = 23$

---

17. $3(2y - 1) = 9 + 3y$

$6y - 3 = 9 + 3y$

$6y - 3y - 3 = 9 + 3y - 3y$

$3y - 3 = 9$

$3y - 3 + 3 = 9 + 3$

$3y = 12$

$\dfrac{3y}{3} = \dfrac{12}{3}$

$y = 4$

Check:

$3(2(4) - 1) \overset{?}{=} 9 + 3(4)$

$3(7) \overset{?}{=} 9 + 12$

$21 = 21$

19. $4y - 6(y - 5) = 2$

$4y - 6y + 30 = 2$

$-2y + 30 = 2$

$-2y + 30 - 30 = 2 - 30$

$-2y = -28$

$\dfrac{-2y}{-2} = \dfrac{-28}{-2}$

$y = 14$

Check:

$4(14) - 6(14 - 5) \stackrel{?}{=} 2$

$56 - 6(9) \stackrel{?}{=} 2$

$56 - 54 \stackrel{?}{=} 2$

$2 = 2$

21. $4(3x - 5) = 6(2x + 3)$

$12x - 20 = 12x + 18$

$12x - 12x - 20 = 12x - 12x + 18$

$-20 = 18$

No solution

23. $\dfrac{4}{5}x - \dfrac{1}{10} = \dfrac{3}{2}$

$10\left[\dfrac{4}{5}x - \dfrac{1}{10}\right] = \left[\dfrac{3}{2}\right]10$

$8x - 1 = 15$

$8x - 1 + 1 = 15 + 1$

$8x = 16$

$\dfrac{8x}{8} = \dfrac{16}{8}$

$x = 2$

Check:

$\dfrac{4}{5}(2) - \dfrac{1}{10} \stackrel{?}{=} \dfrac{3}{2}$

$\dfrac{8}{5} - \dfrac{1}{10} \stackrel{?}{=} \dfrac{3}{2}$

$\dfrac{16}{10} - \dfrac{1}{10} \stackrel{?}{=} \dfrac{3}{2}$

$\dfrac{15}{10} \stackrel{?}{=} \dfrac{3}{2}$

$\dfrac{3}{2} = \dfrac{3}{2}$

25. $1.4t + 2.1 = 0.9t$

$1.4t + 2.1 - 0.9t = 0.9t - 0.9t$

$0.5t + 2.1 = 0$

$0.5t + 2.1 - 2.1 = 0 - 2.1$

$0.5t = -2.1$

$\dfrac{0.5t}{0.5} = \dfrac{-2.1}{0.5}$

$t = -4.2$

Check:

$1.4(-4.2) + 2.1 \stackrel{?}{=} 0.9(-4.2)$

$-5.88 + 2.1 \stackrel{?}{=} -3.78$

$-3.78 = -3.78$

27.

Percent	Parts out of 100	Decimal	Fraction
87%	87	0.87	$\frac{87}{100}$

29. *Verbal Model:* | Compared number | = | Percent | · | Base number |

Labels: Compared number = a

Percent = p

Base number = b

Equation: $a = p \cdot b$

$a = 1.30 \cdot 50$

$a = 65$

31. *Verbal Model:* $\boxed{\text{Compared number}} = \boxed{\text{Percent}} \cdot \boxed{\text{Base number}}$

Labels: Compared number $= a$
Percent $= p$
Base number $= b$

Equation: $a = p \cdot b$

$645 = 0.215 \cdot b$

$\dfrac{645}{0.215} = b$

$3000 = b$

33. *Verbal Model:* $\boxed{\text{Compared number}} = \boxed{\text{Percent}} \cdot \boxed{\text{Base number}}$

Labels: Compared number $= a$
Percent $= p$
Base number $= b$

Equation: $a = p \cdot b$

$250 = p \cdot 200$

$\dfrac{250}{200} = p$

$1.25 = p$ or 125%

35. $\dfrac{16 \text{ feet}}{4 \text{ yards}} = \dfrac{16 \text{ feet}}{12 \text{ feet}} = \dfrac{16}{12} = \dfrac{4}{3}$

37. $\dfrac{45 \text{ seconds}}{5 \text{ minutes}} = \dfrac{45 \text{ seconds}}{300 \text{ seconds}} = \dfrac{45}{300} = \dfrac{3}{20}$

39. $\dfrac{7}{8} = \dfrac{y}{4}$

$8y = 28$

$y = \dfrac{28}{8}$

$y = \dfrac{7}{2}$

41. $\dfrac{b}{6} = \dfrac{5 + b}{15}$

$15b = 6(5 + b)$

$15b = 30 + 6b$

$9b = 30$

$b = \dfrac{30}{9}$

$b = \dfrac{10}{3}$

43. *Verbal Model:* $\boxed{\text{Selling price}} = \boxed{\text{Cost}} + \boxed{\text{Markup}}$

Labels: Selling price $= 149.93$
Cost $= 99.95$
Markup $= x$

Equation: $149.93 = 99.95 + x$

$149.93 - 99.95 = x$

$\$49.98 = x$

Verbal Model: $\boxed{\text{Markup}} = \boxed{\text{Markup rate}} \cdot \boxed{\text{Cost}}$

Labels: Markup $= 49.98$
Markup rate $= x$
Cost $= 99.95$

Equation: $49.98 = x \cdot 99.95$

$\dfrac{49.98}{99.95} = x$

$50\% \approx x$

45. *Verbal Model:* $\boxed{\text{Selling price}} = \boxed{\text{Cost}} + \boxed{\text{Markup}}$

Labels: Selling price $= 125.85$
Cost $= x$
Markup $= 44.13$

Equation: $125.85 = x + 44.13$

$125.85 - 44.13 = x$

$\$81.72 = x$

Verbal Model: $\boxed{\text{Markup}} = \boxed{\text{Markup rate}} \cdot \boxed{\text{Cost}}$

Labels: Markup $= 44.13$
Markup rate $= x$
Cost $= 81.72$

Equation: $44.13 = x \cdot 81.72$

$\dfrac{44.13}{81.72} = x$

$54\% \approx x$

47. *Verbal Model:* $\boxed{\text{Sale price}} = \boxed{\text{List price}} - \boxed{\text{Discount}}$

Labels: Sale price = 53.96

List price = 71.95

Discount = x

Equation: $53.96 = 71.95 - x$

$x = 71.95 - 53.96$

$x = \$17.99$

Verbal Model: $\boxed{\text{Discount}} = \boxed{\text{Discount rate}} \cdot \boxed{\text{List price}}$

Labels: Discount = 17.99

Discount rate = x

List price = 71.95

Equation: $17.99 = x \cdot 71.95$

$\dfrac{17.99}{71.95} = x$

$25\% \approx x$

49. *Verbal Model:* $\boxed{\text{Sale price}} = \boxed{\text{List price}} - \boxed{\text{Discount}}$

Labels: Sale price = x

List price = 1995.50

Discount = 598.65

Equation: $x = 1995.50 - 598.65$

$x = \$1396.85$

Verbal Model: $\boxed{\text{Discount}} = \boxed{\text{Discount rate}} \cdot \boxed{\text{List price}}$

Labels: Discount = 598.65

Discount rate = x

List price = 1995.50

Equation: $598.65 = x \cdot 1995.50$

$\dfrac{598.65}{1995.50} = x$

$30\% = x$

51. $2x - 7y + 4 = 0$

$2x = 7y - 4$

$x = \frac{7}{2}y - 2$

$x = \frac{1}{2}(7y - 4)$

53. $V = \pi r^2 h$

$\dfrac{V}{\pi r^2} = h$

55. $x - 5 \le -1$

$x - 5 + 5 \le -1 + 5$

$x \le 4$

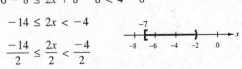

57. $-5x < 30$

$\dfrac{-5x}{-5} > \dfrac{30}{-5}$

$x > -6$

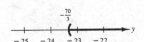

59. $5x + 3 > 18$

$5x > 15$

$x > 3$

61. $8x + 1 \ge 10x - 11$

$8x - 10x + 1 \ge 10x - 10x - 11$

$-2x + 1 \ge -11$

$-2x + 1 - 1 \ge -11 - 1$

$-2x \ge -12$

$\dfrac{-2x}{-2} \le \dfrac{-12}{-2}$

$x \le 6$

63. $\dfrac{1}{3} - \dfrac{1}{2}y < 12$

$2 - 3y < 72$

$-3y < 70$

$y > -\dfrac{70}{3}$

65. $-6 \le 2x + 8 < 4$

$-6 - 8 \le 2x + 8 - 8 < 4 - 8$

$-14 \le 2x < -4$

$\dfrac{-14}{2} \le \dfrac{2x}{2} < \dfrac{-4}{2}$

$-7 \le x < -2$

67. $5 > \dfrac{x+1}{-3} > 0$

$-15 < x + 1 < 0$

$-16 < x < -1$

69. $5x - 4 < 6 \qquad$ and $\qquad 3x + 1 > -8$

$5x - 4 + 4 < 6 + 4 \qquad 3x + 1 - 1 > -8 - 1$

$5x < 10 \qquad\qquad\qquad 3x > -9$

$\dfrac{5x}{5} < \dfrac{10}{5} \qquad\qquad\qquad \dfrac{3x}{3} > \dfrac{-9}{3}$

$x < 2 \qquad$ and $\qquad x > -3$

$-3 < x < 2$

71. $-4(3 - 2x) \le 3(2x - 6)$

$-12 + 8x \le 6x - 18$

$-12 + 8x - 6x \le 6x - 6x - 18$

$-12 + 2x \le -18$

$-12 + 12 + 2x \le -18 + 12$

$2x \le -6$

$\dfrac{2x}{2} \le \dfrac{-6}{2}$

$x \le -3$

73. $z \le 10$

75. $7 \le y < 14$

77. $|x| = 6$

$x = 6$ or $x = -6$

79. $|4 - 3x| = 8$

$4 - 3x = 8 \qquad$ or $\qquad 4 - 3x = -8$

$4 - 4 - 3x = 8 - 4 \qquad 4 - 4 - 3x = -8 - 4$

$-3x = 4 \qquad\qquad\qquad -3x = -12$

$\dfrac{-3x}{-3} = \dfrac{4}{-3} \qquad\qquad \dfrac{-3x}{-3} = \dfrac{-12}{-3}$

$x = \dfrac{4}{-3} \qquad\qquad\qquad x = 4$

81. $|5x + 4| - 10 = -6$

$|5x + 4| = 4$

$5x + 4 = 4 \qquad$ or $\qquad 5x + 4 = -4$

$5x + 4 - 4 = 4 - 4 \qquad 5x + 4 - 4 = -4 - 4$

$5x = 0 \qquad\qquad\qquad 5x = -8$

$\dfrac{5x}{5} = \dfrac{0}{5} \qquad\qquad\qquad \dfrac{5x}{5} = \dfrac{-8}{5}$

$x = 0 \qquad\qquad\qquad x = -\dfrac{8}{5}$

83. $|3x - 4| = |x + 2|$

$3x - 4 = x + 2 \quad$ or $\quad 3x - 4 = -(x + 2)$

$2x = 6 \qquad\qquad 3x - 4 = -x - 2$

$x = 3 \qquad\qquad\qquad 4x = 2$

$x = \tfrac{2}{4} = \tfrac{1}{2}$

85. $|x - 4| > 3$

$x - 4 < -3 \quad$ or $\quad x - 4 > 3$

$x < 1 \qquad$ or $\qquad x > 7$

87. $|3x| > 9$

$3x < -9 \quad$ or $\quad 3x > 9$

$x < -3 \quad$ or $\quad x > 3$

89. $|2x - 7| < 15$

$-15 < 2x - 7 < 15$

$-8 < 2x < 22$

$-4 < x < 11$

91. $|b + 2| - 6 > 1$

$\qquad |b + 2| > 7$

$\quad b + 2 < -7 \quad \text{or} \quad b + 2 > 7$

$\qquad b < -9 \quad \text{or} \qquad b > 5$

93. $|2x - 5| \geq 1$

Keystrokes: $\boxed{\text{Y=}}$ $\boxed{\text{ABS}}$ $\boxed{(}$ 2 $\boxed{\text{X,T,}\theta}$ $\boxed{-}$ 5 $\boxed{)}$ $\boxed{\geq}$ 1 $\boxed{\text{GRAPH}}$

$x \leq 2 \text{ or } x \geq 3$

95. $(1, 5)$

$\qquad 1 < x < 5$

$\quad 1 - 3 < x - 3 < 5 - 3$

$\qquad -2 < x - 3 < 2$

$|x - 3| < 2$

97. *Verbal Model:* $\boxed{\begin{array}{c}\text{First}\\\text{integer}\end{array}} + \boxed{\begin{array}{c}\text{Second}\\\text{integer}\end{array}} = \boxed{\text{Sum}}$

Labels: First integer $= x$

Second integer $= x + 1$

Sum $= 147$

Equation: $x + (x + 1) = 147$

$\qquad\qquad 2x + 1 = 147$

$\quad 2x + 1 - 1 = 147 - 1$

$\qquad\qquad 2x = 146$

$\qquad\qquad \dfrac{2x}{2} = \dfrac{146}{2}$

$\qquad\qquad x = 73, \quad x + 1 = 74$

99. *Verbal Model:* $\boxed{\text{Commission}} = \boxed{\begin{array}{c}\text{Percent}\\\text{rate}\end{array}} \cdot \boxed{\text{Sales}}$

Labels: Commission $= 9000$

Percent rate $= x$

Sales $= 150,000$

Equation: $9000 = x \cdot 150,000$

$\qquad \dfrac{9000}{150,000} = x$

$\qquad\qquad 6\% = x$

101. *Verbal Model:* $\boxed{\begin{array}{c}\text{Total}\\\text{price}\end{array}} = \boxed{\begin{array}{c}\text{List}\\\text{price}\end{array}} + \boxed{\text{Shipping}}$

Labels: Total price $= x$

List price $= 24.95$

Shipping $= 6.95$

Equation: $x = 24.95 + 6.95$

$\qquad x = \$31.90$

Verbal Model: $\boxed{\text{Discount}} = \boxed{\begin{array}{c}\text{Discount}\\\text{rate}\end{array}} \cdot \boxed{\begin{array}{c}\text{List}\\\text{price}\end{array}}$

Labels: Discount $= x$

Discount rate $= 30\%$

List price $= 35.95$

Equation: $x = 0.30 \cdot 35.95$

$\qquad x = \$10.79$

—CONTINUED—

101. —CONTINUED—

Verbal Model: $\boxed{\text{Sale price}} = \boxed{\text{List price}} - \boxed{\text{Discount}}$

Labels: Sale price $= x$

List price $= \$35.95$

Discount $= \$10.79$

Equation: $x = 35.95 - 10.79$

$x = \$25.16$

The department store price is the better buy.

103. *Verbal Model:* $\boxed{\text{Sales tax}} = \boxed{\text{Percent rate}} \cdot \boxed{\text{Cost}}$

Labels: Sales tax $= x$

Percent rate $= 7\frac{1}{4}\%$

Cost $= 34$

Equation: $x = 0.0725 \cdot 34$

$x = \$2.47$

105. *Verbal Model:* $\boxed{\dfrac{\text{Cups}}{\text{Batches}}} = \boxed{\dfrac{\text{Cups}}{\text{Batches}}}$

Proportion: $\dfrac{1\frac{1}{2}}{1} = \dfrac{x}{2\frac{1}{2}}$

$x = 1\frac{1}{2} \cdot 2\frac{1}{2}$

$x = 3\frac{3}{4}$ cups

107. *Verbal Model:* $\boxed{\dfrac{\text{Gasoline}}{\text{Oil}}} = \boxed{\dfrac{\text{Gasoline}}{\text{Oil}}}$

Proportion: $\dfrac{50}{1} = \dfrac{x}{\frac{1}{2}}$

$x = 25$ pints

109. *Verbal Model:* $\boxed{\dfrac{\text{Base}}{\text{Side}}} = \boxed{\dfrac{\text{Base}}{\text{Side}}}$

Proportion: $\dfrac{3}{3.5} = \dfrac{4}{x}$

$3x = 14$

$x = \dfrac{14}{3}$

111. *Verbal Model:* $\boxed{\dfrac{\text{Silo's height}}{\text{Silo's shadow}}} = \boxed{\dfrac{\text{Your height}}{\text{Your shadow}}}$

Proportion: $\dfrac{x}{20} = \dfrac{6}{1\frac{1}{2}}$

$x = \dfrac{120}{1\frac{1}{2}}$

$x = 80$ feet

113. *Verbal Model:* $\boxed{\text{Increase}} = \boxed{\text{Percent}} \cdot \boxed{\text{Base number}}$

Labels: Increase $= x$

Percent $= 5\frac{1}{2}\%$

Base number $= 25{,}750$

Equation: $x = 0.055 \cdot 25{,}750$

$x = \$1416.25$

Verbal Model: $\boxed{\text{New model}} = \boxed{\text{Old price}} + \boxed{\text{Increase}}$

Labels: New model $= x$

Old price $= 25{,}750$

Increase $= 1416.25$

Equation: $x = 25{,}750 + 1416.25$

$x = \$27{,}166.25$

115. *Verbal Model:* $\boxed{\text{Markup}} = \boxed{\text{Selling price}} - \boxed{\text{Cost}}$

Labels: Markup $= x$

Selling price $= 175.00$

Cost $= 95.00$

Equation: $x = 175.00 - 95.00$

$x = \$80.00$

Verbal Model: $\boxed{\text{Markup}} = \boxed{\text{Markup rate}} \cdot \boxed{\text{Cost}}$

Labels: Markup $= 80.00$

Markup rate $= x$

Cost $= 95.00$

Equation: $80.00 = x \cdot 95.00$

$\dfrac{80.00}{95.00} = x$

$84.21\% = x$

117. *Verbal Model:* $\boxed{\text{Total price}} = \boxed{\text{List price}} + \boxed{\text{Shipping}}$

Labels: Total price $= x$

List price $= 99.97$

Shipping $= 4.50$

Equation: $x = 99.97 + 4.50$

$x = \$104.47$

Verbal Model: $\boxed{\text{Discount}} = \boxed{\text{Discount rate}} \cdot \boxed{\text{List price}}$

Labels: Discount $= x$

Discount rate $= 20\%$

List price $= 125.95$

Equation: $x = 0.20 \cdot 125.95$

$x = \$25.19$

Verbal Model: $\boxed{\text{Sale price}} = \boxed{\text{List price}} - \boxed{\text{Discount}}$

Labels: Sale price $= x$

List price $= 125.95$

Discount $= 25.19$

Equation: $x = 125.95 - 25.19$

$x = \$100.76$

The department store price is the better buy.

119. *Verbal Model:* $\boxed{\text{Amount of solution 1}} + \boxed{\text{Amount of solution 2}} = \boxed{\text{Amount of final solution}}$

Labels: Percent of solution 1 $= 30\%$

Liters of solution 1 $= x$

Percent of solution 2 $= 60\%$

Liters of solution 2 $= 10 - x$

Percent of final solution $= 50\%$

Liters of final solution $= 10$

Equation: $0.30x + 0.60(10 - x) = 0.50(10)$

$0.30x + 6 - 0.60x = 5$

$-0.30x = -1$

$x = 3\frac{1}{3}$ liters of 30% solution

$10 - x = 6\frac{2}{3}$ liters of 60% solution

121. *Verbal Model:* $\boxed{\text{Distance}} = \boxed{\text{Rate}} \cdot \boxed{\text{Time}}$

Labels: Distance $= d$

Rate $= 1200$ mph

Time $= 2\frac{1}{3}$ hours

Equation: $d = 1200 \cdot 2\frac{1}{3}$

$d = 2800$ miles

123. *Verbal Model:* $\boxed{\text{Distance}} = \boxed{\text{Rate}} \cdot \boxed{\text{Time}}$

Labels: Distance = 100 miles

Rates = 48 mph and 40 mph

Time = t

Equation: $d = rt$

$t = \dfrac{d}{r}$

$t = \dfrac{100}{48} + \dfrac{100}{40}$

$t = 4.58\overline{3}$ or $\dfrac{55}{12}$

Verbal Model: $\boxed{\begin{array}{c}\text{Average}\\\text{speed}\end{array}} = \boxed{\begin{array}{c}\text{Total}\\\text{distance}\end{array}} \div \boxed{\begin{array}{c}\text{Total}\\\text{time}\end{array}}$

Labels: Average speed = r

Total distance = 200 miles

Total time = $4.58\overline{3}$ hours

Equation: $r = 200 \div 4.58\overline{3}$

$r \approx 43.6$ mph

125. *Verbal Model:* $\boxed{\begin{array}{c}\text{Work}\\\text{done}\end{array}} = \boxed{\begin{array}{c}\text{Work done}\\\text{by person 1}\end{array}} + \boxed{\begin{array}{c}\text{Work done}\\\text{by person 2}\end{array}}$

Labels: Work done = 1

Rate of person 1 = $\dfrac{1}{4.5}$

Rate of person 2 = $\dfrac{1}{6}$

Time = t

Equation: $1 = \dfrac{1}{4.5}(t) + \dfrac{1}{6}(t)$

$27 = 6t + 4.5t$

$27 = 10.5t$

$\dfrac{27}{10.5} = t$

2.57 hours = t

127. *Verbal Model:* $\boxed{\text{Interest}} = \boxed{\text{Principal}} \cdot \boxed{\text{Rate}} \cdot \boxed{\text{Time}}$

Labels: Interest = i

Principal = $1000

Rate = 8.5%

Time = 4

Equation: $i = 1000 \cdot 0.085 \cdot 4$

$i = \$340$

129. *Verbal Model:* $\boxed{\text{Interest}} = \boxed{\text{Principal}} \cdot \boxed{\text{Rate}} \cdot \boxed{\text{Time}}$

Labels: Interest = $20,000

Principal = p

Rate = 9.5%

Time = 1

Equation: $20,000 = p \cdot 0.095 \cdot 1$

$\dfrac{20,000}{0.095} = p$

$\$210,526.32 = p$

131. *Verbal Model:* $\boxed{\text{Interest}} = \boxed{\text{Principal}} \cdot \boxed{\text{Rate}} \cdot \boxed{\text{Time}}$

Labels: Interest = 4700

Principal 1 = p

Rate 1 = 8.5%

Principal 2 = $50,000 - p$

Rate 2 = 10%

Time = 1

Equation: $4700 = 0.085p + 0.10(50,000 - p)$

$4700 = 0.085p + 5000 - 0.10p$

$-300 = -0.015p$

$\dfrac{-300}{-0.015} = p$

$\$20,000 = p$

$\$30,000 = 50,000 - p$

133. *Verbal Model:* $\boxed{\text{Area}} = \boxed{\text{Length}} \cdot \boxed{\text{Width}}$

Labels: Area = 48

Length = x

Width = 6

Equation: $48 = x \cdot 6$

8 inches = x

135. *Verbal Model:* $50 \leq \boxed{\text{Perimeter}} \leq 100$

Label: $\text{Perimeter} = 2x + 2(23)$

Inequality: $50 \leq 2x + 2(23) \leq 100$

$$4 \leq 2x \leq 54$$

$$2 \leq x \leq 27$$

137. $|t - 78.3| < 38.3$

$$-38.3 < t - 78.3 < 38.3$$

$$40 < t < 116.6$$

Chapter Test for Chapter 1

1. $6x - 5 = 19$

$$6x - 5 + 5 = 19 + 5$$

$$6x = 24$$

$$\frac{6x}{6} = \frac{24}{6}$$

$$x = 4$$

2. $5x - 6 = 7x - 12$

$$5x - 7x - 6 = 7x - 7x - 12$$

$$-2x - 6 = -12$$

$$-2x - 6 + 6 = -12 + 6$$

$$-2x = -6$$

$$\frac{-2x}{-2} = \frac{-6}{-2}$$

$$x = 3$$

3. $15 - 7(1 - x) = 3(x + 8)$

$$15 - 7 + 7x = 3x + 24$$

$$8 + 7x = 3x + 24$$

$$8 + 7x - 3x = 3x + 24 - 3x$$

$$8 - 8 + 4x = 24 - 8$$

$$4x = 16$$

$$\frac{4x}{4} = \frac{16}{4}$$

$$x = 4$$

4. $\dfrac{2x}{3} = \dfrac{x}{2} + 4$

$$6\left(\frac{2x}{3}\right) = \left(\frac{x}{2} + 4\right)6$$

$$4x = 3x + 24$$

$$4x - 3x = 3x + 24 - 3x$$

$$x = 24$$

5. *Verbal Model:* $\boxed{\begin{array}{c}\text{Compared} \\ \text{number}\end{array}} = \boxed{\text{Percent}} \cdot \boxed{\begin{array}{c}\text{Base} \\ \text{number}\end{array}}$

Labels: Compared number $= a$

Percent $= p$

Base number $= b$

Equation: $a = p \cdot b$

$$x = 0.27 \cdot 3200$$

$$x = 864$$

6. *Verbal Model:* $\boxed{\begin{array}{c}\text{Compared} \\ \text{number}\end{array}} = \boxed{\text{Percent}} \cdot \boxed{\begin{array}{c}\text{Base} \\ \text{number}\end{array}}$

Labels: Compared number $= a$

Percent $= p$

Base number $= b$

Equation: $a = p \cdot b$

$$1200 = x \cdot 800$$

$$\frac{1200}{800} = x$$

$$1.5 = x$$

$$150\% = x$$

7. *Verbal Model:* $\boxed{\text{Sale price}} = \boxed{\text{Percent}} \cdot \boxed{\text{List price}}$

Labels: Sale price = 6400

Percent = 80%

List price = x

Equation: $6400 = 0.80 \cdot x$

$\dfrac{6400}{0.80} = x$

$\$8000 = x$

8. $\dfrac{\text{Total price}}{\text{Total units}} = \dfrac{2.49}{12} = \dfrac{249}{1200} = 0.2075$ per ounce

$\dfrac{\text{Total price}}{\text{Total units}} = \dfrac{2.99}{15} = \dfrac{299}{1500} = 0.199\overline{3}$ per ounce

The 15-ounce can is the better buy.

9. *Verbal Model:* $\dfrac{\boxed{\text{Tax}}}{\boxed{\text{Assessed value}}} = \dfrac{\boxed{\text{Tax}}}{\boxed{\text{Assessed value}}}$

Proportion: $\dfrac{1200}{90,000} = \dfrac{x}{110,000}$

$x = \dfrac{(1200)(110,000)}{90,000}$

$x \approx \$1466.67$

10. *Verbal Model:* $\boxed{\text{Total bill}} = \boxed{\text{Cost of parts}} + \boxed{\text{Cost of labor}}$

Labels: Total bill = 165

Cost of parts = 85

Number of hours of labor = x

Cost of labor = $6x$

Equation: $165 = 85 + 6x$

$80 = 16x$

5 half hours = x

$x = 2\tfrac{1}{2}$ hours

11. *Verbal Model:* $\boxed{\begin{array}{c}\text{Amount of}\\\text{solution 1}\end{array}} + \boxed{\begin{array}{c}\text{Amount of}\\\text{solution 2}\end{array}} = \boxed{\begin{array}{c}\text{Amount of}\\\text{final solution}\end{array}}$

Labels: Number of liters of solution 1 = x

Percent concentration of solution 1 = 10%

Number of liters of solution 2 = $100 - x$

Percent concentration of solution 2 = 40%

Number of liters of final solution = 100

Percent concentration of final solution = 30%

Equation: $0.10x + 0.40(100 - x) = 0.30(100)$

$0.10x + 40 - 0.40x = 30$

$-0.30x = -10$

$x = 33\tfrac{1}{3}$ liters at 10%

$100 - x = 66\tfrac{2}{3}$ liters at 40%

12. *Verbal Model:* $\boxed{\begin{array}{c}\text{Distance}\\\text{of car 1}\end{array}} + 10 \text{ miles} = \boxed{\begin{array}{c}\text{Distance}\\\text{of car 2}\end{array}}$

Labels: Time = x

Distance of car 1 = $40x$

Distance of car 2 = $55x$

Equation: $40x + 10 = 55x$

$10 = 15x$

$\tfrac{10}{15} = x$

$\tfrac{2}{3}$ hour or 40 minutes = x

13. *Verbal Model:* $\boxed{\text{Interest}} = \boxed{\text{Principal}} \cdot \boxed{\text{Rate}} \cdot \boxed{\text{Time}}$

Labels: Interest $= 300$

Principal $= p$

Rate $= 7.5\%$

Time $= 2$

Equation: $300 = p \cdot 0.075 \cdot 2$

$\$2000 = p$

14. (a) $|2x + 6| = 16$

$2x + 6 = 16$ or $2x + 6 = -16$

$2x = 10$ $2x = -22$

$x = 5$ $x = -11$

(b) $|3x - 5| = |6x - 1|$

$3x - 5 = 6x - 1$ or $3x - 5 = -(6x - 1)$

$-3x - 5 = -1$ $3x - 5 = -6x + 1$

$-3x = 4$ $9x - 5 = 1$

$x = -\frac{4}{3}$ $9x = 6$

$x = \frac{6}{9} = \frac{2}{3}$

(c) $|9 - 4x| - 10 = 1$

$|9 - 4x| = 11$

$9 - 4x = 11$ or $9 - 4x = -11$

$-4x = 2$ $-4x = -20$

$x = -\frac{2}{4}$ $x = 5$

$x = -\frac{1}{2}$

15. (a) $3x + 12 \geq -6$

$3x + 12 - 12 \geq -6 - 12$

$3x \geq -18$

$x \geq -6$

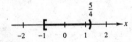

(b) $1 + 2x > 7 - x$

$3x > 6$

$x > 2$

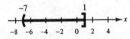

(c) $0 \leq \dfrac{1 - x}{4} < 2$

$0 \leq 1 - x < 8$

$-1 \leq -x < 7$

$1 \geq x > -7$

(d) $-7 < 4(2 - 3x) \leq 20$

$-7 < 8 - 12x \leq 20$

$-15 < -12x \leq 12$

$\dfrac{15}{12} > x \geq -1$

$-1 \leq x < \dfrac{5}{4}$

16. (a) $|x - 3| \le 2$

$-2 \le x - 3 \le 2$

$1 \le x \le 5$

(b) $|5x - 3| > 12$

$5x - 3 > 12$ or $5x - 3 < -12$

$5x > 15 \qquad 5x < -9$

$x > 3 \qquad x < -\dfrac{9}{5}$

(c) $\left|\dfrac{x}{4} + 2\right| < 0.2$

$-0.2 < \dfrac{x}{4} + 2 < 0.2$

$-0.8 < x + 8 < 0.8$

$-8.8 < x < -7.2$

$-\dfrac{44}{5} < x < -\dfrac{36}{5}$

17. $t \ge 8$ denotes the phrase "t is at least 8."

18. *Verbal Model:* $\boxed{\begin{array}{l}\text{Operating} \\ \text{cost}\end{array}} \le 11{,}950$

Label: Number of miles $= m$

Equation: $0.37m + 2700 \le 11{,}950$

$0.37m \le 9250$

$m \le 25{,}000$ miles

CHAPTER 2
Graphs and Functions

CHAPTER 2
Graphs and Functions

Section 2.1   The Rectangular Coordinate System
Solutions to Odd-Numbered Exercises

1.

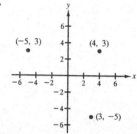

$(4, 3)$ is 4 units to the right of the vertical axis and 3 units above the horizontal axis.

$(-5, 3)$ is 5 units to the left of the vertical axis and 3 units above the horizontal axis.

$(3, -5)$ is 3 units to the right of the vertical axis and 5 units below the horizontal axis.

3.

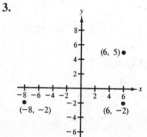

$(-8, -2)$ is 8 units to the left of the vertical axis and 2 units below the horizontal axis.

$(6, -2)$ is 6 units to the right of the vertical axis and 2 units below the horizontal axis.

$(6, 5)$ is 6 units to the right of the vertical axis and 5 units above the horizontal axis.

5.

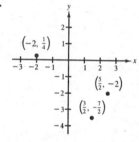

$\left(\frac{5}{2}, -2\right)$ is $\frac{5}{2}$ units to the right of the vertical axis and 2 units below the horizontal axis.

$\left(-2, \frac{1}{4}\right)$ is 2 units to the left of the vertical axis and $\frac{1}{4}$ units above the horizontal axis.

$\left(\frac{3}{2}, -\frac{7}{2}\right)$ is $\frac{3}{2}$ units to the right of the vertical axis and $\frac{7}{2}$ units below the horizontal axis.

7.

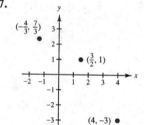

$\left(\frac{3}{2}, 1\right)$ is $\frac{3}{2}$ units to the right of the vertical axis and 1 unit above the horizontal axis.

$(4, -3)$ is 4 units to the right of the vertical axis and 3 units below the horizontal axis.

$\left(-\frac{4}{3}, \frac{7}{3}\right)$ is $\frac{4}{3}$ units to the left of the vertical axis and $\frac{7}{3}$ units above the horizontal axis.

9.

Point	Position	Coordinates
A	2 left, 4 up	$(-2, 4)$
B	0 right or left, 2 down	$(0, -2)$
C	4 right, 2 down	$(4, -2)$

11.

Point	Position	Coordinates
A	4 right, 2 down	$(4, -2)$
B	3 left, $\frac{5}{2}$ down	$\left(-3, -\frac{5}{2}\right)$
C	3 right, $\frac{1}{2}$ up	$\left(3, \frac{1}{2}\right)$

13.

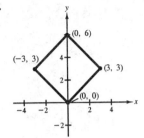

15.

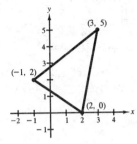

17.

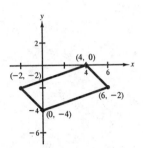

19.

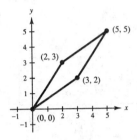

21. Point 5 units left of y-axis and 2 units above x-axis = $(-5, 2)$

23. Point 3 units right of y-axis and 2 units below x-axis = $(3, -2)$

25. The coordinates of the point are equal and located in Quadrant III, 10 units left of y-axis = $(-10, -10)$.

27. Point on positive x-axis 10 units from the origin = $(10, 0)$.

29. $(-3, -5)$ is in Quadrant III.

31. $\left(3, -\frac{5}{8}\right)$ is in Quadrant IV.

33. $(200, 1365.6)$ is in Quadrant I.

35. $(x, y), x > 0, y < 0$ is in Quadrant IV.

37. $(x, 4)$ is in Quadrants I or II.

39. $(-3, y)$ is in Quadrants II or III.

41. $(x, y), xy > 0$ is in Quadrants I or III.

43.

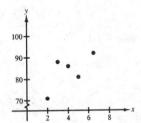

45.

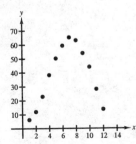

The relationship between x and y is as x increases from 1 to 7, y also increases, but as x increases from 7 to 12, y decreases.

47. $(-2, -1)$ shifted 2 units right and 5 units up = $(0, 4)$

$(-3, -4)$ shifted 2 units right and 5 units up = $(-1, 1)$

$(1, -3)$ shifted 2 units right and 5 units up = $(3, 2)$

49.

x	-2	0	2	4	6
$y = 5x - 1$	-11	-1	9	19	29

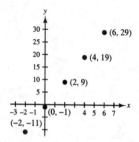

51.

x	-4	$\frac{2}{5}$	4	8	12
$y = -\frac{5}{2}x + 4$	14	3	-6	-16	-26

$y = \dfrac{-5}{2}(-4) + 4$

$= 10 + 4$

$= 14$

$y = \dfrac{-5}{2}\left(\dfrac{2}{5}\right) + 4$

$= -1 + 4$

$= 3$

$y = \dfrac{-5}{2}(4) + 4$

$= -10 + 4$

$= -6$

$y = \dfrac{-5}{2}(8) + 4$

$= -20 + 4$

$= -16$

$y = \dfrac{-5}{2}(12) + 4$

$= -30 + 4$

$= -26$

53.

x	-2	0	2	4	6
$y = 4x^2 + x - 2$	12	-2	16	66	148

Keystrokes: [Y=] 4 [X,T,θ] [x^2] [+] [X,T,θ] [−] 2 [GRAPH]

55. $x^2 + 3y = -5$

(a) $(3, -2)$

$3^2 + 3(-2) \overset{?}{=} -5$

$9 - 6 \overset{?}{=} -5$

$3 \neq -5$

Not a solution

(b) $(-2, -3)$

$(-2)^2 + 3(-3) \overset{?}{=} -5$

$4 - 9 \overset{?}{=} -5$

$-5 = -5$

Solution

(c) $(3, -5)$

$3^2 + 3(-5) \overset{?}{=} -5$

$9 - 15 \overset{?}{=} -5$

$-6 \neq -5$

Not a solution

(d) $(4, -7)$

$4^2 + 3(-7) \overset{?}{=} -5$

$16 - 21 \overset{?}{=} -5$

$-5 = -5$

Solution

57. $4y - 2x + 1 = 0$

(a) $(0, 0)$

$$4(0) - 2(0) + 1 \overset{?}{=} 0$$

$$1 \neq 0$$

Not a solution

(b) $\left(\frac{1}{2}, 0\right)$

$$4(0) - 2\left(\frac{1}{2}\right) + 1 \overset{?}{=} 0$$

$$0 - 1 + 1 \overset{?}{=} 0$$

$$0 = 0$$

Solution

(c) $\left(-3, -\frac{7}{4}\right)$

$$4\left(-\frac{7}{4}\right) - 2(-3) + 1 \overset{?}{=} 0$$

$$-7 + 6 + 1 \overset{?}{=} 0$$

$$0 = 0$$

Solution

(d) $\left(1, -\frac{3}{4}\right)$

$$4\left(-\frac{3}{4}\right) - 2(1) + 1 \overset{?}{=} 0$$

$$-3 - 2 + 1 \overset{?}{=} 0$$

$$-4 \neq 0$$

Not a solution

59. $y = \frac{7}{8}x + 3$

(a) $\left(\frac{8}{7}, 4\right)$

$$4 \overset{?}{=} \frac{7}{8}\left(\frac{8}{7}\right) + 3$$

$$4 \overset{?}{=} 1 + 3$$

$$4 = 4$$

Solution

(b) $(8, 10)$

$$10 \overset{?}{=} \frac{7}{8}(8) + 3$$

$$10 \overset{?}{=} 7 + 3$$

$$10 = 10$$

Solution

(c) $(0, 0)$

$$0 \overset{?}{=} \frac{7}{8}(0) + 3$$

$$0 \overset{?}{=} 0 + 3$$

$$0 \neq 3$$

Not a solution

(d) $(-16, 14)$

$$14 \overset{?}{=} \frac{7}{8}(-16) + 3$$

$$14 \overset{?}{=} -14 + 3$$

$$14 \neq -11$$

Not a solution

61. $d = |5 - (-2)|$

$$= |7|$$

$$= 7$$

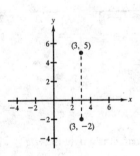

Vertical line

63. $d = |10 - 3|$

$$= |7|$$

$$= 7$$

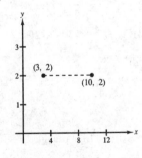

Horizontal line

65. $d = \left| \frac{3}{2} - \frac{9}{4} \right|$

$\qquad = \left| \frac{6}{4} - \frac{9}{4} \right|$

$\qquad = \frac{3}{4}$

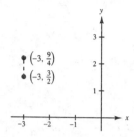

Vertical line

67. $d = \left| \frac{5}{2} - (-4) \right|$

$\qquad = \left| \frac{5}{2} + \frac{8}{2} \right|$

$\qquad = \left| \frac{13}{2} \right|$

$\qquad = \frac{13}{2}$

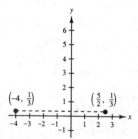

Horizontal line

69. $d = \sqrt{(3 - 4)^2 + (7 - 5)^2}$

$\qquad = \sqrt{(-1)^2 + (2)^2} = \sqrt{1 + 4} = \sqrt{5}$

71. $d = \sqrt{(1 - 5)^2 + (3 - 6)^2}$

$\qquad = \sqrt{16 + 9} = \sqrt{25} = 5$

73. $d = \sqrt{(-3 - 4)^2 + [0 - (-3)]^2}$

$\qquad = \sqrt{(-7)^2 + (3)^2} = \sqrt{49 + 9} = \sqrt{58}$

75. $d = \sqrt{(-2 - 4)^2 + (-3 - 2)^2}$

$\qquad = \sqrt{36 + 25} = \sqrt{61}$

77. $d = \sqrt{(1 - 3)^2 + [3 - (-2)]^2} = \sqrt{4 + 25} = \sqrt{29}$

79.

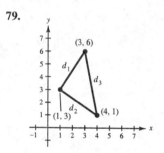

$d_1 = \sqrt{(1 - 3)^2 + (3 - 6)^2} = \sqrt{4 + 9} = \sqrt{13}$

$d_2 = \sqrt{(1 - 4)^2 + (3 - 1)^2} = \sqrt{9 + 4} = \sqrt{13}$

$d_3 = \sqrt{(3 - 4)^2 + (6 - 1)^2} = \sqrt{1 + 25} = \sqrt{26}$

$\left(\sqrt{13} \right)^2 + \left(\sqrt{13} \right)^2 \stackrel{?}{=} \left(\sqrt{26} \right)^2$

$13 + 13 \stackrel{?}{=} 26$

$26 = 26$

By the Pythagorean Theorem, it is a right triangle.

81.

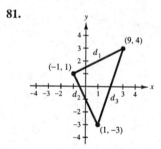

$d_1 = \sqrt{(-1 - 3)^2 + (1 - 3)^2} = \sqrt{16 + 4} = \sqrt{20}$

$d_2 = \sqrt{(-1 - 1)^2 + [1 - (-3)]^2} = \sqrt{4 + 16} = \sqrt{20}$

$d_3 = \sqrt{(1 - 3)^2 + (-3 - 3)^2} = \sqrt{4 + 36} = \sqrt{40}$

$\left(\sqrt{20} \right)^2 + \left(\sqrt{20} \right)^2 \stackrel{?}{=} \left(\sqrt{40} \right)^2$

$20 + 20 \stackrel{?}{=} 40$

$40 = 40$

By the Pythagorean Theorem, it is a right triangle.

83. $d = \sqrt{(2-2)^2 + (3-6)^2} = \sqrt{0+9} = 3$ $3 + 4 \neq 5$ Not collinear

$d = \sqrt{(2-6)^2 + (3-3)^2} = \sqrt{16+0} = 4$

$d = \sqrt{(2-6)^2 + (6-3)^2} = \sqrt{16+9} = 5$

85. $d = \sqrt{(8-5)^2 + (3-2)^2} = \sqrt{9+1} = \sqrt{10}$ $\sqrt{10} + \sqrt{10} = 2\sqrt{10}$ Collinear

$d = \sqrt{(8-2)^2 + (3-1)^2} = \sqrt{36+4} = \sqrt{40} = 2\sqrt{10}$

$d = \sqrt{(5-2)^2 + (2-1)^2} = \sqrt{9+1} = \sqrt{10}$

87. $M = \left(\dfrac{-2+4}{2}, \dfrac{0+8}{2}\right) = (1, 4)$ **89.** $M = \left(\dfrac{1+6}{2}, \dfrac{6+3}{2}\right) = \left(\dfrac{7}{2}, \dfrac{9}{2}\right)$

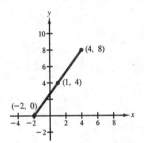   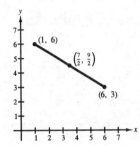

91.

x	100	150	200	250	300
$c = 28x + 3000$	5800	7200	8600	10,000	11,400

$y = 28(100) + 3000$ $y = 28(150) + 3000$ $y = 28(200) + 3000$

$\quad = 2800 + 3000$ $\quad = 4200 + 3000$ $\quad = 5600 + 3000$

$\quad = 5800$ $\quad = 7200$ $\quad = 8600$

$y = 28(250) + 3000$ $y = 28(300) + 3000$

$\quad = 7000 + 3000$ $\quad = 8400 + 3000$

$\quad = 10,000$ $\quad = 11,400$

For each additional 50 units produced, costs increase by $1400.

93. $x^2 = 7^2 + 15^2$ **95.** $d = \sqrt{(-2-0)^2 + (0-5)^2} = \sqrt{4+25} = \sqrt{29}$

$x^2 = 49 + 225$ $d = \sqrt{(0-1)^2 + (5-0)^2} = \sqrt{1+25} = \sqrt{26}$

$x = \sqrt{274} \approx 16.55294536$ $d = \sqrt{(-2-1)^2 + (0-0)^2} = \sqrt{9} = 3$

Rafter $= 2 + x \approx 18.55294536 \approx 18.55$ feet $P = \sqrt{29} + \sqrt{26} + 3 \approx 13.48$

97. The word *ordered* is significant because each number in the pair has a particular interpretation. The first measures horizontal distance and the second measures vertical distance.

99. The x-coordinate of any point on the y-axis is 0.

The y-coordinate of any point on the x-axis is 0.

101. No. The scales on the x and y-axes are determined by the magnitudes of the quantities being measured by x and y.

103.

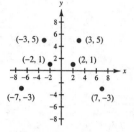

When the sign of the x-coordinate is changed, the point is on the opposite side of the y-axis as the original point.

Section 2.2   Graphs of Equations

1. $y = 2$ matches graph (e).

3. $y = 2 - x$ matched graph (f)

5. $y = x^2 - 4$ matches graph (d).

7.

x	-2	-1	0	1	2
$y = 3x$	-6	-3	0	3	6
Solution	$(-2, -6)$	$(-1, -3)$	$(0, 0)$	$(1, 3)$	$(2, 6)$

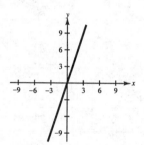

9.

x	-2	-1	0	1	2
$y = 4 - x$	6	5	4	3	2
Solution	$(-2, 6)$	$(-1, 5)$	$(0, 4)$	$(1, 3)$	$(2, 2)$

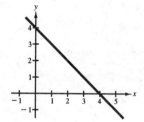

11.

x	-2	-1	0	1	2
$y = 2x - 3$	-7	-5	-3	-1	1
Solution	$(-2, -7)$	$(-1, -5)$	$(0, -3)$	$(1, -1)$	$(2, 1)$

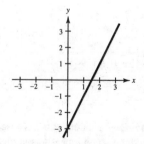

13.

x	-2	-1	0	1	2
$y = -\frac{3}{2}x + 1$	4	$\frac{5}{2}$	1	$-\frac{1}{2}$	-2
Solution	$(-2, 4)$	$\left(-1, \frac{5}{2}\right)$	$(0, 1)$	$\left(1, -\frac{1}{2}\right)$	$(2, -2)$

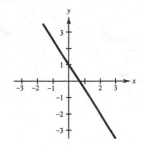

15.

x	-2	-1	0	1	2
$y = -x^2$	-4	-1	0	-1	-4
Solution	$(-2, -4)$	$(-1, -1)$	$(0, 0)$	$(1, -1)$	$(2, -4)$

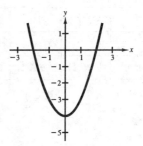

17.

x	-2	-1	0	1	2
$y = x^2 - 4$	0	-3	-4	-3	0
Solution	$(-2, 0)$	$(-1, -3)$	$(0, -4)$	$(1, -3)$	$(2, 0)$

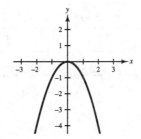

19.

x	-2	-1	0	1	2
$y = x^2 + 3x$	-2	-2	0	4	10
Solution	$(-2, -2)$	$(-1, -2)$	$(0, 0)$	$(1, 4)$	$(2, 10)$

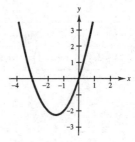

21.

x	-2	-1	0	1	2
$y = x^2 - 2x - 1$	7	2	-1	-2	-1
Solution	$(-2, 7)$	$(-1, 2)$	$(0, -1)$	$(1, -2)$	$(2, -1)$

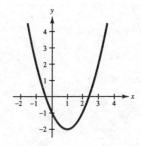

23.

x	-2	-1	0	1	2
$y = \lvert x \rvert$	2	1	0	1	2
Solution	$(-2, 2)$	$(-1, 1)$	$(0, 0)$	$(1, 1)$	$(2, 2)$

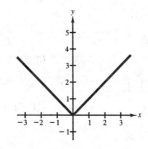

25.

x	-2	-1	0	1	2
$y = \lvert x \rvert + 3$	5	4	3	4	5
Solution	$(-2, 5)$	$(-1, 4)$	$(0, 3)$	$(1, 4)$	$(2, 5)$

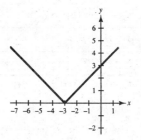

27.

x	-2	-1	0	1	2
$y = \lvert x + 3 \rvert$	1	2	3	4	5
Solution	$(-2, 1)$	$(-1, 2)$	$(0, 3)$	$(1, 4)$	$(2, 5)$

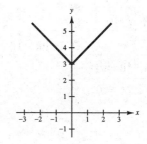

29.

x	-2	-1	0	1	2
$y = -x^3$	8	1	0	-1	-8
Solution	$(-2, 8)$	$(-1, 1)$	$(0, 0)$	$(1, -1)$	$(2, -8)$

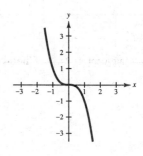

31. $y = 6x - 3$

     y-intercept: $y = 6(0) - 3$

                 $y = -3$ $(0, -3)$

     x-intercept: $0 = 6x - 3$

                 $3 = 6x$

                 $\frac{3}{6} = x$

                 $\frac{1}{2} = x$ $\left(\frac{1}{2}, 0\right)$

33. $y = \frac{3}{4}x + 15$

     y-intercept: $y = \frac{3}{4}(0) + 15$

                 $y = 15$ $(0, 15)$

     x-intercept: $0 = \frac{3}{4}x + 15$

                 $-15 = \frac{3}{4}x$

                 $-20 = x$ $(-20, 0)$

35. $x + 2y = 10$

y-intercept: $0 + 2y = 0$

$\qquad\qquad y = 5 \qquad (0, 5)$

x-intercept: $x + 2(0) = 10$

$\qquad\qquad x = 10 \quad (10, 0)$

37. $4x - y + 3 = 0$

y-intercept: $4(0) - y + 3 = 0$

$\qquad\qquad\qquad 3 = y \qquad (0, 3)$

x-intercept: $4x - 0 + 3 = 0$

$\qquad\qquad\qquad 4x = -3$

$\qquad\qquad\qquad x = -\frac{3}{4} \qquad \left(-\frac{3}{4}, 0\right)$

39. $y = |x| - 1$

y-intercept: $y = |0| - 1$

$\qquad\qquad y = -1 \qquad (0, -1)$

x-intercept: $0 = |x| - 1$

$\qquad\qquad 1 = |x|$

$\qquad\qquad \pm 1 = x \qquad (1, 0), (-1, 0)$

41. $y = |x + 2|$

y-intercept: $y = |0 + 2|$

$\qquad\qquad y = 2 \qquad (0, 2)$

x-intercept: $0 = |x + 2|$

$\qquad\qquad 0 = x + 2$

$\qquad\qquad -2 = x \qquad (-2, 0)$

43. $y = |x - 1| - 3$

y-intercept: $y = |0 - 1| - 3$

$\qquad\qquad y = 1 - 3$

$\qquad\qquad y = -2 \qquad\qquad (0, -2)$

x-intercept: $0 = |x - 1| - 3$

$\qquad\qquad 3 = |x - 1|$

$\qquad\qquad 3 = x - 1 \text{ or } -3 = x - 1$

$\qquad\qquad 4 = x \qquad -2 = x \qquad (4, 0), (-2, 0)$

45. $2x + 3y = 6$

Estimate: y-intercept ≈ 2 **Check:** $2(0) + 3y = 6$

$\qquad\qquad x$-intercept ≈ 3 $\qquad\qquad\qquad 3y = 6$

$\qquad\qquad\qquad\qquad\qquad\qquad\qquad y = 2 \qquad (0, 2)$

$\qquad\qquad\qquad\qquad\qquad 2x + 3(0) = 6$

$\qquad\qquad\qquad\qquad\qquad\qquad 2x = 6$

$\qquad\qquad\qquad\qquad\qquad\qquad x = 3 \qquad (3, 0)$

47. $y = x^2 + 3$

Estimate: y-intercept ≈ 3 **Check:** $\quad y = 0^2 + 3 = 3 \quad (0, 3)$

$\qquad\qquad$ no x-intercepts $\qquad\qquad 0 = x^2 + 3$

$\qquad\qquad\qquad\qquad\qquad\qquad -3 = x^2 \qquad\qquad$ no real solution

49. $y = 4x - 6$

Keystrokes: [Y=] 4 [X,T,θ] [−] 6 [GRAPH]

Estimate: y-intercept ≈ -6

x-intercept $\approx \frac{3}{2}$

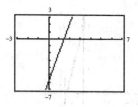

Check: $y = 4(0) - 6$

$y = -6$ $(0, -6)$

Check: $0 = 4x - 6$

$6 = 4x$

$\frac{6}{4} = x$

$\frac{3}{2} = x$ $\left(\frac{3}{2}, 0\right)$

51. $y = (x - 1)(x - 6)$

Keystrokes: [Y=] [(] [X,T,θ] [−] 1 [)] [(] [X,T,θ] [−] 6 [)] [GRAPH]

Estimate: y-intercept ≈ 6

x-intercepts $\approx 1, 6$

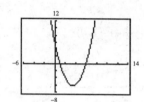

Check: $y = (0 - 1)(0 - 6)$

$y = 6$ $(0, 6)$

Check: $0 = (x - 1)(x - 6)$

$x = 1 \quad x = 6$ $(1, 0), (6, 0)$

53. $y = |4x + 6| - 2$

Keystrokes: [Y=] [ABS] [(] 4 [X,T,θ] [+] 6 [)] [−] 2 [GRAPH]

Estimate: y-intercept ≈ 4

x-intercepts $\approx -1, -2$

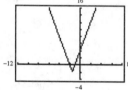

Check: $y = |4(0) + 6| - 2$

$y = 6 - 2$

$y = 4$ $(0, 4)$

Check: $0 = |4x + 6| - 2$

$2 = |4x + 6|$

$2 = 4x + 6$ or $4x + 6 = -2$

$-4 = 4x$ $4x = -8$

$-1 = x$ $x = -2$

$(-1, 0), (-2, 0)$

55. $y = 3 - 0$

$y = 3 \ (0, 3)$

$0 = 3 - x$

$x = 3$ $(3, 0)$

$y = 3 - 1$

$y = 2$ $(1, 2)$

57. $y = 2(0) - 3$

$y = -3$ $(0, -3)$

$0 = 2x - 3$

$3 = 2x$

$\frac{3}{2} = x$ $\left(\frac{3}{2}, 0\right)$

$y = 2(3) - 3$

$y = 3$ $(3, 3)$

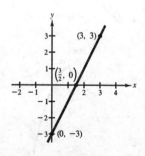

59. $4x + y = 3$

$4(0) + y = 3$

$y = 3 \quad (0, 3)$

$4x + 0 = 3$

$4x = 3$

$x = \frac{3}{4} \quad \left(\frac{3}{4}, 0\right)$

$4(1) + y = 3$

$y = -1 \ (1, -1)$

61. $2x - 3y = 6$

$2(0) - 3y = 6$

$-3y = 6$

$y = -2 \ (0, -2)$

$2x - 3(0) = 6$

$2x = 6$

$x = 3 \quad (3, 0)$

$2(1) - 3y = 6$

$-3y = 4$

$y = -\frac{4}{3} \ \left(1, -\frac{4}{3}\right)$

63. $x + 5y = 10$

$0 + 5y = 10$

$y = 2 \quad (0, 2)$

$x + 5(0) = 10$

$x = 10 \ (10, 0)$

$5 + 5y = 10$

$5y = 5$

$y = 1 \quad (5, 1)$

65. $y = x^2 - 9$

$0 = x^2 - 9$

$0 = (x - 3)(x + 3)$

$3 = x \ x = -3 \qquad (3, 0)(-3, 0)$

$y = 0^2 - 9$

$y = -9 \qquad (0, -9)$

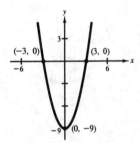

67. $y = 1 - x^2$

$y = 1 - 0$

$y = 1 \qquad (0, 1)$

$y = 1 - (1)^2$

$y = 1 - 1$

$y = 0 \qquad (1, 0)$

$y = 1 - (-1)^2$

$y = 1 - 1$

$y = 0 \qquad (-1, 0)$

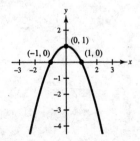

69. $y = x(x - 2)$

$y = 0^2 - 2(0)$

$y = 0 \qquad (0, 0)$

$0 = x^2 - 2x$

$0 = x(x - 2)$

$0 = x \ x = 2 \qquad (0, 0), (2, 0)$

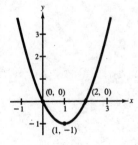

71. $y = |x| - 3$

$y = -3$ $(0, -3)$

$0 = |x| - 3$

$3 = |x|$

$3 = x \quad x = -3$ $(3, 0), (-3, 0)$

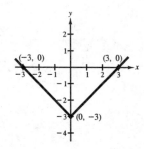

73. $y = |x + 2|$

$= 2$ $(0, 2)$

$y = |-2 + 2|$

$= 0$ $(-2, 0)$

$y = |-4 + 2|$

$= 2$ $(-4, 2)$

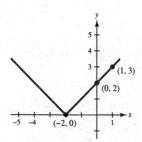

75. $y = -|x| + |x + 1|$

$y = -|0| + |0 + 1|$

$y = 1$ $(0, 1)$

$0 = -|x| + |x + 1|$

$|x| = |x + 1|$

$x = x + 1 \qquad$ or $\qquad -x = x + 1$

$0 \neq 1 \qquad\qquad\qquad -2x = 1$

$\qquad\qquad\qquad\qquad\quad x = -\tfrac{1}{2} \quad \left(-\tfrac{1}{2}, 0\right)$

$y = -|3| + |3 + 1|$

$y = -3 + 4$

$y = 1$ $(3, 1)$

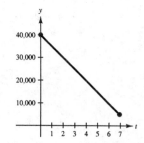

77. $y = 225{,}000 - 20{,}000t$

$y = 225{,}000 - 20{,}000(0)$

$= 225{,}000$ $(0, 225{,}000)$

$y = 225{,}000 - 20{,}000(8)$

$= 225{,}000 - 160{,}000$

$= 65{,}000$ $(8, 65{,}000)$

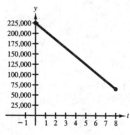

79. $0 \le x \le 7$

$(0, 40{,}000), (7, 5000)$

$m = \dfrac{40{,}000 - 5{,}000}{0 - 7} = \dfrac{35{,}000}{-7} = -5000$

$y = -5000x + 40{,}000$

81. (a)

x	0	3	6	9	12
$\frac{4}{3}x$	0	4	8	12	16

(b)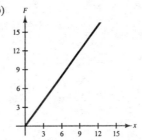

(c) F doubles.

83. The scales on the y-axes are different. From graph (a) it appears that sales have not increased. From graph (b) it appears that sales have increased dramatically.

85. The graph of an equation is the set of all solutions of the equation plotted on a rectangular coordinate system.

87. To find the x-intercepts, let $y = 0$ and solve the equation for x. To find the y-intercepts, let $x = 0$ and solve the equation for y.

Example: $2x - y = 4$

$$2x - 0 = 4 \qquad\qquad 2(0) - y = 4$$
$$2x = 4 \qquad\qquad\qquad -y = 4$$
$$x = 2 \ \ (2, 0) \qquad\qquad y = -4 \ \ (0, -4)$$
$$x\text{-intercept} \qquad\qquad y\text{-intercept}$$

89. (a) It is 6 miles from the person's home.

(b) For time $4 < t < 6$ the person is stopped since the graph is a constant line.

(c) The person's speed was greatest during $6 \leq t \leq 10$ because the graph is steepest there.

Section 2.3   Slope and Graphs of Linear Equations

1. $(0, 2)$ and $(6, 6)$

$$m = \frac{6 - 2}{6 - 0} = \frac{4}{6} = \frac{2}{3}$$

3. $(0, 8)$ and $(4, 0)$

$$m = \frac{0 - 8}{4 - 0} = \frac{-8}{4} = -2$$

5. $(3, 0)$ and $(3, 8)$

$$m = \frac{8 - 0}{3 - 3} = \frac{8}{0} = \text{undefined}$$

7. (a) $m = \frac{3}{4} \Longrightarrow L_3$ (b) $m = 0 \Longrightarrow L_2$

(c) $m = -3 \Longrightarrow L_1$

9. $m = \dfrac{5 - 0}{7 - 0} = \dfrac{5}{7}$ Line rises.

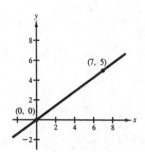

11. $m = \dfrac{-4 - 0}{5 - 0} = \dfrac{-4}{5}$ Line falls.

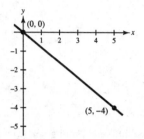

13. $m = \dfrac{3 - 5}{-4 - (-2)} = \dfrac{-2}{-2} = 1$ Line rises.

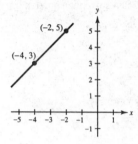

15. $m = \dfrac{4 - (-3)}{-5 - (-5)} = \dfrac{7}{0} =$ undefined

Line is vertical.

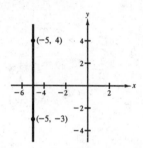

17. $m = \dfrac{-5 - (-5)}{7 - 2} = \dfrac{0}{5} = 0$ Line is horizontal.

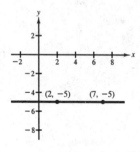

19. $m = \dfrac{2 - \dfrac{-5}{2}}{\dfrac{3}{4} - 5} \cdot \dfrac{4}{4} = \dfrac{8 + 10}{3 - 20} = \dfrac{18}{-17}$ Line falls.

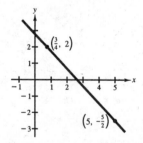

21. $m = \dfrac{\dfrac{1}{4} - \dfrac{1}{8}}{\dfrac{3}{4} - \dfrac{-3}{2}} \cdot \dfrac{8}{8} = \dfrac{2 - 1}{6 + 12} = \dfrac{1}{18}$ Line rises.

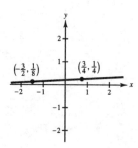

23. $m = \dfrac{5.25 - (-2)}{4.75 - 2.5} = \dfrac{7.25}{2.25} = \dfrac{725}{225} = \dfrac{29}{9}$ Line rises.

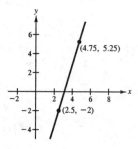

25.

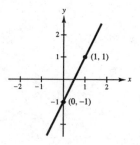

x	-1	0	1
$y = 2x - 1$	-3	-1	1
Solution	$(-1, -3)$	$(0, -1)$	$(1, 1)$

$m = \dfrac{1 - (-1)}{1 - 0} = \dfrac{2}{1} = 2$

27.

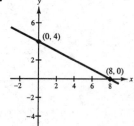

x	-1	0	1
$y = -\frac{1}{2}x + 4$	$\frac{9}{2}$	4	$\frac{7}{2}$
Solution	$\left(-1, \frac{9}{2}\right)$	$(0, 4)$	$\left(1, \frac{7}{2}\right)$

$m = \dfrac{\dfrac{7}{2} - 4}{1 - 0} = \dfrac{7}{2} - \dfrac{8}{2}$

$\quad = -\dfrac{1}{2}$

29.

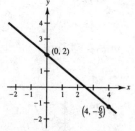

x	-1	0	1
$y = -\frac{4}{5}x + 10$	$\frac{14}{5}$	2	$\frac{6}{5}$
Solution	$\left(-1, \frac{14}{5}\right)$	$(0, 2)$	$\left(1, \frac{6}{5}\right)$

$4x + 5y = 10$

$5y = -4x + 10$

$y = -\dfrac{4}{5}x + 2$

$m = \dfrac{\dfrac{6}{5} - 2}{1 - 0} = \dfrac{6}{5} - \dfrac{10}{5}$

$\quad = -\dfrac{4}{5}$

31. $\dfrac{-2}{3} = \dfrac{7-5}{x-4}$

$-2(x-4) = 6$

$-2x + 8 = 6$

$-2x = -2$

$x = 1$

33. $\dfrac{3}{2} = \dfrac{3-y}{9-(-3)}$

$3(12) = 2(3-y)$

$36 = 6 - 2y$

$30 = -2y$

$-15 = y$

35. $0 = \dfrac{y-2}{x-5}$

Horizontal line: $(1, 2), (0, 2), (3, 2)$

Any points with a y-coordinate of 2

37. $3 = \dfrac{y+4}{x-3}$

$(4, -1), (5, 2)$

let $x = 4$, solve for y:

$3 = \dfrac{y+4}{4-3}$

$3 = y + 4$

$-1 = y$

let $x = 5$, solve for y:

$3 = \dfrac{y+4}{5-3}$

$6 = y + 4$

$2 = y$

39. $-1 = \dfrac{y-3}{x-0}$

$(1, 2), (2, 1)$

let $x = 1$, solve for y:

$-1 = \dfrac{y-3}{1-0}$

$-1 = y - 3$

$2 = y$

let $x = 2$, solve for y:

$-1 = \dfrac{y-3}{2-0}$

$-2 = y - 3$

$1 = y$

41. $\dfrac{4}{3} = \dfrac{y-0}{x+5}$

$(-2, 4), (1, 8)$

let $x = -2$, solve for y:

$\dfrac{4}{3} = \dfrac{y}{-2+5}$

$4 = y$

let $x = 1$, solve for y:

$\dfrac{4}{3} = \dfrac{y}{1+5}$

$8 = y$

43. $6x - 3y = 9$

$-3y = -6x + 9$

$\dfrac{-3y}{-3} = \dfrac{-6x}{-3} + \dfrac{9}{-3}$

$y = 2x - 3$

45. $4y - x = -4$

$4y = x - 4$

$\dfrac{4y}{4} = \dfrac{x}{4} - \dfrac{4}{4}$

$y = \dfrac{1}{4}x - 1$

47. $2x + 5y - 3 = 0$

$5y = -2x + 3$

$\dfrac{5y}{5} = \dfrac{-2x}{5} + \dfrac{3}{5}$

$y = \dfrac{-2}{5}x + \dfrac{3}{5}$

49. $y = \frac{1}{2}x + 2$

51. $y = 3x - 2$

$m = 3; (0, -2)$

53. $3y - 2x = 3$

$3y = 2x + 3$

$y = \frac{2}{3}x + 1$

$m = \frac{2}{3}; (0, 1)$

55. $5x + 3y - 2 = 0$

$3y = -5x + 2$

$y = \dfrac{-5}{3}x + \dfrac{2}{3}$

$m = \dfrac{-5}{3}; \left(0, \dfrac{2}{3}\right)$

57. $3x - y - 2 = 0$

$-y = -3x + 2$

$y = 3x - 2$

slope $= 3$

y-intercept $= -2$

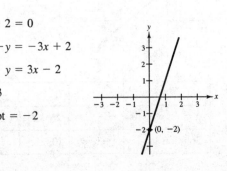

59. $x + y = 0$

$y = -x + 0$

slope $= -1$

y-intercept $= 0$

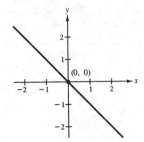

61. $3x + 2y - 2 = 0$

$2y = -3x + 2$

$y = \dfrac{-3}{2}x + 1$

slope $= \dfrac{-3}{2}$

y-intercept $= 1$

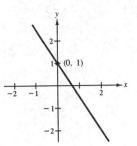

63. $x - 4y + 2 = 0$

$-4y = -x - 2$

$y = \dfrac{1}{4}x + \dfrac{1}{2}$

slope $= \dfrac{1}{4}$

y-intercept $= \dfrac{1}{2}$

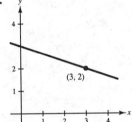

65.

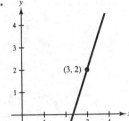

Locate a second point with the slope of 3.

$m = \dfrac{3}{1} = \dfrac{\text{Change in } y}{\text{Change in } x}$

67.

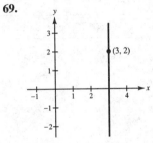

Locate a second point with the slope of $\dfrac{-1}{3}$.

$m = \dfrac{-1}{3} = \dfrac{\text{Change in } y}{\text{Change in } x}$

69.

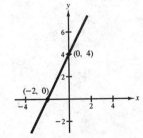

m is undefined so the line is vertical.

71. $2x - y + 4 = 0$

$2(0) - y + 4 = 0$

$4 = y \quad (0, 4)$

$2x - 0 + 4 = 0$

$2x = -4$

$x = -2 \quad (-2, 0)$

73. $-5x + 2y - 20 = 0$

$-5(0) + 2y - 20 = 0$

$2y = 20$

$y = 10$ $(0, 10)$

$-5x + 2(0) - 20 = 0$

$-5x = 20$

$x = -4$ $(-4, 0)$

75. $L_1: y = \dfrac{1}{2}x - 2$

$L_2: y = \dfrac{1}{2}x + 3$

$m_1 = \dfrac{1}{2}$ and $m_2 = \dfrac{1}{2}$

$L_1 = m_2$ so the lines are parallel.

77. $L_1: y = \dfrac{3}{4}x - 3$

$L_2: y = \dfrac{-4}{3}x + 1$

$m_1 = \dfrac{3}{4}$ and $m_2 = \dfrac{-4}{3}$

$m_1 \cdot m_2 = -1$ so the lines are perpendicular.

79. $-\dfrac{12}{100} = \dfrac{-2000}{x}$

$-12x = -200,000$

$x \approx 16,667$

The change in horizontal position is 16,667 feet.

81. $\dfrac{3}{4} = \dfrac{h}{15}$

$45 = 4h$

$\dfrac{45}{4} = h$

The maximum height in the attic is $\dfrac{45}{4}$ feet = 11.25 feet.

83. $y = 192.64t + 2015.79$

(a)

t	0	1	2	3	4	5	6
y	$2015.79	$2208.43	$2401.07	$2593.71	$2786.35	$2978.99	$3171.63

(b)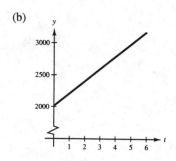

(c) On the average, tuition and fees increased $192.64 each year from 1990 to 1996. The increase is the slope of the graph.

(d) for 2005, $t = 15$ so $y = 192.64(15) + 2015.79$

$= \$4905.39$

85. (a)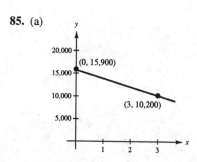

(b) $m = \dfrac{15,900 - 10,200}{0 - 3} = -1900$

(c) The slope is the annual depreciation.

87. Negative slope: line falls to the right.

Zero slope: line is horizontal

Positive slope: line rises to the right

89. In the form $y = mx + b$, m represents the slope and b represents the y-intercept.

91. No, it is not possible for two lines with positive slopes to be perpendicular to each other. Their slopes must be negative reciprocals of each other.

Mid-Chapter Quiz for Chapter 2

1. Quadrants I or II. Since x can be any real number and y is 4, the point $(x, 4)$ can only be located in quadrants in which the y coordinate is positive.

2. $(10, -3)$

3. $4x - 3y = 10$

(a) $(2, 1)$ $4(2) - 3(1) \stackrel{?}{=} 10$

$8 - 3 \stackrel{?}{=} 10$

$5 \neq 10$ not a solution

(b) $(1, -2)$ $4(1) - 3(-2) \stackrel{?}{=} 10$

$4 + 6 \stackrel{?}{=} 10$

$10 = 10$ solution

(c) $(2.5, 0)$ $4(2.5) - 3(0) \stackrel{?}{=} 10$

$10 - 0 \stackrel{?}{=} 10$

$10 = 10$ solution

(d) $\left(2, -\frac{2}{3}\right)$ $4(2) - 3\left(-\frac{2}{3}\right) \stackrel{?}{=} 10$

$8 + 2 \stackrel{?}{=} 10$

$10 = 10$ solution

4.

$d = \sqrt{(-1 - 3)^2 + (5 - 2)^2}$

$= \sqrt{16 + 9}$

$= \sqrt{25}$

$= 5$

5.

$d = \sqrt{(-3 - 2)^2 + (-2 - 10)^2}$

$= \sqrt{25 + 144}$

$= \sqrt{169}$

$= 13$

6. $6x - 8y + 48 = 0$

x-intercept: $6x - 8(0) + 48 = 0$

$6x = -48$

$x = -8$ $(-8, 0)$

y-intercept: $6(0) - 8y + 48 = 0$

$-8y = -48$

$y = 6$ $(0, 6)$

7. $y = 2x - 3$

$y = 2(0) - 3$

$= -3$ $(0, -3)$

$0 = 2x - 3$

$3 = 2x$

$\frac{3}{2} = x$ $\left(\frac{3}{2}, 0\right)$

$y = 2(2) - 3$

$= 1$ $(2, 1)$

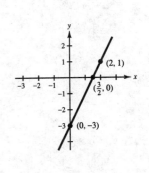

8. $3x + y - 6 = 0$

$3(0) + y - 6 = 0$

$\qquad y = 6 \qquad (0, -6)$

$3x + 0 - 6 = 0$

$\qquad 3x = 6$

$\qquad x = 2 \qquad (2, 0)$

$3(1) + y - 6 = 0$

$\qquad y = 3 \qquad (1, 3)$

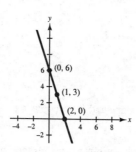

9. $y = 6x - x^2$

$y = 6(0) - 0^2$

$\quad = 0 \qquad (0, 0)$

$y = 6(6) - 6^2$

$\quad = 0 \qquad (6, 0)$

$y = 6(3) - 3^2$

$\quad = 18 - 9$

$\quad = 9 \qquad (3, 9)$

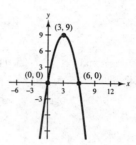

10. $y = x^2 - 4$

$y = 0^2 - 4$

$\quad = -4 \qquad (0, -4)$

$y = 2^2 - 4$

$\quad = 0 \qquad (2, 0)$

$y = (-2)^2 - 4$

$\quad = 0 \qquad (-2, 0)$

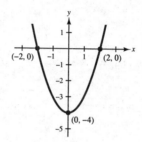

11. $y = |x| + 1$

$y = |0| + 1$

$\quad = 1 \qquad (0, 1)$

$y = |1| + 1$

$\quad = 2 \qquad (1, 2)$

$y = |-1| + 1$

$\quad = 2 \qquad (-1, 2)$

12. $y = |x - 2| - 3$

$y = |0 - 2| - 3$

$\quad = -1 \qquad (0, -1)$

$y = |5 - 2| - 3$

$\quad = 0 \qquad (5, 0)$

$y = |2 - 2| - 3$

$\quad = -3 \qquad (2, -3)$

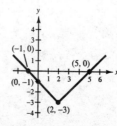

13. $m = \dfrac{-2 - 3}{5 - 5} = \dfrac{-5}{0} =$ undefined

Line is vertical.

14. $m = \dfrac{8 - 8}{7 - (-3)} = \dfrac{0}{10} = 0$ Line is horizontal.

15. $m = \dfrac{5 - 0}{6 - 3} = \dfrac{5}{3}$ Line rises.

16. $m = \dfrac{-6 - 4}{5 - (-1)} = \dfrac{-10}{6} = \dfrac{-5}{3}$ Line falls.

17. $3x + 6y = 6$

$6y = -3x + 6$

$y = \dfrac{-1}{2}x + 1$

$m = \dfrac{-1}{2}; (0, 1)$

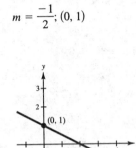

18. $-2x + y = 8$

$y = 2x + 8$

$m = 2; (0, 8)$

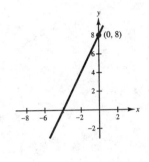

19. $x - 2y = 4$

$-2y = -x + 4$

$y = \dfrac{1}{2}x - 2$

$m = \dfrac{1}{2}; (0, -2)$

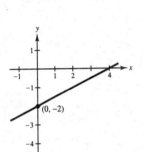

20. $y = 3x + 2; y = \dfrac{-1}{3}x - 4$

$m_1 = 3 \quad m_2 = \dfrac{-1}{3}$

$m_1 \cdot m_2 = -1$

Lines are perpendicular.

21. $y = 2x + 3; y = -2x - 3$

$m_1 = 2 \quad m_2 = -2$

$m_1 \neq m_2$

$m_1 \cdot m_2 \neq -1$

Lines are neither.

22. $y = 4x + 3; y = \dfrac{1}{2}(8x + 5)$

$m_1 = 4 \quad m_2 = 4$

$m_1 = m_2$

Lines are parallel.

23. $(0, \$85{,}000), (10, \$4000)$

$m = \dfrac{4000 - 85{,}000}{10 - 0} = \dfrac{-81{,}000}{10} = -8100$

$V = -8100t + 85{,}000, 0 \leq t \leq 10$

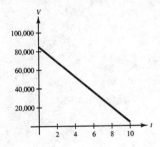

Section 2.4   **Equations of Lines**

1. $y = \frac{2}{3}x + 2$ matches graph (b).

3. $y = -\frac{3}{2}x + 2$ matches graph (a).

5.
$$3 = \frac{y - 5}{x - 2}$$
$$3(x - 2) = y - 5$$
$$3x - 6 = y - 5$$
$$3x - y = 1$$

7.
$$-\frac{1}{2} = \frac{y - 1}{x - (-3)}$$
$$x + 3 = -2(y - 1)$$
$$x + 3 = -2y + 2$$
$$x + 2y = -1$$

9.
$$\frac{4}{5} = \frac{y - (-1)}{x - \frac{3}{4}}$$
$$4\left(x - \frac{3}{4}\right) = 5(y + 1)$$
$$4x - 3 = 5y + 5$$
$$4x - 5y = 8$$

11. $y - 0 = -\frac{1}{2}(x - 0)$
$$y = -\frac{1}{2}x$$

13. $y + 4 = 3(x - 0)$
$$y + 4 = 3x$$

15. $y - 6 = -\frac{3}{4}(x - 0)$
$$y - 6 = -\frac{3}{4}x$$

17. $y - 8 = -2[x - (-2)]$
$$y - 8 = -2(x + 2)$$

19. $y - (-7) = \frac{5}{4}[x - (-4)]$
$$y + 7 = \frac{5}{4}(x + 4)$$

21. $y - \frac{7}{2} = -4[x - (-2)]$
$$y - \frac{7}{2} = -4(x + 2)$$

23. $y - \frac{5}{2} = \frac{4}{3}\left(x - \frac{3}{4}\right)$

25. $y - (-1) = 0(x - 2)$
$$y + 1 = 0$$

27. $m = \frac{3 - 0}{2 - 0} = \frac{3}{2}$
$$y - 0 = \frac{3}{2}(x - 0)$$
$$y = \frac{3}{2}x$$
$$2y = 3x$$
$$3x - 2y = 0$$

29. $m = \frac{0 - 4}{4 - 0} = \frac{-4}{4} = -1$
$$y - 4 = -1(x - 0)$$
$$y - 4 = -x$$
$$x + y - 4 = 0$$

31. $m = \frac{0 - 3}{4 - (-2)} = \frac{-3}{6} = \frac{-1}{2}$
$$y - 0 = \frac{-1}{2}(x - 4)$$
$$y = \frac{-1}{2}x + 2$$
$$2y = -x + 4$$
$$x + 2y - 4 = 0$$

33. $m = \frac{-2 - 2}{5 + 5} = -\frac{4}{10} = -\frac{2}{5}$
$$y - 2 = -\frac{2}{5}(x + 5)$$
$$y - 2 = -\frac{2}{5}x - 2$$
$$y = -\frac{2}{5}x$$
$$5y = -2x$$
$$2x + 5y = 0$$

35. $m = \dfrac{4-3}{\frac{9}{2}-\frac{3}{2}} = \dfrac{1}{\frac{6}{2}} = \dfrac{1}{3}$

$$y - 3 = \frac{1}{3}\left(x - \frac{3}{2}\right)$$

$$y - 3 = \frac{1}{3}x - \frac{1}{2}$$

$$6y - 18 = 2x - 3$$

$$2x - 6y + 15 = 0$$

37. $m = \dfrac{\frac{7}{4}-\frac{1}{2}}{\left(\frac{3}{2}\right)-10} \cdot \dfrac{4}{4} = \dfrac{7-2}{6-40} = \dfrac{5}{-34}$

$$y - \frac{1}{2} = -\frac{5}{34}(x - 10)$$

$$y - \frac{1}{2} = -\frac{5}{34}x + \frac{50}{34}$$

$$34y - 17 = -5x + 50$$

$$5x + 34y - 67 = 0$$

39. $m = \dfrac{-1.4-9}{8-5} = \dfrac{-10.4}{3} = \dfrac{-104}{30} = \dfrac{-52}{15}$

$$y - 9 = \frac{-52}{15}(x - 5)$$

$$y - 9 = \frac{-52}{15}x + \frac{52}{3}$$

$$15y - 135 = -52x + 260$$

$$52x + 15y - 395 = 0$$

41. $m = \dfrac{-4.2-0.6}{8-2} = -\dfrac{4.8}{6} = -0.8$

$$y - 0.6 = -0.8(x - 2)$$

$$y - 0.6 = -0.8x + 1.6$$

$$0.8x + y - 2.2 = 0$$

$$8x + 10y - 22 = 0$$

$$4x + 5y - 11 = 0$$

43. $m = \dfrac{5-2}{4+2} = \dfrac{3}{6} = \dfrac{1}{2}$

$$y - 5 = \frac{1}{2}(x - 4)$$

$$y - 5 = \frac{1}{2}x - 2$$

$$y = \frac{1}{2}x + 3$$

45. $m = \dfrac{3-3}{4+2} = \dfrac{0}{6} = 0$

$$y - 3 = 0(x - 4)$$

$$y - 3 = 0$$

$$y = 3$$

47. $x = -1$ because every x-coordinate is -1.

49. $y = 6$ because every y-coordinate is 6.

51. $x = -7$ because both points have an x-coordinate of -7.

53. $6x - 2y = 3$ slope $= 3$

$$-2y = -6x + 3$$

$$y = 3x - \frac{3}{2}$$

(a) $y - 1 = 3(x - 2)$

$$y - 1 = 3x - 6$$

$$y = 3x - 5$$

(b) $y - 1 = -\frac{1}{3}(x - 2)$

$$y - 1 = -\frac{1}{3}x + \frac{2}{3}$$

$$y = -\frac{1}{3}x + \frac{2}{3} + \frac{3}{3}$$

$$y = -\frac{1}{3}x + \frac{5}{3}$$

55. $5x + 4y = 24$

$$4y = -5x + 24$$

$$y = -\frac{5}{4}x + 6$$ slope $= -\frac{5}{4}$

(a) $y - 4 = -\frac{5}{4}[x - (-5)]$

$$y - 4 = -\frac{5}{4}(x + 5)$$

$$y - 4 = -\frac{5}{4}x - \frac{25}{4}$$

$$y = -\frac{5}{4}x - \frac{25}{4} + \frac{16}{4}$$

$$y = -\frac{5}{4}x - \frac{9}{4}$$

(b) $y - 4 = \frac{4}{5}[x - (-5)]$

$$y - 4 = \frac{4}{5}(x + 5)$$

$$y - 4 = \frac{4}{5}x + 4$$

$$y = \frac{4}{5}x + 8$$

57. $4x - y - 3 = 0$ slope $= 4$

$\qquad 4x - 3 = y$

(a) $y - 7 = 4(x - 3)$

$\qquad y - 7 = 4x - 12$

$\qquad\quad y = 4x - 5$

(b) $y - 7 = -\frac{1}{4}(x - 3)$

$\qquad y - 7 = -\frac{1}{4}x + \frac{3}{4}$

$\qquad\quad y = -\frac{1}{4}x + \frac{3}{4} + \frac{28}{4}$

$\qquad\quad y = -\frac{1}{4}x + \frac{31}{4}$

59. $x - 5 = 0$

$\qquad x = 5$ The slope is undefined.

(a) $\qquad x = \frac{2}{3}$

$\qquad x - \frac{2}{3} = 0$ or

$\qquad 3x - 2 = 0$

(b) $\qquad y = \frac{4}{3}$

$\qquad y - \frac{4}{3} = 0$ or

$\qquad 3y - 4 = 0$

61. $y + 5 = 0$

$\qquad y = -5$ The slope is zero.

(a) $y - 2 = 0(x + 1)$

$\qquad y - 2 = 0$

(b) $\qquad x = -1$

$\qquad x + 1 = 0$

63. $\dfrac{x}{a} + \dfrac{y}{b} = 1,\ a \neq 0,\ b \neq 0$

$\qquad \dfrac{x}{3} + \dfrac{y}{2} = 1$

65. $\dfrac{x}{a} + \dfrac{y}{b} = 1,\ a \neq 0,\ b \neq 0$

$\qquad \dfrac{x}{\frac{-5}{6}} + \dfrac{y}{\frac{-7}{3}} = 1$

$\qquad -\dfrac{6x}{5} - \dfrac{3y}{7} = 1$

67. $M = \dfrac{6000 - 5000}{50 - 0} = \dfrac{1000}{50} = 20$

$\qquad C - 5000 = 20(x - 0)$

$\qquad\qquad C = 20x + 5000$

$\qquad C = 20(400) + 5000$

$\qquad\quad = \$13{,}000$

69. $M = \dfrac{200{,}000 - 500{,}000}{2 - 5}$

$\qquad = \dfrac{-300{,}000}{-3}$

$\qquad = 100{,}000$

$\qquad S - 500{,}000 = 100{,}000(t - 5)$

$\qquad S - 500{,}000 = 100{,}000t - 500{,}000$

$\qquad\qquad\qquad S = 100{,}000t$

$\qquad\qquad\qquad S = 100{,}000(6) = \$600{,}000$

71. $M = \dfrac{1530 - 1500}{1000 - 0}$

$\qquad = \dfrac{30}{1000}$

$\qquad = \dfrac{3}{100}$

$\qquad S - 1500 = \dfrac{3}{100}(M - 0)$

$\qquad\qquad S = \dfrac{3}{100}M + 1500$ or

$\qquad\qquad S = 0.03M + 1500$

$\qquad 0.03 = 3\%$

73. (a) $S = 0.70L$

(b) $S = 0.70(135)$

$S = \$94.50$

75. (a) $(0, 7400)$ $(4, 1500)$

$$m = \frac{7400 - 1500}{0 - 4} = \frac{5900}{-4} = -1475$$

$$V - 7400 = -1475(t - 0)$$

$$V - 7400 = -1475t$$

$$V = -1475t + 7400$$

(b) $V = -1475(2) + 7400$

$V = -2950 + 7400$

$V = 4450$

Thus, after 2 years, the photocopier has a value of \$4450.

77. (a) $N = 1500 + 60t$

(b) $N = 1500 + 60(15)$

$= 1500 + 900$

$= 2400$

(c) $N = 1500 + 60(5)$

$= 1500 + 300$

$= 1800$

79. (a) & (b)

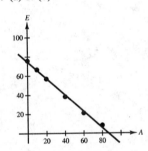

(c) Two points taken from the "best-fitting" line sketched in part (b) are 0 and 10.

$$m = \frac{38.3 - 21.1}{40 - 60} = \frac{17.2}{-20} = -0.86$$

$$E - 38.3 = -0.86(A - 40)$$

$$E = -0.86A + 72.7$$

$$E = -0.86A + 74.56$$

(d) $E = -0.86(30) + 74.56$

$E = -25.8 + 74.56$

$E \approx 48.8$ years

81. $(0, 0), (40, 5)$

$$m = \frac{5 - 0}{40 - 0} = \frac{5}{40} = \frac{1}{8}$$

$$y - 0 = \tfrac{1}{8}(x - 0)$$

$$y = \tfrac{1}{8}x$$

$$8y = x$$

$$x - 8y = 0$$

Distance from deep end	0	8	16	24	32	40
Depth of water	9	8	7	6	5	4

—CONTINUED—

81. —CONTINUED—

Depth of water $= 9 - y$

(a)   Depth $= 9 - y$

$9 = 9 - y$

$0 = y$

$x - 8(0) = 0$

$x = 0$

(b)   Depth $= 9 - y$

$8 = 9 - y$

$-1 = -y$

$1 = y$

$x - 8(1) = 0$

$x = 8$

(c)   Depth $= 9 - y$

$7 = 9 - y$

$-2 = -y$

$2 = y$

$x - 8(2) = 0$

$x = 16$

(d)   Depth $= 9 - y$

$6 = 9 - y$

$-3 = -y$

$3 = y$

$x - 8(3) = 0$

$x = 24$

(e)   Depth $= 9 - y$

$5 = 9 - y$

$-4 = -y$

$4 = y$

$x - 8(4) = 0$

$x = 32$

(f)   Depth $= 9 - y$

$4 = 9 - y$

$-5 = -y$

$5 = y$

$x - 8(5) = 0$

$x = 40$

83. Yes. When different pairs of points are selected, the change in y and the change in x are the lengths of the sides of similar triangles. Corresponding sides of similar triangles are proportional.

85. In the equation $y = 3x + 5$, 3 is the slope and 5 is the y-intercept.

Section 2.5   Relations and Functions

1. Domain $= \{-2, 0, 1\}$

Range $= \{-1, 0, 1, 4\}$

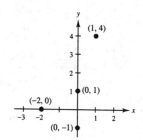

3. Domain $= \{0, 2, 4, 5, 6\}$

Range $= \{-3, 0, 5, 8\}$

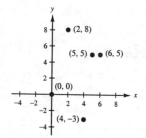

5. $(3, 150), (2, 100), (8, 400), (6, 300), \left(\frac{1}{2}, 25\right)$

7. $(1, 1), (2, 8), (3, 27), (4, 64), (5, 125), (6, 216), (7, 343)$

9. (1995, Atlanta Braves), (1996, New York Yankees), (1997, Florida Marlins), (1998, New York Yankees)

11. No, this relation is not a function because -1 in the domain is paired to 2 numbers (6 and 7) in the range.

13. Yes, this relation is a function as each number in the domain is paired with exactly one number in the range.

15. No, this relation is not a function as 0 in the domain is paired with 2 numbers in the range (5 and 9).

17. No, this relation is not a function because both CBS and ABC in the domain are each paired to 3 different TV shows in the range.

19. Yes, this relation is a function as each number in the domain is paired with exactly one number in the range.

21. No, this relation is not a function as the 4 and the 7 in the domain are each paired with 2 different numbers in the range.

23. (a) Yes, this relation is a function as each number in the domain is paired with exactly one number in the range.

    (b) No, this relation is not a function as the 1 in the domain is paired with 2 different numbers in the range.

    (c) Yes, this relation is a function as each number in the domain is paired with exactly one number in the range.

    (d) No, this relation is not a function as each number in the domain is not paired with a number.

25. $x^2 + y^2 = 25$

$$0^2 + 5^2 \overset{?}{=} 25 \qquad 0^2 + (-5)^2 \overset{?}{=} 25$$
$$25 = 25 \qquad\qquad 25 = 25$$

Both $(0, 5)$ and $(0, -5)$ are solutions of $x^2 + y^2 = 25$ which implies y is not a function of x.

27. $|y| = x + 2$

$$|3| \overset{?}{=} 1 + 2 \qquad |-3| \overset{?}{=} 1 + 2$$
$$3 = 3 \qquad\qquad 3 = 3$$

Both $(1, 3)$ and $(1, -3)$ are solutions of $|y| = x + 2$ which implies y is not a function of x.

29. $y = 10x + 12$ represents y as a function of x because there is one value of y associated with one value of x.

31. $3x + 7y - 2 = 0$ represents y as a function of x because there is one value of y associated with one value of x.

33. $y = x(x - 10)$ represents y as a function of x because there is one value of y associated with one value of x.

35. $f(x) = 3x + 5$

    (a) $f(2) = 3(2) + 5 = 11$

    (b) $f(-2) = 3(-2) + 5 = -1$

    (c) $f(k) = 3(k) + 5 = 3k + 5$

    (d) $f(k + 1) = 3(k + 1) + 5 = 3k + 3 + 5 = 3k + 8$

37. $f(x) = 3 - x^2$

    (a) $f(0) = 3 - 0^2 = 3$

    (b) $f(-3) = 3 - (-3)^2 = 3 - 9 = -6$

    (c) $f(m) = 3 - m^2$

    (d) $f(2t) = 3 - (2t)^2 = 3 - 4t^2$

39. $f(x) = \dfrac{x}{x + 2}$

    (a) $f(3) = \dfrac{3}{3 + 2} = \dfrac{3}{5}$

    (b) $f(-4) = \dfrac{-4}{-4 + 2} = \dfrac{-4}{-2} = 2$

    (c) $f(s) = \dfrac{s}{s + 2}$

    (d) $f(s - 2) = \dfrac{s - 2}{(s - 2) + 2} = \dfrac{s - 2}{s}$

41. $f(x) = 12x - 7$

    (a) $f(3) = 12(3) - 7 = 29$

    (b) $f\left(\frac{3}{2}\right) = 12\left(\frac{3}{2}\right) - 7 = 11$

    (c) $f(a) + f(1) = [12(a) - 7] + [12(1) - 7] = 12a - 7 + 12 - 7 = 12a - 2$

    (d) $f(a + 1) = 12(a + 1) - 7 = 12a + 12 - 7 = 12a + 5$

43. $g(x) = 2 - 4x + x^2$

    (a) $g(4) = 2 - 4(4) + 4^2 = 2 - 16 + 16 = 2$

    (b) $g(0) = 2 - 4(0) + 0^2 = 2$

    (c) $g(2y) = 2 - 4(2y) + (2y)^2 = 2 - 8y + 4y^2$

    (d) $g(4) + g(6) = [2 - 4(4) + 4^2] + [2 - 4(6) + 6^2] = (2 - 16 + 16) + (2 - 24 + 36) = 2 + 14 = 16$

45. $f(x) = \sqrt{x + 5}$

    (a) $f(-1) = \sqrt{-1 + 5} = 2$ (b) $f(4) = \sqrt{4 + 5} = 3$

    (c) $f(z - 5) = \sqrt{z - 5 + 5} = \sqrt{z}$ (d) $f(5z) = \sqrt{5z + 5}$

47. $g(x) = 8 - |x - 4|$

    (a) $g(0) = 8 - |0 - 4| = 8 - 4 = 4$

    (b) $g(8) = 8 - |8 - 4| = 8 - 4 = 4$

    (c) $g(16) - g(-1) = \left(8 - |16 - 4|\right) - \left(8 - |-1 - 4|\right) = (8 - 12) - (8 - 5) = -4 - 3 = -7$

    (d) $g(x - 2) = 8 - |x - 2 - 4| = 8 - |x - 6|$

49. $f(x) = \dfrac{3x}{x - 5}$

    (a) $f(0) = \dfrac{3(0)}{0 - 5} = 0$

    (b) $f\left(\dfrac{5}{3}\right) = \dfrac{3\left(\dfrac{5}{3}\right)}{\dfrac{5}{3} - 5} \cdot \dfrac{3}{3} = \dfrac{15}{5 - 15} = \dfrac{15}{-10} = \dfrac{3}{-2}$

    (c) $f(2) - f(-1) = \left[\dfrac{3(2)}{2 - 5}\right] - \left[\dfrac{3(-1)}{-1 - 5}\right] = \dfrac{6}{-3} = \dfrac{-3}{-6} = -2 - \dfrac{1}{2} = \dfrac{-5}{2}$

    (d) $f(x + 4) = \dfrac{3(x + 4)}{x + 4 - 5} = \dfrac{3x + 12}{x - 1}$

51. $f(x) = \begin{cases} x + 8, & \text{if} \quad x < 0 \\ 10 - 2x, & \text{if} \quad x \geq 0 \end{cases}$

    (a) $f(4) = 10 - 2(4) = 10 - 8 = 2$

    (b) $f(-10) = -10 + 8 = -2$

    (c) $f(0) = 10 - 2(0) = 10$

    (d) $f(6) - f(-2) = [10 - 2(6)] - [-2 + 8] = 10 - 12 - 6 = -8$

53. $h(x) = \begin{cases} 4 - x^2, \text{ if } & x \leq 2 \\ x - 2, \text{ if } & x > 2 \end{cases}$

(a) $h(2) = 4 - 2^2 = 0$

(b) $h\left(-\frac{3}{2}\right) = 4 - \left(-\frac{3}{2}\right)^2 = 4 - \frac{9}{4} = \frac{16}{4} - \frac{9}{4} = \frac{7}{4}$

(c) $h(5) = 5 - 2 = 3$

(d) $h(-3) + h(7) = [4 - (-3)^2] + [7 - 2] = 4 - 9 + 5 = 0$

55. $f(x) = 2x + 5$

(a) $\dfrac{f(x + 2) - f(2)}{x} = \dfrac{[2(x + 2) + 5] - [2(2) + 5]}{x} = \dfrac{2x + 4 + 5 - 4 - 5}{x} = \dfrac{2x}{x} = 2$

(b) $\dfrac{f(x - 3) - f(3)}{x} = \dfrac{[2(x - 3) + 5] - [2(3) + 5]}{x} = \dfrac{2x - 6 + 5 - 6 - 5}{x} = \dfrac{2x - 12}{x}$

57. Domain of $f(x) = 5 - 2x$ is all real numbers x.

59. Domain of $f(x) = \dfrac{2x}{x - 3}$ is all real numbers x such that $x \neq 3$ because $x - 3 \neq 0$ means $x \neq 3$.

61. Domain of $f(t) = \dfrac{t + 3}{t(t + 2)}$ is all real numbers t such that $t \neq 0, -2$ because $t(t + 2) \neq 0$ means $t \neq 0$ and $t \neq -2$.

63. Domain of $g(x) = \sqrt{x + 4}$ is all real numbers x such that $x \geq -4$ because $x + 4 \geq 0$ means $x \geq -4$.

65. Domain of $f(x) = \sqrt{2x - 1}$ is all real numbers x such that $x \geq \frac{1}{2}$ because $2x - 1 \geq 0$ means $x \geq \frac{1}{2}$.

67. Domain of $f(t) = |t - 4|$ is all real numbers t.

69. Domain = $\{0, 2, 4, 6\}$

Range = $\{0, 1, 8, 27\}$

71. Domain = $\{-3, -1, 4, 10\}$

Range = $\left\{-\dfrac{17}{2}, -\dfrac{5}{2}, 2, 11\right\}$

73. Domain = $r > 0$

Range = $C > 0$

75. Domain = $r > 0$

Range = $A > 0$

77. *Verbal model:* $\boxed{\text{Perimeter}} = 4 \cdot \boxed{\text{Length of side}}$

Labels: Perimeter = $P(x)$

Length of side = x

Function: $P(x) = 4x$

79. *Verbal model:* $\boxed{\text{Volume}} = \boxed{\text{Length of side}}^3$

Labels: Volume = $V(x)$

Length of side = x

Function: $V(x) = x^3$

81. *Verbal model:* | Distance | = | Rate | · | Time |

   Labels: Distance = $d(t)$

   Rate = 230

   Time = t

   Function: $d(t) = 230t$

83. *Verbal model:* | Volume | = | Length | · | Width | · | Height |

   Labels: Volume = $V(x)$

   Length = $(24 - 2x)$

   Width = $(24 - 2x)$

   Height = x

   Function: $V(x) = x(24 - 2x)^2$ or $4x(12 - x)^2$

85. *Verbal model:* | Area | = | Length | · | Width |

   Labels: Area = $A(x)$

   Length = $(32 - x)$

   Width = $(32 - x)$

   Function: $A(x) = (32 - x)(32 - x)$

   $A(x) = (32 - x)^2$

87. $S(L) = \dfrac{128,160}{L}$

   (a) $S(12) = \dfrac{128,160}{12} = 10,680$ pounds   (b) $S(16) = \dfrac{128,160}{16} = 8010$ pounds

89. Yes to both questions. For each year there is associated one public school enrollment and one private school enrollment.

91. (g) $y(x) = 15,900 - 1900x$

   $y(7) = 15,900 - 1900(7)$

   $= 15,900 - 13,300$

   $= \$2600$

   (i) Domain: all real numbers x such that $0 < x \le 8.37$

   Range: all real numbers y such that $0 < y \le 15,900$

   (h) Straight-line depreciation might not be a fair model for automobile depreciation because the car depreciates more slowly as the car ages.

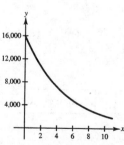

93. (a) This is not a correct mathematical use of the word function.

   (b) This is a correct mathematical use of the word function.

95. No, every relation is not a function because some relations have more than one *y* value paired with each *x* value. For example, {(4, 3), (4, −2)} is a relation, but not a function.

97. You can name the function (*f*, *g*, etc.). That is convenient when there is more than one function used in solving a problem. The values of the independent and the dependent variables are easily seen in function notation.

Section 2.6   Graphs of Functions

1.

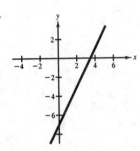

Domain: −∞ < *x* < ∞

Range: −∞ < *y* < ∞

3.

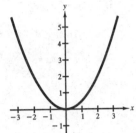

Domain: −∞ < *x* < ∞

Range: [0, ∞) or 0 ≤ *y* < ∞

5.

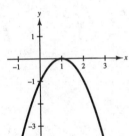

Domain: −∞ < *x* < ∞

Range: (−∞, 0] or −∞ < *y* ≤ 0

7.

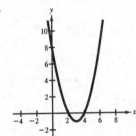

Domain: −∞ < *x* < ∞

Range: [−1, ∞) or −1 ≤ *y* < ∞

9.

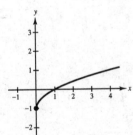

Domain: 0 ≤ *x* < ∞

Range: −1 ≤ *y* < ∞

11.

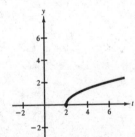

Domain: [2, ∞) or 2 ≤ *t* < ∞

Range: [0, ∞) or 0 ≤ *y* < ∞

13.

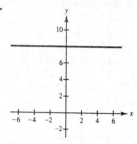

Domain: $-\infty < x < \infty$

Range: $y = 8$

15.

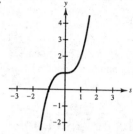

Domain: $-\infty < s < \infty$

Range: $-\infty < y < \infty$

17.

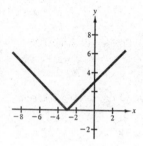

Domain: $-\infty < x < \infty$

Range: $[0, \infty)$ or $0 \le y < \infty$

19.

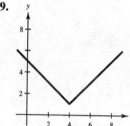

Domain: $-\infty < x < \infty$

Range: $[1, \infty)$ or $1 \le y < \infty$

21.

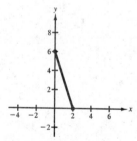

Domain: $0 \le x \le 2$ or $[0, 2]$

Range: $0 \le y \le 6$ or $[0, 6]$

23.

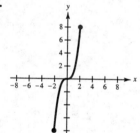

Domain: $-2 \le x \le 2$ or $[-2, 2]$

Range: $-8 \le y \le 8$ or $[-8, 8]$

25.

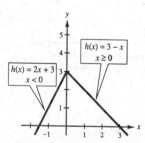

Domain: $-\infty < x < \infty$

Range: $(-\infty, 3]$ or $\infty < y \le 3$

27.

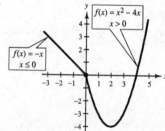

Domain: $-\infty < x < \infty$

Range: $-4 \le y < \infty$ or $[-4, \infty)$

29. *Keystrokes:*

$\boxed{Y=}\,1\,\boxed{-}\,\boxed{X,T,\theta}\,\boxed{x^2}\,\boxed{GRAPH}$

Domain $= -\infty < x < \infty$ Range $= (-\infty, 1]$ or $-\infty < y \leq 1$

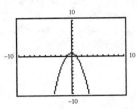

31. *Keystrokes:*

$\boxed{Y=}\,\boxed{\sqrt{\ }}\,\boxed{(}\,\boxed{X,T,\theta}\,\boxed{-}\,2\,\boxed{)}\,\boxed{GRAPH}$

Domain $= [2, \infty)$ or $x \geq 2$ Range $= [0, \infty)$ or $0 \leq y < \infty$

$\qquad\qquad 2 \leq x < \infty$

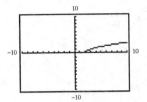

33. Yes, $y = \frac{1}{3}x^3$ passes the Vertical Line Test and is a function of x.

35. Yes, y is a function of x by the Vertical Line Test.

37. No, y is not a function of x by the Vertical Line Test.

39. No, $y^2 = x$ does not pass the Vertical Line Test and y is not a function of x.

41.

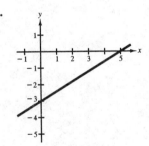

y is a function of x.

43.

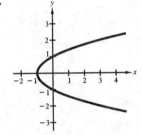

y is not a function of x.

45. (b) graph matches $f(x) = x^2 - 1$.

47. (a) graph matches $f(x) = 2 - |x|$.

49. (b) shows the most complete graph.

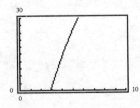

(a)

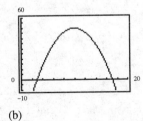

(b)

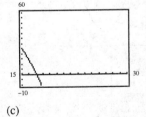

(c)

51. (a) Vertical shift 2 units upward

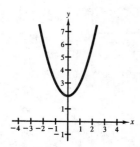

(b) Vertical shift 4 units downward

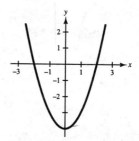

(c) Horizontal shift 2 units to the left

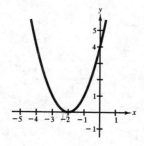

(d) Horizontal shift 4 units to the right

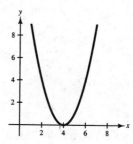

(e) Reflection in the *x*-axis.

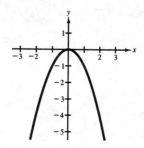

(f) Reflection in the *x*-axis and a vertical shift 4 units upward

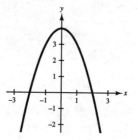

(g) Horizontal shift 3 units to the right and a vertical shift 1 unit upward

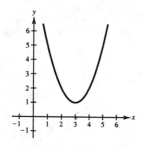

(h) Reflection in the *x*-axis, a horizontal shift 2 units to the left, and a vertical shift 3 units downward

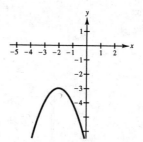

53. *Keystrokes:*

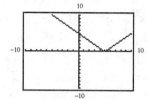

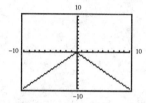

Horizontal shift 5 units to the right

55. *Keystrokes:*

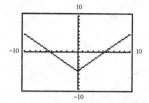

Vertical shift 5 units downward

57. *Keystrokes:*

Y= (−) ABS X,T,θ GRAPH

Reflection in the *x*-axis

59. Graph is shifted 3 units left

$h(x) = (x + 3)^2$

61. Graph is reflected in the *x*-axis

$h(x) = -x^2$

63. Graph is shifted 3 units left and reflected in the *x*-axis

$h(x) = -(x + 3)^2$

65. Graph is reflected in the *x*-axis and shifted up 2 units

$h(x) = -x^2 + 2$

67. $f(x) = -\sqrt{x}$

69. $f(x) = \sqrt{x + 2}$

71. $f(x) = \sqrt{-x}$

73. (a) $y = f(x) + 2$

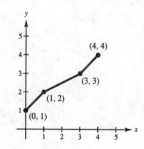

(b) $y = -f(x)$

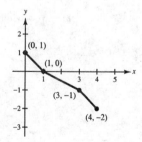

—**CONTINUED**—

73. —CONTINUED—

(c) $y = f(x - 2)$

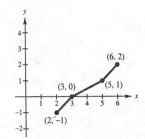

(d) $y = f(x + 2)$

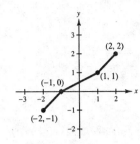

(e) $y = f(x) - 1$

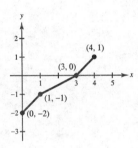

(f) $y = f(-x)$

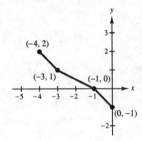

75. (a) *Keystrokes:*

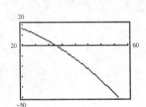

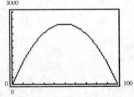

(b) $\approx 46\%$

77. (a)

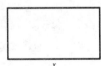

$100 - x$

x

Let x = length

$100 - x$ = width

$P = 2l + 2w$

$200 = 2l + 2w$

$100 = l + w$

$100 - l = w$

$A = l \cdot w$

$A = x(100 - x)$

Keystrokes:

Y= X,T,θ (100 − X,T,θ) GRAPH

(b)

(c) When $x = 50$, the largest value of A is 2500. $(50, 2500)$ is the highest point on the graph of A giving the largest value of the function.

79. (a) *Keystrokes:*

Y= (−) 5.46 X,T,θ x² + 2665.56 X,T,θ + 153,363 GRAPH

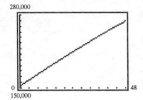

(b) $t = 0$ corresponds to the year 1970 (20 years later).

(c) *Keystrokes:*

Y= (−) 5.46 (X,T,θ + 20) x² + 2665.56 (X,T,θ + 20) + 153,363 GRAPH

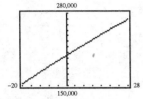

81. If the domain of the function $f(x) = 2x$ changes from $[0, 2]$ to $[0, 4]$, then the range changed from $[0, 4]$ to $[0, 8]$.

83. The four types of shifts of the graph of a function are vertical shift upward, vertical shift downward, horizontal shift to the left, horizontal shift to the right.

85. $g(x) = f(-x)$ is a reflection in the y-axis of the graph of $f(x)$.

Review Exercises for Chapter 2

1.

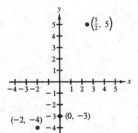

3.

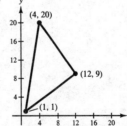

5. Quadrant IV

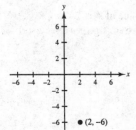

7. Quadrant I, IV

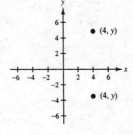

9. (a) $(4, 2)$ $\quad 2 \overset{?}{=} 4 - \frac{1}{2}(4)$

$\qquad\qquad\quad 2 \overset{?}{=} 4 - 2$

$\qquad\qquad\quad 2 = 2$ yes

(c) $(-4, 0)$ $\quad 0 \overset{?}{=} 4 - \frac{1}{2}(-4)$

$\qquad\qquad\quad 0 \overset{?}{=} 4 + 2$

$\qquad\qquad\quad 0 \neq 6$ no

(b) $(-1, 5)$ $\quad 5 \overset{?}{=} 4 - \frac{1}{2}(-1)$

$\qquad\qquad\quad 5 \overset{?}{=} 4 + \frac{1}{2}$

$\qquad\qquad\quad 5 \neq 4\frac{1}{2}$ no

(d) $(8, 0)$ $\quad 0 \overset{?}{=} 4 - \frac{1}{2}(8)$

$\qquad\qquad\quad 0 \overset{?}{=} 4 - 4$

$\qquad\qquad\quad 0 = 0$ yes

11. $d = \sqrt{(4 - 4)^2 + (3 - 8)^2}$

$\quad = \sqrt{0 + 25}$

$\quad = \sqrt{25}$

$\quad = 5$

13. $d = \sqrt{(-5 - 1)^2 + (-1 - 2)^2}$

$\quad = \sqrt{36 + 9}$

$\quad = \sqrt{45}$

$\quad = 3\sqrt{5}$

15. $y = 5 - \frac{3}{2}x$ matches graph (c).

17. $y = |x| + 4$ matched graph (a).

19. $\quad y = 6 - \frac{1}{3}x$

$\qquad y = 6 - \frac{1}{3}(0)$

$\qquad y = 6 \quad (0, 6)$

$\qquad 0 = 6 - \frac{1}{3}x$

$\qquad \frac{1}{3}x = 6$

$\qquad x = 18 \quad (18, 0)$

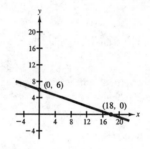

21. $\quad 3y - 2x - 3 = 0$

$\qquad 3y - 2(0) - 3 = 0$

$\qquad\qquad\quad 3y = 3$

$\qquad\qquad\qquad y = 1 \qquad (0, 1)$

$\qquad 3(0) - 2x - 3 = 0$

$\qquad\qquad\quad -2x = 3$

$\qquad\qquad\qquad x = -\frac{3}{2} \quad \left(-\frac{3}{2}, 0\right)$

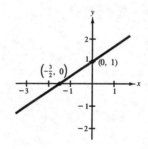

23. $\quad y = x^2 - 1$

$\qquad y = 0^2 - 1$

$\qquad\quad = -1 \quad (0, -1)$

$\qquad 0 = x^2 - 1$

$\qquad 0 = (x - 1)(x + 1)$

$\qquad x = 1 \quad x = -1 \qquad (1, 0), (-1, 0)$

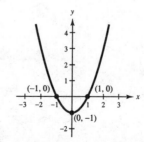

25. $y = |x| - 2$

$y = |0| - 2$

$\quad = -2$

$0 = |x| - 2$

$2 = |x|$

$\pm 2 = x \quad (2, 0), (-2, 0)$

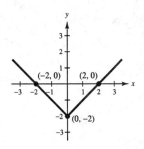

27. $y = 4x - 6$

y-intercept

$y = 4(0) - 6$

$\quad = -6 \quad (0, -6)$

x-intercept

$0 = 4x - 6$

$6 = 4x$

$\frac{6}{4} = x$

$\frac{3}{2} = x \quad \left(\frac{3}{2}, 0\right)$

29. $7x - 2y = -14$

y-intercept

$7(0) - 2y = -14$

$-2y = -14$

$\quad y = 7 \quad (0, 7)$

x-intercept

$7x - 2(0) = -14$

$7x = -14$

$\quad x = -2 \quad (-2, 0)$

31. $y = |x - 5|$

y-intercept

$y = |0 - 5|$

$\quad = 5 \quad (0, 5)$

x-intercept

$0 = |x - 5|$

$0 = x - 5$

$5 = x \quad (5, 0)$

33. $y = |2x + 1| - 5$

y-intercept

$y = |2(0) + 1| - 5$

$\quad = -5$

$\quad = -4 \quad (0, -4)$

x-intercepts

$0 = |2x + 1| - 5$

$5 = |2x + 1|$

$5 = 2x + 1 \qquad \text{or} \qquad -5 = 2x + 1$

$4 = 2x \qquad\qquad\qquad\quad -6 = 2x$

$2 = x \qquad\qquad\qquad\quad -3 = x$

$(2, 0), (-3, 0)$

35. *Keystrokes:*

$\boxed{Y=}\ \boxed{(}\ \boxed{X,T,\theta}\ \boxed{-}\ 3\ \boxed{)}\ \boxed{x^2}\ \boxed{-}\ 3\ \boxed{\text{GRAPH}}$

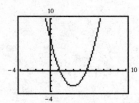

$(1.27, 0), (4.73, 0), (0, 6)$

37. *Keystrokes:*

$\boxed{Y=}\ \boxed{(-)}\ \boxed{\text{ABS}}\ \boxed{(}\ \boxed{X,T,\theta}\ \boxed{-}\ 4\ \boxed{)}\ \boxed{-}\ 7\ \boxed{\text{GRAPH}}$

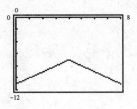

$(0, -11)$

no x-intercepts

39. *Keystrokes:*

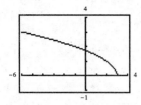

(3, 0), (0, 1.73)

41. $m = \dfrac{3 - 1}{6 - (-1)} = \dfrac{2}{7}$

43. $m = \dfrac{3 - 3}{4 - (-1)} = \dfrac{0}{5} = 0$

45. $m = \dfrac{0 - 6}{8 - 0} = \dfrac{-6}{8} = \dfrac{-3}{4} = -\dfrac{3}{4}$

47. $m = \dfrac{3 - (-3)}{1 - (-3)} = \dfrac{6}{4} = \dfrac{3}{2}$

$\dfrac{3}{2} = \dfrac{3 - t}{1 - 0}$

$3 = 6 - 2t$

$-3 = -2t$

$\dfrac{3}{2} = t$

49. $-3 = \dfrac{y + 4}{x - 2}$

(0, 2), (1, −1)

51. $\dfrac{5}{4} = \dfrac{y - 1}{x - 3}$

(7, 6), (11, 11)

53. Since m is undefined the line is a vertical line so points such as (3, 0), (3, 1), and (3, −2) are on this line.

55. $5x - 2y - 4 = 0$

$-2y = -5x + 4$

$y = \tfrac{5}{2}x - 2$

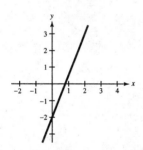

57. $x + 2y - 2 = 0$

$2y = -x + 2$

$y = -\tfrac{1}{2}x + 1$

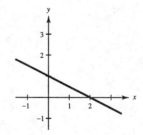

59. $L_1: y = \frac{3}{2}x + 1$

$L_2: y = \frac{2}{3}x - 1$

$m_1 = \frac{3}{2}, m_2 = \frac{2}{3}$

$m_1 \neq m_2, m_1 \cdot m_2 \neq -1$

So lines are neither

61. $L_1: y = \frac{3}{2}x - 2$

$L_2: y = -\frac{2}{3}x + 1$

$m_1 = \frac{3}{2}, m_2 = -\frac{2}{3}$

$m_1 \cdot m_2 = -1$

So lines are perpendicular

63. $L_1: 2x - 3y - 5 = 0$

$L_2: x + 2y - 6 = 0$

$L_1: -3y = -2x + 5$

$y = \frac{2}{3}x - \frac{5}{3}$

$m_1 = \frac{2}{3}$

$L_2: 2y = -x + 6$

$y = -\frac{1}{2}x + 3$

$m_2 = -\frac{1}{2}$

$m_1 \neq m_2, m_1 \cdot m_2 \neq -1$

So lines are neither

65. $y + 4 = 2(x - 1)$

$y + 4 = 2x - 2$

$2x - y - 6 = 0$

67. $y - 4 = -4(x + 1)$

$y - 4 = -4x - 4$

$4x + y = 0$

69. $y - 4 = -\frac{2}{3}\left(x - \frac{5}{2}\right)$

$y - 4 = -\frac{2}{3}x + \frac{5}{3}$

$3y - 12 = -2x + 5$

$2x + 3y - 17 = 0$

71. $y - 5 = 0[x - (-6)]$

$y - 5 = 0$

73. $m = \frac{0 + 3}{-6 - 0} = \frac{3}{-6} = -\frac{1}{2}$

$y - 0 = -\frac{1}{2}(x + 6)$

$y = -\frac{1}{2}x - 3$

$2y = -x - 6$

$x + 2y + 6 = 0$

75. $m = \frac{6 - (-3)}{4 - (-2)} = \frac{6 + 3}{4 + 2} = \frac{9}{6} = \frac{3}{2}$

$y - 6 = \frac{3}{2}(x - 4)$

$y - 6 = \frac{3}{2}x - 6$

$2(y - 6) = 2\left(\frac{3}{2}x - 6\right)$

$2y - 12 = 3x - 12$

$3x - 2y = 0$

77. $m = \dfrac{\frac{7}{6} - \frac{1}{6}}{4 - \frac{4}{3}} \cdot \frac{6}{6} = \frac{7 - 1}{24 - 8} = \frac{6}{16} = \frac{3}{8}$

$y - \frac{7}{6} = \frac{3}{8}(x - 4)$

$y - \frac{7}{6} = \frac{3}{8}x - \frac{12}{8}$

$48y - 56 = 18x - 72$

$18x - 48y - 16 = 0$

$9x - 24y - 8 = 0$

79. $3x + y = 2$

$y = -3x + 2$

(a) $y + \frac{4}{5} = -3\left(x - \frac{3}{5}\right)$ or $3x + y - 1 = 0$

(b) $y + \frac{4}{5} = \frac{1}{3}\left(x - \frac{3}{5}\right)$ or $x - 3y - 3 = 0$

81. $5x = 3$

$x = \frac{3}{5}$ $m = $ undefined

(a) $x = 12$ or $x - 12 = 0$

(b) $y = 1$ or $y - 1 = 0$

83. No, this relation is not a function because the 8 in the domain is paired to two numbers (1 and 2) in the range.

85. Yes, this relation is a function because each number in the domain is paired to only one number in the range.

87. $f(x) = 4 - \frac{5}{2}x$

  (a) $f(-10) = 4 - \frac{5}{2}(-10) = 4 + 25 = 29$

  (b) $f\left(\frac{2}{5}\right) = 4 - \frac{5}{2}\left(\frac{2}{5}\right) = 4 - 1 = 3$

  (c) $f(t) + f(-4) = \left(4 - \frac{5}{2}t\right) + \left[4 - \frac{5}{2}(-4)\right] = 4 - \frac{5}{2}t + 4 + 10 = 18 - \frac{5}{2}t$

  (d) $f(x + h) = 4 - \frac{5}{2}(x + h) = 4 - \frac{5}{2}x - \frac{5}{2}h$

89. $f(t) = \sqrt{5 - t}$

  (a) $f(-4) = \sqrt{5 - (-4)} = \sqrt{9} = 3$

  (b) $f(5) = \sqrt{5 - 5} = 0$

  (c) $f(3) = \sqrt{5 - 3} = \sqrt{2}$

  (d) $f(5z) = \sqrt{5 - 5z}$

91. $\begin{cases} -3x, & \text{if} \quad x \le 0 \\ 1 - x^2, \text{if} \quad x > 0 \end{cases}$

  (a) $f(2) = 1 - 2^2 = -3$

  (b) $f\left(-\frac{2}{3}\right) = -3\left(-\frac{2}{3}\right) = 2$

  (c) $f(1) = 1 - 1^2 = 0$

  (d) $f(4) - f(3) = (1 - 4^2) - (1 - 3^2) = 1 - 16 - 1 + 9 = -7$

93. (a) $\dfrac{f(x + 2) - f(2)}{x} = \dfrac{[3 - 2(x + 2)] - [3 - 2(2)]}{x} = \dfrac{3 - 2x - 4 - 3 + 4}{x} = \dfrac{-2x}{x} = -2$

  (b) $\dfrac{f(x - 3) - f(3)}{x} = \dfrac{[3 - 2(x - 3)] - [3 - 2(3)]}{x} = \dfrac{3 - 2x + 6 - 3 + 6}{x} = \dfrac{-2x + 12}{x}$

95. Find the domain of $h(x) = 4x^2 - 7$.

  Domain: $-\infty < x < \infty$ or $(-\infty, \infty)$

97. Find the domain of $f(x) = \sqrt{5 - 2x}$.

  Domain: $\left(-\infty, \frac{5}{2}\right]$ or $-\infty < x \le \frac{5}{2}$

99.

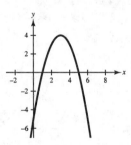

101.

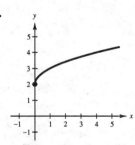

103.

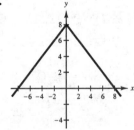

105.

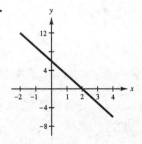

107.

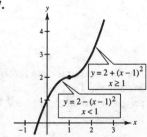

109. No, y is not a function of x.

111. Yes, y is a function of x.

113. $h(x) = -\sqrt{x}$ is a reflection in the x-axis of $f(x) = \sqrt{x}$

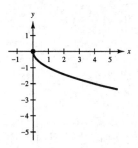

115. $h(x) = \sqrt{x - 1}$ is a horizontal shift 1 unit to the right of $f(x) = \sqrt{x}$

117. $y = x^2 - 2$

Vertical shift 2 units downward

119. $y = -(x + 3)^2$

Reflection in the x-axis and a horizontal shift 3 units to the left

121. *Verbal model:* $\boxed{\dfrac{\text{Rise}}{\text{Run}}} = \boxed{\dfrac{\text{Rise}}{\text{Run}}}$

Proportion: $\dfrac{1}{12} = \dfrac{3}{x}$

$x = 36$

Verbal model: $\boxed{\text{Leg} \atop 1}^2 + \boxed{\text{Leg} \atop 2}^2 = \boxed{\text{Hypotenuse}}^2$

Labels: Leg 1 = 3

Leg 2 = 36

Hypotenuse = x

Equation: $3^2 + 36^2 = x^2$

$9 + 1296 = x^2$

$\sqrt{1305} = x$

$3\sqrt{145} = x \approx 36.12$ feet

123. $(0, \$20{,}000), (7, \$6000)$

$m = \dfrac{6{,}000 - 20{,}000}{7 - 0} = \dfrac{-14{,}000}{7} = -2{,}000$

$V - 20{,}000 = -2{,}000(t - 0)$

$V - 20{,}000 = -2{,}000t$

$V = -2{,}000t + 20{,}000, \ 0 \leq t \leq 7$

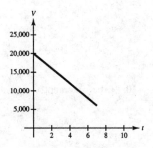

125. $m = \dfrac{-0.88 - 4.75}{4.75 - (-0.88)} = \dfrac{-5.63}{5.63} = -1$

$y + 0.88 = -1(x - 4.75)$

$y = -x + 4.75 - 0.88$

$y = -x + 3.87$

127.

$\dfrac{150-2x}{2}$

x x

$\dfrac{150-2x}{2}$

Verbal model:

$\boxed{\text{Perimeter}} = 2\,\boxed{\text{Length}} + 2\,\boxed{\text{Width}}$

$$150 = 2\text{Length} + 2x$$

$$\dfrac{150-2x}{2} = \text{Length}$$

$$75 - x = \text{Length}$$

Verbal model: $\boxed{\text{Area}} = \boxed{\text{Length}} \cdot \boxed{\text{Width}}$

Labels: Area $= A(x)$

                  Length $= 75 - x$

                  Width $= x$

Function: $A(x) = (75 - x)x$

                  Domain: $0 < x < \dfrac{75}{2}$

129. (a) $v = -32(2) + 80$

           $v = -64 + 80$

           $v = 16$ feet per second

(b) $0 = -32t + 80$

      $32t = 80$

         $t = \frac{80}{32}$

         $t = \frac{5}{2}$ seconds

(c) $v = -32(3) + 80$

         $v = -96 + 80$

         $v = -16$ feet per second

Chapter Test for Chapter 2

1. (x, y) lies in Quadrant IV if $x > 0$ and $y < 0$.

2. $d = \sqrt{(0-3)^2 + (5-1)^2} = \sqrt{9 + 16} = \sqrt{25} = 5$

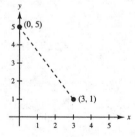

3. (a) $y = -3(0 + 1) = -3$ $(0, -3)$; y-intercept

    (b) $0 = -3(x + 1)$

        $x = -1$, $(-1, 0)$; x-intercept

4.

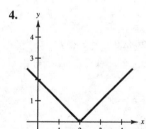

5. (a) $m = \dfrac{3-7}{2+4} = -\dfrac{4}{6} = -\dfrac{2}{3}$

   (b) $m = \dfrac{6+2}{3-3} = \dfrac{8}{0} = $ undefined

6.

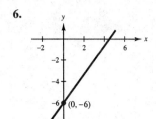

7. $2x + 5y = 10$

   $2(0) + 5y = 10$

   $5y = 10$

   $y = 2 \quad (0, 2)$

   $2x + 5(0) = 10$

   $2x = 10$

   $x = 5 \quad (5, 0)$

8. $5x + 3y - 9 = 0$

   $3y = -5x + 9$

   $y = \dfrac{-5}{3}x + 3$

   $m = \dfrac{3}{5}$

9. $m = \dfrac{10 + 15}{75 - 25} = \dfrac{25}{50} = \dfrac{1}{2}$

   $y - 10 = \dfrac{1}{2}(x - 75)$

   $y - 10 = \dfrac{1}{2}x - \dfrac{75}{2}$

   $2y - 20 = x - 75$

   $x - 2y - 55 = 0$

10. $y - (-4) = -2(x - 2)$

   $y + 4 = -2x + 4$

   $2x + y = 0$

11. $x = -2$

   $x + 2 = 0$

12. No, $y^2(4 - x) = x^3$ is not a function of x, because the graph does not pass the Vertical Line Test.

13. (a) The relation is a function because each x number is paired with exactly one y number.

   (b) The relation is not a function because 0 is paired with two numbers, 0 and -4.

14. (a) $g(2) = \dfrac{2}{2 - 3} = -2$

   (b) $g\!\left(\dfrac{7}{2}\right) = \dfrac{\dfrac{7}{2}}{\dfrac{7}{2} - 3} = \dfrac{7}{7 - 6} = 7$

   (c) $g(x + 2) = \dfrac{x + 2}{(x + 2) - 3} = \dfrac{x + 2}{x - 1}$

15. (a) $h(t) = \sqrt{9 - t}$

   $9 - t \geq 0$

   $-t \geq -9$

   $t \leq 9$

   Domain: $t \leq 9$ or $(-\infty, 9]$

   (b) $f(x) = \dfrac{x + 1}{x - 4}$

   Domain: $x \neq 4$

16.

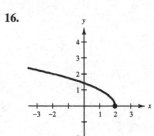

17. $g(x) = -(x - 2)^2 + 1$ is a reflection in the x-axis, horizontal shift 2 units to the right and a vertical shift 1 unit upward.

18. (0, \$26,000), (4, \$10,000)

$$m = \frac{10,000 - 26,000}{4 - 0} = \frac{-16,000}{4} = -4000$$

$$V - 26,000 = -4000(t - 0)$$

$$V = -4000t + 26,000$$

$$16,000 = -4000t + 26,000$$

$$-10,000 = -4000t$$

$$\frac{-10,000}{-4000} = t$$

$$2.5 = \frac{5}{2} = t$$

19. (a) $y = |x - 2|$

(b) $y = |x| - 2$

(c) $y = -|x| + 2$ or $2 - |x|$

CHAPTER 3
Polynomials and Factoring

CHAPTER 3
Polynomials and Factoring

Section 3.1   Adding and Subtracting Polynomials
Solutions to Odd-Numbered Exercises

1. Standard form: $10x - 4$

Degree: 1

Leading coefficient: 10

3. Standard form: $3x^2 - x + 2$

Degree: 2

Leading coefficient: 3

5. Standard form: $y^5 - 3y^4 - 2y^3 + 5$

Degree: 5

Leading coefficient: 1

7. Standard form: $-3x^3 - 2x^2 - 3$

Degree: 3

Leading coefficient: -3

9. Standard form: -4

Degree: 0

Leading coefficient: -4

11. Standard form: $-16t^2 + v_0 t$

Degree: 2

Leading coefficient: -16

13. $12 - 5y^2$ is a binomial.

15. $x^3 + 2x^2 - 4$ is a trinomial.

17. 5 is a monomial.

19. A monomial of degree 3 is any term of form ax^3 where a is any real number.

21. A binomial of degree 2 and leading coefficient of 8 is any binomial beginning $8x^2$ and containing one other term of degree less than 2 such as $8x^2 + 4$ or $8x^2 + x$.

23. $y^{-3} - 2$ is not a polynomial because the first term is not of the form ax^k (k must be nonnegative).

25. $\dfrac{8}{x}$ is not a polynomial because the term is not of the form ax^k (k must be nonnegative).

27. $5 + (2 + 3x) = (5 + 2) + 3x = 7 + 3x$

29. $(2x^2 - 3) + (5x^2 + 6) = (2x^2 + 5x^2) + (-3 + 6) = 7x^2 + 3$

31. $(5y + 6) + (4y^2 - 6y - 3) = 4y^2 + (5y - 6y) + (6 - 3) = 4y^2 - y + 3$

33. $(2 - 8y) + (-2y^4 + 3y + 2) = (-2y^4) + (-8y + 3y) + (2 + 2) = -2y^4 - 5y + 4$

35. $(8 - t^4) + (5 + t^4) = (8 + 5) + (-t^4 + t^4) = 13$

37. $(x^2 - 3x + 8) + (2x^2 - 4x) + 3x^2 = (x^2 + 2x^2 + 3x^2) + (-3x - 4x) + (8) = 6x^2 - 7x + 8$

39. $\left(\frac{2}{3}x^3 - 4x + 1\right) + \left(-\frac{3}{5} + 7x - \frac{1}{2}x^3\right) = \left(\frac{2}{3}x^3 - \frac{1}{2}x^3\right) + (-4x + 7x) + \left(1 - \frac{3}{5}\right) = \left(\frac{4}{6}x^3 - \frac{3}{6}x^3\right) + 3x + \left(\frac{5}{5} - \frac{3}{5}\right) = \frac{1}{6}x^3 + 3x + \frac{2}{5}$

41. $(6.32t - 4.51t^2) + (7.2t^2 + 1.03t - 4.2) = (-4.51t^2 + 7.2t^2) + (6.32t + 1.03t) - 4.2 = 2.69t^2 + 7.35t - 4.2$

43. $5x^2 - 3x + 4$
$\underline{-3x^2 \qquad\;\; - 4}$
$\quad 2x^2 - 3x$

45. $4x^3 - 2x^2 + 8x$
$\underline{\qquad\quad 4x^2 + \;\; x - 6}$
$\;4x^3 + \;\; 2x^2 + 9x - 6$

47. $5p^2 - 4p + 2$
$\underline{\;\; -3p^2 + 2p - 7}$
$\quad 2p^2 - 2p - 5$

49. $-3.6b^2 + 2.5b$
$\quad -2.4b^2 - 3.1b + 7.1$
$\underline{\quad\;\; 6.6b^2 \qquad\qquad}$
$\quad\; 0.6b^2 - 0.6b + 7.1$

51. $(4 - y^3) - (4 + y^3) = (4 - y^3) + (-4 - y^3)$
$\qquad\qquad\qquad\qquad = (4 - 4) + (-y^3 - y^3)$
$\qquad\qquad\qquad\qquad = -2y^3$

53. $(3x^2 - 2x + 1) - (2x^2 + x - 1) = (3x^2 - 2x + 1) + (-2x^2 - x + 1)$
$\qquad\qquad\qquad\qquad\qquad\qquad\; = (3x^2 - 2x^2) + (-2x - x) + (1 + 1)$
$\qquad\qquad\qquad\qquad\qquad\qquad\; = x^2 - 3x + 2$

55. $(6t^3 - 12) - (-t^3 + t - 2) = (6t^3 - 12) + (t^3 - t + 2)$
$\qquad\qquad\qquad\qquad\qquad\; = (6t^3 + t^3) - t + (-12 + 2)$
$\qquad\qquad\qquad\qquad\qquad\; = 7t^3 - t - 10$

57. $\left(\frac{1}{4}y^2 - 5y\right) - \left(12 + 4y - \frac{3}{2}y^2\right) = \left(\frac{1}{4}y^2 - 5y\right) + \left(-12 - 4y + \frac{3}{2}y^2\right)$
$\qquad\qquad\qquad\qquad\qquad\qquad\quad = \left(\frac{1}{4}y^2 + \frac{3}{2}y^2\right) + (-5y - 4y) - 12$
$\qquad\qquad\qquad\qquad\qquad\qquad\quad = \frac{7}{4}y^2 - 9y - 12$

59. $(10.4t^4 - 0.23t^5 + 1.3t^2) - (2.6 - 7.35t + 6.7t^2 - 9.6t^5) = (10.4t^4 - 0.23t^5 + 1.3t^2) + (-2.6 + 7.35t - 6.7t^2 + 9.6t^5)$
$\qquad\qquad\qquad\qquad\qquad\qquad\qquad\qquad\qquad\qquad\quad = (-0.23t^5 + 9.6t^5) + 10.4t^4 + (1.3t^2 - 6.7t^2) + 7.35t - 2.6$
$\qquad\qquad\qquad\qquad\qquad\qquad\qquad\qquad\qquad\qquad\quad = 9.37t^5 + 10.4t^4 - 5.4t^2 + 7.35t - 2.6$

61. $(x^3 - 3x) - [3x^3 - (x^2 + 5x)] = (x^3 - 3x) - [3x^3 - x^2 - 5x]$ **63.**
$\qquad\qquad\qquad\qquad\qquad\quad\; = x^3 - 3x - 3x^3 + x^2 + 5x$
$\qquad\qquad\qquad\qquad\qquad\quad\; = -2x^3 + x^2 + 2x$

63. $\qquad\quad x^2 - x + \;\; 3 \Longrightarrow x^2 - \;\; x + 3$
$\underline{-\qquad\quad (x - 2) \Longrightarrow \quad - x + 2}$
$\qquad\qquad\qquad\qquad\qquad\;\; x^2 - 2x + 5$

65. $\quad 25 - 15x - 2x^3 \Longrightarrow -2x^3 - 15x + 25$
$\underline{-(12 - 13x + 2x^3) \Longrightarrow -2x^3 + 13x - 12}$
$\qquad\qquad\qquad\qquad\qquad\;\; -4x^3 - \;\; 2x + 13$

67. $-3x^7 \qquad\qquad + 6x^4 + \;\; 4 \Longrightarrow -3x^7 \qquad\qquad + 6x^4 + \;\; 4$
$\underline{-(8x^7 + 10x^5 - 2x^4 - 12) \Longrightarrow -8x^7 - 10x^5 + 2x^4 + 12}$
$\qquad\qquad\qquad\qquad\qquad\qquad\qquad\;\; -11x^7 - 10x^5 + 8x^4 + 16$

69. $-(2x^3 - 3) + (4x^3 - 2x) = -2x^3 + 3 + 4x^3 - 2x$
$\qquad\qquad\qquad\qquad\qquad\;\; = (-2x^3 + 4x^3) + (-2x) + (3)$
$\qquad\qquad\qquad\qquad\qquad\;\; = 2x^3 - 2x + 3$

71. $(4x^5 - 10x^3 + 6x) - (8x^5 - 3x^3 + 11) + (4x^5 + 5x^3 - x^2) = (4x^5 - 10x^3 + 6x) + (-8x^5 + 3x^3 - 11) + (4x^5 + 5x^3 - x^2)$
$\qquad\qquad\qquad\qquad\qquad\qquad\qquad\qquad\qquad\qquad\qquad\quad = (4x^5 - 8x^5 + 4x^5) + (-10x^3 + 3x^3 + 5x^3) - x^2 + 6x - 11$
$\qquad\qquad\qquad\qquad\qquad\qquad\qquad\qquad\qquad\qquad\qquad\quad = -2x^3 - x^2 + 6x - 11$

73. $(5y^2 - 2y) - [(y^2 + y) - (3y^2 - 6y + 2)] = (5y^2 - 2y) - [(y^2 + y) + (-3y^2 + 6y - 2)]$

$$= (5y^2 - 2y) - [(y^2 - 3y^2) + (y + 6y) - 2]$$

$$= (5y^2 - 2y) - [-2y^2 + 7y - 2]$$

$$= (5y^2 - 2y) + (2y^2 - 7y + 2)$$

$$= (5y^2 + 2y^2) + (-2y - 7y) + 2$$

$$= 7y^2 - 9y + 2$$

75. $(8x^3 - 4x^2 + 3x) - [(x^3 - 4x^2 + 5) + (x - 5)] = (8x^3 - 4x^2 + 3x) - [x^3 - 4x^2 + x]$

$$= (8x^3 - 4x^2 + 3x) + (-x^3 + 4x^2 - x)$$

$$= (8x^3 - x^3) + (-4x^2 + 4x^2) + (3x - x)$$

$$= 7x^3 + 2x$$

77. $3(4x^2 - 1) + (3x^3 - 7x^2 + 5) = 12x^2 - 3 + 3x^3 - 7x^2 + 5$

$$= 3x^3 + 5x^2 + 2$$

79. $2(t^2 + 12) - 5(t^2 + 5) + 6(t^2 + 5) = 2t^2 + 24 - 5t^2 - 25 + 6t^2 + 30$

$$= (2t^2 - 5t^2 + 6t^2) + (24 - 25 + 30)$$

$$= 3t^2 + 29$$

81. $15v - 3(3v - v^2) + 9(8v + 3) = 15v - 9v + 3v^2 + 72v + 27$

$$= (3v^2) + (15v - 9v + 72v) + 27$$

$$= 3v^2 + 78v + 27$$

83. $5s - [6s - (30s + 8)] = 5s - [6s - 30s - 8]$

$$= (5s - 6s + 30s) + (8)$$

$$= 29s + 8$$

85. *Keystrokes:*

y_1 [Y=] [(] [X,T,θ] [^] 3 [−] 3 [X,T,θ] [x²] [−] 2 [)] [−] [(] [X,T,θ] [x²] [+] 1 [)] [ENTER]

y_2 [X,T,θ] [^] 3 [−] 4 [X,T,θ] [x²] [−] 3 [GRAPH]

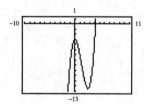

y_1 and y_2 represent equivalent expressions since the graphs of y_1 and y_2 are identical.

87. $h(x) = f(x) + g(x)$

$$= (4x^3 - 3x^2 + 7) + (9 - x - x^2 - 5x^3)$$

$$= (4x^3 - 5x^3) + (-3x^2 - x^2) - x + (7 + 9)$$

$$= -x^3 - 4x^2 - x + 16$$

89. *Polynomial*   *Value*   *Substitute*   *Simplify*

$h(t) = -16t^2 + 64$ (a) $t = 0$ $-16(0)^2 + 64$ 64 feet

(b) $t = \frac{1}{2}$ $-16\left(\frac{1}{2}\right)^2 + 64$ 60 feet

(c) $t = 1$ $-16(1)^2 + 64$ 48 feet

(d) $t = 2$ $-16(2)^2 + 64$ 0 feet

At time $t = 0$, the object is at 64 feet and continues to fall, reaching the ground at time $t = 2$.

91. *Polynomial*   *Value*   *Substitute*   *Simplify*

$h(t) = -16t^2 + 80t + 50$ (a) $t = 0$ $-16(0)^2 + 80(0) + 50$ 50 feet

(b) $t = 2$ $-16(2)^2 + 80(2) + 50$ 146 feet

(c) $t = 4$ $-16(4)^2 + 80(4) + 50$ 114 feet

(d) $t = 5$ $-16(5)^2 + 80(5) + 50$ 50 feet

At time $t = 0$, the object is at a height of 50 feet. The object moves upward, reaches a maximum height and returns downward. At time $t = 5$, object is again at a height of 50 feet.

93. The free-falling object was dropped.

$-16(0)^2 + 100 = 100$ feet

95. The free-falling object was thrown downward.

$-16(0)^2 - 24(0) + 50 = 50$ feet

97. $h = -16(1)^2 + 40(1) + 200 = 224$ feet

$h = -16(2)^2 + 40(2) + 200 = 216$ feet

$h = -16(3)^2 + 40(3) + 200 = 176$ feet

99. *Verbal model:* $\boxed{\text{Profit}} = \boxed{\text{Revenue}} - \boxed{\text{Cost}}$

Equation: $P = R - C$

$P = 14x - (8x + 15,000)$

$P = 6x - 15,000$

$P = 6(5000) - 15,000$

$P = \$15,000$

101. Perimeter of region $= 2(2x + 4) + 4x + 2(3x)$

$= 4x + 8 + 4x + 6x$

$= 14x + 8$

103. Area of region $= \left(6 \cdot \frac{3}{2}x\right) + \left(6 \cdot \frac{9}{2}x\right)$ or $6 \cdot \left[\frac{3}{2}x + \frac{9}{2}x\right]$

$= 9x + 27x$ or $6\left[\frac{12}{2}x\right]$

$= 36x$ or $36x$

105. Area $= 12(x + 6) - 7x$

$= 12x + 72 - 7x$

$= 5x + 72$

107. (a) *Verbal model:*

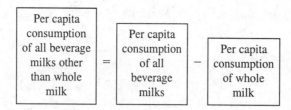

| Per capita consumption of all beverage milks other than whole milk | = | Per capita consumption of all beverage milks | − | Per capita consumption of whole milk |

Equation: $y = (231.06 + 0.009t - 0.095t^2) - (171.17 - 11.415t + 0.325t^2)$

$y = 231.06 + 0.009t - 0.095t^2 + (-171.17 + 11.415t - 0.325t^2)$

$= (231.06 - 171.17) + (0.009t + 11.415t) + (-0.095t^2 - 0.325t^2)$

$= 59.89 + 11.424t - 0.42t^2$

$= -0.42t^2 + 11.424t + 59.89$

(b) *Keystrokes:*

$\boxed{Y=}$ 59.89 $\boxed{+}$ 11.4141 $\boxed{X,T,\theta}$ $\boxed{-}$ .42 $\boxed{X,T,\theta}$ $\boxed{x^2}$ $\boxed{GRAPH}$

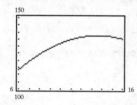

No, this model was increasing over the interval $6 \le t \le 13.6$.

109. The degree of the term ax^k is k. The term of highest degree in a polynomial has the same degree as the polynomial.

111. $8x^2 - 3x^2 = (8 - 3)x^2 = 5x^2$

113. No, not every trinomial is a second-degree polynomial. For example, $x^3 + 2x + 3$ is a trinomial of third-degree.

Section 3.2   Multiplying Polynomials

1. $t^3 \cdot t^4 = (t \cdot t \cdot t)(t \cdot t \cdot t \cdot t) = t^{3+4} = t^7$

3. $(-5x)^5 = -5x \cdot -5x \cdot -5x \cdot -5x \cdot -5x$

$= -5 \cdot -5 \cdot -5 \cdot -5 \cdot -5 \cdot x \cdot x \cdot x \cdot x \cdot x$

$= (-5)^5 x^5 = -3125x^5$

5. $(u^4)^2 = u^4 \cdot u^4$

$= u^{4+4}$

$= u^8$

7. $\dfrac{x^6}{x^4} = \dfrac{x \cdot x \cdot x \cdot x \cdot x \cdot x}{x \cdot x \cdot x \cdot x} = x^{6-4} = x^2$

9. $\left(\dfrac{y}{5}\right)^4 = \dfrac{y}{5} \cdot \dfrac{y}{5} \cdot \dfrac{y}{5} \cdot \dfrac{y}{5} = \dfrac{y \cdot y \cdot y \cdot y}{5 \cdot 5 \cdot 5 \cdot 5} = \dfrac{y^4}{5^4} = \dfrac{y^4}{625}$

11. (a) $-3x^3 \cdot x^5 = -3(x^3 \cdot x^5) = -3x^{3+5} = -3x^8$ (b) $(-3x)^2 \cdot x^5 = 9x^2 \cdot x^5 = 9x^{2+5} = 9x^7$

13. (a) $(-5z^2)^3 = (-5)^3 \cdot (z^2)^3 = -125z^{2\cdot3} = -125z^6$ (b) $(-5z^4)^2 = (-5)^2(z^4)^2 = 25z^{4\cdot2} = 25z^8$

15. (a) $(u^3v)(2v^2) = 2 \cdot u^3 \cdot v^{1+2} = 2u^3v^3$ (b) $(-4u^4)(u^5v) = -4 \cdot u^{4+5} \cdot v = -4u^9v$

17. (a) $5u^2 \cdot (-3u^6) = 5 \cdot -3 \cdot u^2 \cdot u^6 = -15u^{2+6} = -15u^8$ (b) $(2u)^4(4u) = 2^4u^4 \cdot 4u = 16 \cdot 4 \cdot u^{4+1} = 64u^5$

19. (a) $-(m^5n)^3(-m^2n^2)^2 = -m^{5\cdot3}n^3 \cdot m^{2\cdot2}n^{2\cdot2}$

$$= -m^{15}n^3 \cdot m^4n^4$$

$$= -m^{15+4} \cdot n^{3+4} = -m^{19}n^7$$

(b) $(-m^5n)(m^2n^2) = -m^{5+2}n^{1+2} = -m^7n^3$

21. (a) $\dfrac{27m^5n^6}{9mn^3} = \dfrac{27}{9} \cdot \dfrac{m^5}{m} \cdot \dfrac{n^6}{n^3}$

$$= 3 \cdot m^{5-1} \cdot n^{6-3}$$

$$= 3m^4n^3$$

(b) $\dfrac{-18m^3n^6}{-6mn^3} = \dfrac{-18}{-6} \cdot \dfrac{m^3}{m} \cdot \dfrac{n^6}{n^3}$

$$= 3 \cdot m^{3-1} \cdot n^{6-3}$$

$$= 3m^2n^3$$

23. (a) $\left(\dfrac{3x}{4y}\right)^2 = \dfrac{3^2 \cdot x^2}{4^2 \cdot y^2}$

$$= \dfrac{9x^2}{16y^2}$$

(b) $\left(\dfrac{5u}{3v}\right)^3 = \dfrac{5^3 \cdot u^3}{3^3 \cdot v^3}$

$$= \dfrac{125u^3}{27v^3}$$

25. (a) $\dfrac{(-3x^2y)^3}{9x^2y^2} = -\dfrac{(-3)^3(x^2)^3y^3}{9x^2y^2}$

$$= \dfrac{(-27)x^6y^3}{9x^2y^2}$$

$$= \dfrac{27x^{6-2}y^{3-2}}{9}$$

$$= 3x^4y$$

(b) $-\dfrac{(-2xy^3)^2}{6y^2} = -\dfrac{(-2)^2x^2(y^3)^2}{6y^2}$

$$= -\dfrac{4x^2y^6}{6y^2}$$

$$= -\dfrac{2x^2y^{6-2}}{3}$$

$$= -\dfrac{2x^2y^4}{3}$$

27. (a) $\left[\dfrac{(-5u^3v)^2}{10u^2v}\right]^2 = \left[\dfrac{(-5)^2 \cdot (u^3)^2 \cdot (v)^2}{10u^2v}\right]^2$

$$= \left[\dfrac{25u^6v^2}{10u^2v}\right]^2$$

$$= \left[\dfrac{25}{10} \cdot \dfrac{u^6}{u^2} \cdot \dfrac{v^2}{v}\right]^2$$

$$= \left[\dfrac{5}{2} \cdot u^{6-2} \cdot v^{2-1}\right]^2$$

$$= \left[\dfrac{5}{2}u^4v\right]^2$$

$$= \dfrac{25}{4}u^8v^2$$

(a) $\left[\dfrac{-5(u^3v)^2}{10u^2v}\right]^2 = \left[\dfrac{-5 \cdot (u^3)^2 \cdot (v)^2}{10u^2v}\right]^2$

$$= \left[\dfrac{-5u^6v^2}{10u^2v}\right]^2$$

$$= \left[\dfrac{-5}{10} \cdot \dfrac{u^6}{u^2} \cdot \dfrac{v^2}{v}\right]^2$$

$$= \left[-\dfrac{1}{2} \cdot u^{6-2} \cdot v^{2-1}\right]^2$$

$$= \left[\dfrac{-1}{2}u^4v\right]^2$$

$$= \dfrac{1}{4}u^8v^2$$

29. (a) $\dfrac{x^{2n+4}y^{4n}}{x^5 y^{2n+1}} = x^{2n+4-5}y^{4n-(2n+1)} = x^{2n-1}y^{4n-2n-1} = x^{2n-1}y^{2n-1}$

(b) $\dfrac{x^{6n}y^{n-7}}{x^{4n+2}y^5} = x^{6n-(4n+2)}y^{n-7-5} = x^{6n-4n-2}y^{n-12} = x^{2n-2}y^{n-12}$

31. $(-2a^2)(-8a) = (-2)(-8)a^2 \cdot a = 16a^{2+1} = 16a^3$ **33.** $2y(5-y) = (2y)(5) - (2y)(y) = 10y - 2y^2$

35. $4x(2x^2 - 3x + 5) = (4x)(2x^2) - (4x)(3x) + (4x)(5) = 8x^3 - 12x^2 + 20x$

37. $-2x^2(5 + 3x^2 - 7x^3) = (-2x^2)(5) + (-2x^2)(3x^2) - (-2x^2)(7x^3) = -10x^2 - 6x^4 + 14x^5$

39. $-x^3(x^4 - 2x^3 + 5x - 6) = -x^3(x^4) - x^3(-2x^3) - x^3(5x) - x^3(-6) = -x^7 + 2x^6 - 5x^4 + 6x^3$

41. $-3x(-5x)(5x+2) = (-3x)(-5x)(5x+2) = 15x^2(5x+2) = 15x^2(5x) + 15x^2(2) = 75x^3 + 30x^2$

43. $u^2v(3u^4 - 5u^2 + 6uv^3) = u^2v(3u^4) + u^2v(-5u^2) + u^2v(6uv^3) = 3u^6v - 5u^4v + 6u^3v^4$

45. $(x+2)(x+4) = x^2 + 4x + 2x + 8 = x^2 + 6x + 8$

47. $(x-6)(x+5) = x^2 + 5x - 6x - 30 = x^2 - x - 30$

49. $(x-4)(x-4) = x^2 - 4x - 4x + 16 = x^2 - 8x + 16$

51. $(2x-3)(x+5) = 2x^2 + 10x - 3x - 15 = 2x^2 + 7x - 15$

53. $(5x-2)(2x-6) = 10x^2 - 30x - 4x + 12 = 10x^2 - 34x + 12$

55. $(8 - 3x^2)(4x+1) = 32x + 8 - 12x^3 - 3x^2 = -12x^3 - 3x^2 + 32x + 8$

57. $\left(4y - \frac{1}{3}\right)(12y + 9) = 48y^2 + 36y - 4y - 3 = 48y^2 + 32y - 3$

59. $(2x+y)(3x+2y) = 6x^2 + 4xy + 3xy + 2y^2 = 6x^2 + 7xy + 2y^2$

61. $(2t-1)(t+1) + 1(2t-5)(t-1) = 2t^2 + 2t - t - 1 + 2t^2 - 2t - 5t + 5 = 4t^2 - 6t + 4$

63. $(x-1)(x^2 - 4x + 6) = (x-1)(x^2) + (x-1)(-4x) + (x-1)(6)$

$$= x^3 - x^2 - 4x^2 + 4x + 6x - 6$$

$$= x^3 - 5x^2 + 10x - 6$$

65. $(3a+2)(a^2 + 3a + 1) = (3a+2)(a^2) + (3a+2)(3a) + (3a+2)(1)$

$$= 3a^3 + 2a^2 + 9a^2 + 6a + 3a + 2$$

$$= 3a^3 + 11a^2 + 9a + 2$$

67. $(2u^2 + 3u - 4)(4u + 5) = (4u + 5)(2u^2) + (4u + 5)(3u) + (4u + 5)(-4)$

$= 8u^3 + 10u^2 + 12u^2 + 15u - 16u - 20$

$= 8u^3 + 22u^2 - u - 20$

69. $(x^3 - 3x + 2)(x - 2) = x^3(x - 2) + (-3x)(x - 2) + 2(x - 2)$

$= x^4 - 2x^3 - 3x^2 + 6x + 2x - 4$

$= x^4 - 2x^3 - 3x^2 + 8x - 4$

71. $(5x^2 + 2)(x^2 + 4x - 1) = (5x^2 + 2)(x^2) + (5x^2 + 2)(4x) + (5x^2 + 2)(-1)$

$= 5x^4 + 2x^2 + 20x^3 + 8x - 5x^2 - 2$

$= 5x^4 + 20x^3 - 3x^2 + 8x - 2$

73. $(t^2 + t - 2)(t^2 - t + 2) = t^2(t^2 - t + 2) + t(t^2 - t + 2) - 2(t^2 - t + 2)$

$= t^4 - t^3 + 2t^2 + t^3 - t^2 + 2t - 2t^2 + 2t - 4$

$= t^4 - t^2 + 4t - 4$

75.

$$\begin{array}{r} 7x^2 - 14x + 9 \\ \underline{4x^3 \qquad\qquad + 3} \\ + 21x^2 - 42x + 27 \\ \underline{28x^5 - 56x^4 + 36x^3} \\ 28x^5 - 56x^4 + 36x^3 + 21x^2 - 42x + 27 \end{array}$$

77.

$$\begin{array}{r} 2u^2 + 5u + 3 \\ \underline{u - 2} \\ -4u^2 - 10u - 6 \\ \underline{2u^3 + 5u^2 + 3u} \\ 2u^3 + u^2 - 7u - 6 \end{array}$$

79.

$$\begin{array}{r} -x^2 + 2x - 1 \\ \underline{2x + 1} \\ -x^2 + 2x - 1 \\ \underline{-2x^3 + 4x^2 - 2x} \\ -2x^3 + 3x^2 \quad - 1 \end{array}$$

81.

$$\begin{array}{r} t^2 + t - 2 \\ \underline{t^2 - t + 2} \\ + 2t^2 + 2t - 4 \\ - t^3 - t^2 + 2t \\ \underline{t^4 + t^3 - 2t^2} \\ t^4 \quad - t^2 + 4t - 4 \end{array}$$

83. $(x + 2)(x - 2) = (x)^2 - (2)^2$

$= x^2 - 4$

85. $(x - 7)(x + 7) = (x)^2 - (7)^2$

$= x^2 - 49$

87. $(2 + 7y)(2 - 7y) = (2)^2 - (7y)^2 = 4 - 49y^2$

89. $(6 - 4x)(6 + 4x) = (6)^2 - (4x)^2 = 36 - 16x^2$

91. $(2a + 5b)(2a - 5b) = (2a)^2 - (5b)^2 = 4a^2 - 25b^2$

93. $(6x - 9y)(6x + 9y) = (6x)^2 - (9y)^2 = 36x^2 - 81y^2$

95. $\left(2x - \frac{1}{4}\right)\left(2x + \frac{1}{4}\right) = (2x)^2 - \left(\frac{1}{4}\right)^2 = 4x^2 - \frac{1}{16}$

97. $(0.2t + 0.5)(0.2t - 0.5) = (0.2t)^2 - (0.5)^2$

$= 0.04t^2 - 0.25$

99. $(x + 5)^2 = (x)^2 + 2(x)(5) + (5)^2 = x^2 + 10x + 25$

101. $(x - 10)^2 = (x)^2 - 2(x)(10) + 10^2 = x^2 - 20x + 100$

103. $(2x + 5)^2 = (2x)^2 + 2(2x)(5) + (5)^2 = 4x^2 + 20x + 25$ **105.** $(6x - 1)^2 = (6x)^2 - 2(6x)(1) + (1)^2 = 36x^2 - 12x + 1$

107. $(2x - 7y)^2 = (2x)^2 - 2(2x)(7y) + (7y)^2 = 4x^2 - 28xy + 49y^2$

109. $[(x + 2) + y]^2 = (x + 2)^2 + 2(x + 2)y + y^2 = (x)^2 + 2(x)(2) + (2)^2 + 2xy + 4y + y^2 = x^2 + 4x + 4 + 2xy + 4y + y^2$

111. $[u - (v - 3)][u + (v - 3)] = (u)^2 - (v - 3)^2 = u^2 - [v^2 - 2(v)(3) + (3)^2] = u^2 - (v^2 - 6v + 9) = u^2 - v^2 + 6v - 9$

113. $(x + 3)^3 = (x + 3)(x + 3)(x + 3)$

$\qquad = (x^2 + 3x + 3x + 9)(x + 3)$

$\qquad = (x^2 + 6x + 9)(x + 3)$

$$\begin{array}{r} x^2 + 6x + 9 \\ x + 3 \\ \hline 3x^2 + 18x + 27 \\ x^3 + 6x^2 + 9x \\ \hline x^3 + 9x^2 + 27x + 27 \end{array}$$

115. $(u + v)^3 = (u + v)(u + v)(u + v)$

$\qquad = (u^2 + uv + uv + v^2)(u + v)$

$\qquad = (u^2 + 2uv + v^2)(u + v)$

$$\begin{array}{r} u^2 + 2uv + v^2 \\ u + v \\ \hline u^2v + 2uv^2 + v^3 \\ u^3 + 2u^2v + uv^2 \\ \hline u^3 + 3u^2v + 3uv^2 + v^3 \end{array}$$

117. *Keystrokes:*

y_1 [Y=] [(] [X,T,θ] [+] 1 [)] [(] [X,T,θ] [x^2] [−] [X,T,θ] [+] 2 [)] [ENTER]

y_2 [X,T,θ] [^] 3 [+] [X,T,θ] [+] 2 [GRAPH]

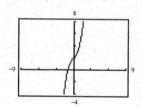

$y_1 = y_2$ because $(x + 1)(x^2 - x + 2) = x^3 - x^2 + 2x + x^2 - x + 2 = x^3 + x + 2$

119. *Keystrokes:*

y_1 [Y=] [(] 2 [X,T,θ] [−] 3 [)] [(] [X,T,θ] [+] 2 [)] [ENTER]

y_2 2 [X,T,θ] [x^2] [+] [X,T,θ] [−] 6 [GRAPH]

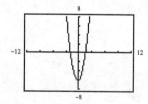

$y_1 = y_2$ because $(2x - 3)(x + 2) = 2x^2 + 4x - 3x - 6 = 2x^2 + x - 6$

121. (a) $f(t - 3) = (t - 3)^2 - 2(t - 3)$

$\qquad = t^2 - 6t + 9 - 2t + 6$

$\qquad = t^2 - 8t + 15$

(b) $f(2 + h) - f(2) = [(2 + h)^2 - 2(2 + h)] - [2^2 - 2(2)]$

$\qquad = (4 + 4h + h^2 - 4 - 2h) - (0)$

$\qquad = 2h + h^2$

123. (a) *Verbal model:* $\boxed{\text{Volume}}$ $=$ $\boxed{\text{Length}}$ $\cdot$ $\boxed{\text{Width}}$ $\cdot$ $\boxed{\text{Height}}$

 Function: $V(n) = n \cdot (n + 2) \cdot (n + 4)$

$= n(n^2 + 6n + 8)$

$= n^3 + 6n^2 + 8n$

(b) $V(2) = 2 \cdot (2 + 2) \cdot (2 + 4)$

$= 2(4)(6)$

$= 48$ cubic inches

(c) *Verbal model:* $\boxed{\text{Area}}$ $=$ $\boxed{\text{Length}}$ $\cdot$ $\boxed{\text{Width}}$

 Function: $A(n) = n \cdot (n + 2)$

$= n^2 + 2n$

(d) *Function:* $\text{Area} = (n + 4)(n + 2 + 4)$

$= (n + 4)(n + 6)$

$= n^2 + 6n + 4n + 24$

$= n^2 + 10n + 24 = A(n + 4)$

$A(n + 4) = (n + 4)(n + 4 + 2)$

$= (n + 4)(n + 6)$

$= n^2 + 10n + 24$

125. *Verbal model:* $\boxed{\begin{array}{c}\text{Area of}\\\text{Shaded}\\\text{Region}\end{array}}$ $=$ $\boxed{\begin{array}{c}\text{Area of}\\\text{Outside}\\\text{Rectangle}\end{array}}$ $-$ $\boxed{\begin{array}{c}\text{Area of}\\\text{Inside}\\\text{Rectangle}\end{array}}$

 Function: $A(x) = 3x(3x + 10) - x(x + 4)$

$= 9x^2 + 30x - x^2 - 4x$

$= 8x^2 + 26x$

127. *Verbal model:* $\boxed{\begin{array}{c}\text{Area of}\\\text{Shaded}\\\text{Region}\end{array}}$ $=$ $\boxed{\begin{array}{c}\text{Area of}\\\text{Larger}\\\text{Triangle}\end{array}}$ $-$ $\boxed{\begin{array}{c}\text{Area of}\\\text{Smaller}\\\text{Triangle}\end{array}}$

 Function: $A(x) = \frac{1}{2}(2x)(1.6x) - \frac{1}{2}(x)(0.8x)$

$= 1.6x^2 - 0.4x^2$

$= 1.2x^2$

129. (a) *Verbal model:* $\boxed{\text{Perimeter}}$ $= 2$ $\boxed{\text{Length}}$ $+ 2$ $\boxed{\text{Width}}$ (b) *Verbal model:* $\boxed{\text{Area}}$ $=$ $\boxed{\text{Length}}$ $\cdot$ $\boxed{\text{Width}}$

$P = 2\left(\frac{3}{2}w\right) + 2w$ $A = \left(\frac{3}{2}w\right)(w)$

$= 3w + 2w$ $A = \frac{3}{2}w^2$

$P = 5w$

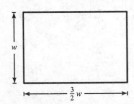

131. Interest $= 1000(1 + r)^2$

$\qquad\qquad = 1000(1 + r)(1 + r)$

$\qquad\qquad = 1000(1 + 2r + r^2)$

$\qquad\qquad = 1000 + 2000r + 1000r^2$

133. Area $= l \cdot w$

$\qquad\qquad = (x + a)(x + b)$

$\qquad\qquad = x^2 + ax + bx + ab$

Area $= (x \cdot x) + (x \cdot a) + (x \cdot b) + (a \cdot b)$

$\qquad\quad = x^2 + ax + bx + ab$

Formula: $(x + a)(x + b) = x^2 + ax + bx + ab$.

Distributive Property

135. (a) $(x - 1)(x + 1) = x^2 - 1$

(b) $(x - 1)(x^2 + x + 1) = x^3 + x^2 + x - x^2 - x - 1 = x^3 - 1$

(c) $(x - 1)(x^3 + x^2 + x + 1) = x^4 + x^3 + x^2 + x - x^3 - x^2 - x - 1 = x^4 - 1$

$(x - 1)(x^4 + x^3 + x^2 + x + 1) = x^5 - 1$

137. (a) *Verbal model:* $\boxed{\text{Volume}} = \boxed{\text{Length}} \cdot \boxed{\text{Width}} \cdot \boxed{\text{Height}}$

Labels: Volume $= V_B(x)$

Length $= 3x - 2$

Width $= x + 5$

Height $= x$

Function: $V_B(x) = (3x - 2)(x + 5)x$

$\qquad\qquad = (3x^2 + 15x - 2x - 10)x$

$\qquad\qquad = (3x^2 + 13x - 10)x$

$\qquad\qquad = 3x^3 + 13x^2 - 10x$

(b) *Verbal model:* $\boxed{\text{Volume}} = \frac{1}{3} \cdot \boxed{\text{Area of base}} \cdot \boxed{\text{Height}}$

Labels: Volume $= V_P(x)$

Area of base $= (2x - 6)(x - 1)$

Height $= x - 3$

Function: $V_P(x) = \frac{1}{3}(2x - 6)(x - 1)(x - 3)$

$\qquad\qquad = \frac{1}{3}(2x^2 - 8x + 6)(x - 3)$

$\qquad\qquad = \frac{1}{3}(2x^3 - 8x^2 + 6x - 6x^2 + 24x - 18)$

$\qquad\qquad = \frac{1}{3}(2x^3 - 14x^2 + 30x - 18)$

$\qquad\qquad = \frac{2}{3}x^3 - \frac{14}{3}x^2 + 10x - 6$

(c) *Verbal model:* $\boxed{\begin{array}{c}\text{Volume}\\\text{of grain}\end{array}} = \boxed{\begin{array}{c}\text{Volume}\\\text{of bin}\end{array}} - \boxed{\begin{array}{c}\text{Volume}\\\text{of pyramid}\end{array}}$

Function: $V_S(x) = (3x^3 + 13x^2 - 10x) - \left(\frac{2}{3}x^3 - \frac{14}{3}x^2 + 10x - 6\right)$

$\qquad\qquad = 3x^3 + 13x^2 - 10x - \frac{2}{3}x^3 + \frac{14}{3}x^2 - 10x + 6$

$\qquad\qquad = \frac{7}{3}x^3 + \frac{53}{3}x^2 - 20x + 6$

139. $(2x)^3 = 2^3 \cdot x^3 = 8x^3 \neq 2x^3$

141. F = First

O = Outer

I = Inner

L = Last

143. (a) True, the product of two monomials is a monomial.

(b) False, the product of two binomials can be a trinomial. For example, $(x + 2)(x - 3) = x^2 - x - 6$.

Section 3.3   Factoring Polynomials

1. $48 = 2^4 \cdot 3$

$90 = 5 \cdot 2 \cdot 3^2$

$96 = 2^5 \cdot 3$

GCF $= 2 \cdot 3 = 6$

3. $3x^2 = 3 \cdot x \cdot x$

$12x = 2^2 \cdot 3 \cdot x$

GCF $= 3x$

5. $30z^2 = 2 \cdot 3 \cdot 5 \cdot z \cdot z$

$-12z^3 = -1 \cdot 2^2 \cdot 3 \cdot z \cdot z \cdot z$

GCF $= 2 \cdot 3 \cdot z \cdot z$

$= 6z^2$

7. $28b^2 = 7 \cdot 2^2 \cdot b \cdot b$

$14b^3 = 7 \cdot 2 \cdot b \cdot b \cdot b$

$42b^5 = 7 \cdot 2 \cdot 3 \cdot b \cdot b \cdot b \cdot b \cdot b$

GCF $= 7 \cdot 2 \cdot b \cdot b$

$= 14b^2$

9. $42(x + 8)^2 = 7 \cdot 3 \cdot 2 \cdot (x + 8)^2$

$63(x + 8)^3 = 7 \cdot 3^2 \cdot (x + 8)^3$

GCF $= 7 \cdot 3(x + 8)^2$

$= 21(x + 8)^2$

11. $8z - 8 = 8(z - 1)$

13. $4u + 10 = 2(2u + 5)$

15. $24x^2 - 18 = 6(4x^2 - 3)$

17. $2x^2 + x = x(2x + 1)$

19. $21u^2 - 14u = 7u(3u - 2)$

21. $11u^2 + 9$ is prime (No common factor other than 1.)

23. $28x^2 + 16x - 8 = 4(7x^2 + 4x - 2)$

25. $3x^2y^2 - 15y = 3y(x^2y - 5)$

27. $15xy^2 - 3x^2y + 9xy = 3xy(5y - x + 3)$

29. $14x^4y^3 + 21x^3y^2 + 9x^2 = x^2(14x^2y^3 + 21xy^2 + 9)$

31. $10 - x = -1(-10 + x) = -1(x - 10)$

33. $7 - 14x = -7(-1 + 2x) = -7(2x - 1)$

35. $16 + 4x - 6x^2 = -1(-16 - 4x + 6x^2) = -1(6x^2 - 4x - 16) = -2(3x^2 - 2x - 8)$

37. $y - 3y^3 - 2y^2 = -1(-y + 3y^3 + 2y^2) = -1(3y^3 + 2y^2 - y) = -y(3y^2 + 2y - 1)$

39. $2y - \frac{3}{5} = \frac{1}{5}(10y - 3)$

41. $\frac{3}{2}x + \frac{5}{4} = \frac{1}{4}(6x + 5)$

43. $2y(y - 3) + 5(y - 3) = (y - 3)(2y + 5)$

45. $5x(3x + 2) - 3(3x + 2) = (3x + 2)(5x - 3)$

47. $2(7a + 6) - 3a^2(7a + 6) = (7a + 6)(2 - 3a^2)$

49. $8t^3(4t - 1)^2 + 3(4t - 1)^2 = (4t - 1)^2(8t^3 + 3)$

51. $(x - 5)(4x + 9) - (3x + 4)(4x + 9) = (4x + 9)(x - 5 - 3x - 4) = (4x + 9)(-2x - 9)$

53. $x^2 + 25x + x + 25 = (x^2 + 25x) + (x + 25) = x(x + 25) + 1(x + 25) = (x + 25)(x + 1)$

55. $y^2 - 6y + 2y - 12 = (y^2 - 6y) + (2y - 12)$

$= y(y - 6) + 2(y - 6)$

$= (y - 6)(y + 2)$

57. $x^3 + 2x^2 + x + 2 = (x^3 + 2x^2) + (x + 2)$

$= x^2(x + 2) + 1(x + 2)$

$= (x + 2)(x^2 + 1)$

59. $3a^3 - 12a^2 - 2a + 8 = (3a^3 - 12a^2) + (-2a + 8)$

$= 3a^2(a - 4) - 2(a - 4)$

$= (a - 4)(3a^2 - 2)$

61. $z^4 - 2z + 3z^3 - 6 = (z^4 - 2z) + (3z^3 - 6)$

$= z(z^3 - 2) + 3(z^3 - 2)$

$= (z^3 - 2)(z + 3)$

63. $5x^3 - 10x^2y + 7xy^2 - 14y^3 = (5x^3 - 10x^2y) + (7xy^2 - 14y^3)$

$= 5x^2(x - 2y) + 7y^2(x - 2y)$

$= (x - 2y)(5x^2 + 7y^2)$

65. $x^2 - 64 = x^2 - 8^2$

$= (x - 8)(x + 8)$

67. $1 - a^2 = 1^2 - a^2$

$= (1 - a)(1 + a)$

69. $16y^2 - 9 = (4y)^2 - 3^2$

$= (4y - 3)(4y + 3)$

71. $81 - 4x^2 = 9^2 - (2x)^2$

$= (9 - 2x)(9 + 2x)$

73. $4z^2 - y^2 = (2z - y)(2z + y)$

75. $36x^2 - 25y^2 = (6x)^2 - (5y)^2$

$= (6x - 5y)(6x + 5y)$

77. $u^2 - \frac{1}{16} = u^2 - \left(\frac{1}{4}\right)^2$

$= \left(u - \frac{1}{4}\right)\left(u + \frac{1}{4}\right)$

79. $\frac{4}{9}x^2 - \frac{16}{25}y^2 = \left(\frac{2}{3}x\right)^2 - \left(\frac{4}{5}y\right)^2$

$= \left(\frac{2}{3}x - \frac{4}{5}y\right)\left(\frac{2}{3}x + \frac{4}{5}y\right)$

81. $(x - 1)^2 - 16 = [(x - 1) - 4][(x - 1) + 4] = (x - 5)(x + 3)$

83. $81 - (z + 5)^2 = 9^2 - (z + 5)^2 = [9 - (z + 5)][9 + (z + 5)] = [9 - z - 5][9 + z + 5] = (4 - z)(14 + z)$

85. $(2x + 5)^2 - (x - 4)^2 = [(2x + 5) - (x - 4)][(2x + 5) + (x - 4)] = [2x + 5 - x + 4][2x + 5 + x - 4] = (x + 9)(3x + 1)$

87. $x^3 - 8 = x^3 - 2^3$

$= (x - 2)(x^2 + 2x + 4)$

89. $y^3 + 64 = y^3 + 4^3$

$= (y + 4)(y^2 - 4y + 16)$

91. $8t^3 - 27 = (2t)^3 - 3^3$

$= (2t - 3)(4t^2 + 6t + 9)$

93. $27u^3 + 1 = (3u)^3 + 1^3$

$= (3u + 1)(9u^2 - 3u + 1)$

95. $64a^3 + b^3 = (4a)^3 + b^3$

$= (4a + b)(16a^2 - 4ab + b^2)$

97. $x^3 + 27y^3 = x^3 + (3y)^3$

$= (x + 3y)(x^2 - 3xy + 9y^2)$

99. $8 - 50x^2 = 2(4 - 25x^2)$

$= 2[2^2 - (5x)^2]$

$= 2[2 - 5x][2 + 5x]$

101. $8x^3 + 64 = 8(x^3 + 8)$

$\qquad\qquad = 8(x^3 + 2^3)$

$\qquad\qquad = 8(x + 2)(x^2 - 2x + 4)$

103. $y^4 - 81 = (y^2)^2 - 9^2$

$\qquad\qquad = (y^2 - 9)(y^2 + 9)$

$\qquad\qquad = (y - 3)(y + 3)(y^2 + 9)$

105. $3x^4 - 300x^2 = 3x^2(x^2 - 100)$

$\qquad\qquad\quad = 3x^2(x - 10)(x + 10)$

107. $6x^6 - 48y^6 = 6(x^6 - 8y^6)$

$\qquad\qquad\quad = 6[(x^2)^3 - (2y^2)^3]$

$\qquad\qquad\quad = 6(x^2 - 2y^2)(x^4 + 2x^2y^2 + 4y^4)$

109. $4x^{2n} - 25 = (2x^n)^2 - 5^2$

$\qquad\qquad\quad = (2x^n - 5)(2x^n + 5)$

111. *Keystrokes:*

y_1 [Y=] 3 [X,T,θ] [−] 6 [ENTER]

y_2 3 [(] [X,T,θ] [−] 2 [)] [GRAPH]

$y_1 = y_2$

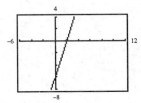

113. *Keystrokes:*

y_1 [Y=] [X,T,θ] [x^2] [−] 4 [ENTER]

y_2 [(] [X,T,θ] [+] 2 [)] [(] [X,T,θ] [−] 2 [)] [GRAPH]

$y_1 = y_2$

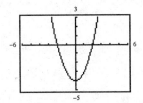

115. $3x^3 + 4x^2 - 3x - 4 = (3x^3 + 4x^2) + (-3x - 4)$

$\qquad\qquad\qquad\qquad\quad = x^2(3x + 4) - 1(3x + 4)$ or

$\qquad\qquad\qquad\qquad\quad = (x^2 - 1)(3x + 4)$

$\qquad\qquad\qquad\qquad\quad = (x - 1)(x + 1)(3x + 4)$

$\qquad\qquad\qquad\qquad\quad = (3x^3 - 3x) + (4x^2 - 4)$

$\qquad\qquad\qquad\qquad\quad = 3x(x^2 - 1) + 4(x^2 - 1)$

$\qquad\qquad\qquad\qquad\quad = (x^2 - 1)(3x + 4)$

$\qquad\qquad\qquad\qquad\quad = (x - 1)(x + 1)(3x + 4)$

117. $R = 800x - 0.25x^2$

$\qquad = x(800 - 0.25x)$

$R = xp$

$p = 800 - 0.25x$

119. $P + Prt = P(1 + rt)$

121. $A = 45l - l^2$

$\qquad = l(45 - l)$ so

$w = 45 - l$

123. $S = 2x^2 + 4xh$

$S = 2x(x + 2h)$

125. $A = \pi R^2 - \pi r^2$

$\qquad = \pi(R^2 - r^2)$

$\qquad = \pi(R - r)(R + r)$

127. A polynomial is in factored form when the polynomial is written as a product of polynomials.

129. The method of finding the greatest common factor of two or more integers is first determine the prime factorization of each integer. Then the greatest common factor is the product of each common prime factor raised to its lowest power in either one of the integers.

131. The Distributive Property is used to factor a polynomial in this example $x^2 + 2x = x(x + 2)$.

Mid-Chapter Quiz for Chapter 3

1. degree $= 4$

leading coefficient $= -2$

2. $2x - 3x^{1/2} + 5$ is not a polynomial because the term $-3x^{1/2}$ has degree $\frac{1}{2}$. The degree of the variable x is not an integer.

3. $(2t^3 + 3t^2 - 2) + (t^3 + 9) = 3t^3 + 3t^2 + 7$

4. $(3 - 7y) + (7y^2 + 2y - 3) = 7y^2 - 5y$

5. $(7x^3 - 3x^2 + 1) - (x^2 - 2x^3) = 7x^3 - 3x^2 + 1 - x^2 + 2x^3$
$$= 9x^3 - 4x^2 + 1$$

6. $(5 - u) - 2[3 - (u^2 + 1)] = (5 - u) - 2[3 - u^2 - 1]$
$$= (5 - u) - 2[2 - u^2]$$
$$= 5 - u - 4 + 2u^2$$
$$= 2u^2 - u + 1$$

7. $(-5n^2)(-2n^3) = 10n^5$

8. $(-2x^2)^3(x^4) = (-2)^3(x^2)^3(x^4)$
$$= -8x^6 \cdot x^4$$
$$= -8x^{10}$$

9. $\dfrac{6x^7}{(-2x^2)^3} = \dfrac{6x^7}{-8x^6}$
$$= -\dfrac{3x}{4}$$

10. $\left(\dfrac{4y^2}{5x}\right) = \left(\dfrac{4y^2}{5x}\right)\left(\dfrac{4y^2}{5x}\right)$
$$= \dfrac{16y^4}{25x^2}$$

11. $7y(4 - 3y) = 28y - 21y^2$

12. $(x - 7)(x + 3) = x^2 + 3x - 7x - 21$
$$= x^2 - 4x - 21$$

13. $(4x - y)(6x - 5y) = 24x^2 - 20xy - 6xy + 5y^2$
$$= 24x^2 - 26xy + 5y^2$$

14. $2z(z + 5) - 7(z + 5) = 2z^2 + 10z - 7z - 35$
$$= 2z^2 + 3z - 35$$

15. $(6r + 5)(6r - 5) = 36r^2 - 25$

16. $(2x - 3)^2 = (2x - 3)(2x - 3)$
$$= 4x^2 - 12x + 9$$

17. $(x + 1)(x^2 - x + 1) = x^3 - x^2 + x + x^2 - x + 1$
$$= x^3 + 1$$

18. $(x^2 - 3x + 2)(x^2 + 5x - 10) = x^2(x^2 + 5x - 10) - 3x(x^2 + 5x - 10) + 2(x^2 + 5x - 10)$
$$= x^4 + 5x^3 - 10x^2 - 3x^3 - 15x^2 + 30x + 2x^2 + 10x - 20$$
$$= x^4 + 2x^3 - 23x^2 + 40x - 20$$

19. $28a^2 - 21a = 7a(4a - 3)$

20. $25 - 4x^2 = (5 - 2x)(5 + 2x)$

21. $z^3 + 3z^2 - 9z - 27 = z^2(z + 3) - 9(z + 3)$
$$= (z + 3)(z^2 - 9)$$
$$= (z + 3)(z + 3)(z - 3)$$
$$= (z + 3)^2(z - 3)$$

22. $4y^3 - 32x^3 = 4(y^3 - 8x^3)$
$$= 4[y^3 - (2x)^3]$$
$$= 4(y - 2x)(y^2 + 2xy + 4x^2)$$

23. $(5x + 10)(2x + 1)$ $(5x - 10)(2x - 1)$

     $(5x + 1)(2x + 10)$ $(5x - 1)(2x - 10)$

     $(5x + 2)(2x + 5)$ $(5x - 2)(2x - 5)$

     $(5x + 5)(2x + 2)$ $(5x - 5)(2x - 2)$

24. *Verbal model:*

Area of shaded region	=	Area of large triangle	−	Area of small triangle

     Equation: $A = \frac{1}{2}(x + 2)^2 - \frac{1}{2}x^2$

$$= \frac{1}{2}(x^2 + 4x + 4) - \frac{1}{2}x^2$$

$$= \frac{1}{2}x^2 + 2x + 2 - \frac{1}{2}x^2$$

$$= 2x + 2$$

25. $h(1) = -16(1)^2 - 5(1) + 100$

$$= -16 - 5 + 100$$

$$= 79 \text{ feet}$$

$h(2) = -16(2)^2 - 5(2) + 100$

$$= -16(4) - 10 + 100$$

$$= -64 + 90$$

$$= 26 \text{ feet}$$

26. $P(x) = R(x) - C(x)$

$$= 19x - (5x + 2000)$$

$$= 19x - 5x - 2000$$

$$= 14x - 2000$$

$P(1000) = 14(1000) - 2000 = \$12,000$

Section 3.4 Factoring Trinomials

1. $x^2 + 4x + 4 = x^2 + 2(2x) + 2^2 = (x + 2)^2$

3. $a^2 - 12a + 36 = a^2 - 2(6a) + 6^2 = (a - 6)^2$

5. $25y^2 - 10y + 1 = (5y)^2 - 2(5y) + 1 = (5y - 1)^2$

7. $9b^2 + 12b + 4 = (3b)^2 + 2(3b)(2) + 2^2 = (3b + 2)^2$

9. $u^2 + 8uv + 16v^2 = u^2 + 2(4uv) + (4v)^2 = (u + 4v)^2$

11. $36x^2 - 60xy + 25y^2 = (6x)^2 - 2(6x)(5y) + (5y)^2 = (6x - 5y)^2$

13. $5x^2 + 30x + 45 = 5(x^2 + 6x + 9) = 5[x^2 + 2(3)(x) + 3^2] = 5(x + 3)^2$

15. $2x^2 + 24x^2 + 72x = 2x(x^2 + 12x + 36) = 2x[x^2 + 2(6)x + 6^2] = 2x(x + 6)^2$

17. $20v^4 - 60v^3 + 45v^2 = 5v^2(4v^2 - 12v + 9) = 5v^2[(2v)^2 - 2(2v)(3) + 3^2] = 5v^2(2v - 3)^2$

19. $\frac{1}{4}x^2 - \frac{2}{3}x + \frac{4}{9} = \left(\frac{1}{2}x\right)^2 - 2\left(\frac{1}{2}x\right)\left(\frac{2}{3}\right) + \left(\frac{2}{3}\right)^2$ or $= \frac{9}{36}x^2 - \frac{24}{36}x + \frac{16}{36}$

$\qquad\qquad = \left(\frac{1}{2}x - \frac{2}{3}\right)^2$ $= \frac{1}{36}(9x^2 - 24x + 16)$

$\qquad\qquad\qquad\qquad\qquad\qquad\qquad\qquad\qquad\qquad = \frac{1}{36}[(3x)^2 - 2(3x)(4) + 4^2]$

$\qquad\qquad\qquad\qquad\qquad\qquad\qquad\qquad\qquad\qquad = \frac{1}{36}(3x - 4)^2$

21. $x^2 + bx + 81 = x^2 + bx + 9^2$

    (a) $b = 18$ or   (b) $b = -18$

        $x^2 + 18x + 9^2 = x^2 + 2(9x) + 9^2$ $\qquad\qquad x^2 - 18x + 9^2 = x^2 - 2(9x) + 9^2$

                    $= (x + 9)^2$ $\qquad\qquad\qquad\qquad\qquad\qquad = (x - 9)^2$

23. $4x^2 + bx + 9 = (2x)^2 + bx + 3^2$

    (a) $b = 12$ or   (b) $b = -12$

        $(2x)^2 + 12x + 3^2 = (2x)^2 + 2(2x)(3) + 3^2$ $\qquad (2x)^2 - 12x + 3^2 = (2x)^2 - 2(2x)(3) + 3^2$

                    $= (2x + 3)^2$ $\qquad\qquad\qquad\qquad\qquad\qquad = (2x - 3)^2$

25. $c = 16$ **27.** $c = 9$

    $x^2 + 8x + c = x^2 + 2(4x) + c$ $\qquad\qquad\qquad y^2 - 6y + c = y^2 - 2(3y) + c$

                $= x^2 + 2(4x) + 4^2$ $\qquad\qquad\qquad\qquad\qquad = y^2 - 2(3y) + 3^2$

                $= (x + 4)^2$ $\qquad\qquad\qquad\qquad\qquad\qquad = (y - 3)^2$

29. $x^2 + 5x + 4 = (x + 4)(x + 1)$ **31.** $y^2 - y - 20 = (y + 4)(y - 5)$ **33.** $x^2 - 2x - 24 = (x + 4)(x - 6)$

35. $z^2 - 6z + 8 = (z - 4)(z - 2)$ **37.** $x^2 + 4x + 3 = (x + 3)(x + 1)$ **39.** $x^2 - 5x + 6 = (x - 3)(x - 2)$

41. $y^2 + 7y - 30 = (y + 10)(y - 3)$ **43.** $t^2 - 4t - 21 = (t - 7)(t + 3)$ **45.** $x^2 - 20x + 96 = (x - 12)(x - 8)$

47. $x^2 - 2xy - 35y^2 = (x - 7y)(x + 5y)$ **49.** $x^2 + 30xy + 216y^2 = (x + 12y)(x + 18y)$

51. $b = 19$: $x^2 + 19x + 18 = (x + 18)(x + 1)$ **53.** $b = 20$: $x^2 + 20x - 21 = (x + 21)(x - 1)$

     $b = -19$: $x^2 - 19x + 18 = (x - 18)(x - 1)$ $b = -20$: $x^2 - 20x - 21 = (x - 21)(x + 1)$

     $b = 9$: $x^2 + 9x + 18 = (x + 6)(x + 3)$ $b = 4$: $x^2 + 4x - 21 = (x + 7)(x - 3)$

     $b = -9$: $x^2 - 9x + 18 = (x - 6)(x - 3)$ $b = -4$: $x^2 - 4x - 21 = (x - 7)(x + 3)$

     $b = 11$: $x^2 + 11x + 18 = (x + 9)(x + 2)$

     $b = -11$: $x^2 - 11x + 18 = (x - 9)(x - 2)$

55. $b = 36$: $x^2 + 36x + 35 = (x + 35)(x + 1)$

     $b = -36$: $x^2 - 36x + 35 = (x - 35)(x - 1)$

     $b = 12$: $x^2 + 12x + 35 = (x + 7)(x + 5)$

     $b = -12$: $x^2 - 12x + 35 = (x - 7)(x - 5)$

57. There are many possibilities, such as:

$c = 5$ $\qquad$ $x^2 + 6x + 5 = (x + 5)(x + 1)$

$c = 8$ $\qquad$ $x^2 + 6x + 8 = (x + 4)(x + 2)$

$c = 9$ $\qquad$ $x^2 + 6x + 9 = (x + 3)(x + 3)$

Also note that if $c = $ a negative number, there are many possibilities for c such as the following.

$c = -7$ $\qquad$ $x^2 + 6x - 7 = (x + 7)(x - 1)$

$c = -16$ $\qquad$ $x^2 + 6x - 16 = (x + 8)(x - 2)$

$c = -27$ $\qquad$ $x^2 + 6x - 27 = (x + 9)(x - 3)$

59. There are many possibilities, such as:

$c = 2$ $\qquad$ $x^2 - 3x + 2 = (x - 2)(x - 1)$

$c = -4$ $\qquad$ $x^2 - 3x - 4 = (x - 4)(x + 1)$

$c = -10$ $\qquad$ $x^2 - 3x - 10 = (x - 5)(x + 2)$

$c = -18$ $\qquad$ $x^2 - 3x - 18 = (x - 6)(x + 3)$

There are more possibilities.

61. $5x^2 + 18x + 9 = (x + 3)(5x + 3)$ $\qquad$ **63.** $5a^2 + 12a - 9 = (a + 3)(5a - 3)$ $\qquad$ **65.** $2y^2 - 3y - 27 = (y + 3)(2y - 9)$

67. $3x^2 + 4x + 1 = (3x + 1)(x + 1)$ $\qquad$ **69.** $7x^2 + 15x + 2 = (7x + 1)(x + 2)$ $\qquad$ **71.** $2x^2 - 9x + 9 = (2x - 3)(x - 3)$

73. $6x^2 - 11x + 3 = (3x - 1)(2x - 3)$ $\qquad$ **75.** $3t^2 - 4t - 10 = $ prime $\qquad$ **77.** $6b^2 + 19b - 7 = (3b - 1)(2b + 7)$

79. $18y^2 + 35y + 12 = (2y + 3)(9y + 4)$ $\qquad$ **81.** $-2x^2 - x + 6 = -1(2x^2 + x - 6) = -1(2x - 3)(x + 2)$

83. $1 - 11x - 60x^2 = -60x^2 - 11x + 1$

$\qquad = -1(60x^2 + 11x - 1)$

$\qquad = -1(15x - 1)(4x + 1)$

85. $6x^2 - 3x - 84 = 3(2x^2 - x - 28)$

$\qquad = 3(2x + 7)(x - 4)$

87. $60y^3 + 35y^2 - 50y = 5y(12y^2 + 7y - 10)$

$\qquad = 5y(3y - 2)(4y + 5)$

89. $10a^2 + 23ab + 6b^2 = (a + 2b)(10a + 3b)$

91. $24x^2 - 14xy - 3y^2 = (6x + y)(4x - 3y)$

93. $3x^2 + 10x + 8 = 3x^2 + 6x + 4x + 8$

$\qquad = (3x^2 + 6x) + (4x + 8)$

$\qquad = 3x(x + 2) + 4(x + 2)$

$\qquad = (3x + 4)(x + 2)$

95. $6x^2 + x - 2 = 6x^2 + 4x - 3x - 2$

$\qquad = (6x^2 + 4x) + (-3x - 2)$

$\qquad = 2x(3x + 2) - 1(3x + 2)$

$\qquad = (2x - 1)(3x + 2)$

97. $15x^2 - 11x + 2 = 15x^2 - 6x - 5x + 2$

$\qquad = (15x^2 - 6x) + (-5x + 2)$

$\qquad = 3x(5x - 2) - 1(5x - 2)$

$\qquad = (3x - 1)(5x - 2)$

99. $3x^4 - 12x^3 = 3x^3(x - 4)$

101. $10t^3 + 2t^2 - 36t = 2t(5t^2 + t - 18)$

$\qquad = 2t(5t - 9)(t + 2)$

103. $54x^3 - 2 = 2(27x^3 - 1)$

$\qquad = 2(3x - 1)(9x^2 + 3x + 1)$

105. $27a^3b^4 - 9a^2b^3 - 18ab^2 = 9ab^2(3a^2b^2 - ab - 2)$

$\qquad = 9ab^2(3ab + 2)(ab - 1)$

107. $x^3 + 2x^2 - 16x - 32 = (x^3 + 2x^2) + (-16x - 32)$

$\qquad = x^2(x + 2) - 16(x + 2)$

$\qquad = (x + 2)(x^2 - 16)$

$\qquad = (x + 2)(x - 4)(x + 4)$

109. $36 - (z + 3)^2 = [6 - (z + 3)][6 + (z + 3)]$

$\qquad = [6 - z - 3][6 + z + 3]$

$\qquad = (3 - z)(9 + z)$

111. $x^2 - 10x + 25 - y^2 = (x - 5)^2 - y^2$

$\qquad = [(x - 5) + y][(x - 5) - y]$

$\qquad = (x - 5 + y)(x - 5 - y)$

113. $x^8 - 1 = (x^4)^2 - 1^2 = (x^4 - 1)(x^4 + 1)$

$\qquad = [(x^2)^2 - 1^2](x^4 + 1)$

$\qquad = (x^2 - 1)(x^2 + 1)(x^4 + 1)$

$\qquad = (x - 1)(x + 1)(x^2 + 1)(x^4 + 1)$

115. *Keystrokes:*

y_1 [Y=] [X,T,θ] [x^2] [+] 6 [X,T,θ] [+] 9 [ENTER]

y_2 [(] [X,T,θ] [+] 3 [)] [x^2] [GRAPH]

$y_1 = y_2$

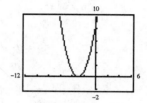

117. *Keystrokes:*

y_1 [Y=] [X,T,θ] [x^2] [+] 2 [X,T,θ] [−] 3 [ENTER]

y_2 [(] [X,T,θ] [−] 1 [)] [(] [X,T,θ] [+] 3 [)] [GRAPH]

$y_1 = y_2$

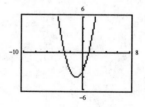

119. $a^2 - b^2 = (a + b)(a - b)$ matches graph (c).

121. $a^2 + 2ab + b^2 = (a + b)^2$ matches graph (b).

123. *Verbal model:*

$$\boxed{\begin{array}{c}\text{Area of}\\\text{shaded}\\\text{region}\end{array}} = \boxed{\begin{array}{c}\text{Area of}\\\text{rectangle}\end{array}} - \boxed{\begin{array}{c}\text{Area of}\\\text{squares}\end{array}}$$

Equation: $\text{Area} = (8 \cdot 18) - 4 \cdot x^2$

$\qquad = 144 - 4x^2$

$\qquad = 4(36 - x^2)$

$\qquad = 4(6 + x)(6 - x)$

125. (a) $8n^3 - 8n = 2n(4n^2 - 4)$

$\qquad = 2n[(2n)^2 - 2^2]$

$\qquad = 2n(2n - 2)(2n + 2)$

(b) If $n = 10$, $2n = 2(10) = 20$

$\qquad 2n - 2 = 2(10) - 2 = 18$

$\qquad 2n + 2 = 2(10) + 2 = 22$

127. To factor $x^2 - 5x + 6$ begin by finding the factors of 6 whose sum is -5. They are -2 and -3. The factorization is $(x - 2)(x - 3)$.

129. Check the factors of a trinomial by multiplication. The factors of $x^2 - 5x + 6$ are $x - 2$ and $x - 3$ because

$(x - 2)(x - 3) = x^2 - 5x + 6$.

131. No, $x(x + 2) - 2(x + 2)$ is not in factored form. It is not yet a product. $x(x + 2) - 2(x + 2) = (x + 2)(x - 2)$

Section 3.5   Solving Polynomial Equations

1. $2x(x - 8) = 0$

$2x = 0 \qquad x - 8 = 0$

$x = 0 \qquad\quad x = 8$

3. $(y - 3)(y + 10) = 0$

$y - 3 = 0 \quad y + 10 = 0$

$y = 3 \qquad y = -10$

5. $25(a + 4)(a - 2) = 0$

$a + 4 = 0 \qquad a - 2 = 0$

$a = -4 \qquad\quad a = 2$

7. $(2t + 5)(3t + 1) = 0$

$2t + 5 = 0 \qquad\qquad 3t + 1 = 0$

$t = -\frac{5}{2} \qquad\qquad\quad t = -\frac{1}{3}$

9. $4x(2x - 3)(2x + 25) = 0$

$4x = 0 \qquad 2x - 3 = 0 \qquad 2x + 25 = 0$

$x = 0 \qquad\quad x = \frac{3}{2} \qquad\qquad x = -\frac{25}{2}$

11. $(x - 3)(2x + 1)(x + 4) = 0$

$x - 3 = 0 \qquad 2x + 1 = 0 \qquad x + 4 = 0$

$x = 3 \qquad\quad x = -\frac{1}{2} \qquad\quad x = -4$

13. $5y - y^2 = 0$

$y(5 - y) = 0$

$y = 0 \qquad\quad 5 - y = 0$

$\qquad\qquad\qquad 5 = y$

15. $9x^2 + 15x = 0$

$3x(3x + 5) = 0$

$3x = 0 \qquad\quad 3x + 5 = 0$

$x = 0 \qquad\qquad x = -\frac{5}{3}$

17. $x(x + 2) - 10(x + 2) = 0$

$(x + 2)(x - 10) = 0$

$x + 2 = 0 \qquad\quad x - 10 = 0$

$x = -2 \qquad\qquad x = 10$

19. $u(u - 3) + 3(u - 3) = 0$

$(u - 3)(u + 3) = 0$

$u - 3 = 0 \qquad\qquad u + 3 = 0$

$u = 3 \qquad\qquad\quad u = -3$

21. $\qquad x^2 - 25 = 0$

$(x + 5)(x - 5) = 0$

$x + 5 = 0 \qquad\quad x - 5 = 0$

$x = -5 \qquad\qquad x = 5$

23. $\qquad 3y^2 - 48 = 0$

$3(y^2 - 16) = 0$

$3(y + 4)(y - 4) = 0$

$y + 4 = 0 \qquad\qquad y - 4 = 0$

$y = -4 \qquad\qquad\quad y = 4$

25. $x^2 - 3x - 10 = 0$

$(x - 5)(x + 2) = 0$

$x - 5 = 0 \qquad\qquad x + 2 = 0$

$x = 5 \qquad\qquad\quad x = -2$

27. $x^2 - 10x + 24 = 0$

$(x - 6)(x - 4) = 0$

$x - 6 = 0 \qquad\quad x - 4 = 0$

$x = 6 \qquad\qquad x = 4$

29. $4x^2 + 15x - 25 = 0$

$(4x - 5)(x + 5) = 0$

$4x - 5 = 0 \qquad\quad x + 5 = 0$

$4x = 5 \qquad\qquad\quad x = -5$

$x = \frac{5}{4}$

31. $7 + 13x - 2x^2 = 0$

$(7 - x)(1 + 2x) = 0$

$7 - x = 0 \qquad 1 + 2x = 0$

$7 = x \qquad\qquad -\frac{1}{2} = x$

33. $m^2 - 8m + 18 = 2$

$m^2 - 8m + 16 = 0$

$(m - 4)^2 = 0$

$m - 4 = 0$

$m = 4$

35. $x^2 + 16x + 57 = -7$

$x^2 + 16x + 64 = 0$

$(x + 8)^2 = 0$

$x + 8 = 0$

$x = -8$

37. $4z^2 - 12z + 15 = 6$

$4z^2 - 12z + 9 = 0$

$(2z - 3)^2 = 0$

$2z - 3 = 0$

$z = \frac{3}{2}$

39. $x(x - 5) = 36$

$x^2 - 5x = 36$

$x^2 - 5x - 36 = 0$

$(x - 9)(x + 4) = 0$

$x - 9 = 0 \qquad x + 4 = 0$

$x = 9 \qquad\qquad x = -4$

41. $y(y + 6) = 72$

$y^2 + 6y - 72 = 0$

$(y + 12)(y - 6) = 0$

$y + 12 = 0 \qquad y - 6 = 0$

$y = -12 \qquad\qquad y = 6$

43. $t(2t - 3) = 35$

$2t^2 - 3t - 35 = 0$

$(2t + 7)(t - 5) = 0$

$2t + 7 = 0 \qquad t - 5 = 0$

$t = -\frac{7}{2} \qquad\qquad t = 5$

45. $(a + 2)(a + 5) = 10$

$a^2 + 7a + 10 - 10 = 0$

$a^2 + 7a = 0$

$a(a + 7) = 0$

$a = 0 \qquad a + 7 = 0$

$a = 0 \qquad\qquad a = -7$

47. $(x - 4)(x + 5) = 10$

$x^2 + x - 20 - 10 = 0$

$x^2 + x - 30 = 0$

$(x + 6)(x - 5) = 0$

$x + 6 = 0 \qquad x - 5 = 0$

$x = -6 \qquad\qquad x = 5$

49. $(t - 2)^2 - 16 = 0$

$(t - 2 + 4)(t - 2 - 4) = 0$

$(t + 2)(t - 6) = 0$

$t + 2 = 0 \qquad t - 6 = 0$

$t = -2 \qquad\qquad t = 6$

51. $(x + 2)^2 = 9$

$[(x + 2) - 3][(x + 2) + 3] = 0$

$(x - 1)(x + 5) = 0$

$(x - 1) = 0 \qquad (x + 5) = 0$

$x = 1 \qquad\qquad x = -5$

53. $x^3 - 19x^2 + 84x = 0$

$x(x^2 - 19x + 84) = 0$

$x(x - 12)(x - 7) = 0$

$x = 0 \qquad x - 12 = 0 \qquad x - 7 = 0$

$x = 0 \qquad\quad x = 12 \qquad\quad x = 7$

55. $6t^3 - t^2 - t = 0$

$t(6t^2 - t - 1) = 0$

$t(3t + 1)(2t - 1) = 0$

$t = 0 \qquad 3t + 1 = 0 \qquad 2t - 1 = 0$

$t = 0 \qquad\quad t = -\frac{1}{3} \qquad\quad t = \frac{1}{2}$

57. $z^2(z + 2) - 4(z + 2) = 0$

$\qquad (z + 2)(z^2 - 4) = 0$

$\qquad (z + 2)(z - 2)(z + 2) = 0$

$\quad z + 2 = 0 \qquad z - 2 = 0 \qquad\qquad z + 2 = 0$

$\qquad z = -2 \qquad\quad z = 2 \qquad\qquad\quad z = -2$

59. $a^3 + 2a^2 - 9a - 18 = 0$

$\qquad (a^3 + 2a^2) + (-9a - 18) = 0$

$\qquad\quad a^2(a + 2) - 9(a + 2) = 0$

$\qquad\qquad (a + 2)(a^2 - 9) = 0$

$\qquad\quad (a + 2)(a - 3)(a + 3) = 0$

$\quad a + 2 = 0 \qquad a - 3 = 0 \qquad\quad a + 3 = 0$

$\qquad a = -2 \qquad\quad a = 3 \qquad\qquad\quad a = -3$

61. $c^3 - 3c^2 - 9c + 27 = 0$

$\quad c^2(c - 3) - 9(c - 3) = 0$

$\qquad (c - 3)(c^2 - 9) = 0$

$\quad (c - 3)(c - 3)(c + 3) = 0$

$\; c - 3 = 0 \quad c - 3 = 0 \qquad c + 3 = 0$

$\qquad c = 3 \qquad\quad c = 3 \qquad\qquad c = -3$

63. $x^4 - 3x^3 - x^2 + 3x = 0$

$\quad x^3(x - 3) - x(x - 3) = 0$

$\qquad (x - 3)(x^3 - x) = 0$

$\qquad (x - 3)\,x(x^2 - 1) = 0$

$\quad (x - 3)\,x(x - 1)(x + 1) = 0$

$x - 3 = 0 \quad x = 0 \quad x - 1 = 0 \qquad x + 1 = 0$

$\quad x = 3 \qquad\qquad\quad x = 1 \qquad\qquad x = -1$

65. $8x^4 + 12x^3 - 32x^2 - 48x = 0$

$\quad 4x^3(2x + 3) - 16x(2x + 3) = 0$

$\qquad\quad (2x + 3)(4x^3 - 16x) = 0$

$\qquad\quad (2x + 3)\,4x(x^2 - 4) = 0$

$\quad (2x + 3)(4x)(x - 2)(x + 2) = 0$

$2x + 3 = 0 \qquad 4x = 0 \quad x - 2 = 0 \quad x + 2 = 0$

$\; x = -\frac{3}{2} \qquad\quad x = 0 \qquad x = 2 \qquad x = -2$

67. From the graph, the x-intercepts are $(-3, 0)$ and $(3, 0)$. The solutions of the equation $0 = x^2 - 9$ are 3 and -3.

$0 = (x - 3)(x + 3)$

$\quad 0 = x - 3 \qquad\qquad 0 = x + 3$

$\quad 3 = x \qquad\qquad\quad -3 = x$

69. From the graph, the x-intercepts are $(-1, 0)$ and $(3, 0)$. The solutions of the equation $0 = x^2 - 2x - 3$ are -1 and 3.

$0 = x^2 - 2x - 3$

$0 = (x - 3)(x + 1)$

$\quad 0 = x - 3 \qquad\quad x + 1 = 0$

$\quad 3 = x \qquad\qquad\quad x = -1$

71. *Keystrokes:*

$\boxed{Y=}\ \boxed{X,T,\theta}\ \boxed{x^2}\ \boxed{-}\ 6\ \boxed{X,T,\theta}\ \boxed{\text{GRAPH}}$

The x-intercepts are 0 and 6, so the solutions are 0 and 6.

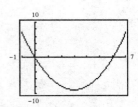

73. *Keystrokes:*

$\boxed{Y=}\ \boxed{X,T,\theta}\ \boxed{x^2}\ \boxed{-}\ 8\ \boxed{X,T,\theta}\ \boxed{+}\ 12\ \boxed{\text{GRAPH}}$

The x-intercepts are 2 and 6, so the solutions are 2 and 6.

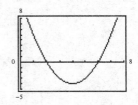

75. *Keystrokes:*

$\boxed{Y=}$ 2 $\boxed{X,T,\theta}$ $\boxed{x^2}$ $\boxed{+}$ 5 $\boxed{X,T,\theta}$ $\boxed{-}$ 12 $\boxed{\text{GRAPH}}$

The x-intercepts are -4 and $\frac{3}{2}$, so the solutions are -4 and $\frac{3}{2}$.

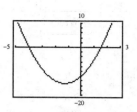

77. *Keystrokes:*

$\boxed{Y=}$ 2 $\boxed{X,T,\theta}$ $\boxed{\wedge}$ 3 $\boxed{-}$ 5 $\boxed{X,T,\theta}$ $\boxed{x^2}$ $\boxed{-}$ 12 $\boxed{X,T,\theta}$ $\boxed{\text{GRAPH}}$

The x-intercepts are $-\frac{3}{2}$, 0, and 4, so the solutions are $-\frac{3}{2}$, 0, and 4.

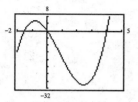

79. $ax^2 + bx = 0$

$x(ax + b) = 0$

$x = 0$ $\qquad$ $ax + b = 0$

$\qquad\qquad$ $ax = -b$

$\qquad\qquad$ $x = -\frac{b}{a}$

81. $x = -3, x = 5$

$[x - (-3)](x - 5) = 0$

$(x + 3)(x - 5) = 0$

$x^2 - 2x - 15 = 0$

83. *Verbal model:* $\boxed{\text{Number}} + \boxed{\text{Its Square}} = \boxed{240}$

Labels: $\qquad$ Number $= x$

$\qquad\qquad$ Its square $= x^2$

Equation: $\qquad\qquad\qquad$ $x + x^2 = 240$

$\qquad\qquad\qquad$ $x^2 + x - 240 = 0$

$\qquad\qquad$ $(x + 16)(x - 15) = 0$

$\qquad\qquad\qquad\qquad$ $x + 16 = 0$ $\qquad$ $x - 15 = 0$

$\qquad\qquad\qquad\qquad\qquad$ $x = -16$ $\qquad\qquad$ $x = 15$

$\qquad\qquad$ reject

85. *Verbal model:* $\boxed{\begin{array}{c}\text{First}\\\text{Integer}\end{array}} \cdot \boxed{\begin{array}{c}\text{Second}\\\text{Integer}\end{array}} = \boxed{132}$

Labels: $\qquad$ First integer $= x$

$\qquad\qquad$ Second integer $x + 1$

Equation: $\qquad\qquad$ $x \cdot (x + 1) = 132$

$\qquad\qquad$ $x^2 + x - 132 = 0$

$\qquad\qquad$ $(x + 12)(x - 11) = 0$

$\qquad\qquad\qquad\qquad$ $x + 12 = 0$ $\qquad$ $x - 11 = 0$

$\qquad\qquad\qquad\qquad\qquad$ $x = -12$ $\qquad\qquad$ $x = 11$ $\quad$ 1st integer

$\qquad\qquad$ reject $\qquad\qquad\qquad\qquad\qquad$ $x + 1 = 12$ $\quad$ 2nd integer

87. *Verbal model:*   Length · Width = Area

Labels: Length = $x + 7$

Width = x

Equation: $(x + 7) \cdot x = 330$

$x^2 + 7x = 330$

$x^2 + 7x - 330 = 0$

$(x + 22)(x - 15) = 0$

$x + 22 = 0 \qquad\qquad x - 15 = 0$

$x = -22 \qquad\qquad x = 15$ feet width

reject $\qquad\qquad\qquad x + 7 = 22$ feet length

89. *Verbal model:* $\dfrac{1}{2}$ · Base · Height = Area

Labels: Base = x

Height = $\frac{3}{2}x$

Equation: $\frac{1}{2} \cdot x \cdot \frac{3}{2}x = 48$

$\frac{3}{4}x^2 - 48 = 0$

$3x^2 - 192 = 0$

$3(x^2 - 64) = 0$

$(x + 8)(x - 8) = 0$

$x + 8 = 0 \qquad\qquad x - 8 = 0$

$x = -8 \qquad\qquad x = 8$ inches base

reject $\qquad\qquad\qquad \frac{3}{2}x = 12$ inches height

91. (a) Volume V = Length · Width · Height

$V = (5 - 2x)(4 - 2x)x$

(b) $0 = (5 - 2x)(4 - 2x)x$ $\qquad\qquad$ Domain: Each side must be positive.

$5 - 2x = 0 \qquad 4 - 2x = 0 \qquad\quad x = 0 \quad x > 0 \quad 5 - 2x > 0 \qquad 4 - 2x > 0$ so $0 < x < 2$

$x = \frac{5}{2} \qquad\qquad x = 2 \qquad\qquad x = 0 \qquad\qquad x < \frac{5}{2} \qquad\qquad x < 2$

(c)

x	0.25	0.50	0.75	1.00	1.25	1.50	1.75
V	3.94	6	6.56	6	4.69	3	1.31

(d) If $V = 3$, then $x = 1.5$.

$3 = [5 - 2(1.5)][4 - 2(1.5)](1.5)$

$3 = (5 - 3)(4 - 3)(1.5)$

$3 = (2)(1)(1.5)$

$3 = 3$

(e) *Keystrokes:*

Y= (5 − 2 X,T,θ) (4 − 2 X,T,θ) X,T,θ GRAPH

$x = 0.74$ yields the box of greatest volume.

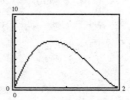

93.
$$-16t^2 + 6400 = 0$$
$$-16(t^2 - 400) = 0$$
$$-16(t - 20)(t + 20) = 0$$

$$t - 20 = 0 \qquad t + 20 = 0$$
$$t = 20 \qquad t = -20$$
$$\text{reject}$$

The object reaches the ground after 20 seconds.

95. *Verbal model:* | Revenue | = | Cost |

Equation:
$$90x - x^2 = 200 + 60x$$
$$0 = x^2 - 30x + 200$$
$$0 = (x - 20)(x - 10)$$
$$x - 20 = 0 \qquad x - 10 = 0$$
$$x = 20 \qquad x = 10$$
$$\text{units} \qquad \text{units}$$

97. (a)
$$2(x + 3)^2 + (x + 3) - 15 = 0$$
$$2u^2 + u - 15 = 0$$
$$(2u - 5)(u + 3) = 0$$

$$2u - 5 = 0 \qquad u + 3 = 0$$
$$2u = 5 \qquad u = -3$$
$$u = \tfrac{5}{2}$$

$$u = x + 3 \qquad u = x + 3$$
$$\tfrac{5}{2} = x + 3 \qquad -3 = x + 3$$
$$-\tfrac{1}{2} = x \qquad -6 = x$$

(b)
$$2(x + 3)^2 + (x + 3) - 15 = 0$$
$$2(x^2 + 6x + 9) + (x + 3) - 15 = 0$$
$$2x^2 + 12x + 18 + x + 3 - 15 = 0$$
$$2x^2 + 13x + 6 = 0$$
$$(2x + 1)(x + 6) = 0$$
$$2x + 1 = 0 \qquad x + 6 = 0$$
$$2x = -1 \qquad x = -6$$
$$x = -\tfrac{1}{2}$$

(c) Answers will vary.

99. (d) *Verbal model:* | Area | = | Length | · | Width |

Labels:
Area = 30
Length = $2x - 6$
Width = $x - 1$

Equation:
$$30 = (2x - 6)(x - 1)$$
$$30 = 2x^2 - 8x + 6$$
$$0 = 2x^2 - 8x - 24$$
$$0 = x^2 - 4x - 12$$
$$0 = (x - 6)(x + 2)$$
$$0 = x - 6 \qquad x + 2 = 0$$
$$6 = x \qquad x = -2 \text{ reject}$$

Length = $2(6) - 6$ Width = $6 - 1$ Height = $6 - 3$
= 6 feet   = 5 feet   = 3 feet

(e) Volume = $V_S(x) = \tfrac{7}{3}x^3 + \tfrac{53}{3}x^2 - 20x + 6$
$$V_S(6) = \tfrac{7}{3}(6)^3 + \tfrac{53}{3}(6)^2 - 20(6) + 6$$
$$= \tfrac{7}{3}(216) + \tfrac{53}{3}(36) - 120 + 6$$
$$= 504 + 636 - 120 + 6$$
$$= 1026 \text{ cubic feet}$$

(f) Domain of $V_B(x)$

101. False. This is not an application of the Zero Factor Property because there are unlimited number of factors whose product is 1.

103. The maximum number of solutions of an nth degree polynomial equation is n. The third-degree equation $(x + 1)^3 = 0$ has only one solution, $x = -1$.

Review Exercises for Chapter 3

1. $x^2 + 2 + 3x^{1/2}$ is not a polynomial because the exponent of a variable must be a natural number.

3. Standard form: $-x^4 + 6x^3 + 5x^2 - 4x$

Leading coefficient: -1

Degree: 4

5. Standard form: $-7x^3 + 3x^2 - 6x + 14$

Leading coefficient: -7

Degree: 3

7. Binomial of degree 4: $3x^4 - 2$

9. Monomial of degree 3 and leading coefficient 5: $5x^3$

11. $(5x + 3x^2) + (6 - x - 4x^2) = (3x^2 - 4x^2) + (5x - x) + 6 = -x^2 + 4x + 6$

13. $(5x^3 - 6x + 11) + (5 + 6x - x^2 - 8x^3) = (5x^3 - 8x^3) - x^2 + (-6x + 6x) + (11 + 5) = -3x^3 - x^2 + 16$

15. $(3t - 5) - (t^2 - t - 5) = (3t - 5) + (-t^2 + t + 5) = -t^2 + (3t + t) + (-5 + 5) = -t^2 + 4t$

17. $(3x^5 + 4x^2 - 8x + 12) - (2x^5 + x) + (3x^2 - 4x^3 - 9) = (3x^5 - 2x^5) - 4x^3 + (4x^2 + 3x^2) + (-8x - x) + (12 - 9)$

$$= x^5 - 4x^3 + 7x^2 - 9x + 3$$

19. $(-x^3 - 3x) - 4(2x^3 - 3x + 1) = -x^3 - 3x - 8x^3 + 12x - 4$

$$= (-x^3 - 8x^3) + (-3x + 12x) + (-4)$$

$$= -9x^3 + 9x - 4$$

21. $3y^2 - [2y + 3(y^2 + 5)] = 3y^2 - [2y + 3y^2 + 15]$

$$= 3y^2 - 2y - 3y^2 - 15$$

$$= (3y^2 - 3y^2) - 2y - 15$$

$$= -2y - 15$$

23. $x^2 \cdot x^3 = x^{2+3} = x^5$

25. $(u^2)^3 = u^{2 \cdot 3} = u^6$

27. $(-2z)^3 = (-2)^3 z^3$

$$= -8z^3$$

29. $-(u^2v)^2(-4u^3v) = -(u^4v^2)(-4u^3v)$

$$= 4u^{4+3}v^{2+1}$$

$$= 4u^7v^3$$

31. $\dfrac{12z^5}{6z^2} = \left(\dfrac{12}{6}\right) \cdot z^{5-2} = 2z^3$

33. $\dfrac{120u^5v^3}{15u^3v} = \dfrac{120}{15} \cdot \dfrac{u^5}{u^3} \cdot \dfrac{v^3}{v}$

$$= 8u^2v^2$$

35. $\left(\dfrac{72x^4}{6x^2}\right)^2 = (12x^{4-2})^2$

$$= (12x^2)^2$$

$$= 144x^4$$

37. $(-2x)^3(x + 4) = -8x^3(x + 4)$
$\qquad\qquad\qquad\quad = -8x^4 - 32x^3$

39. $3x(2x^2 - 5x + 3) = 6x^3 - 15x^2 + 9x$

41. $(x - 2)(x + 7) = x^2 + 7x - 2x - 14$
$\qquad\qquad\qquad = x^2 + 5x - 14$

43. $(5x + 3)(3x - 4) = 15x^2 - 20x + 9x - 12 = 15x^2 - 11x - 12$

45. $(4x^2 + 3)(6x^2 + 1) = 24x^4 + 4x^2 + 18x^2 + 3 = 24x^4 + 22x^2 + 3$

47. $(2x^2 - 3x + 2)(2x + 3) = 2x^2(2x + 3) - 3x(2x + 3) + 2(2x + 3)$
$\qquad\qquad\qquad\qquad\qquad = 4x^3 + 6x^2 - 6x^2 - 9x + 4x + 6$
$\qquad\qquad\qquad\qquad\qquad = 4x^3 + (6x^2 - 6x^2) + (-9x + 4x) + 6$
$\qquad\qquad\qquad\qquad\qquad = 4x^3 - 5x + 6$

49. $2u(u - 7) - (u + 1)(u - 7) = 2u(u - 7) - u(u - 7) - 1(u - 7)$
$\qquad\qquad\qquad\qquad\qquad\qquad = 2u^2 - 14u - u^2 + 7u - u + 7$
$\qquad\qquad\qquad\qquad\qquad\qquad = (2u^2 - u^2) + (-14u + 7u - u) + 7$
$\qquad\qquad\qquad\qquad\qquad\qquad = u^2 - 8u + 7$

51. $(4x - 7)^2 = (4x)^2 - 2(4x)(7) + (-7)^2$
$\qquad\qquad\quad = 16x^2 - 56x + 49$

53. $(2x + 3y)^2 = (2x)^2 + 2(2x)(3y) + (3y)^2$
$\qquad\qquad\qquad = 4x^2 + 12xy + 9y^2$

55. $(5u - 8)(5u + 8) = (5u)^2 - 8^2$
$\qquad\qquad\qquad\quad = 25u^2 - 64$

57. $(2u + v)(2u - v) = (2u)^2 - v^2 = 4u^2 - v^2$

59. $[(u - 3) + v][(u - 3) - v] = (u - 3)^2 - v^2 = u^2 - 2(u)(3) + (-3)^2 - v^2 = u^2 - 6u + 9 - v^2$

61. $6x^2 + 15x^3 = 3x^2(2 + 5x)$

63. $28(x + 5) - 70(x + 5)^2 = 14(x + 5)[2 - 5(x + 5)]$
$\qquad\qquad\qquad\qquad\qquad = 14(x + 5)(2 - 5x - 25)$
$\qquad\qquad\qquad\qquad\qquad = 14(x + 5)(-5x - 23)$
$\qquad\qquad\qquad\qquad\qquad = -14(x + 5)(5x + 23)$

65. $v^3 - 2v^2 - v + 2 = v^2(v - 2) - 1(v - 2)$
$\qquad\qquad\qquad\qquad = (v - 2)(v^2 - 1)$
$\qquad\qquad\qquad\qquad = (v - 2)(v - 1)(v + 1)$

67. $t^3 + 3t^2 + 3t + 9 = t^2(t + 3) + 3(t + 3)$
$\qquad\qquad\qquad\qquad = (t^2 + 3)(t + 3)$

69. $x^2 - 36 = x^2 - 6^2 = (x - 6)(x + 6)$

71. $9a^2 - 100 = (3a - 10)(3a + 10)$

73. $(u + 6)^2 - 81 = (u + 6 - 9)(u + 6 + 9)$
$\qquad\qquad\qquad = (u - 3)(u + 15)$

75. $u^3 - 1 = (u - 1)(u^2 + u + 1)$

77. $8x^3 + 27 = (2x)^3 + (3)^3$

$\quad\quad = (2x + 3)(4x^2 - 6x + 9)$

79. $x^2 - 18x + 81 = x^2 - 2(9)x + 9^2 = (x - 9)^2$

81. $4s^2 + 40st + 100t^2 = (2s)^2 + 2(2s)(10) + (10t)^2$

$\quad\quad\quad = (2s + 10t)^2$

83. $x^2 + 2x - 35 = (x + 7)(x - 5)$

85. $2x^2 - 7x + 6 = (2x - 3)(x - 2)$

87. $18x^2 + 27x + 10 = (3x + 2)(6x + 5)$

89. $4a - 64a^3 = 4a(1 - 16a^2)$

$\quad\quad = 4a(1 - 4a)(1 + 4a)$

91. $8x(2x - 3) - 4(2x - 3) = (2x - 3)(8x - 4)$

$\quad\quad = (2x - 3)(2x - 1)$

$\quad\quad = 4(2x - 3)(2x - 1)$

93. $\frac{1}{4}x^2 + xy + y^2 = \left(\frac{1}{2}x\right)^2 + 2\left(\frac{1}{2}\right)xy + y^2$

$\quad\quad = \left(\frac{1}{2}x + y\right)^2$

95. $4u^2 - 28u + 49 = (2u)^2 - 2(2u)(7) + 7^2$

$\quad\quad = (2u - 7)^2$

97. $x^2 - 10x + 25 - y^2 = (x - 5)^2 - y^2$

$\quad\quad = [(x - 5) - y][(x - 5) + y]$

$\quad\quad = (x - 5 - y)(x - 5 + y)$

$\quad\quad = (x - y - 5)(x + y - 5)$

99. $3s^2 - 2s - 8 = 0$

$(3s + 4)(s - 2) = 0$

$3s + 4 = 0 \quad\quad s - 2 = 0$

$s = -\frac{4}{3} \quad\quad s = 2$

101. $v^2 - 100 = 0$

$(v - 10)(v + 10) = 0$

$v - 10 = 0 \quad\quad v + 10 = 0$

$v = 10 \quad\quad v = -10$

103. $10x(x - 3) = 0$

$10x = 0 \quad\quad x - 3 = 0$

$x = 0 \quad\quad x = 3$

105. $z(5 - z) + 36 = 0$

$5z - z^2 + 36 = 0$

$z^2 - 5z - 36 = 0$

$(z - 9)(z + 4) = 0$

$z - 9 = 0 \quad\quad z + 4 = 0$

$z = 9 \quad\quad z = -4$

107. $2y^4 + 2y^3 - 24y^2 = 0$

$2y^2(y^2 + y - 12) = 0$

$2y^2(y + 4)(y - 3) = 0$

$2y^2 = 0 \quad y + 4 = 0 \quad y - 3 = 0$

$y = 0 \quad\quad y = -4 \quad\quad y = 3$

109. *Keystrokes:*

$\boxed{Y=}\ \boxed{X,T,\theta}\ \boxed{x^2}\ \boxed{-}\ 10\ \boxed{X,T,\theta}\ \boxed{+}\ 21\ \boxed{GRAPH}$

The x-intercepts are 3 and 7, so the solutions are 3 and 7.

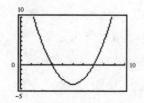

111. $x = 5 \quad x = -9$

$$(x - 5)(x + 9) = 0$$

$$x^2 + 9x - 5x - 45 = 0$$

$$x^2 + 4x - 45 = 0$$

113. $x = 0 \quad x = -\frac{3}{2} \quad x = 2$

$$x\left(x + \frac{3}{2}\right)(x - 2) = 0$$

$$x(2x + 3)(x - 2) = 0$$

$$x(2x^2 - 4x + 3x - 6) = 0$$

$$2x^3 - x^2 - 6x = 0$$

115. (a) *Keystrokes:*

y_1 [Y=] [(-)] .022 [X,T,θ] [x²] [+] 1.33 [X,T,θ] [+] 270.71 [ENTER]

y_2 2.386 [X,T,θ] [+] 274.857 [ENTER]

y_3 .028 [X,T,θ] [x²] [+] 3.4 [X,T,θ] [+] 278.18 [GRAPH]

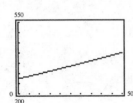

(b) $\dfrac{P_L + P_H}{2} = \dfrac{-0.022t^2 + 1.33t + 270.71 + 0.028t^2 + 3.40t + 278.18}{2}$

$$= \dfrac{0.006t^2 + 4.73t + 548.89}{2}$$

$$= 0.003t^2 + 2.365t + 274.445$$

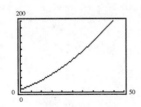

This graph is most like the graph of P_M, the average of the high and low projections.

(c) $P_H - P_L = (0.028t^2 + 3.40t + 278.18) - (-0.022t^2 + 1.33t + 270.71)$

$$= (0.028t^2 + 0.022t^2) + (3.40t - 1.33t) + (278.18 - 270.71)$$

$$= 0.05t^2 + 2.07t + 7.47$$

Keystrokes: [Y=] .003 [X,T,θ] [x²] [+] 2.365 [X,T,θ] [+] 274.495 [GRAPH]

Keystrokes: [Y=] .05 [X,T,θ] [x²] [+] 2.07 [X,T,θ] [+] 7.47 [GRAPH]

The difference between the high and low projections is increasing.

117. *Verbal model:* | Profit | = | Revenue | − | Cost |

Equation:

$$P(x) = 1.1x - (0.5x + 1000)$$

$$= 1.1x - 0.5x - 1000$$

$$= 0.6x - 1000$$

$$P(5000) = 0.6(5000) - 1000$$

$$= 3000 - 1000$$

$$= \$2000$$

119. Perimeter $= x + 3x + 4 + 4x + 3 + 1 = 8x + 8$

Area $= 1.3x + 3.4x = 3x + 12x = 15x$

121. *Verbal model:*

$$\boxed{\begin{array}{c}\text{Area of}\\\text{shaded}\\\text{region}\end{array}} = \boxed{\begin{array}{c}\text{Area of}\\\text{larger}\\\text{rectangle}\end{array}} - \boxed{\begin{array}{c}\text{Area of}\\\text{smaller}\\\text{rectangle}\end{array}}$$

Labels:

Width of larger rectangle $= 2x$

Length of larger rectangle $= 2x + 5$

Width of smaller rectangle $= 2x - 3$

Length of smaller rectangle $= 2x + 1$

Equation:

$$\begin{aligned}\text{Area} &= 2x(2x + 5) - (2x + 1)(2x - 3)\\&= 4x^2 + 10x - (4x^2 - 6x + 2x - 3)\\&= 4x^2 + 10x - 4x^2 + 4x + 3\\&= 14x + 3\end{aligned}$$

123. (a) $\begin{aligned}\text{Perimeter} &= 2l + 2w\\&= 2l + 2(l - 5)\\&= 2l + 2l - 10\\&= 4l - 10\end{aligned}$

(b) $\begin{aligned}\text{Area} &= l \cdot w\\&= l(l - 5)\\&= l^2 - 5l\end{aligned}$

125. *Verbal model:*

$$\boxed{\begin{array}{c}\text{Cost of}\\\text{fencing}\\\text{2 widths}\end{array}} + \boxed{\begin{array}{c}\text{Cost of}\\\text{fencing}\\\text{front}\end{array}} + \boxed{\begin{array}{c}\text{Cost of}\\\text{fencing}\\\text{back}\end{array}} = \boxed{9500}$$

Labels:

Width $= x$

Front $= 400 - x$

Back $= 400 - x$

Equation:

$$\begin{aligned}10(2x) + 15(400 - x) + 10(400 - x) &= 9500\\20x + 6000 - 15x + 4000 - 10x &= 9500\\-5x &= -500\\x &= 100 \text{ feet}\\400 - x &= 300 \text{ feet}\end{aligned}$$

127. $-16t^2 + 16t + 32 = 0$

$-16(t^2 - t - 2) = 0$

$-16(t - 2)(t + 1) = 0$

$t - 2 = 0 \qquad t + 1 = 0$

$\quad t = 2 \qquad\qquad t = -1$

$\qquad\qquad\qquad\qquad$ reject

The object reaches the ground after 2 seconds.

129. *Verbal model:*
$$\boxed{\begin{array}{c}\text{First even}\\\text{integer}\end{array}} \cdot \boxed{\begin{array}{c}\text{Second even}\\\text{integer}\end{array}} = \boxed{224}$$

Labels: First even integer $= 2n$

Second even integer $= 2n + 2$

Equation: $2n \cdot (2n + 2) = 224$

$4n^2 + 4n - 224 = 0$

$4(n^2 + n - 56) = 0$

$4(n + 8)(n - 7) = 0$

$\begin{array}{ll} n + 8 = 0 & n - 7 = 0 \\ n = -8 & n = 7 \\ \text{reject} & 2n = 14 \\ & 2n + 2 = 16 \end{array}$

Chapter Test for Chapter 3

1. $-5.2x^3 + 3x^2 - 8$

Degree $= 3$ Leading coefficient $= -5.2$

2. $\dfrac{4}{x^2 + 2}$ is not a polynomial because the variable appears in the denominator.

3. (a) $(5a^2 - 3a + 4) + (a^2 - 4) = 6a^2 - 3a$

(b) $(16 - y^2) - (16 + 2y + y^2)$

$= 16 - y^2 - 16 - 2y - y^2$

$= -2y^2 - 2y$

4. (a) $-2(2x^4 - 5) + 4x(x^3 + 2x - 1)$

$= -4x^4 - 10 + 4x^4 + 8x^2 - 4x$

$= 8x^2 - 4x + 10$

(b) $4t - [3t - (10t + 7)] = 4t - [3t - 10t - 7]$

$= 4t - 3t + 10t + 7$

$= 11t + 7$

5. (a) $(-2u^2v)^3(3v^2) = (-8u^6v^3)(3v^2)$

$= -24u^6v^5$

(b) $3(5x)(2xy)^2 = 3(5x)(4x^2y^2)$

$= 60x^3y^2$

6. (a) $2y\left(\dfrac{y}{4}\right)^2 = 2y\left(\dfrac{y^2}{16}\right)$

$= \dfrac{y^3}{8}$

(b) $\dfrac{(-3x^2y)^4}{6x^2} = \dfrac{81x^8y^4}{6x^2}$

$= \dfrac{27x^6y^4}{2}$

7. (a) $-3x(x - 4) = -3x^2 + 12x$

(b) $(2x - 3y)(x + 5y) = 2x^2 + 7xy - 15y^2$

8. (a) $(x - 1)[2x + (x - 3)] = (x - 1)(3x - 3) = 3x^2 - 6x + 3$

(b) $(2s - 3)(3s^2 - 4s + 7) = 6s^3 - 8s^2 + 14s - 9s^2 + 12s - 21$

$= 6s^3 - 17s^2 + 26s - 21$

9. (a) $(4x - 3)^2 = 16x^2 - 24x + 9$

(b) $[4 - (a + b)][4 + (a + b)] = 16 - (a + b)^2$

$$= 16 - (a^2 + 2ab + b^2)$$
$$= 16 - a^2 - 2ab - b^2$$

10. $18y^2 - 12y = 6y(3y - 2)$

11. $v^2 - \frac{16}{9} = \left(v - \frac{4}{3}\right)\left(v + \frac{4}{3}\right)$

12. $x^3 - 3x^2 - 4x + 12 = x^2(x - 3) - 4(x - 3)$

$$= (x - 3)(x^2 - 4)$$
$$= (x - 3)(x - 2)(x + 2)$$

13. $9u^2 - 6u + 1 = (3u - 1)(3u - 1)$ or $(3u - 1)^2$

14. $6x^2 - 26x - 20 = 2(3x^2 - 13x - 10)$

$$= 2(3x + 2)(x - 5)$$

15. $x^3 + 27 = (x + 3)(x^2 - 3x + 9)$

16.

$$(y + 2)^2 - 9 = 0$$

$$[(y + 2) - 3][(y + 2) + 3] = 0$$

$$y - 1 = 0 \qquad\qquad y + 5 = 0$$

$$y = 1 \qquad\qquad y = -5$$

17. $12 + 5y - 3y^2 = 0$

$$(3 - y)(4 + 3y) = 0$$

$$3 - y = 0 \qquad\qquad 4 + 3y = 0$$

$$3 = y \qquad\qquad -\frac{4}{3} = y$$

18. Area $= 2x(x + 15) - x(x + 4)$

Shaded region $= 2x^2 + 30x - x^2 - 4x$

$$= x^2 + 26x$$

19. *Verbal model:* | Area rectangle | $=$ | Length | $\cdot$ | Width |

Labels: Length $= \frac{3}{2}w$

Width $= w$

Equation: $54 = \frac{3}{2}w \cdot w$

$$108 = 3w^2$$

$$36 = w^2$$

6 centimeters $=$ width

9 centimeters $=$ length

20. $0 = -16t^2 - 40t + 144$

$$0 = 2t^2 + 5t - 18$$

$$0 = (2t + 9)(t - 2)$$

$$2t + 9 = 0 \qquad\qquad t - 2 = 0$$

$$t = -\frac{9}{2} \qquad\qquad t = 2 \text{ sec}$$

reject

21. *Verbal model:* $\boxed{\text{Area}} = \frac{1}{2} \cdot \boxed{\text{Base}} \cdot \boxed{\text{Height}}$

Labels: Base $= x$

Height $= 2x + 4$

Equation: $35 = \frac{1}{2} \cdot x \cdot (2x + 4)$

$70 = 2x^2 + 4x$

$0 = 2x^2 + 4x - 70$

$0 = x^2 + 2x - 35$

$0 = (x + 7)(x - 5)$

$x + 7 = 0$ $x - 5 = 0$

$x = -7$ $x = 5$ feet; base

reject $2x + 4 = 14$ feet; height

Cumulative Test for Chapters P–3

1. (a) $-2 < 5$

(b) $\frac{1}{3} < \frac{1}{2}$

(c) $|2.3| > -|-4.5|$

2. "The number n is tripled and the product is decreased by 8," is expressed by $3n - 8$.

3. (a) $t(3t - 1) - 2t(t + 4) = 3t^2 - t - 2t^2 - 8t$

$= t^2 - 9t$

(b) $3x(x^2 - 2) - x(x^2 + 5) = 3x^3 - 6x - x^3 - 5x$

$= 2x^3 - 11x$

4. (a) $(2a^2b)^3(-ab^2)^2 = (8a^6b^3)(a^2b^4)$

$= 8a^8b^7$

(b) $\left(\dfrac{2x^4y^2}{4x^3y}\right)^2 = \left(\dfrac{xy}{2}\right)^2 = \dfrac{x^2y^2}{4}$

5. (a) $(2x + 1)(x - 5) = 2x^2 - 10x + x - 5$

$= 2x^2 - 9x - 5$

(b) $[2 + (x - y)]^2 = 4 + 4(x - y) + (x - y)^2$

$= 4 + 4x - 4y + x^2 - 2xy + y^2$

6. (a) $12 - 5(3 - x) = x + 3$

$12 - 15 + 5x = x + 3$

$-3 + 5x = x + 3$

$-3 + 5x - x = x + 3 - x$

$3 - 3 + 4x = 3 + 3$

$4x = 6$

$\dfrac{4x}{4} = \dfrac{6}{4}$

$x = \dfrac{3}{2}$

(b) $1 - \dfrac{x + 2}{4} = \dfrac{7}{8}$

$8\left[1 - \dfrac{x + 2}{4}\right] = \left[\dfrac{7}{8}\right]8$

$8 - 2(x + 2) = 7$

$8 - 2x - 4 = 7$

$4 - 2x = 7$

$4 - 4 - 2x = 7 - 4$

$-2x = 3$

$\dfrac{-2x}{-2} = -\dfrac{3}{2}$

$x = -\dfrac{3}{2}$

7. (a) $|3x - 5| = 7$

$3x - 5 = 7$ $3x - 5 = -7$

$3x = 12$ $3x = -2$

$x = 4$ $x = -\frac{2}{3}$

(b) $2t^2 - 5t - 3 = 0$

$(2t + 1)(t - 3) = 0$

$2t + 1 = 0$ $t - 3 = 0$

$t = -\frac{1}{2}$ $t = 3$

8. (a) $3(1 - x) > 6$

$3 - 3x > 6$

$-3x > 3$

$x < -1$

(b) $-12 \le 4x - 6 < 10$

$-6 \le 4x < 16$

$-\frac{6}{4} \le x < 4$

$-\frac{3}{2} \le x < 4$

9. *Verbal model:* $\boxed{\begin{array}{c}\text{Total annual} \\ \text{premium}\end{array}} = \boxed{\begin{array}{c}\text{Annual} \\ \text{premium}\end{array}} + \boxed{\text{Surcharge}}$

Labels: Total annual premium $= x$

Equation: $x = 1225 + 0.15(1225)$

$x = 1225 + 183.75$

$x = \$1408.75$

10. $\dfrac{9}{4.5} = \dfrac{13}{x}$

$9x = 13(4.5)$

$x = \dfrac{13(4.5)}{9}$

$x = 6.5$

11. $x - 2 \le -3$ or $x - 2 \ge 3$

$x \le -1$ $x \ge 5$

12. *Verbal model:* $\boxed{\text{Revenue}} > \boxed{\text{Cost}}$

Equation: $12.90x \ge 8.50x + 450$

$4.4x \ge 450$

$x \ge 102.27273$

$x \ge 103$

13. $x - y^3 = 0$ does represent y as a function of x.

14. $f(x) = \sqrt{x - 2}$ $D = x \ge 2$ $x - 2 \ge 0$

$2 \le x < \infty$

15. $f(x) = x^2 - 3x$

(a) $f(4) = 4^2 - 3(4) = 16 - 12 = 4$

(b) $f(c + 3) = (c + 3)^2 - 3(c + 3)$

$= c^2 + 6c + 9 - 3c - 9$

$= c^2 + 3c$

16. $m = \dfrac{6-0}{4+4} = \dfrac{6}{8} = \dfrac{3}{4}$

$d = \sqrt{(-4-4)^2 + (0-6)^2}$

$= \sqrt{64 + 36}$

$= \sqrt{100}$

$= 10$

17. (a) $2x - y = 1$

$-y = -2x + 1$

$y = 2x - 1$

$m = 2$

$y - 1 = 2(x + 2)$

$y - 1 = 2x + 4$

$2x - y + 5 = 0$

(b) $3x + 2y = 5$

$2y = -3x + 5$

$y = -\frac{3}{2}x + 5$

$m = \frac{2}{3}$

$y - 1 = \frac{2}{3}(x + 2)$

$y - 1 = \frac{2}{3}x + \frac{4}{3}$

$y = \frac{2}{3}x + \frac{7}{3}$

$3y = 2x + 7$

$2x - 3y + 7 = 0$

18. (a) $3x^2 - 8x - 35 = (3x + 7)(x - 5)$

(b) $9x^2 - 144 = (3x)^2 - (12)^2$

$= (3x - 12)(3x + 12)$

$= 3(x - 4)\,3(x + 4)$

$= 9(x - 4)(x + 4)$

19. (a) $y^3 - 3y^2 - 9y + 27 = y^2(y - 3) - 9(y - 3)$

$= (y - 3)(y^2 - 9)$

$= (y - 3)(y - 3)(y + 3)$

(b) $8t^3 - 40t^2 + 50t = 2t(4t^2 - 20t + 25)$

$= 2t[(2t)^2 - 2(2t)(5) + 5^2]$

$= 2t(2t - 5)^2$

20. $4x + 3y - 12 = 0$

$4(0) + 3y - 12 = 0$ $4x + 3(0) - 12 = 0$

$3y = 12$ $4x = 12$

$y = 4 \quad (0, 4)$ $x = 3 \quad (3, 0)$

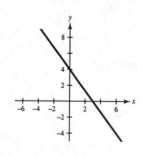

21. $y = 1 - (x - 2)^2$

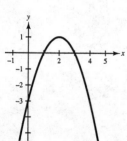

C H A P T E R 4
Rational Expressions, Equations, and Functions

CHAPTER 4
Rational Expressions, Equations, and Functions

Section 4.1   Integer Exponents and Scientific Notation
Solutions to Odd-Numbered Exercises

1. $5^{-2} = \dfrac{1}{5^2} = \dfrac{1}{25}$

3. $-10^{-3} = -\dfrac{1}{10^3} = -\dfrac{1}{1000}$

5. $(-3)^0 = 1$

7. $\dfrac{1}{4^{-3}} = \dfrac{1}{(1/4)^3} = 4^3 = 64$

9. $\dfrac{1}{(-2)^{-5}} = \dfrac{1}{\left(-\dfrac{1}{2}\right)^5}$

$= \dfrac{1}{-\dfrac{1}{32}} = -32$

11. $\left(\dfrac{2}{3}\right)^{-1} = \dfrac{3}{2}$

13. $\left(\dfrac{3}{16}\right)^0 = 1$

15. $27 \cdot 3^{-3} = 3^3 \cdot 3^{-3}$

$= 3^{3+(-3)}$

$= 3^0$

$= 1$

17. $\dfrac{3^4}{3^{-2}} = 3^{4-(-2)}$

$= 3^{4+2}$

$= 3^6$

$= 729$

19. $\dfrac{10^3}{10^{-2}} = 10^{3-(-2)}$

$= 10^{3+2}$

$= 10^5$

$= 100,000$

21. $(4^2 \cdot 4^{-1})^{-2} = (4^{2+(-1)})^{-2}$

$= (4^1)^{-2}$

$= 4^{-2}$

$= \dfrac{1}{4^2}$

$= \dfrac{1}{16}$

23. $(2^{-3})^2 = 2^{-6}$

$= \dfrac{1}{2^6}$

$= \dfrac{1}{64}$

25. $2^{-3} + 2^{-4} = \dfrac{1}{2^3} + \dfrac{1}{2^4}$

$= \dfrac{1}{8} + \dfrac{1}{16}$

$= \dfrac{2}{16} + \dfrac{1}{16}$

$= \dfrac{3}{16}$

27. $\left(\dfrac{3}{4} + \dfrac{5}{8}\right)^{-2} = \left(\dfrac{6}{8} + \dfrac{5}{8}\right)^{-2}$

$= \left(\dfrac{11}{8}\right)^{-2}$

$= \left(\dfrac{8}{11}\right)^2$

$= \dfrac{64}{121}$

29. $(5^0 - 4^{-2})^{-1} = \left(1 - \dfrac{1}{4^2}\right)^{-1}$

$= \left(\dfrac{16}{16} - \dfrac{1}{16}\right)^{-1}$

$= \left(\dfrac{15}{16}\right)^{-1}$

$= \dfrac{16}{15}$

31. $y^4 \cdot y^{-2} = y^{4+(-2)} = y^2$

33. $z^5 \cdot z^{-3} = z^{5+(-3)} = z^2$

35. $7x^{-4} = \dfrac{7}{x^4}$

37. $(4x)^{-3} = \dfrac{1}{(4x)^3} = \dfrac{1}{64x^3}$ **39.** $\dfrac{1}{x^{-6}} = x^6$

41. $\dfrac{8a^{-6}}{6a^{-7}} = \dfrac{4}{3}a^{(-6)-(-7)}$

$= \dfrac{4}{3}a^{-6+7}$

$= \dfrac{4}{3}a$

43. $\dfrac{(4t)^0}{t^{-2}} = \dfrac{1}{t^{-2}} = t^2$

45. $(2x^2)^{-2} = \dfrac{1}{(2x^2)^2} = \dfrac{1}{4x^4}$

47. $(-3x^{-3}y^2)(4x^2y^{-5}) = -3 \cdot 4 \cdot x^{-3+2} \cdot y^{2+(-5)}$

$= -12x^{-1}y^{-3}$

$= -\dfrac{12}{xy^3}$

49. $(3x^2y^{-2}) = 3^{-2}x^{-4}y^4 = \dfrac{1y^4}{9x^4}$

51. $\left(\dfrac{x}{10}\right)^{-1} = \dfrac{10}{x}$

53. $\dfrac{6x^3y^{-3}}{12x^{-2}y} = \dfrac{6x^{3-(-2)}y^{-3-1}}{6 \cdot 2}$

$= \dfrac{x^5y^{-4}}{2}$

$= \dfrac{x^5}{2y^4}$

55. $\left(\dfrac{3u^2v^{-1}}{3^3u^{-1}v^3}\right)^{-2} = \left(\dfrac{3u^{2-(-1)}v^{-1-3}}{3^3}\right)^{-2}$

$= \left(\dfrac{u^3v^{-4}}{3^2}\right)^{-2}$

$= \left(\dfrac{3^2}{u^3v^{-4}}\right)^2$

$= \dfrac{3^4}{u^6v^{-8}}$

$= \dfrac{81v^8}{u^6}$

57. $\left(\dfrac{a^{-2}}{b^{-2}}\right)\left(\dfrac{b}{a}\right)^3 = \left(\dfrac{b^2}{a^2}\right)\left(\dfrac{b^3}{a^3}\right)$

$= \dfrac{b^5}{a^5}$

59. $(2x^3y^{-1})^{-3}(4xy^{-6}) = (2^{-3}x^{-9}y^3)(4xy^{-6})$

$= \dfrac{4x^{-9+1}y^{3+(-6)}}{2^3}$

$= \dfrac{4x^{-8}y^{-3}}{8}$

$= \dfrac{1}{2x^8y^3}$

61. $u^4(6u^{-3}v^0)(7v)^0 = u^4(6u^{-3})(1)$

$= 6u^{4+(-3)}$

$= 6u$

63. $[(x^{-4}y^{-6})^{-1}]^2 = (x^4y^6)^2 = x^8y^{12}$

65. $\dfrac{(2a^{-2}b^4)^3b}{(10a^3b)^2} = \dfrac{2^3a^{-6}b^{12} \cdot b}{10^2a^6b^2}$

$= \dfrac{8a^{-6-6}b^{12+1-2}}{100}$

$= \dfrac{2a^{-12}b^{11}}{25}$

$= \dfrac{2b^{11}}{25a^{12}}$

67. $(u + v^{-2})^{-1} = \dfrac{1}{u + v^{-2}}$

$= \dfrac{1}{u + \left(\dfrac{1}{v^2}\right)} \cdot \dfrac{v^2}{v^2}$

$= \dfrac{v^2}{uv^2 + 1}$

69. $\dfrac{a + b}{ba^{-1} - ab^{-1}} = \dfrac{a + b}{\dfrac{b}{a} - \dfrac{a}{b}} \cdot \dfrac{ab}{ab}$

$= \dfrac{a^2 b + ab^2}{b^2 - a^2}$

$= \dfrac{ab(a + b)}{(b - a)(b + a)}$

$= \dfrac{ab}{b - a}$

71. $3,600,000 = 3.6 \times 10^6$

73. $47,620,000 = 4.762 \times 10^7$

75. $0.00031 = 3.1 \times 10^{-4}$

77. $0.0000000381 = 3.81 \times 10^{-8}$

79. $57,500,000 = 5.75 \times 10^7$

81. $9,461,000,000,000,000 = 9.461 \times 10^{15}$

83. $0.0000899 = 8.99 \times 10^{-5}$

85. $6 \times 10^7 = 60,000,000$

87. $1.359 \times 10^{-7} = 0.0000001359$

89. $\$3.17 \times 10^{10} = 31,700,000,000$

91. $1.3 \times 10^7 = 13,000,000$

93. $4.8 \times 10^{-10} = 0.00000000048$

95. $(2 \times 10^9)(3.4 \times 10^{-4}) = (2)(3.4)(10^5)$
$= 6.8 \times 10^5$

97. $(5 \times 10^4)^2 = 5^2 \times 10^8$
$= 25 \times 10^8$
$= 2.5 \times 10^9$

99. $\dfrac{3.6 \times 10^{12}}{6 \times 10^5} = \dfrac{3.6}{6} \times 10^{12-5}$
$= 0.6 \times 10^7$
$= 6.0 \times 10^6$

101. $(4,500,000)(2,000,000,000) = (4.5 \times 10^6)(2 \times 10^9)$
$= (4.5)(2) \times 10^{15}$
$= 9 \times 10^{15}$

103. $\dfrac{64,000,000}{0.00004} = \dfrac{6.4 \times 10^7}{4.0 \times 10^{-5}}$
$= 1.6 \times 10^{7-(-5)}$
$= 1.6 \times 10^{12}$

105. $\dfrac{(0.0000565)(2,850,000,000,000)}{0.00465} = \dfrac{(5.65 \times 10^{-5})(2.85 \times 10^{12})}{4.65 \times 10^{-3}}$

$= \dfrac{(5.65)(2.85)}{4.65} \times 10^{10}$

$\approx 3.4629032 \times 10^{10}$

$\approx 3.46 \times 10^{10}$

107. $\dfrac{1.357 \times 10^{12}}{(4.2 \times 10^2)(6.87 \times 10^{-3})} = \dfrac{1.357}{(4.2)(6.87)} \times 10^{13}$

$= 0.0470299 \times 10^{13}$

$= 4.70299 \times 10^{11}$

$\approx 4.70 \times 10^{11}$

109. $72,400 \times 2,300,000,000 = (7.24 \times 10^4)(2.3 \times 10^9)$
$= 16.652 \times 10^{4+9}$
$= 16.652 \times 10^{13}$
$= 1.6652 \times 10^{14}$
$\approx 1.67 \times 10^{14}$

111. $\dfrac{(5{,}000{,}000)^3(0.000037)^2}{(0.005)^4} = \dfrac{(5.0 \times 10^6)^3(3.7 \times 10^{-5})^2}{(5.0 \times 10^{-3})^4}$

$= \dfrac{(5^3 \times 10^{18})(3.7^2 \times 10^{-10})}{5^4 \times 10^{-12}}$

$= \dfrac{(125)(13.69)}{625} \times 10^{18+(-10)-(-12)}$

$= 2.738 \times 10^{18-10+12}$

$= 2.738 \times 10^{20}$

$\approx 2.74 \times 10^{20}$

113. $93{,}000{,}000 = 9.3 \times 10^7$

115. $\dfrac{1.49 \times 10^{11}}{9.45 \times 10^{15}} = \dfrac{1.49}{9.45} \times 10^{-4}$

$\approx 0.157672 \times 10^{-4}$

$\approx 1.58 \times 10^{-5}$

$\approx 8.3 \text{ minutes}$

117. $\dfrac{1.99 \times 10^{30}}{5.975 \times 10^{24}} = \dfrac{1.99}{5.975} \times 10^6$

$\approx 0.3330544 \times 10^6$

$\approx 3.33 \times 10^5$

119. $\dfrac{\$5506 \text{ billion}}{270 \text{ million}} = \dfrac{\$5{,}506{,}000{,}000{,}000}{270{,}000{,}000}$

$= \dfrac{5.506 \times 10^{12}}{2.7 \times 10^8}$

$\approx 2.03925 \times 10^4$

$\approx \$20{,}393$

121. In $(3x)^4$, $3x$ is called the base and 4 is called the exponent.

123. You can "move" a factor from the numerator to the denominator by changing the sign of the exponent of the factor.

125. Scientific notation is an efficient way of writing and computing real numbers when the numbers are very large or very small.

Section 4.2 Rational Expressions and Functions

1. $x - 8 \neq 0$

$x \neq 8$

$D = (-\infty, 8) \cup (8, \infty)$

3. $x + 4 \neq 0$

$x \neq -4$

$D = (-\infty, -4) \cup (-4, \infty)$

5. $4 \neq 0$

$D = (-\infty, \infty)$

7. $D = (-\infty, \infty)$

9. $x^2 + 4 \neq 0$

$D = (-\infty, \infty)$

11. $y(y + 3) \neq 0$

$y \neq 0 \quad y \neq -3$

$D = (-\infty, -3) \cup (-3, 0) \cup (0, \infty)$

13. $\quad t^2 - 16 \neq 0$

$\quad\quad (t - 4)(t + 4) \neq 0$

$\quad\quad\quad t \neq 4 \quad t \neq -4$

$\quad\quad D = (-\infty, -4) \cup (-4, 4) \cup (4, \infty)$

15. $\quad y^2 - 3y \neq 0$

$\quad\quad y(y - 3) \neq 0$

$\quad\quad y \neq 0 \quad y \neq 3$

$\quad\quad D = (-\infty, 0) \cup (0, 3) \cup (3, \infty)$

17. $\quad x^2 - 5x + 6 \neq 0$

$\quad\quad (x - 3)(x - 2) \neq 0$

$\quad\quad\quad x \neq 3 \quad x \neq 2$

$\quad\quad D = (-\infty, 2) \cup (2, 3) \cup (3, \infty)$

19. $\quad 3u^2 - 2u - 5 \neq 0$

$\quad\quad (3u - 5)(u + 1) \neq 0$

$\quad\quad\quad u \neq \frac{5}{3} \quad u \neq -1$

$\quad\quad D = (-\infty, -1) \cup \left(-1, \frac{5}{3}\right) \cup \left(\frac{5}{3}, \infty\right)$

21. (a) $f(1) = \dfrac{4(1)}{1 + 3} = \dfrac{4}{4} = 1$

(b) $f(-2) = \dfrac{4(-2)}{-2 + 3} = \dfrac{-8}{1} = -8$

(c) $f(-3) = \dfrac{4(-3)}{-3 + 3} = \dfrac{-12}{0}$

$\quad\quad\quad = \text{not possible; undefined}$

(d) $f(0) = \dfrac{4(0)}{0 + 3} = \dfrac{0}{3} = 0$

23. (a) $g(0) = \dfrac{0^2 - 4(0)}{0^2 - 9} = 0$

(b) $g(4) = \dfrac{4^2 - 4(4)}{4^2 - 9} = \dfrac{16 - 16}{16 - 9} = \dfrac{0}{7} = 0$

(c) $g(3) = \dfrac{3^2 - 4(3)}{3^2 - 9} = \dfrac{9 - 12}{9 - 9} = \dfrac{-3}{0}$

$\quad\quad\quad = \text{not possible; undefined}$

(d) $g(-3) = \dfrac{(-3)^2 - 4(-3)}{(-3)^2 - 9} = \dfrac{9 + 12}{9 - 9} = \dfrac{21}{0}$

$\quad\quad\quad = \text{not possible; undefined}$

25. (a) $h(10) = \dfrac{10^2}{10^2 - 10 - 2} = \dfrac{100}{88} = \dfrac{25}{22}$

(b) $h(0) = \dfrac{0^2}{0^2 - 0 - 2} = \dfrac{0}{-2} = 0$

(c) $h(-1) = \dfrac{(-1)^2}{(-1)^2 - (-1) - 2} = \dfrac{1}{1 + 1 - 2} = \dfrac{1}{0}$

$\quad\quad\quad = \text{not possible; undefined}$

(d) $h(2) = \dfrac{2^2}{2^2 - 2 - 2} = \dfrac{4}{4 - 2 - 2} = \dfrac{4}{0}$

$\quad\quad\quad = \text{not possible; undefined}$

27. Since length must be positive, $x \geq 0$. Since $\dfrac{500}{x}$ must be defined, $x \neq 0$. Therefore, the domain is $x > 0$ or $(0, \infty)$.

29. $x = $ units of a product

$\quad D = \{1, 2, 3, 4, \ldots\}$

31. Since p is the percent of air pollutants in the stack emission of a utility, $0 \leq p \leq 100$. Since

$$\dfrac{80,000p}{100 - p}$$

must be defined, $p \neq 100$. Therefore, the domain is $[0, 100)$.

33. $\dfrac{5}{6} = \dfrac{5(x + 3)}{6(x + 3)}, \quad x \neq -3$

35. $\dfrac{x}{2} = \dfrac{3x(x + 16)^2}{2(3(x + 16)^2)}, \quad x \neq -16$

37. $\dfrac{x + 5}{3x} = \dfrac{(x + 5)(x(x - 2))}{3x^2(x - 2)}, \quad x \neq 2$

39. $\dfrac{8x}{x - 5} = \dfrac{8x(x + 2)}{x^2 - 3x - 10}, \quad x \neq -2$

41. $\dfrac{5x}{25} = \dfrac{5x}{5 \cdot 5} = \dfrac{x}{5}$

43. $\dfrac{12y^2}{2y} = \dfrac{2 \cdot 6 \cdot y \cdot y}{2 \cdot y}$

$\quad\quad = 6y, \quad y \neq 0$

45. $\dfrac{18x^2y}{15xy^4} = \dfrac{3 \cdot 6 \cdot x \cdot x \cdot y}{3 \cdot 5 \cdot x \cdot y \cdot y^3}$

$= \dfrac{6x}{5y^3}, \quad x \neq 0$

47. $\dfrac{3x^2 - 9x}{12x^2} = \dfrac{3x(x-3)}{12x^2} = \dfrac{(x-3)}{4x}$

49. $\dfrac{x^2(x-8)}{x(x-8)} = \dfrac{x \cdot x(x-8)}{x(x-8)}$

$= x, \quad x \neq 0, x \neq 8$

51. $\dfrac{2x-3}{4x-6} = \dfrac{2x-3}{2(2x-3)} = \dfrac{1}{2}, \quad x \neq \dfrac{3}{2}$

53. $\dfrac{5-x}{3x-15} = \dfrac{-1(x-5)}{3(x-5)}$

$= -\dfrac{1}{3}, \quad x \neq 5$

55. $\dfrac{a+3}{a^2+6a+9} = \dfrac{a+3}{(a+3)(a+3)}$

$= \dfrac{1}{a+3}$

57. $\dfrac{x^2-7x}{x^2-14x+49} = \dfrac{x(x-7)}{(x-7)(x-7)}$

$= \dfrac{x}{x-7}$

59. $\dfrac{y^3-4y}{y^2+4y-12} = \dfrac{y(y^2-4)}{(y+6)(y-2)}$

$= \dfrac{y(y-2)(y+2)}{(y+6)(y-2)}$

$= \dfrac{y(y+2)}{y+6}, \quad y \neq 2$

61. $\dfrac{x^3-4x}{x^2-5x+6} = \dfrac{x(x^2-4)}{(x-3)(x-2)}$

$= \dfrac{x(x-2)(x+2)}{(x-3)(x-2)}$

$= \dfrac{x(x+2)}{x-3}, \quad x \neq 2$

63. $\dfrac{3x^2-7x-20}{12+x-x^2} = \dfrac{(3x+5)(x-4)}{-1(x^2-x-12)}$

$= \dfrac{(3x+5)(x-4)}{-1(x-4)(x+3)}$

$= -\dfrac{3x+5}{x+3}, \quad x \neq 4$

65. $\dfrac{2x^2+19x+24}{2x^2-3x-9} = \dfrac{(2x+3)(x+8)}{(2x+3)(x-3)}$

$= \dfrac{x+8}{x-3}, \quad x \neq -\dfrac{3}{2}$

67. $\dfrac{15x^2+7x-4}{25x^2-16} = \dfrac{(5x+4)(3x-1)}{(5x+4)(5x-4)}$

$= \dfrac{3x-1}{5x-4}, \quad x \neq -\dfrac{4}{5}$

69. $\dfrac{3xy^2}{xy^2+x} = \dfrac{3xy^2}{x(y^2+1)}$

$= \dfrac{3y^2}{y^2+1}, \quad x \neq 0$

71. $\dfrac{y^2-64x^2}{5(3y+24x)} = \dfrac{(y-8x)(y+8x)}{15(y+8x)}$

$= \dfrac{y-8x}{15}, \quad y \neq -8x$

73. $\dfrac{5xy+3x^2y^2}{xy^3} = \dfrac{xy(5+3xy)}{xy \cdot y^2}$

$= \dfrac{5+3xy}{y^2}, \quad x \neq 0$

75. $\dfrac{u^2-4v^2}{u^2+uv-2v^2} = \dfrac{(u-2v)(u+2v)}{(u-v)(u+2v)}$

$= \dfrac{u-2v}{u-v}, \quad u \neq -2v$

77. $\dfrac{3m^2-12n^2}{m^2+4mn+4n^2} = \dfrac{3(m^2-4n^2)}{(m+2n)(m+2n)}$

$= \dfrac{3(m-2n)(m+2n)}{(m+2n)(m+2n)}$

$= \dfrac{3(m-2n)}{m+2n}$

79. $\dfrac{x-4}{4} \neq x-1$

$\dfrac{10-4}{4} \neq 10-1$ Choose a value such as 10 for x and evaluate both sides.

$\dfrac{6}{4} \neq 9$

81. $\dfrac{3x+2}{4x+2} \neq \dfrac{3}{4}$

$\dfrac{3(0)+2}{4(0)+2} \neq \dfrac{3}{4}$ Choose a value such as 0 for x and evaluate both sides.

$1 \neq \dfrac{3}{4}$

83.

x	-2	-1	0	1	2	3	4
$\dfrac{x^2 - x - 2}{x - 2}$	-1	0	1	2	Undefined	4	5
$x + 1$	-1	0	1	2	3	4	5

Domain of $\dfrac{x^2 - x - 2}{x - 2}$ is $(-\infty, 2) \cup (2, \infty)$.

Domain of $x + 1$ is $(-\infty, \infty)$.

The two expressions are equal for all replacements of the variable x except 2.

85. $\dfrac{\text{Area of shaded portion}}{\text{Area of total figure}} = \dfrac{x(x + 1)}{(x + 1)(x + 3)} = \dfrac{x}{x + 3}, \quad x > 0$

87. (a) *Verbal Model:* $\boxed{\begin{array}{c}\text{Total}\\\text{cost}\end{array}} = \boxed{\begin{array}{c}\text{Number}\\\text{of units}\end{array}} \cdot \boxed{\begin{array}{c}\text{Cost per}\\\text{unit}\end{array}} + \boxed{\begin{array}{c}\text{Initial}\\\text{cost}\end{array}}$

    Labels: Total cost $= C$

    Number of units $= x$

    Equation: $2500 + 9.25x = C$

(b) *Verbal Model:* $\boxed{\begin{array}{c}\text{Average}\\\text{cost}\end{array}} = \boxed{\begin{array}{c}\text{Total}\\\text{cost}\end{array}} \div \boxed{\begin{array}{c}\text{Number}\\\text{of units}\end{array}}$

    Label: Average cost $= \overline{C}$

    Equation: $\overline{C} = \dfrac{2500 + 9.25x}{x}$

(c) Domain $= \{1, 2, 3, 4, \ldots\}$

(d) $\dfrac{2500 + 9.25(100)}{100} = \$34.25$

89. (a) *Verbal Model:* $\boxed{\text{Distance}} = \boxed{\text{Rate}} \cdot \boxed{\text{Time}}$

    Van: $45(t + 3)$

    Car: $60t$

(b) Distance between van and car $= d$

    $= 45(t + 3) - 60t$

    $= 45t + 135 - 60t$

    $= 135 - 15t$

    $= 15(9 - t)$

(c) $\dfrac{\text{Distance of car}}{\text{Distance of van}} = \dfrac{60t}{45(t + 3)} = \dfrac{4t}{3(t + 3)}$

91. $\dfrac{\text{Circular pool volume}}{\text{Rectangular pool volume}} = \dfrac{\pi(3d)^2(d + 2)}{d(3d)(3d + 6)}$

$= \dfrac{\pi(3d)^2(d + 2)}{3d^2 \cdot 3(d + 2)}$

$= \dfrac{\pi(3d)^2(d + 2)}{(3d)^2(d + 2)}$

$= \pi$

93. Average cost of Medicare per person $= \dfrac{107.30 + 15.09t \text{ billion}}{34.26 + 0.65t \text{ million}} = \dfrac{(10{,}730 + 1509t)1000}{3426 + 65t}$

95. Let u and v be polynomials. The algebraic expression u/v is a rational expression.

97. The rational expression is in simplified form if the numerator and denominator have no factors in common (other than ± 1).

99. You can cancel only common factors.

Section 4.3   Multiplying and Dividing Rational Expressions

1. (a) $x = 10$: $\dfrac{10 - 10}{4(10)} = \dfrac{0}{40} = 0$ (b) $x = 0$: $\dfrac{0 - 10}{4(0)} = \dfrac{-10}{0} =$ undefined

  (c) $x = -2$: $\dfrac{-2 - 10}{4(-2)} = \dfrac{-12}{-8} = \dfrac{3}{2}$ (d) $x = 12$: $\dfrac{12 - 10}{4(12)} = \dfrac{2}{48} = \dfrac{1}{24}$

3. $\dfrac{7}{3y} = \dfrac{7x^2}{3y(x^2)}, \quad x \neq 0$

5. $\dfrac{3x}{x - 4} = \dfrac{3x(x + 2)^2}{(x - 4)(x + 2)^2}, \quad x \neq -2$

7. $\dfrac{3u}{7v} = \dfrac{3u(u + 1)}{7v(u + 1)}, \quad u \neq -1$

9. $\dfrac{13x}{x - 2} = \dfrac{13x((-1)(2 + x))}{4 - x^2}, \quad x \neq -2$

11. $\dfrac{45}{28} \cdot \dfrac{77}{60} = \dfrac{9 \cdot 5 \cdot 7 \cdot 11}{7 \cdot 4 \cdot 6 \cdot 10} = \dfrac{33}{16}$

13. $7x \cdot \dfrac{9}{14x} = \dfrac{7x \cdot 3 \cdot 3}{7 \cdot 2 \cdot x} = \dfrac{9}{2}$

15. $\dfrac{8s^3}{9s} \cdot \dfrac{6s^2}{32s} = \dfrac{8s^3 \cdot 3 \cdot 2s \cdot s}{3 \cdot 3 \cdot s \cdot 8 \cdot 2 \cdot 2 \cdot s} = \dfrac{s^3}{6}, \quad s \neq 0$

17. $16u^4 \cdot \dfrac{12}{8u^2} = \dfrac{8 \cdot 2 \cdot u^2 \cdot u^2 \cdot 12}{8 \cdot u^2} = 24u^2, \quad u \neq 0$

19. $\dfrac{8}{3 + 4x} \cdot (9 + 12x) = \dfrac{8 \cdot 3(3 + 4x)}{3 + 4x}$

$= 24, \quad x \neq -\dfrac{3}{4}$

21. $\dfrac{8u^2v}{3u + v} \cdot \dfrac{u + v}{12u} = \dfrac{4 \cdot 2 \cdot u \cdot u \cdot v(u + v)}{(3u + v) \cdot 4 \cdot 3 \cdot u}$

$= \dfrac{2uv(u + v)}{3(3u + v)}, \quad u \neq 0$

23. $\dfrac{12 - r}{3} \cdot \dfrac{3}{r - 12} = \dfrac{-1(r - 12) \cdot 3}{3(r - 12)} = -1, \quad r \neq 12$

25. $\dfrac{(2x - 3)(x + 8)}{x^3} \cdot \dfrac{x}{3 - 2x} = \dfrac{(2x - 3)(x + 8)x}{x \cdot x^2 \cdot -1(2x - 3)}$

$= \dfrac{x + 8}{-x^2}, \quad x \neq \dfrac{3}{2}$

27. $\dfrac{4r - 12}{r - 2} \cdot \dfrac{r^2 - 4}{r - 3} = \dfrac{4(r - 3)(r - 2)(r + 2)}{(r - 2) \cdot (r - 3)} = 4(r + 2), \quad r \neq 3, r \neq 2$

29. $\dfrac{2t^2 - t - 15}{t + 2} \cdot \dfrac{t^2 - t - 6}{t^2 - 6t + 9} = \dfrac{(2t + 5)(t - 3)(t - 3)(t + 2)}{(t + 2)(t - 3)(t - 3)} = 2t + 5, \quad t \neq 3, t \neq -2$

31. $(x^2 - 4y^2) \cdot \dfrac{xy}{(x - 2y)^2} = (x - 2y)(x + 2y) \cdot \dfrac{xy}{(x - 2y)^2} = \dfrac{(x + 2y)xy}{x - 2y}$

33. $\dfrac{x^2 + 2xy - 3y^2}{(x + y)^2} \cdot \dfrac{x^2 - y^2}{x + 3y} = \dfrac{(x + 3y)(x - y)}{(x + y)^2} \cdot \dfrac{(x - y)(x + y)}{x + 3y} = \dfrac{(x - y)^2}{x + y}, \quad x \neq -3y$

35. $\dfrac{x + 5}{x - 5} \cdot \dfrac{2x^2 - 9x - 5}{3x^2 + x - 2} \cdot \dfrac{x^2 - 1}{x^2 + 7x + 10} = \dfrac{x + 5}{x - 5} \cdot \dfrac{(2x + 1)(x - 5)}{(3x - 2)(x + 1)} \cdot \dfrac{(x - 1)(x + 1)}{(x + 5)(x + 2)}$

$= \dfrac{(x + 5)(2x + 1)(x - 5)(x - 1)(x + 1)}{(x - 5)(3x - 2)(x + 1)(x + 5)(x + 2)}$

$= \dfrac{(2x + 1)(x - 1)}{(3x - 2)(x + 2)}, \quad x \neq \pm 5, -1$

37. $\dfrac{9 - x^2}{2x + 3} \cdot \dfrac{4x^2 + 8x - 5}{4x^2 - 8x + 3} \cdot \dfrac{6x^4 - 2x^3}{8x^2 + 4x} = \dfrac{(3 - x)(3 + x)}{2x + 3} \cdot \dfrac{(2x + 5)(2x - 1)}{(2x - 3)(2x - 1)} \cdot \dfrac{2x^3(3x - 1)}{4x(2x + 1)}$

$$= \dfrac{-1(x - 3)(x + 3)(2x + 5)x^2(3x - 1)}{(2x + 3)(2x - 3)2(2x + 1)}$$

$$= \dfrac{(x^2 - 9)(2x + 5)x^2(3x - 1)}{(2x + 3)(3 - 2x)2(2x + 1)}, \quad x \neq 0, \dfrac{1}{2}$$

39. $\dfrac{x^3 + 3x^2 - 4x - 12}{x^3 - 3x^2 - 4x + 12} \cdot \dfrac{x^2 - 9}{x} = \dfrac{x^2(x + 3) - 4(x + 3)}{x^2(x - 3) - 4(x - 3)} \cdot \dfrac{(x + 3)(x - 3)}{x}$

$$= \dfrac{(x + 3)(x^2 - 4)(x + 3)(x - 3)}{(x - 3)(x^2 - 4) \cdot x}$$

$$= \dfrac{(x + 3)^2}{x}, \quad x \neq -2, 2, 3$$

41. $\dfrac{-5}{12} \div \dfrac{45}{32} = \dfrac{-5}{12} \cdot \dfrac{32}{45} = \dfrac{-5 \cdot 8 \cdot 4}{4 \cdot 3 \cdot 5 \cdot 9} = \dfrac{-8}{27}$

43. $x^2 \div \dfrac{3x}{4} = x^2 \cdot \dfrac{4}{3x} = \dfrac{4x}{3}, \quad x \neq 0$

45. $\dfrac{7xy^2}{10u^2v} \div \dfrac{21x^3}{45uv} = \dfrac{7xy^2}{10u^2v} \cdot \dfrac{45uv}{21x^3}$

$$= \dfrac{7xy^2 \cdot 3 \cdot 3 \cdot 5 \cdot u \cdot v}{5 \cdot 2 \cdot u \cdot u \cdot v \cdot 7 \cdot 3x \cdot x^2}$$

$$= \dfrac{3y^2}{2ux^2}, \quad v \neq 0$$

47. $\dfrac{3(a + b)}{4} \div \dfrac{(a + b)^2}{2} = \dfrac{3(a + b)}{4} \cdot \dfrac{2}{(a + b)^2}$

$$= \dfrac{3(a + b) \cdot 2}{2 \cdot 2 \cdot (a + b)(a + b)}$$

$$= \dfrac{3}{2(a + b)}$$

49. $\dfrac{(x^3y)^2}{(x + 2y)^2} \div \dfrac{x^2y}{(x + 2y)^3} = \dfrac{(x^3y)^2}{(x + 2y)^2} \cdot \dfrac{(x + 2y)^3}{x^2y}$

$$= \dfrac{(x^3y)(x^3y)(x + 2y)^2(x + 2y)}{(x + 2y)^2x^2y}$$

$$= \dfrac{(x^3y)(x^2 \cdot xy)(x + 2y)}{x^2y}$$

$$= x^4y(x + 2y), \quad x \neq 0, y \neq 0, x \neq -2y$$

51. $\dfrac{\left(\dfrac{x^2}{12}\right)}{\left(\dfrac{5x}{18}\right)} = \dfrac{x^2}{12} \div \dfrac{5x}{18}$

$$= \dfrac{x^2}{12} \cdot \dfrac{18}{5x}$$

$$= \dfrac{x^2 \cdot 3 \cdot 3 \cdot 2}{2 \cdot 2 \cdot 3 \cdot 5 \cdot x}$$

$$= \dfrac{3x}{10}, \quad x \neq 0$$

53. $\dfrac{\left(\dfrac{25x^2}{x - 5}\right)}{\left(\dfrac{10x}{5 + 4x - x^2}\right)} = \dfrac{25x^2}{x - 5} \div \dfrac{10x}{5 + 4x - x^2}$

$$= \dfrac{25x^2}{x - 5} \cdot \dfrac{5 + 4x - x^2}{10x}$$

$$= \dfrac{5 \cdot 5 \cdot x \cdot x \cdot (-1)(x^2 - 4x - 5)}{(x - 5) \cdot 5 \cdot 2 \cdot x}$$

$$= \dfrac{5 \cdot x \cdot (-1)(x - 5)(x + 1)}{(x - 5)2}$$

$$= \dfrac{-5x(x + 1)}{2}, \quad x \neq 0, 5, -1$$

55. $\dfrac{16x^2 + 8x + 1}{3x^2 + 8x - 3} \div \dfrac{4x^2 - 3x - 1}{x^2 + 6x + 9} = \dfrac{16x^2 + 8x + 1}{3x^2 + 8x - 3} \cdot \dfrac{x^2 + 6x + 9}{4x^2 - 3x - 1}$

$$= \dfrac{(4x + 1)(4x + 1)}{(3x - 1)(x + 3)} \cdot \dfrac{(x + 3)(x + 3)}{(4x + 1)(x - 1)}$$

$$= \dfrac{(4x + 1)(4x + 1)(x + 3)(x + 3)}{(3x - 1)(x + 3)(4x + 1)(x - 1)}$$

$$= \dfrac{(4x + 1)(x + 3)}{(3x - 1)(x - 1)}, \quad x \neq -3, -\dfrac{1}{4}$$

57. $\dfrac{x^2 + 3x - 2x - 6}{x^2 - 4} \div \dfrac{x + 3}{x^2 + 4x + 4} = \dfrac{x(x + 3) - 2(x + 3)}{x^2 - 4} \cdot \dfrac{x^2 + 4x + 4}{x + 3}$

$$= \dfrac{(x + 3)(x - 2)}{(x - 2)(x + 2)} \cdot \dfrac{(x + 2)(x + 2)}{x + 3}$$

$$= \dfrac{(x + 3)(x - 2)(x + 2)(x + 2)}{(x - 2)(x + 2)(x + 3)}$$

$$= (x + 2), \quad x \neq \pm 2, -3$$

59. $\dfrac{\left(\dfrac{x^2 - 3x - 10}{x^2 - 4x + 4}\right)}{\left(\dfrac{21 + 4x - x^2}{x^2 - 5x - 14}\right)} = \dfrac{x^2 - 3x - 10}{x^2 - 4x + 4} \div \dfrac{21 + 4x - x^2}{x^2 - 5x - 14}$

$$= \dfrac{x^2 - 3x - 10}{x^2 - 4x + 4} \cdot \dfrac{x^2 - 5x - 14}{1(x^2 - 4x - 21)}$$

$$= \dfrac{(x - 5)(x + 2)}{(x - 2)(x - 2)} \cdot \dfrac{(x - 7)(x + 2)}{-1(x - 7)(x + 3)}$$

$$= -\dfrac{(x^2 - 3x - 10)(x + 2)}{(x^2 - 4x + 4)(x + 3)}, \quad x \neq \pm 2, 7$$

61. $\left[\dfrac{x^2}{9} \cdot \dfrac{3(x + 4)}{x^2 + 2x}\right] \div \dfrac{x}{x + 2} = \dfrac{x^2}{9} \cdot \dfrac{3(x + 4)}{x(x + 2)} \cdot \dfrac{x + 2}{x}$

$$= \dfrac{x + 4}{3}, \quad x \neq -2, 0$$

63. $\left[\dfrac{xy + y}{4x} \div (3x + 3)\right] \div \dfrac{y}{3x} = \dfrac{y(x + 1)}{4x} \cdot \dfrac{1}{3(x + 1)} \cdot \dfrac{3x}{y} = \dfrac{1}{4}, \quad x \neq -1, 0, y \neq 0$

65. $\dfrac{2x^2 + 5x - 25}{3x^2 + 5x + 2} \cdot \dfrac{3x^2 + 2x}{x + 5} \div \left(\dfrac{x}{x + 1}\right)^2 = \dfrac{(2x - 5)(x + 5)}{(3x + 2)(x + 1)} \cdot \dfrac{x(3x + 2)}{x + 5} \cdot \left(\dfrac{x + 1}{x}\right)^2$

$$= \dfrac{(2x - 5)(x + 5)x(3x + 2)(x + 1)(x + 1)}{(3x + 2)(x + 1)(x + 5)x \cdot x}$$

$$= \dfrac{(2x - 5)(x + 1)}{x}, x \neq -1, -5, -\dfrac{2}{3}$$

67. $x^3 \cdot \dfrac{x^{2n} - 9}{x^{2n} + 4x^n + 3} \div \dfrac{x^{2n} - 2x^n - 3}{x} = x^3 \cdot \dfrac{(x^n - 3)(x^n + 3)}{(x^n + 3)(x^n + 1)} \cdot \dfrac{x}{(x^n - 3)(x^n + 1)}$

$$= \dfrac{x^4}{(x^n + 1)^2}, \quad x^n \neq -3, 3, 0$$

69. *Keystrokes:*

y_1 [Y=] [( ] [( ] 3 [X,T,θ] [+] 2 [ )] [÷] [X,T,θ] [ )] [×]
[( ] [X,T,θ] [x^2] [÷] [( ] 9 [X,T,θ] [x^2] [−] 4 [ )] [ )] [ENTER]

y_2 [X,T,θ] [÷] [( ] 3 [X,T,θ] [−] 2 [ )] [GRAPH]

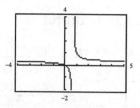

71. *Keystrokes:*

y_1 [Y=] [( ] [( ] 3 [X,T,θ] [+] 15 [ )] [÷] [X,T,θ] [^] 4 [ )] [÷]
[( ] [( ] [X,T,θ] [+] 5 [ )] [÷] [X,T,θ] [x^2] [ )] [ENTER]

y_2 3 [÷] [X,T,θ] [x^2] [GRAPH]

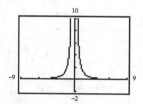

73. Area $= \left(\dfrac{2w + 3}{3}\right)\left(\dfrac{w}{2}\right) = \dfrac{(2w + 3)w}{6}$

75. $\dfrac{\text{Unshaded Area}}{\text{Total Area}} = \dfrac{\frac{x}{2} \cdot \frac{x}{2}}{x(2x + 1)} = \left[\dfrac{x}{2} \cdot \dfrac{x}{2}\right] \div [x(2x + 1)]$

$= \dfrac{x}{2} \cdot \dfrac{x}{2} \cdot \dfrac{1}{x(2x + 1)}$

$= \dfrac{x}{4(2x + 1)}$

77. $\dfrac{\text{Unshaded Area}}{\text{Total Area}} = \dfrac{x \cdot \frac{x}{2}}{x(2x + 1)} = \dfrac{x}{2(2x + 1)}$

79. (a) $\dfrac{20 \text{ pages}}{1 \text{ minute}} = \dfrac{20 \text{ pages}}{60 \text{ seconds}} = \dfrac{1 \text{ page}}{3 \text{ seconds}}$,

$t = 3$ seconds or $\dfrac{1}{20}$ minutes

(b) $\dfrac{3 \text{ seconds}}{1 \text{ page}} \cdot x$ pages $= 3x$ seconds or $\dfrac{x}{20}$ minutes

(c) $\dfrac{3 \text{ seconds}}{1 \text{ page}} \cdot 35$ pages $= 3 \cdot 35$ seconds

$= 105$ seconds or $\dfrac{7}{4}$ minutes

81. (a) *Keystrokes:*

y_1 [Y=] 6357 [+] 1070 [X,T,θ] [x^2] [ENTER]

y_2 6115.2 [+] 590.7 [X,T,θ] [x^2] [GRAPH]

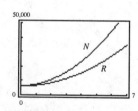

(b) *Verbal Model:*

$$\boxed{\text{Average monthly bill}} = \dfrac{\boxed{\text{Revenue}}}{\boxed{\text{Number of subscribers}}}$$

Equation: $AMB = \dfrac{(6115.2 + 590.7t^2)1000}{(6357 + 1070t^2)12} = \dfrac{6115200 + 590700t^2}{(6357 + 1070t^2)12}$

(c)

Year, t	0	2	4	6
Monthly bill	\$80.16	\$66.40	\$55.21	\$50.70

(d) The number of subscribers was increasing at a faster rate than the revenue.

83. Divide a rational expression by a polynomial by multiplying the rational expression by the reciprocal of the polynomial.

85. Invert the divisor, not the dividend.

Mid-Chapter Quiz for Chapter 4

1. $(t^3)^{-4}(3t^3) = t^{-12}(3t^3)$

$\qquad\qquad = 3t^{-12+3}$

$\qquad\qquad = 3t^{-9}$

$\qquad\qquad = \dfrac{3}{t^9}$

2. $(3x^2y^{-1})(4x^{-2}y)^{-2} = 3x^2y^{-1} \cdot 4^{-2}x^4y^{-2}$

$\qquad\qquad\qquad\qquad = 3 \cdot \dfrac{1}{4^2} \cdot x^{2+4}y^{-1+(-2)}$

$\qquad\qquad\qquad\qquad = \dfrac{3}{16}x^6y^{-3}$

$\qquad\qquad\qquad\qquad = \dfrac{3x^6}{16y^3}$

3. $\dfrac{10u^{-2}}{15u} = \dfrac{10}{15}u^{-2-1} = \dfrac{2}{3}u^{-3} = \dfrac{2}{3u^3}$

4. $\dfrac{(10x)^0 x^{-2}}{(x^2)^{-1}} = \dfrac{x^{-2}}{x^{-2}} = 1$

5. (a) $13{,}400{,}000 = 1.34 \times 10^7$

    (b) $0.00075 = 7.5 \times 10^{-4}$

6. (a) $(3 \times 10^3)^4 = 3^4 \times 10^{12} = 81 \times 10^{12} = 8.1 \times 10^{13}$

    (b) $\dfrac{3.2 \times 10^4}{16 \times 10^7} = \dfrac{3.2}{16} \times 10^{-3} = 0.2 \times 10^{-3} = 2 \times 10^{-4}$

7. $y(y - 4) \neq 0$

$y \neq 0$

$y - 4 \neq 0$

$y \neq 4$

$D = (-\infty, 0) \cup (0, 4) \cup (4, \infty)$

8. $h(x) = \dfrac{x^2 - 9}{x^2 - x - 2}$

    (a) $h(-3) = \dfrac{(-3)^2 - 9}{(-3)^2 - (-3) - 2}$

$\qquad\qquad\quad = \dfrac{9 - 9}{9 + 3 - 2} = \dfrac{0}{10} = 0$

    (c) $h(-1) = \dfrac{(-1)^2 - 9}{(-1)^2 - (-1) - 2}$

$\qquad\qquad\quad = \dfrac{1 - 9}{1 + 1 - 2} = \dfrac{-8}{0} = \text{undefined}$

    (b) $h(0) = \dfrac{0^2 - 9}{0^2 - 0 - 2}$

$\qquad\qquad = \dfrac{-9}{-2} = \dfrac{9}{2}$

    (d) $h(5) = \dfrac{5^2 - 9}{5^2 - 5 - 2}$

$\qquad\qquad = \dfrac{25 - 9}{25 - 5 - 2} = \dfrac{16}{18} = \dfrac{8}{9}$

9. $\dfrac{9y^2}{6y} = \dfrac{3y}{2}$

10. $\dfrac{8u^3v^2}{36uv^3} = \dfrac{2u^2}{9v}$

11. $\dfrac{4x^2 - 1}{x - 2x^2} = \dfrac{(2x - 1)(2x + 1)}{x(1 - 2x)}$

$\qquad\qquad\quad = \dfrac{(2x - 1)(2x + 1)}{-x(2x - 1)}$

$\qquad\qquad\quad = \dfrac{2x + 1}{-x}$

12. $\dfrac{(z + 3)^2}{2z^2 + 5z - 3} = \dfrac{(z + 3)(z + 3)}{(2z - 1)(z + 3)}$

$\qquad\qquad\qquad = \dfrac{z + 3}{2z - 1}$

13. $\dfrac{7ab + 3a^2b^2}{a^2b} = \dfrac{ab(7 + 3ab)}{a^2b}$

$\qquad\qquad\quad = \dfrac{7 + 3ab}{a}$

14. $\dfrac{2mn^2 - n^3}{2m^2 + mn - n^2} = \dfrac{n^2(2m - n)}{(2m - n)(m + n)}$

$\qquad\qquad\qquad = \dfrac{n^2}{m + n}$

15. $\dfrac{11t^2}{6} \cdot \dfrac{9}{33t} = \dfrac{11t^2(9)}{6(33t)} = \dfrac{t}{2}$

16. $(x^2 + 2x) \cdot \dfrac{5}{x^2 - 4} = \dfrac{x(x + 2)5}{(x - 2)(x + 2)}$

$$= \dfrac{5x}{x - 2}$$

17. $\dfrac{4}{3(x - 1)} \cdot \dfrac{12x}{6(x^2 + 2x - 3)} = \dfrac{4(12x)}{3(x - 1)6(x + 3)(x - 1)}$

$$= \dfrac{8x}{3(x - 1)^2(x + 3)}$$

$$= \dfrac{8x}{3(x - 1)(x^2 + 2x - 3)}$$

18. $\dfrac{5u}{3(u + v)} \cdot \dfrac{2(u^2 - v^2)}{3v} \div \dfrac{25u^2}{18(u - v)} = \dfrac{5u \cdot 2(u - v)(u + v) \cdot 18(u - v)}{3(u + v)(3v)(25u^2)}$

$$= \dfrac{4(u - v)^2}{5uv}$$

19. $\dfrac{\dfrac{9t^2}{3 - t}}{\dfrac{6t}{t - 3}} \cdot \dfrac{t - 3}{t - 3} = \dfrac{-9t^2}{6t} = -\dfrac{3t}{2}$

20. $\dfrac{\dfrac{10}{x^2 + 2x}}{\dfrac{15}{x^2 + 3x + 2}} = \dfrac{\dfrac{10}{x(x + 2)}}{\dfrac{15}{(x + 2)(x + 1)}} \cdot \dfrac{x(x + 2)(x + 1)}{x(x + 2)(x + 1)}$

$$= \dfrac{10(x + 1)}{15x}$$

$$= \dfrac{2(x + 1)}{3x}$$

21. (a) *Verbal Model:* $\boxed{\text{Average cost}} = \boxed{\text{Total cost}} \div \boxed{\text{Number of units}}$

Equation: Average cost $= \dfrac{6000 + 10.50x}{x}$

(b) Average cost when $x = 500$ units are produced $= \dfrac{6000 + 10.50(500)}{500} = \$22.50$

Section 4.4   Adding and Subtracting Rational Expressions

1. $\dfrac{5}{8} + \dfrac{7}{8} = \dfrac{5 + 7}{8} = \dfrac{12}{8} = \dfrac{3}{2}$

3. $\dfrac{5x}{8} - \dfrac{7x}{8} = \dfrac{-2x}{8} = \dfrac{-x}{4}$

5. $\dfrac{2}{3a} - \dfrac{11}{3a} = \dfrac{2 - 11}{3a} = \dfrac{-9}{3a} = \dfrac{-3}{a}$

7. $\dfrac{x}{9} - \dfrac{x + 2}{9} = \dfrac{x - (x + 2)}{9} = \dfrac{x - x - 2}{9} = -\dfrac{2}{9}$

9. $\dfrac{z^2}{3} + \dfrac{z^2 - 2}{3} = \dfrac{z^2 + z^2 - 2}{3} = \dfrac{2z^2 - 2}{3}$

11. $\dfrac{2x + 5}{3} + \dfrac{1 - x}{3} = \dfrac{2x + 5 + 1 - x}{3} = \dfrac{x + 6}{3}$

13. $\dfrac{3y}{3} - \dfrac{3y - 3}{3} - \dfrac{7}{3} = \dfrac{3y - (3y - 3) - 7}{3}$

$$= \dfrac{3y - 3y + 3 - 7}{3}$$

$$= -\dfrac{4}{3}$$

15. $\dfrac{3y - 22}{y - 6} - \dfrac{2y - 16}{y - 6} = \dfrac{3y - 22 - (2y - 16)}{y - 6}$

$$= \dfrac{3y - 22 - 2y + 16}{y - 6}$$

$$= \dfrac{y - 6}{y - 6}$$

$$= 1, \, y \ne 6$$

17. $\dfrac{2x-1}{x(x-3)} + \dfrac{1-x}{x(x-3)} + \dfrac{2x-1+1-x}{x(x-3)}$

$\qquad\qquad + \dfrac{x}{x(x-3)}$

$\qquad\qquad + \dfrac{1}{x-3}, \quad x \neq 0$

19. $5x^2 + 5 \cdot x \cdot x$

$20x^3 + 5 \cdot 2 \cdot 2 \cdot x \cdot x \cdot x$

LCM $+ 20x^3$

21. $9y^3 + 3 \cdot 3 \cdot y \cdot y \cdot y$

$12y + 2 \cdot 2 \cdot 3 \cdot y$

LCM $+ 3 \cdot 3 \cdot 2 \cdot 2 \cdot y \cdot y \cdot y + 36y^3$

23. $15x^2 + 5 \cdot 3 \cdot x \cdot x$

$3(x+5) + 3 \cdot (x+5)$

LCM $+ 15x^2(x+5)$

25. $63z^2(z+1) + 7 \cdot 9 \cdot z \cdot z(z+1)$

$14(z+1)^4 + 7 \cdot 2 \cdot (z+1)^4$

LCM $+ 126z^2(z+1)^4$

27. $8t(t+2) + 2 \cdot 2 \cdot 2 \cdot t \cdot (t+2)$

$14(t^2-4) + 2 \cdot 7 \cdot (t+2)(t-2)$

LCM $+ 2 \cdot 2 \cdot 2 \cdot 7 \cdot t \cdot (t+2)(t-2) + 56t(t^2-4)$

29. $6(x^2-4) + 6(x-2)(x+2)$

$2x(x+2) + 2 \cdot x \cdot (x+2)$

LCM $+ 6x(x-2)(x+2)$

31. $\dfrac{7x^2}{4a(x^2)} + \dfrac{7}{4a}, \quad x \neq 0$

33. $\dfrac{5r(u+1)}{3v(u+1)} + \dfrac{5r}{3v}, \quad u \neq -1$

35. $\dfrac{7y(-1(x+2))}{4-x^2} + \dfrac{7y}{x-2}, \quad x \neq -2$

$\qquad 4 - x^2 + (2-x)(2+x)$

$\qquad\qquad + -1(x-2)(2+x)$

37. $\dfrac{n+8}{3n-12} + \dfrac{n+8}{3(n-4)} + \dfrac{n+8(2n^2)}{3(n-4)(2n^2)} + \dfrac{2n^2(n+8)}{6n^2(n-4)}$

$\dfrac{10}{6n^2} + \dfrac{10}{3 \cdot 2n^2} + \dfrac{10(n-4)}{3 \cdot 2n^2(n-4)} + \dfrac{10(n-4)}{6n^2(n-4)}$

LCD $+ 6n^2(n-4)$

39. $\dfrac{2}{x^2(x-3)} + \dfrac{2(x+3)}{x^2(x-3)(x+3)}$

$\dfrac{5}{x(x+3)} + \dfrac{5x(x-3)}{x^2(x+3)(x-3)}$

LCD $+ x^2(x-3)(x+3) \neq x^2(x^2-9)$

41. $\dfrac{v}{2v^2+2v} + \dfrac{v}{2v(v+1)} + \dfrac{v(3v)}{2v(v+1)(3v)} + \dfrac{3v^2}{6v^2(v+1)}$

$\dfrac{4}{3v^2} + \dfrac{4(2(v+1))}{3v^2(2(v+1))} + \dfrac{8v+8}{6v^2(v+1)}$

LCD $+ 6v^2(v+1)$

43. $\dfrac{x-8}{x^2-25} + \dfrac{x-8}{(x-5)(x+5)}$

$\qquad\qquad + \dfrac{(x-8)(x-5)}{(x-5)(x+5)(x-5)} + \dfrac{(x-8)(x-5)}{(x-5)^2(x+5)}$

$\dfrac{9x}{x^2-10x+25} + \dfrac{9x}{(x-5)^2}$

$\qquad\qquad + \dfrac{9x(x+5)}{(x-5)^2(x+5)} + \dfrac{9x(x+5)}{(x-5)^2(x+5)}$

LCD $+ (x-5)^2(x+5)$

45. $\dfrac{5}{4x} - \dfrac{3}{5} + \dfrac{5(5)}{4x(5)} - \dfrac{3(4x)}{5(4x)} + \dfrac{25}{20x} - \dfrac{12x}{20x} + \dfrac{25-12x}{20x}$

47. $\dfrac{7}{a} + \dfrac{14}{a^2} + \dfrac{7(a)}{a(a)} + \dfrac{14(1)}{a^2(1)} + \dfrac{7a}{a^2} + \dfrac{14}{a^2} + \dfrac{7a+14}{a^2}$

49. $\dfrac{20}{x-4} + \dfrac{20}{4-x} + \dfrac{20(1)}{(x-4)(1)} + \dfrac{20(-1)}{(4-x)(-1)}$

$\qquad + \dfrac{20}{x-4} - \dfrac{20}{x-4}$

$\qquad + \dfrac{20-20}{x-4} + 0, \quad x \neq 4$

51. $\dfrac{3x}{x-8} - \dfrac{6}{8-x} + \dfrac{3x(1)}{(x-8)(1)} - \dfrac{6(-1)}{(8-x)(-1)}$

$\qquad + \dfrac{3x}{x-8} + \dfrac{6}{x-8}$

$\qquad + \dfrac{3x+6}{x-8}$

53. $25 + \dfrac{10}{x+4} + \dfrac{25(x+4)}{1(x+4)} + \dfrac{10(1)}{(x+4)(1)}$

$\qquad + \dfrac{25(x+4)}{x+4} + \dfrac{10}{x+4}$

$\qquad + \dfrac{25x+100+10}{x+4} + \dfrac{25x+110}{x+4}$

55. $\dfrac{3x}{3x-2} + \dfrac{2}{2-3x} + \dfrac{3x(1)}{3x-2(1)} + \dfrac{2(-1)}{(2-3x)(-1)}$

$\qquad + \dfrac{3x}{3x-2} + \dfrac{-2}{3x-2}$

$\qquad + \dfrac{3x-2}{3x-2} + 1, \quad x \neq \dfrac{2}{3}$

57. $-\dfrac{1}{6x} + \dfrac{1}{6(x-3)} + \dfrac{-1(x-3)}{6x(x-3)} + \dfrac{1(x)}{6(x-3)x}$

$\qquad + \dfrac{-(x-3)}{6x(x-3)} + \dfrac{x}{6x(x-3)}$

$\qquad + \dfrac{-x+3+x}{6x(x-3)}$

$\qquad + \dfrac{3}{6x(x-3)}$

$\qquad + \dfrac{1}{2x(x-3)}$

59. $\dfrac{x}{x+3} - \dfrac{5}{x-2} + \dfrac{x(x-2)}{(x+3)(x-2)} - \dfrac{5(x+3)}{(x-2)(x+3)}$

$\qquad + \dfrac{x(x-2)}{(x+3)(x-2)} - \dfrac{5(x+3)}{(x-2)(x+3)}$

$\qquad + \dfrac{x^2-2x-5x-15}{(x+3)(x-2)}$

$\qquad + \dfrac{x^2-7x-15}{(x+3)(x-2)}$

61. $\dfrac{3}{x+1} - \dfrac{2}{x} + \dfrac{3x}{(x+1)x} - \dfrac{2(x+1)}{x(x+1)}$

$\qquad + \dfrac{3x}{x(x+1)} - \dfrac{2(x+1)}{x(x+1)}$

$\qquad + \dfrac{3x-2x-2}{x(x+1)}$

$\qquad + \dfrac{x-2}{x(x+1)}$

63. $\dfrac{3}{x-5} + \dfrac{2}{x+5} + \dfrac{3(x+5)}{(x-5)(x+5)} + \dfrac{2(x-5)}{(x+5)(x-5)}$

$\qquad + \dfrac{3(x+5)}{(x-5)(x+5)} + \dfrac{2(x-5)}{(x+5)(x-5)}$

$\qquad + \dfrac{3x+15+2x-10}{(x-5)(x+5)}$

$\qquad + \dfrac{5x+5}{(x-5)(x+5)}$

65. $\dfrac{4}{x^2} - \dfrac{4}{x^2+1} + \dfrac{4(x^2+1)}{x^2(x^2+1)} - \dfrac{4x^2}{(x^2+1)x^2}$

$\qquad + \dfrac{4(x^2+1)}{x^2(x^2+1)} - \dfrac{4x^2}{x^2(x^2+1)}$

$\qquad + \dfrac{4x^2+4-4x^2}{x^2(x^2+1)}$

$\qquad + \dfrac{4}{x^2(x^2+1)}$

67. $\dfrac{x}{x^2 - 9} + \dfrac{3}{x^2 - 5x + 6} + \dfrac{x}{(x-3)(x+3)} + \dfrac{3}{(x-3)(x-2)}$

$$+ \dfrac{x(x-2)}{(x-2)(x-3)(x+3)} + \dfrac{3(x+3)}{(x-2)(x-3)(x+3)}$$

$$+ \dfrac{x^2 - 2x + 3x + 9}{(x-2)(x-3)(x+3)}$$

$$+ \dfrac{x^2 + x + 9}{(x-2)(x-3)(x+3)}$$

69. $\dfrac{4}{x-4} + \dfrac{16}{(x-4)^2} + \dfrac{4(x-4)}{(x-4)(x-4)} + \dfrac{16(1)}{(x-4)^2(1)}$

$$+ \dfrac{4x - 16}{(x-4)^2} + \dfrac{16}{(x-4)^2}$$

$$+ \dfrac{4x - 16 + 16}{(x-4)^2}$$

$$+ \dfrac{4x}{(x-4)^2}$$

71. $\dfrac{y}{x^2 + xy} - \dfrac{x}{xy + y^2} + \dfrac{y}{x(x+y)} - \dfrac{x}{y(x+y)}$

$$+ \dfrac{y(y)}{x(x+y)(y)} - \dfrac{x(x)}{y(x+y)(x)}$$

$$+ \dfrac{y^2}{xy(x+y)} - \dfrac{x^2}{xy(x+y)}$$

$$+ \dfrac{y^2 - x^2}{xy(x+y)}$$

$$+ \dfrac{(y-x)(y+x)}{xy(x+y)} = \dfrac{y-x}{xy}, \quad x \neq -y$$

73. $\dfrac{4}{x} - \dfrac{2}{x^2} + \dfrac{4}{x+3} + \dfrac{4x(x+3)}{x(x)(x+3)} - \dfrac{2(x+3)}{x^2(x+3)} + \dfrac{4(x^2)}{(x+3)x^2}$

$$+ \dfrac{4x^2 + 12x}{x^2(x+3)} - \dfrac{2x + 6}{x^2(x+3)} + \dfrac{4x^2}{x^2(x+3)}$$

$$+ \dfrac{4x^2 + 12x - 2x - 6 + 4x^2}{x^2(x+3)}$$

$$+ \dfrac{8x^2 + 10x - 6}{x^2(x+3)}$$

$$+ \dfrac{2(4x^2 + 5x - 3)}{x^2(x+3)}$$

75. $\dfrac{3u}{u^2 - 2uv + v^2} + \dfrac{2}{u-v} - \dfrac{u}{u-v}$

$$+ \dfrac{3u}{(u-v)^2} + \dfrac{2-u}{u-v}$$

$$+ \dfrac{3u(1)}{(u-v)^2(1)} + \dfrac{(2-u)(u-v)}{(u-v)(u-v)}$$

$$+ \dfrac{3u}{(u-v)^2} + \dfrac{2u - 2v - u^2 + uv}{(u-v)^2}$$

$$+ \dfrac{3u + 2u - 2v - u^2 + uv}{(u-v)^2}$$

$$+ \dfrac{5u - 2v - u^2 + uv}{(u-v)^2}$$

$$+ -\dfrac{u^2 - uv - 5u + 2v}{(u-v)^2}$$

77. $\dfrac{x+2}{x-1} - \dfrac{2}{x+6} - \dfrac{14}{x^2 + 5x - 6} = \dfrac{(x+2)(x+6)}{(x-1)(x+6)} - \dfrac{2(x-1)}{(x+6)(x-1)} - \dfrac{14(1)}{(x+6)(x-1)(1)}$

$(x+6)(x-1)$

$$= \dfrac{x^2 + 8x + 12}{(x-1)(x+6)} - \dfrac{2x-2}{(x+6)(x-1)} - \dfrac{14}{(x+6)(x-1)}$$

$$= \dfrac{x^2 + 8x + 12 - 2x + 2 - 14}{(x-1)(x+6)} \quad \text{CD}$$

$$= \dfrac{x^2 + 6x}{(x-1)(x+6)}$$

$$= \dfrac{x(x+6)}{(x-1)(x+6)}$$

$$= \dfrac{x}{x-1}, \quad x \neq -6$$

79. *Keystrokes:*

y_1 Y= (2 ÷ X,T,θ) + (4 ÷

(X,T,θ − 2)) ENTER

y_2 (6 X,T,θ − 4) ÷ (X,T,θ (X,T,θ − 2)) GRAPH

$$\frac{2}{x} + \frac{4}{(x-2)} + \frac{2(x-2)}{x(x-2)} + \frac{4x}{x(x-2)} + \frac{2x-4+4x}{x(x-2)} + \frac{6x-4}{x(x-2)}$$

$y_1 + y_2$

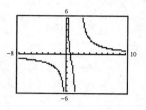

81. $\dfrac{\dfrac{1}{2}}{\left(3+\dfrac{1}{x}\right)} + \dfrac{\dfrac{1}{2}}{\left(3+\dfrac{1}{x}\right)} \cdot \dfrac{2x}{2x}$

$+ \dfrac{\dfrac{1}{2}\cdot 2x}{3(2x)+\dfrac{1}{x}(2x)}$

$+ \dfrac{x}{6x+2}$

$+ \dfrac{x}{2(3x+1)}, \quad x \neq 0$

83. $\dfrac{\left(\dfrac{4}{x}+3\right)}{\left(\dfrac{4}{x}-3\right)} + \dfrac{\left(\dfrac{4}{x}+3\right)}{\left(\dfrac{4}{x}-3\right)} \cdot \dfrac{x}{x}$

$+ \dfrac{4+3x}{4-3x}, \quad x \neq 0$

85. $\dfrac{\left(16x-\dfrac{1}{x}\right)}{\left(\dfrac{1}{x}-4\right)} + \dfrac{\left(16x-\dfrac{1}{x}\right)}{\left(\dfrac{1}{x}-4\right)} \cdot \dfrac{x}{x}$

$+ \dfrac{16x(x)-\dfrac{1}{x}(x)}{\dfrac{1}{x}(x)-4(x)}$

$+ \dfrac{16x^2-1}{1-4x}$

$+ \dfrac{(4x-1)(4x+1)}{-1(4x-1)}$

$+ \dfrac{4x+1}{-1}$

$+ -4x-1, \quad x \neq 0, \dfrac{1}{4}$

87. $\dfrac{\left(3+\dfrac{9}{x-3}\right)}{\left(4+\dfrac{12}{x-3}\right)} + \dfrac{\left(3+\dfrac{9}{x-3}\right)}{\left(4+\dfrac{12}{x-3}\right)} \cdot \dfrac{x-3}{x-3}$

$+ \dfrac{3(x-3)+\dfrac{9}{x-3}(x-3)}{4(x-3)+\dfrac{12}{x-3}(x-3)}$

$+ \dfrac{3x-9+9}{4x-12+12}$

$+ \dfrac{3x}{4x} + \dfrac{3}{4}, \quad x \neq 0, 3$

89. $\dfrac{\left(\dfrac{3}{x^2}+\dfrac{1}{x}\right)}{\left(2-\dfrac{4}{5x}\right)}+\dfrac{\left(\dfrac{3}{x^2}+\dfrac{1}{x}\right)}{\left(2-\dfrac{4}{5x}\right)}\cdot\dfrac{5x^2}{5x^2}$

$+\dfrac{15+5x}{10x^2-4x}$

$+\dfrac{5(3+x)}{2x(5x-2)}$

91. $\dfrac{\left(\dfrac{y}{x}-\dfrac{x}{y}\right)}{\left(\dfrac{x+y}{xy}\right)}+\dfrac{\left(\dfrac{y}{x}-\dfrac{x}{y}\right)}{\left(\dfrac{x+y}{xy}\right)}\cdot\dfrac{xy}{xy}$

$+\dfrac{\dfrac{y}{x}(xy)-\dfrac{x}{y}(xy)}{\left(\dfrac{x+y}{xy}\right)xy}$

$+\dfrac{y^2-x^2}{x+y}$

$+\dfrac{(y-x)(y+x)}{x+y}$

$+y-x,\quad x\neq 0, y\neq 0, x\neq -y$

93. $\dfrac{\left(1-\dfrac{1}{y}\right)}{\left(\dfrac{1-4y}{y-3}\right)}+\dfrac{\left(1-\dfrac{1}{y}\right)}{\left(\dfrac{1-4y}{y-3}\right)}\cdot\dfrac{y(y-3)}{y(y-3)}$

$+\dfrac{y(y-3)-(y-3)}{y(1-4y)}$

$+\dfrac{y^2-3y-y+3}{y-4y^2}$

$+\dfrac{y^2-4y+3}{-y(-1+4y)}$

$+-\dfrac{(y-3)(y-1)}{y(4y-1)},\quad y\neq 3$

95. $\dfrac{\left(\dfrac{x}{x-3}-\dfrac{2}{3}\right)}{\left(\dfrac{10}{3x}+\dfrac{x^2}{x-3}\right)}+\dfrac{\left(\dfrac{x}{x-3}-\dfrac{2}{3}\right)}{\left(\dfrac{10}{3x}+\dfrac{x^2}{x-3}\right)}\cdot\dfrac{3x(x-3)}{3x(x-3)}$

$+\dfrac{3x^2-2x(x-3)}{10(x-3)+3x^2}$

$+\dfrac{3x^2-2x^2+6x}{10x-30+3x^3}$

$+\dfrac{x^2+6x}{3x^3+10x-30},\quad x\neq 0,\quad x\neq 3$

97. $\dfrac{f(2+h)-f(2)}{h}+\dfrac{\dfrac{1}{2+h}-\dfrac{1}{2}}{h}$

$+\dfrac{\dfrac{1}{2+h}-\dfrac{1}{2}}{h}\cdot\dfrac{2(2+h)}{2(2+h)}$

$+\dfrac{2-(2+h)}{2h(2+h)}$

$+\dfrac{2-2-h}{2h(2+h)}$

$+\dfrac{-h}{2h(2+h)}$

$+\dfrac{-1}{2(2+h)}$

99.

x	-3	-2	-1	0	1	2	3
$\dfrac{\left(1-\dfrac{1}{x}\right)}{\left(1-\dfrac{1}{x^2}\right)}$	$\dfrac{3}{2}$	2	Undef.	Undef.	Undef.	$\dfrac{2}{3}$	$\dfrac{3}{4}$
$\dfrac{x}{x+1}$	$\dfrac{3}{2}$	2	Undef.	0	$\dfrac{1}{2}$	$\dfrac{2}{3}$	$\dfrac{3}{4}$

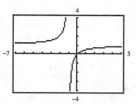

Keystrokes:

y_1 [Y=] [(] 1 [−] 1 [÷] [X,T,θ] [)] [÷]

[(] 1 [−]1 [÷] [X,T,θ] [x^2] [)] [ENTER]

y_2 [X,T,θ] [÷] [(] [X,T,θ] [+] 1 [)] [GRAPH]

Zero and one are not in the domain of

$$\frac{1-\dfrac{1}{x}}{1-\dfrac{1}{x^2}}$$

but are in the domain of $\dfrac{x}{x+1}$. The two expressions are equivalent except at $x+0$ and $x+1$.

101. $\dfrac{t}{4}+\dfrac{t}{6}+\dfrac{t(3)}{4(3)}+\dfrac{t(2)}{6(2)}$

$+\dfrac{3t}{12}+\dfrac{2t}{12}$

$+\dfrac{5t}{12}$

103. $\dfrac{\dfrac{x}{4}+\dfrac{x}{6}}{2}+\dfrac{\left(\dfrac{x}{4}+\dfrac{x}{6}\right)}{2}\cdot\dfrac{12}{12}$

$+\dfrac{\dfrac{x}{4}(12)+\dfrac{x}{6}(12)}{2(12)}$

$+\dfrac{3x+2x}{24}$

$+\dfrac{5x}{24}$

105. $\dfrac{\dfrac{x}{3}-\dfrac{x}{5}}{3}\cdot\dfrac{15}{15}+5x-3x+\dfrac{2x}{45}$

Thus,

$x_1+\dfrac{x}{5}+\dfrac{2x}{45}+\dfrac{9x}{45}+\dfrac{2x}{45}+\dfrac{11x}{45}$

$x_2+\dfrac{11x}{45}+\dfrac{2x}{45}+\dfrac{13x}{45}.$

107. $\dfrac{1}{\left(\dfrac{1}{R_1}+\dfrac{1}{R_2}\right)}+\dfrac{1}{\left(\dfrac{1}{R_1}+\dfrac{1}{R_2}\right)}\cdot\dfrac{R_1R_2}{R_1R_2}$

$+\dfrac{R_1R_2}{\dfrac{1}{R_1}(R_1R_2)+\dfrac{1}{R_2}(R_1R_2)}$

$+\dfrac{R_1R_2}{R_2+R_1}$

109. (a) *Verbal Model:*   Distance + Rate · Time

$\dfrac{\text{Distance}}{\text{Rate}}+\text{Time}$

Equation: Upstream $t+\dfrac{10}{5-x}$

Downstream $t+\dfrac{10}{5+x}$

(b) Total time $+ t(x)+\dfrac{10}{5-x}+\dfrac{10}{5+x}$

(c) $t(x)+\dfrac{10(5+x)}{(5-x)(5+x)}+\dfrac{10(5-x)}{(5-x)(5+x)}$

$+\dfrac{50+10x+50-10x}{(5-x)(5+x)}$

$+\dfrac{100}{(5-x)(5+x)}$

111. Rewrite each fraction in terms of the lowest common denominator, combine the numerators, and place the result over the lowest common denominator.

113. $\dfrac{x-1}{x+4} - \dfrac{4x-11}{x+4} = \dfrac{(x-1)-(4x-11)}{x+4}$

$$= \dfrac{x-1-4x+11}{x+4}$$

$$= \dfrac{-3x+10}{x+4}$$

The subtraction must be distributed to both terms of the numerator of the second fraction.

Section 4.5   Dividing Polynomials

1. $\dfrac{6z+10}{2} = \dfrac{6z}{2} + \dfrac{10}{2} = 3z + 5$

3. $\dfrac{10z^2 + 4z - 12}{4} = \dfrac{10z^2}{4} + \dfrac{4z}{4} - \dfrac{12}{4}$

$$= \dfrac{5z^2}{2} + z - 3$$

5. $(7x^3 - 2x^2) \div x = \dfrac{7x^3 - 2x^2}{x}$

$$= \dfrac{7x^3}{x} - \dfrac{2x^2}{x}$$

$$= 7x^2 - 2x, \quad x \neq 0$$

7. $\dfrac{m^4 + 2m^2 - 7}{m} = \dfrac{m^4}{m} + \dfrac{2m^2}{m} - \dfrac{7}{m}$

$$= m^3 + 2m - \dfrac{7}{m}, \, m \neq 0$$

9. $\dfrac{50z^3 + 30z}{-5z} = \dfrac{50z^3}{-5z} + \dfrac{30z}{-5z}$

$$= -10z^2 - 6, \quad z \neq 0$$

11. $\dfrac{8z^3 + 3z^2 - 2z}{2z} = \dfrac{8z^3}{2z} + \dfrac{3z^2}{2z} - \dfrac{2z}{2z}$

$$= 4z^2 + \dfrac{3}{2}z - 1, \quad z \neq 0$$

13. $(5x^2y - 8xy + 7xy^2) \div 2xy = \dfrac{5x^2y - 8xy + 7xy^2}{2xy}$

$$= \dfrac{5x^2y}{2xy} - \dfrac{8xy}{2xy} + \dfrac{7xy^2}{2xy}$$

$$= \dfrac{5x}{2} - 4 + \dfrac{7}{2}y, \quad x \neq 0, y \neq 0$$

15. $\dfrac{x^2 - 8x + 15}{x - 3} = $

$$
\begin{array}{r}
x - 5, \quad x \neq 3 \\
x - 3 \overline{) x^2 - 8x + 15} \\
\underline{x^2 - 3x} \\
-5x + 15 \\
\underline{-5x + 15}
\end{array}
$$

17. $(x^2 + 15x + 50) \div (x + 5) = $

$$
\begin{array}{r}
x + 10, \quad x \neq -5 \\
x + 5 \overline{) x^2 + 15x + 50} \\
\underline{x^2 + 5x} \\
10x + 50 \\
\underline{10x + 50}
\end{array}
$$

19.
$$
\begin{array}{r}
x - 3 + \dfrac{2}{x-2} \\
x - 2 \overline{) x^2 - 5x + 8} \\
\underline{x^2 - 2x} \\
-3x + 8 \\
\underline{-3x + 6} \\
2
\end{array}
$$

21.
$$
\begin{array}{r}
x + 7, \quad x \neq 3 \\
-x + 3 \overline{) -x^2 - 4x + 21} \\
\underline{-x^2 + 3x} \\
-7x + 21 \\
\underline{-7x + 21}
\end{array}
$$

23.
$$5x - 8 + \frac{19}{x+2}$$

$$x + 2 \overline{)5x^2 + 2x + 3}$$
$$\underline{5x^2 + 10x}$$
$$-8x + 3$$
$$\underline{-8x - 16}$$
$$19$$

25.
$$4x + 3 + \frac{-11}{3x+2}$$

$$3x + 2 \overline{)12x^2 + 17x - 5}$$
$$\underline{12x^2 + 8x}$$
$$9x - 5$$
$$\underline{9x + 6}$$
$$-11$$

27.
$$6t - 5, \quad t \neq \frac{5}{2}$$

$$2t - 5 \overline{)12t^2 - 40t + 25}$$
$$\underline{12t^2 - 30t}$$
$$-10t + 25$$
$$\underline{-10t + 25}$$

29.
$$y + 3, \quad y \neq -\frac{1}{2}$$

$$2y + 1 \overline{)2y^2 + 7y + 3}$$
$$\underline{2y^2 + y}$$
$$6y + 3$$
$$\underline{6y + 3}$$

31.
$$x^2 \qquad + 4, \quad x \neq 2$$

$$x - 2 \overline{)x^3 - 2x^2 + 4x - 8}$$
$$\underline{x^3 - 2x^2}$$
$$4x - 8$$
$$\underline{4x - 8}$$

33.
$$2x^2 + x + 4 + \frac{6}{x-3}$$

$$x - 3 \overline{)2x^3 - 5x^2 + x - 6}$$
$$\underline{2x^3 - 6x^2}$$
$$x^2 + x$$
$$\underline{x^2 - 3x}$$
$$4x - 6$$
$$\underline{4x - 12}$$
$$6$$

35.
$$2 + \frac{5}{x+2}$$

$$x + 2 \overline{)2x + 9}$$
$$\underline{2x + 4}$$
$$5$$

37.
$$x - 4 + \frac{32}{x+4}$$

$$x + 4 \overline{)x^2 + 0x + 16}$$
$$\underline{x^2 + 4x}$$
$$-4x + 16$$
$$\underline{-4x - 16}$$
$$32$$

39.
$$\frac{6}{5}z + \frac{41}{25} + \frac{41}{25(5z-1)}$$

$$5z - 1 \overline{)6z^2 + 7z + 0}$$
$$\underline{6z^2 - \frac{6}{5}z}$$
$$\frac{41}{5}z + 0$$
$$\underline{\frac{41}{5}z - \frac{41}{25}}$$
$$\frac{41}{25}$$

41.
$$4x - 1, \quad x \neq -\frac{1}{4}$$

$$4x + 1 \overline{)16x^2 + 0x - 1}$$
$$\underline{16x^2 + 4x}$$
$$-4x - 1$$
$$\underline{-4x - 1}$$

43.
$$
\begin{array}{r}
x^2 - 5x + 25, \quad x \neq -5 \\
x + 5 \overline{)\ x^3 + 0x^2 + 0x + 125} \\
\underline{x^3 + 5x^2} \\
-5x^2 + 0x \\
\underline{-5x^2 - 25x} \\
25x + 125 \\
\underline{25x + 125}
\end{array}
$$

45.
$$
\begin{array}{r}
x + 2 \\
x^2 + 2x + 3 \overline{)\ x^3 + 4x^2 + 7x + 6} \\
\underline{x^3 + 2x^2 + 3x} \\
2x^2 + 4x + 6 \\
\underline{2x^2 + 4x + 6}
\end{array}
$$

47.
$$
\begin{array}{r}
4x^2 + 12x + 25 + \dfrac{52x - 55}{x^2 - 3x + 2} \\
x^2 - 3x + 2 \overline{)\ 4x^4 + 0x^3 - 3x^2 + x - 5} \\
\underline{4x^4 - 12x^3 + 8x^2} \\
12x^3 - 11x^2 + x \\
\underline{12x^3 - 36x^2 + 24x} \\
25x^2 - 23x - 5 \\
\underline{25x^2 - 75x + 50} \\
52x - 55
\end{array}
$$

49.
$$
\begin{array}{r}
x^5 + x^4 + x^3 + x^2 + x + 1, \quad x \neq 1 \\
x - 1 \overline{)\ x^6 - 1} \\
\underline{x^6 - x^5} \\
x^5 \\
\underline{x^5 - x^4} \\
x^4 \\
\underline{x^4 - x^3} \\
x^3 \\
\underline{x^3 - x^2} \\
x^2 \\
\underline{x^2 - x} \\
x - 1 \\
\underline{x - 1} \\
0
\end{array}
$$

51.
$$
\begin{array}{r}
x^3 - x + \dfrac{x}{x^2 + 1} \\
x^2 + 1 \overline{)\ x^5} \\
\underline{x^5 + x^3} \\
-x^3 \\
\underline{-x^3 - x} \\
x
\end{array}
$$

53. $\dfrac{4x^4}{x^3} - 2x = 4x - 2x = 2x, \quad x \neq 0$

55. $\dfrac{8u^2v}{2u} + \dfrac{3(uv)^2}{uv} = 4uv + \dfrac{3u^2v^2}{uv}$

$\phantom{\dfrac{8u^2v}{2u} + \dfrac{3(uv)^2}{uv}} = 4uv + 3uv$

$\phantom{\dfrac{8u^2v}{2u} + \dfrac{3(uv)^2}{uv}} = 7uv, \quad u \neq 0, v \neq 0$

57. $\dfrac{x^3 - 5x^2 + 3x - 4}{x - 2}$

$$
\begin{array}{r|rrrr}
2 & 1 & -5 & 3 & -4 \\
  &   & 2 & -6 & -6 \\
\hline
  & 1 & -3 & -3 & -10
\end{array}
$$

$\dfrac{x^3 - 5x^2 + 3x - 4}{x - 2} = x^2 - 3x - 3 - \dfrac{10}{x - 2}$

59. $\dfrac{x^3 + 3x^2 - 1}{x + 4}$

$$
\begin{array}{r|rrrr}
-4 & 1 & 3 & 0 & -1 \\
   &   & -4 & 4 & -16 \\
\hline
   & 1 & -1 & 4 & -17
\end{array}
$$

$\dfrac{x^3 + 3x^2 - 1}{x + 4} = x^2 - x + 4 + \dfrac{-17}{x + 4}$

61. $\dfrac{x^4 - 4x^3 + x + 10}{x - 2}$

$$
\begin{array}{r|rrrrr}
2 & 1 & -4 & 0 & 1 & 10 \\
  &   & 2 & -4 & -8 & -14 \\
\hline
  & 1 & -2 & -4 & -7 & -4
\end{array}
$$

$\dfrac{x^4 - 4x^3 + x + 10}{x - 2} = x^3 - 2x^2 - 4x - 7 + \dfrac{-4}{x - 2}$

63. $\dfrac{5x^3 - 6x^2 + 8}{x - 4}$

$$
\begin{array}{r|rrrr}
4 & 5 & -6 & 0 & 8 \\
  &   & 20 & 56 & 224 \\
\hline
  & 5 & 14 & 56 & 232
\end{array}
$$

$\dfrac{5x^3 - 6x^2 + 8}{x - 4} = 5x^2 + 14x + 56 + \dfrac{232}{x - 4}$

65. $\dfrac{10x^4 - 50x^3 - 800}{x - 6}$

$$
\begin{array}{r|rrrrr}
6 & 10 & -50 & 0 & 0 & -800 \\
  &   & 60 & 60 & 360 & 2160 \\
\hline
  & 10 & 10 & 60 & 360 & 1360
\end{array}
$$

$\dfrac{10x^4 - 50x^3 - 800}{x - 6} = 10x^3 + 10x^2 + 60x + 360 + \dfrac{1360}{x - 6}$

67. $\dfrac{0.1x^2 + 0.8x + 1}{x - 0.2}$

$$
\begin{array}{r|rrr}
0.2 & 0.1 & 0.8 & 1 \\
    &   & 0.02 & 0.164 \\
\hline
    & 0.1 & 0.82 & 1.164
\end{array}
$$

$\dfrac{0.1x^2 + 0.8x + 1}{x - 0.2} = 0.1x + 0.82 + \dfrac{1.164}{x - 0.2}$

69.
$$
\begin{array}{r|rrrr}
3 & 1 & 0 & -13 & 12 \\
  &   & 3 & 9 & -12 \\
\hline
  & 1 & 3 & -4 & 0
\end{array}
$$

$x^2 + 3x - 4 = (x + 4)(x - 1)$

$x^3 - 13x + 12 = (x - 3)(x + 4)(x - 1)$

71.
$$
\begin{array}{r|rrrr}
1 & 6 & -13 & 9 & -2 \\
  &   & 6 & -7 & 2 \\
\hline
  & 6 & -7 & 2 & 0
\end{array}
$$

$6x^2 - 7x + 2 = (2x - 1)(3x - 2)$

$6x^3 - 13x^2 + 9x - 2 = (x - 1)(2x - 1)(3x - 2)$

73.
$$
\begin{array}{r|rrrr}
-5 & 9 & 45 & -4 & -20 \\
   &   & -45 & 0 & 20 \\
\hline
   & 9 & 0 & -4 & 0
\end{array}
$$

$9x^2 - 4 = (3x - 2)(3x + 2)$

$9x^3 + 45x^2 - 4x - 20 = (x + 5)(3x - 2)(3x + 2)$

75.
$$
\begin{array}{r|rrrrr}
-3 & 1 & 7 & 3 & -63 & -108 \\
   &   & -3 & -12 & 27 & 108 \\
\hline
   & 1 & 4 & -9 & -36 & 0
\end{array}
$$

$$
\begin{aligned}
x^3 + 4x^2 - 9x - 36 &= x^2(x + 4) - 9(x + 4) \\
&= (x + 4)(x^2 - 9) \\
&= (x + 4)(x - 3)(x + 3)
\end{aligned}
$$

$x^4 + 7x^3 + 3x^2 - 63x - 108 = (x + 3)^2(x + 4)(x - 3)$

77. $\dfrac{15x^2 - 2x - 8}{x - \frac{4}{5}}$

$$
\begin{array}{r|rrr}
\frac{4}{5} & 15 & -2 & -8 \\
            &   & 12 & 8 \\
\hline
            & 15 & 10 & 0
\end{array}
$$

$15x^2 - 2x - 8 = (15x + 10)\left(x - \dfrac{4}{5}\right)$

$\qquad\qquad\qquad = 5(3x + 2)\left(x - \dfrac{4}{5}\right)$

79. $\dfrac{x^3 - 2x^2 - 4x + c}{x - 2}$

$$
\begin{array}{r|rrrr}
2 & 1 & 2 & -4 & c \\
  &   & 2 & 8 & 8 \\
\hline
  & 1 & 4 & 4 & 0
\end{array}
$$

$c + 8 = 0$

$\qquad c = -8$

81. Keystrokes:

y_1 [Y=] [(] [X,T,θ] [+] 4 [)] [÷] 2 [X,T,θ] [ENTER]

y_2 [(] 1 [÷] 2 [)] [+] [(] 2 [÷] [X,T,θ] [)] [GRAPH]

$\dfrac{x + 4}{2x} = \dfrac{x}{2x} + \dfrac{4}{2x} = \dfrac{1}{2} + \dfrac{2}{x}$

So, $y_1 = y_2$.

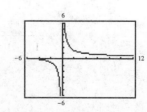

83. Keystrokes:

y_1 [Y=] [(] [X,T,θ] [^] 3 [+] 1 [)] [÷] [(] [X,T,θ] [+] 1 [)] [ENTER]

y_2 [X,T,θ] [x^2] [−] [X,T,θ] [+] 1 [GRAPH]

$$\frac{x^3 + 1}{x + 1} = \frac{(x + 1)(x^2 - x + 1)}{x + 1} = x^2 - x + 1, \quad x \neq 1$$

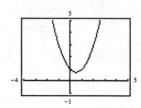

85.
$$x^n + 2 \overline{\smash{\big)}\, x^{3n} + 3x^{2n} + 6x^n + 8} \quad \overset{x^{2n} + \ x^n + 4, \quad x^n \neq -2}{}$$

$$\underline{x^{3n} + 2x^{2n}}$$
$$x^{2n} + 6x^n$$
$$\underline{x^{2n} + 2x^n}$$
$$4x^n + 8$$
$$\underline{4x^n + 8}$$

87. Dividend = Divisor · Quotient + Remainder

$$= (x - 6) \cdot (x^2 - x + 1) - 4$$
$$= x^3 + x^2 + x - 6x^2 - 6x - 6 - 4$$
$$= x^3 - 5x^2 - 5x - 10$$

89.

x	Polynomial value	Divisor	Remainder
-2	-8	$x + 2$	-8
-1	0	$x + 1$	0
0	0	x	0
$\frac{1}{2}$	$-\frac{9}{8}$	$x - \frac{1}{2}$	$-\frac{9}{8}$
1	-2	$x - 1$	-2
2	0	$x - 2$	0

$$f(-1) = (-1)^3 - (-1)^2 - 2(-1)$$
$$= -1 - 1 + 2$$
$$= 0$$

$$\begin{array}{r|rrrr} -1 & 1 & -1 & -2 & 0 \\ & & -1 & 2 & 0 \\ \hline & 1 & -2 & 0 & 0 \end{array}$$

$$f(0) = 0^3 - 0^2 - 2(0)$$
$$= 0$$

$$\begin{array}{r|rrrr} 0 & 1 & -1 & -2 & 0 \\ & & 0 & 0 & 0 \\ \hline & 1 & -1 & -2 & 0 \end{array}$$

$$f\left(\tfrac{1}{2}\right) = \left(\tfrac{1}{2}\right)^3 - \left(\tfrac{1}{2}\right)^2 - 2\left(\tfrac{1}{2}\right)$$
$$= \tfrac{1}{8} - \tfrac{1}{4} - 1$$
$$= \tfrac{1}{8} - \tfrac{2}{8} - \tfrac{8}{8}$$
$$= -\tfrac{9}{8}$$

$$\begin{array}{r|rrrr} \tfrac{1}{2} & 1 & -1 & -2 & 0 \\ & & \tfrac{1}{2} & -\tfrac{1}{4} & -\tfrac{9}{8} \\ \hline & 1 & -\tfrac{1}{2} & -\tfrac{9}{4} & -\tfrac{9}{8} \end{array}$$

$$f(1) = 1^3 - 1^2 - 2(1)$$
$$= 1 - 1 - 2$$
$$= -2$$

$$\begin{array}{r|rrrr} 1 & 1 & -1 & -2 & 0 \\ & & 1 & 0 & -2 \\ \hline & 1 & 0 & -2 & -2 \end{array}$$

$$f(2) = 2^3 - 2^2 - 2(2)$$
$$= 8 - 4 - 4$$
$$= 0$$

$$\begin{array}{r|rrrr} 2 & 1 & -1 & -2 & 0 \\ & & 2 & 2 & 0 \\ \hline & 1 & 1 & 0 & 0 \end{array}$$

The polynomial values equal the remainders.

91. Area = Length · Width, so Width = $\dfrac{\text{Area}}{\text{Length}}$.

Length = $\dfrac{2x^3 + 3x^2 - 6x - 9}{2x + 3} = x^2 - 3$

$$
\begin{array}{r}
x^2 \qquad\quad - 3 \\
2x + 3 \overline{)\, 2x^3 + 3x^2 - 6x - 9} \\
\underline{2x^3 + 3x^2} \\
-6x - 9 \\
\underline{-6x - 9}
\end{array}
$$

93. Volume = Area of triangle · Height (of prism)

Area of triangle = $\dfrac{\text{Volume}}{\text{Height (of prism)}}$

$$= \dfrac{x^3 + 18x^2 + 80x + 96}{x + 12}$$

$$= x^2 + 6x + 8$$

Area of triangle = $\dfrac{1}{2}$ · Base · Height

Height = $\dfrac{2(\text{Area of triangle})}{\text{Base}}$

$$= \dfrac{2(x^2 + 6x + 8)}{x + 2}$$

$$= 2x + 8 \text{ or } 2(x + 4)$$

95. x is not a factor of the numerator.

97. A divisor divides evenly into a dividend when the remainder is 0 and the divisor is a factor of the dividend.

99. True. If $\dfrac{n(x)}{d(x)} = q(x)$, then $n(x) = d(x) \cdot q(x)$.

Section 4.6 Solving Rational Equations

1. (a) $x = 0$

$$\dfrac{0}{3} - \dfrac{0}{5} \overset{?}{=} \dfrac{4}{3}$$

$$0 \neq \dfrac{4}{3}$$

Not a solution

(b) $x = -1$

$$\dfrac{-1}{3} - \dfrac{-1}{5} \overset{?}{=} \dfrac{4}{3}$$

$$\dfrac{-5}{15} - \dfrac{-3}{15} \overset{?}{=} \dfrac{20}{15}$$

$$\dfrac{-5}{15} + \dfrac{3}{15} \overset{?}{=} \dfrac{20}{15}$$

$$\dfrac{-2}{15} \neq \dfrac{20}{15}$$

Not a solution

(c) $x = \dfrac{1}{8}$

$$\dfrac{1/8}{3} - \dfrac{1/8}{5} \overset{?}{=} \dfrac{4}{3}$$

$$\dfrac{1}{24} - \dfrac{1}{40} \overset{?}{=} \dfrac{4}{3}$$

$$\dfrac{5}{120} - \dfrac{3}{120} \overset{?}{=} \dfrac{160}{120}$$

$$\dfrac{2}{120} \neq \dfrac{160}{120}$$

Not a solution

(d) $x = 10$

$$\dfrac{10}{3} - \dfrac{10}{5} \overset{?}{=} \dfrac{4}{3}$$

$$\dfrac{50}{15} - \dfrac{30}{15} \overset{?}{=} \dfrac{20}{15}$$

$$\dfrac{20}{15} = \dfrac{20}{15}$$

Solution

3. (a) $x = -1$

$$\dfrac{-1}{4} + \dfrac{3}{4(-1)} \overset{?}{=} 1$$

$$\dfrac{-1}{4} + \dfrac{-3}{4} \overset{?}{=} 1$$

$$-1 \neq 1$$

Not a solution

(b) $x = 1$

$$\dfrac{1}{4} + \dfrac{3}{4(1)} \overset{?}{=} 1$$

$$\dfrac{1}{4} + \dfrac{3}{4} \overset{?}{=} 1$$

$$1 = 1$$

Solution

(c) $x = 3$

$$\dfrac{3}{4} + \dfrac{3}{4(3)} \overset{?}{=} 1$$

$$\dfrac{3}{4} + \dfrac{3}{12} \overset{?}{=} 1$$

$$\dfrac{3}{4} + \dfrac{1}{4} \overset{?}{=} 1$$

$$1 = 1$$

Solution

(d) $x = 2$

$$\dfrac{2}{4} + \dfrac{3}{4(2)} \overset{?}{=} 1$$

$$\dfrac{4}{8} + \dfrac{3}{8} \overset{?}{=} 1$$

$$\dfrac{7}{8} \neq 1$$

Not a solution

5. $\dfrac{x}{6} - 1 = \dfrac{2}{3}$

Check: $\dfrac{10}{6} - 1 \overset{?}{=} \dfrac{2}{3}$

$6\left(\dfrac{x}{6} - 1\right) = \left(\dfrac{2}{3}\right)6$

$\dfrac{5}{3} - \dfrac{3}{3} \overset{?}{=} \dfrac{2}{3}$

$x - 6 = 4$

$\dfrac{2}{3} = \dfrac{2}{3}$

$x = 10$

7. $\dfrac{z + 2}{3} = 4 - \dfrac{z}{12}$

Check: $\dfrac{8 + 2}{3} \overset{?}{=} 4 - \dfrac{8}{12}$

$12\left(\dfrac{z + 2}{3}\right) = \left(4 - \dfrac{z}{12}\right)12$

$\dfrac{10}{3} \overset{?}{=} \dfrac{12}{3} - \dfrac{2}{3}$

$4(z + 2) = 48 - z$

$\dfrac{10}{3} = \dfrac{10}{3}$

$4z + 8 = 48 - z$

$5z = 40$

$z = 8$

9. $\dfrac{2y - 9}{6} = 3y - \dfrac{3}{4}$

Check: $\dfrac{2\left(-\frac{9}{32}\right) - 9}{6} \overset{?}{=} 3\left(-\dfrac{9}{32}\right) - \dfrac{3}{4}$

$(12)\left(\dfrac{2y - 9}{6}\right) = \left(3y - \dfrac{3}{4}\right)(12)$

$\dfrac{1}{6}\left(-\dfrac{18}{32} - \dfrac{288}{32}\right) \overset{?}{=} -\dfrac{27}{32} - \dfrac{24}{32}$

$2(2y - 9) = 36y - 9$

$\dfrac{1}{6}\left(-\dfrac{306}{32}\right) \overset{?}{=} -\dfrac{51}{32}$

$4y - 18 = 36y - 9$

$-\dfrac{51}{32} = -\dfrac{51}{32}$

$-9 = 32y$

$-\dfrac{9}{32} = y$

11. $\dfrac{4t}{3} = 15 - \dfrac{t}{6}$

Check: $\dfrac{4(10)}{3} \overset{?}{=} 15 - \dfrac{10}{6}$

$6\left(\dfrac{4t}{3}\right) = \left(15 - \dfrac{t}{6}\right)6$

$\dfrac{40}{3} \overset{?}{=} \dfrac{45}{3} - \dfrac{5}{3}$

$8t = 90 - t$

$\dfrac{40}{3} = \dfrac{40}{3}$

$9t = 90$

$t = 10$

13. $\dfrac{5y - 1}{12} + \dfrac{y}{3} = -\dfrac{1}{4}$

$12\left(\dfrac{5y - 1}{12} + \dfrac{y}{3}\right) = \left(-\dfrac{1}{4}\right)12$

$5y - 1 + 4y = -3$

$9y = -2$

$y = -\dfrac{2}{9}$

15. $\dfrac{h + 2}{5} - \dfrac{h - 1}{9} = \dfrac{2}{3}$

Check: $\dfrac{\frac{7}{4} + 2}{5} - \dfrac{\frac{7}{4} - 1}{9} \overset{?}{=} \dfrac{2}{3}$

$45\left(\dfrac{h + 2}{5} - \dfrac{h - 1}{9}\right) = \left(\dfrac{2}{3}\right)45$

$\dfrac{1}{5}\left(\dfrac{7}{4} + \dfrac{8}{4}\right) - \dfrac{1}{9}\left(\dfrac{7}{4} - \dfrac{4}{4}\right) \overset{?}{=} \dfrac{2}{3}$

$9(h + 2) - 5(h - 1) = 30$

$\dfrac{1}{5}\left(\dfrac{15}{4}\right) - \dfrac{1}{9}\left(\dfrac{3}{4}\right) \overset{?}{=} \dfrac{2}{3}$

$9h + 18 - 5h + 5 = 30$

$\dfrac{3}{4} - \dfrac{1}{12} \overset{?}{=} \dfrac{2}{3}$

$4h + 23 = 30$

$\dfrac{9}{12} - \dfrac{1}{12} \overset{?}{=} \dfrac{2}{3}$

$4h = 7$

$\dfrac{8}{12} \overset{?}{=} \dfrac{2}{3}$

$h = \dfrac{7}{4}$

$\dfrac{2}{3} = \dfrac{2}{3}$

17. $\dfrac{x+5}{4} - \dfrac{3x-8}{3} = \dfrac{4-4}{12}$

$12\left(\dfrac{x+5}{4} - \dfrac{3x-8}{3}\right) = \left(\dfrac{4-x}{12}\right)12$

$3(x+5) - 4(3x-8) = 4-x$

$3x + 15 - 12x + 32 = 4 - x$

$-9x + 47 = 4 - x$

$-8x = -43$

$x = \dfrac{43}{8}$

Check: $\dfrac{\frac{43}{8}+5}{4} - \dfrac{3\left(\frac{43}{8}\right)-8}{3} \overset{?}{=} \dfrac{4-\left(\frac{43}{8}\right)}{12}$

$\dfrac{1}{4}\left(\dfrac{43}{8} + \dfrac{40}{8}\right) - \dfrac{1}{3}\left(\dfrac{129}{8} - \dfrac{64}{8}\right) \overset{?}{=} \dfrac{1}{12}\left(\dfrac{32}{8} - \dfrac{43}{8}\right)$

$\dfrac{1}{4}\left(\dfrac{83}{8}\right) - \dfrac{1}{3}\left(\dfrac{65}{8}\right) \overset{?}{=} \dfrac{1}{12}\left(-\dfrac{11}{8}\right)$

$\dfrac{1}{8}\left(\dfrac{83}{4} - \dfrac{65}{3}\right) \overset{?}{=} \dfrac{1}{8}\left(-\dfrac{11}{12}\right)$

$\dfrac{1}{8}\left(\dfrac{249}{12} - \dfrac{260}{12}\right) \overset{?}{=} \dfrac{1}{8}\left(-\dfrac{11}{12}\right)$

$\dfrac{1}{8}\left(-\dfrac{11}{12}\right) = \dfrac{1}{8}\left(-\dfrac{11}{12}\right)$

19. $\dfrac{9}{25-y} = -\dfrac{1}{4}$

$4(25-y)\left(\dfrac{9}{25-y}\right) = \left(-\dfrac{1}{4}\right)4(25-y)$

$36 = -(25-y)$

$36 = -25 + y$

$61 = y$

Check: $\dfrac{9}{25-61} \overset{?}{=} -\dfrac{1}{4}$

$-\dfrac{9}{36} = -\dfrac{1}{4}$

$-\dfrac{1}{4} = -\dfrac{1}{4}$

21. $5 - \dfrac{12}{a} = \dfrac{5}{3}$

$3a\left(5 - \dfrac{12}{a}\right) = \left(\dfrac{5}{3}\right)3a$

$15a - 36 = 5a$

$10a = 36$

$a = \dfrac{36}{10}$

$a = \dfrac{18}{5}$

Check: $5 - \dfrac{12}{\frac{18}{5}} \overset{?}{=} \dfrac{5}{3}$

$5 - \dfrac{60}{18} = \dfrac{5}{3}$

$\dfrac{15}{3} - \dfrac{10}{3} = \dfrac{5}{3}$

$\dfrac{5}{3} = \dfrac{5}{3}$

23. $\dfrac{4}{x} - \dfrac{7}{5x} = -\dfrac{1}{2}$

$10x\left(\dfrac{4}{x} - \dfrac{7}{5x}\right) = \left(-\dfrac{1}{2}\right)10x$

$40 - 14 = -5x$

$26 = -5x$

$\dfrac{26}{-5} = x$

Check: $\dfrac{4}{\frac{26}{-5}} - \dfrac{7}{5\left(\frac{26}{-5}\right)} \overset{?}{=} -\dfrac{1}{2}$

$-\dfrac{20}{26} + \dfrac{7}{26} \overset{?}{=} -\dfrac{1}{2}$

$-\dfrac{13}{26} \overset{?}{=} -\dfrac{1}{2}$

$-\dfrac{1}{2} = -\dfrac{1}{2}$

25. $\dfrac{12}{y+5} + \dfrac{1}{2} = 2$

$2(y+5)\left(\dfrac{12}{y+5} + \dfrac{1}{2}\right) = (2)2(y+5)$

$24 + y + 5 = 4(y+5)$

$y + 29 = 4y + 20$

$9 = 3y$

$3 = y$

Check: $\dfrac{12}{3+5} + \dfrac{1}{2} \overset{?}{=} 2$

$\dfrac{3}{2} + \dfrac{1}{2} = 2$

$\dfrac{4}{2} = 2$

$2 = 2$

27. $\dfrac{5}{x} = \dfrac{25}{3(x+2)}$ **Check:** $\dfrac{5}{3} \overset{?}{=} \dfrac{25}{3(3+2)}$

$3x(x+2)\left(\dfrac{5}{x}\right) = \left(\dfrac{25}{3(x+2)}\right)3x(x+2)$ $\dfrac{5}{3} = \dfrac{25}{15}$

$15(x+2) = 25x$ $\dfrac{5}{3} = \dfrac{5}{3}$

$15x + 30 = 25x$

$30 = 10x$

$3 = x$

29. $\dfrac{8}{3x+5} = \dfrac{1}{x+2}$ **Check:** $\dfrac{8}{3\left(-\frac{11}{5}\right)+5} \overset{?}{=} \dfrac{1}{-\frac{11}{5}+2}$

$(3x+5)(x+2)\left(\dfrac{8}{3x+5}\right) = \left(\dfrac{1}{x+2}\right)(3x+5)(x+2)$ $\dfrac{8}{-\frac{33}{5}+\frac{25}{5}} = \dfrac{1}{-\frac{11}{5}+\frac{10}{5}}$

$8(x+2) = 3x+5$ $\dfrac{8}{-\frac{8}{5}} = \dfrac{1}{-\frac{1}{5}}$

$8x + 16 = 3x + 5$ $-5 = -5$

$5x = -11$

$x = -\dfrac{11}{5}$

31. $\dfrac{3}{x+2} - \dfrac{1}{x} = \dfrac{1}{5x}$ **Check:** $\dfrac{1}{\frac{4}{3}+2} - \dfrac{1}{\frac{4}{3}} \overset{?}{=} \dfrac{1}{5\left(\frac{4}{3}\right)}$

$5x(x+2)\left(\dfrac{3}{x+2} - \dfrac{1}{x}\right) = \left(\dfrac{1}{5x}\right)5x(x+2)$ $\dfrac{3}{\frac{10}{3}} - \dfrac{1}{\frac{4}{3}} = \dfrac{1}{\frac{20}{3}}$

$15x - 5(x+2) = x + 2$ $\dfrac{9}{10} - \dfrac{3}{4} = \dfrac{3}{20}$

$15x - 5x - 10 = x + 2$ $\dfrac{18}{20} - \dfrac{15}{20} = \dfrac{3}{20}$

$10x - 10 = x + 2$ $\dfrac{3}{20} = \dfrac{3}{20}$

$9x = 12$

$x = \dfrac{12}{9}$

$x = \dfrac{4}{3}$

33. $\dfrac{1}{2} = \dfrac{18}{x^2}$ **Check:** $\dfrac{1}{2} \overset{?}{=} \dfrac{18}{6^2}$ $\dfrac{1}{2} \overset{?}{=} \dfrac{18}{(-6)^2}$

$2x^2\left(\dfrac{1}{2}\right) = \left(\dfrac{18}{x^2}\right)2x^2$ $\dfrac{1}{2} = \dfrac{18}{36}$ $\dfrac{1}{2} = \dfrac{18}{36}$

$x^2 = 36$ $\dfrac{1}{2} = \dfrac{1}{2}$ $\dfrac{1}{2} = \dfrac{1}{2}$

$x^2 - 36 = 0$

$(x-6)(x+6) = 0$

$x = 6 \quad x = -6$

35. $\dfrac{32}{t} = 2t$

Check: $\dfrac{32}{4} \overset{?}{=} 2(4)$ $\dfrac{32}{-4} \overset{?}{=} 2(-4)$

$\qquad\quad 8 = 8 \qquad\qquad -8 = -8$

$t\left(\dfrac{32}{t}\right) = (2t)t$

$32 = 2t^2$

$16 = t^2$

$0 = t^2 - 16$

$0 = (t-4)(t+4)$

$t = 4 \quad t = -4$

37. $x + 1 = \dfrac{72}{x}$

Check: $-9 + 1 \overset{?}{=} \dfrac{72}{-9}$ $\qquad 8 + 1 \overset{?}{=} \dfrac{72}{8}$

$\qquad\qquad\qquad -8 = -8 \qquad\qquad\qquad 9 = 9$

$x(x+1) = \left(\dfrac{72}{x}\right)x$

$x^2 + x = 72$

$x^2 + x - 72 = 0$

$(x+9)(x-8) = 0$

$x = -9 \quad x = 8$

39. $1 = \dfrac{16}{y} - \dfrac{39}{y^2}$

Check: $1 \overset{?}{=} \dfrac{16}{13} - \dfrac{39}{13^2}$ $\qquad 1 \overset{?}{=} \dfrac{16}{3} - \dfrac{39}{3^2}$

$\qquad\qquad\qquad 1 = \dfrac{16}{13} - \dfrac{3}{13} \qquad\quad 1 = \dfrac{16}{3} - \dfrac{13}{3}$

$y^2(1) = \left[\dfrac{16}{y} - \dfrac{39}{y^2}\right]y^2$

$\qquad\qquad\qquad 1 = 1 \qquad\qquad\qquad 1 = 1$

$y^2 = 16y - 39$

$y^2 - 16y + 39 = 0$

$(y-13)(y-3) = 0$

$y = 13 \quad y = 3$

41. $\dfrac{2x}{3x - 10} - \dfrac{5}{x} = 0$

$x(3x - 10)\left(\dfrac{2x}{3x - 10} - \dfrac{5}{x}\right) = (0)x(3x - 10)$

$2x^2 - 5(3x - 10) = 0$

$2x^2 - 15x + 50 = 0$

No real solution

43. $5x\left(\dfrac{2x}{5}\right) = \left(\dfrac{x^2 - 5x}{5x}\right)5x$

Check: $x = 0$ $\qquad\qquad\qquad x = -5$

$\qquad\qquad\qquad\qquad\quad \dfrac{2(0)}{5} \overset{?}{=} \dfrac{0^2 - 5(0)}{5(0)} \qquad \dfrac{2(-5)}{5} \overset{?}{=} \dfrac{(-5)^2 - 5(-5)}{5(-5)}$

$2x^2 = x^2 - 5x$

$\qquad\qquad\qquad\qquad\quad 0 \neq \text{undefined} \qquad\qquad \dfrac{-10}{5} = \dfrac{25 + 25}{-25}$

$x^2 + 5x = 0$

$\qquad\qquad\qquad\quad \text{so } x = 0 \text{ is extraneous.}$

$x(x+5) = 0$

$\qquad\qquad\qquad\qquad\qquad\qquad\qquad\qquad\qquad -2 = -2$

$x = 0 \quad x + 5 = 0$

$\qquad\qquad x = -5$

45.
$$\frac{2}{6q + 5} - \frac{3}{4(6q + 5)} = \frac{1}{28}$$

$$28(6q + 5)\left(\frac{2}{6q + 5} - \frac{3}{4(6q + 5)}\right) = \left(\frac{1}{28}\right)28(6q + 5)$$

$$28(2) - 7(3) = 6q + 5$$

$$56 - 21 = 6q + 5$$

$$35 = 6q + 5$$

$$30 = 6q$$

$$5 = q$$

Check: $\quad \dfrac{2}{6(5) + 5} - \dfrac{3}{4[6(5) + 5]} \stackrel{?}{=} \dfrac{1}{28}$

$$\frac{2}{30 + 5} - \frac{3}{4(30 + 5)} \stackrel{?}{=} \frac{1}{28}$$

$$\frac{2}{35} - \frac{3}{4(35)} \stackrel{?}{=} \frac{1}{28}$$

$$\frac{8}{140} - \frac{3}{140} \stackrel{?}{=} \frac{1}{28}$$

$$\frac{5}{140} \stackrel{?}{=} \frac{1}{28}$$

$$\frac{1}{28} = \frac{1}{28}$$

47.
$$\frac{4}{2x + 3} + \frac{17}{5x - 3} = 3$$

$$(5x - 3)(2x + 3)\left(\frac{4}{2x + 3} + \frac{17}{5x - 3}\right) = (3)(2x + 3)(5x - 3)$$

$$4(5x - 3) + 17(2x + 3) = 3(10x^2 + 9x - 9)$$

$$20x - 12 + 34x + 51 = 30x^2 + 27x - 27$$

$$0 = 30x^2 - 27x - 66$$

$$0 = 10x^2 - 9x - 22$$

$$0 = (10x + 11)(x - 2)$$

$$x = -\frac{11}{10} \quad x = 2$$

Check: $\quad \dfrac{4}{2\left(-\frac{11}{10}\right) + 3} + \dfrac{17}{5\left(-\frac{11}{10}\right) - 3} \stackrel{?}{=} 3$

$$\frac{4}{-\frac{22}{10} + \frac{30}{10}} + \frac{17}{-\frac{55}{10} - \frac{30}{10}} \stackrel{?}{=} 3$$

$$\frac{4}{\frac{8}{10}} + \frac{17}{-\frac{85}{10}} \stackrel{?}{=} 3$$

$$\frac{4}{\frac{4}{5}} + \frac{17}{-\frac{17}{2}} \stackrel{?}{=} 3$$

$$5 + -2 \stackrel{?}{=} 3$$

$$3 = 3$$

Check: $\quad \dfrac{4}{2(2) + 3} + \dfrac{17}{5(2) - 3} \stackrel{?}{=} 3$

$$\frac{4}{7} + \frac{17}{7} \stackrel{?}{=} 3$$

$$3 = 3$$

49.
$$\frac{2}{x - 10} - \frac{3}{x - 2} = \frac{6}{x^2 - 12x + 20}$$

$$\frac{2}{x - 10} - \frac{3}{x - 2} = \frac{6}{(x - 10)(x - 2)}$$

$$(x - 10)(x - 2)\left(\frac{2}{x - 10} - \frac{3}{x - 2}\right) = \left(\frac{6}{(x - 10)(x - 2)}\right)(x - 10)(x - 2)$$

$$2(x - 2) - 3(x - 10) = 6$$

$$2x - 4 - 3x + 30 = 6$$

$$-x + 26 = 6$$

$$-x = -20$$

$$x = 20$$

Check:

$$\frac{2}{20 - 10} - \frac{3}{20 - 2} \stackrel{?}{=} \frac{6}{(20)^2 - 12(20) + 20}$$

$$\frac{2}{10} - \frac{3}{18} \stackrel{?}{=} \frac{6}{400 - 240 + 20}$$

$$\frac{1}{5} - \frac{1}{6} \stackrel{?}{=} \frac{6}{180}$$

$$\frac{6}{30} - \frac{5}{30} = \frac{1}{30}$$

$$\frac{1}{30} = \frac{1}{30}$$

51.

$$\frac{x+3}{x^2-9}+\frac{4}{3-x}-2=0$$

$$\frac{\cancel{x+3}}{(x-3)\cancel{(x+3)}}-\frac{4}{x-3}-2=0$$

$$(x-3)\left(\frac{1}{x-3}-\frac{4}{x-3}-2\right)=0(x-3)$$

$$1-4-2(x-3)=0$$

$$-3-2x+6=0$$

$$-2x=-3$$

$$x=\frac{3}{2}$$

Check: $\dfrac{\frac{3}{2}+3}{\left(\frac{3}{2}\right)^2-9}+\dfrac{4}{3-\frac{3}{2}}-2\overset{?}{=}0$

$$\frac{\frac{3}{2}+\frac{6}{2}}{\frac{9}{4}-\frac{36}{4}}+\frac{4}{\frac{6}{2}-\frac{3}{2}}-2\overset{?}{=}0$$

$$\frac{\frac{9}{2}}{-\frac{27}{4}}+\frac{4}{\frac{3}{2}}-2\overset{?}{=}0$$

$$-\frac{2}{3}+\frac{8}{3}-\frac{6}{3}\overset{?}{=}0$$

$$0=0$$

53.

$$\frac{x}{x-2}+\frac{3x}{x-4}=\frac{-2(x-6)}{x^2-6x+8}$$

$$(x-2)(x-4)\left(\frac{x}{x-2}+\frac{3x}{x-4}\right)=\left(\frac{-2(x-6)}{(x-4)(x-2)}\right)(x-2)(x-4)$$

$$x(x-4)+3x(x-2)=-2(x-6)$$

$$x^2-4x+3x^2-6x=-2x+12$$

$$4x^2-8x-12=0$$

$$x^2-2x-3=0$$

$$(x-3)(x+1)=0$$

$$x=3 \quad x=-1$$

Check: $\dfrac{3}{3-2}+\dfrac{3(3)}{3-4}\overset{?}{=}\dfrac{-2(3-6)}{3^2-6(3)+8}$

$$3+\frac{9}{-1}\overset{?}{=}\frac{6}{-1}$$

$$-6=-6$$

Check:

$$\frac{-1}{-1-2}+\frac{3(-1)}{-1-4}\overset{?}{=}\frac{-2(-1-6)}{(-1)^2-6(-1)+8}$$

$$\frac{1}{3}+\frac{3}{5}\overset{?}{=}\frac{14}{15}$$

$$\frac{5}{15}+\frac{9}{15}\overset{?}{=}\frac{14}{15}$$

$$\frac{14}{15}=\frac{14}{15}$$

55.

$$\frac{2(x+7)}{x+4}-2=\frac{2x+20}{2x+8}$$

$$2(x+4)\left(\frac{2(x+7)}{x+4}-2\right)=\left(\frac{2x+20}{2(x+4)}\right)2(x+4)$$

$$4(x+7)-2\cdot2(x+4)=2x+20$$

$$4x+28-4x-16=2x+20$$

$$12=2x+20$$

$$-8=2x$$

$$-4=x$$

Check: $\dfrac{2[-4+7]}{-4+4}-2\overset{?}{=}\dfrac{2(-4)+20}{2(-4)+8}$

$$\frac{6}{0}-2\neq\frac{12}{0}\cdot$$

Division by zero is undefined. Solution is extraneous, so equation has no solution.

57.
$$\frac{x}{2} = \frac{2 - \dfrac{3}{x}}{1 - \dfrac{1}{x}}$$

$$\frac{x}{2} = \frac{2 - \dfrac{3}{x}}{1 - \dfrac{1}{x}} \cdot \frac{x}{x}$$

$$2(x - 1)\left(\frac{x}{2}\right) = \left(\frac{2x - 3}{x - 1}\right)2(x - 1)$$

$$x(x - 1) = (2x - 3)2$$

$$x^2 - x = 4x - 6$$

$$x^2 - 5x + 6 = 0$$

$$(x - 3)(x - 2) = 0$$

$$x = 3 \quad x = 2$$

Check:
$$\frac{3}{2} \overset{?}{=} \frac{2 - \dfrac{3}{3}}{1 - \dfrac{1}{3}}$$

$$\frac{3}{2} = \frac{1}{\dfrac{2}{3}}$$

$$\frac{3}{2} = \frac{3}{2}$$

$$\frac{2}{2} \overset{?}{=} \frac{2 - \dfrac{3}{2}}{1 - \dfrac{1}{2}}$$

$$1 = \frac{\dfrac{1}{2}}{\dfrac{1}{2}}$$

$$1 = 1$$

59. x-intercept: $(-2, 0)$

$$0 = \frac{x + 2}{x - 2}$$

$$(x - 2)(0) = \left(\frac{x + 2}{x - 2}\right)(x - 2)$$

$$0 = x + 2$$

$$-2 = x$$

61. x-intercepts: $(-1, 0)$ and $(1, 0)$

$$0 = x - \frac{1}{x}$$

$$x(0) = \left(x - \frac{1}{x}\right)x$$

$$0 = x^2 - 1$$

$$0 = (x - 1)(x + 1)$$

$$x - 1 = 0 \quad x + 1 = 0$$

$$x = 1 \qquad x = -1$$

63. (a) *Keystrokes:*

Y= (X,T,θ − 4) ÷ (X,T,θ + 5) GRAPH

x-intercept: $(4, 0)$

(b) $0 = \dfrac{x - 4}{x + 5}$

$$0 = x - 4$$

$$4 = x$$

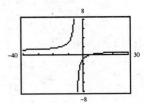

65. *Keystrokes:*

Y= 1 ÷ X,T,θ + 4 ÷ (X,T,θ − 5) GRAPH

x-intercept: $(1, 0)$

$$0 = \frac{1}{x} + \frac{4}{x - 5}$$

$$x(x - 5)(0) = \left(\frac{1}{x} + \frac{4}{x - 5}\right)x(x - 5)$$

$$0 = x - 5 + 4x$$

$$5 = 5x$$

$$1 = x$$

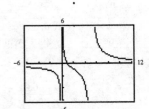

67. *Keystrokes:*

Y= (X,T,θ + 1) − 6 ÷ X,T,θ GRAPH

x-intercepts: $(-3, 0)$ and $(2, 0)$

$$0 = (x + 1) - \frac{6}{x}$$

$$x(0) = \left[(x + 1) - \frac{6}{x} \right] x$$

$$0 = x^2 + x - 6$$

$$0 = (x + 3)(x - 2)$$

$$x + 3 = 0 \qquad x - 2 = 0$$

$$x = -3 \qquad x = 2$$

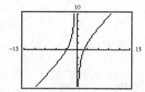

69. (a) *Keystrokes:*

Y= (X,T,θ − 1) − 12 ÷ X,T,θ GRAPH

x-intercepts: $(-3, 0)$ and $(4, 0)$

(b)
$$0 = (x - 1) - \frac{12}{x}$$

$$0 = x^2 - x - 12$$

$$0 = (x - 4)(x + 3)$$

$$x - 4 = 0 \qquad x + 3 = 0$$

$$x = 4 \qquad x = -3$$

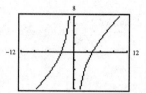

71. *Verbal Model:* $\boxed{\text{Number}} + \boxed{\text{Reciprocal}} = \boxed{\dfrac{65}{8}}$

Labels: Number $= x$

Reciprocal $= \dfrac{1}{x}$

Equation:
$$x + \frac{1}{x} = \frac{65}{8}$$

$$8x\left(x + \frac{1}{x} \right) = \left(\frac{65}{8} \right) 8x$$

$$8x^2 + 8 = 65x$$

$$8x^2 - 65x + 8 = 0$$

$$(8x - 1)(x - 8) = 0$$

$$x = \frac{1}{8} \quad x = 8$$

73. *Verbal Model:* $\boxed{\text{Distance}} \div \boxed{\text{Rate}} = \boxed{\text{Time}}$

$$\dfrac{\boxed{\text{Distance}}}{\boxed{\text{Rate}}} = \boxed{\text{Time}}$$

$$\boxed{\begin{array}{c}\text{Time traveled}\\\text{with wind}\end{array}} = \boxed{\begin{array}{c}\text{Time traveled}\\\text{without wind}\end{array}}$$

Labels: Speed of the wind $= x$

Equation:
$$\frac{680}{300 + x} = \frac{520}{300 - x}$$

$$(300 + x)(300 - x)\left(\frac{680}{300 + x} \right) = \left(\frac{520}{300 - x} \right)(300 + x)(300 - x)$$

$$680(300 - x) = 520(300 + x)$$

$$204{,}000 - 680x = 156{,}000 + 520x$$

$$-1200x = -48{,}000$$

$$x = 40 \text{ miles per hour}$$

75. *Verbal Model:* $\boxed{\text{Distance}} = \boxed{\text{Rate}} \cdot \boxed{\text{Time}}$

$$\frac{\boxed{\text{Distance person 1}}}{\boxed{\text{Rate person 1}}} = \frac{\boxed{\text{Distance person 2}}}{\boxed{\text{Rate person 2}}}$$

Labels: Rate person 1 $= x + 2$

Rate person 2 $= x$

Equation:
$$\frac{5}{x+2} = \frac{4}{x}$$

$$x(x+2)\left(\frac{5}{x+2}\right) = \left(\frac{4}{x}\right)x(x+2)$$

$$5x = 4(x+2)$$

$$5x = 4x + 8$$

$$x = 8 \text{ mph person 2}$$

$$x + 2 = 10 \text{ mph person 1}$$

77. *Verbal Model:* $\boxed{\text{Distance}} = \boxed{\text{Rate}} \cdot \boxed{\text{Time}}$

$$\frac{\text{Distance}}{\text{Rate}} = \text{Time}$$

$$\boxed{\begin{array}{c}\text{Time traveled}\\\text{upstream}\end{array}} + \boxed{\begin{array}{c}\text{Time traveled}\\\text{downstream}\end{array}} = \boxed{\begin{array}{c}\text{Total}\\\text{time}\end{array}}$$

Labels: Speed of the current $= x$

Equation:
$$\frac{48}{20-x} + \frac{48}{20+x} = 5$$

$$(20-x)(20+x)\left(\frac{48}{20-x} + \frac{48}{20+x}\right) = (5)(20-x)(20+x)$$

$$48(20+x) + 48(20-x) = 5(400 - x^2)$$

$$960 + 48x + 960 - 48x = 2000 - 5x^2$$

$$1920 = 2000 - 5x^2$$

$$5x^2 = 80$$

$$x^2 = 16$$

$$x = 4 \text{ mph}$$

79. *Verbal Model:* $\boxed{\begin{array}{c}\text{Cost per person}\\\text{current group}\end{array}} - \boxed{\begin{array}{c}\text{Cost per person}\\\text{new group}\end{array}} = \boxed{4000}$

Labels: Persons in current group $= x$

Persons in new group $= x + 2$

Equation:
$$\frac{240,000}{x} - \frac{240,000}{x+2} = 4000$$

$$x(x+2)\left(\frac{240,000}{x} - \frac{240,000}{x+2}\right) = (4000)x(x+2)$$

$$240,000(x+2) - 240,000x = 4000(x^2 + 2x)$$

$$240,000x + 480,000 - 240,000x = 4000x^2 + 8000x$$

$$0 = 4000x^2 + 8000x - 480,000$$

$$0 = x^2 + 2x - 120$$

$$0 = (x+12)(x-10)$$

$$x + 12 = 0 \qquad x - 10 = 0$$

$$x = -12 \qquad x = 10 \text{ people}$$

81. *Verbal Model:*   Cost per person original group − Cost per person new group = 1300

Labels: Persons in current group = x

Persons in new group = $x + 3$

Equation:

$$\frac{78{,}000}{x} - \frac{78{,}000}{x + 3} = 1300$$

$$x(x + 3)\left(\frac{78{,}000}{x} - \frac{78{,}000}{x + 3}\right) = (1300)x(x + 3)$$

$$78{,}000(x + 3) - 78{,}000x = 1300x(x + 3)$$

$$78{,}000x + 234{,}000 - 78{,}000x = 1300x^2 + 3900x$$

$$0 = 1300x^2 + 3900x - 234{,}000$$

$$0 = x^2 + 3x - 180$$

$$0 = (x + 15)(x - 12)$$

$$x = -15 \quad x = 12 \text{ persons}$$

83. (a) *Keystrokes:*

(b) *Verbal Model:*   Cost = $\dfrac{120{,}000p}{100 - p}$

Equation:

$$680{,}000 = \frac{120{,}000p}{100 - p}$$

$$(100 - p)(680{,}000) = \left(\frac{120{,}000p}{100 - p}\right)(100 - p)$$

$$68{,}000{,}000 - 680{,}000p = 120{,}000p$$

$$68{,}000{,}000 = 800{,}000p$$

$$85\% = p$$

85.

$$\frac{1}{6} + \frac{1}{6} = \frac{1}{t}$$

$$t + t = 6$$

$$2t = 6$$

$$t = 3 \text{ hours}$$

$$\frac{1}{3} + \frac{1}{5} = \frac{1}{t}$$

$$5t + 3t = 15$$

$$8t = 15$$

$$t = \frac{15}{8} \text{ minutes}$$

$$\frac{1}{5} + \frac{1}{2\frac{1}{2}} = \frac{1}{t}$$

$$\frac{1}{5} + \frac{1}{\frac{5}{2}} = \frac{1}{t}$$

$$\frac{1}{5} + \frac{2}{5} = \frac{1}{t}$$

$$t + 2t = 5$$

$$3t = 5$$

$$t = \frac{5}{3} \text{ hours}$$

Person #1	Person #2	Together
6 hours	6 hours	3 hours
3 minutes	5 minutes	$\frac{15}{8}$ minutes
5 hours	$2\frac{1}{2}$ hours	$\frac{5}{3}$ hours

87. *Verbal Model:* $\boxed{\text{Rate Person 1}} + \boxed{\text{Rate Person 2}} = \boxed{\text{Rate Together}}$

Labels: Second landscaper's time $= x$

First landscaper's time $= \dfrac{3}{2}x$

Equation:

$$\frac{1}{x} + \frac{1}{\frac{3}{2}x} = \frac{1}{9}$$

$$9x\left(\frac{1}{x} + \frac{2}{3x}\right) = \left(\frac{1}{9}\right)9x$$

$$9 + 6 = x$$

$$15 \text{ hours} = x$$

$$22\frac{1}{2} \text{ hours} = \frac{45}{2} = \frac{3}{2}x$$

89. *Verbal Model:* $\boxed{\text{Rate Pipe 1}} + \boxed{\text{Rate Pipe 2}} = \boxed{\text{Rate Together}}$

Labels: Second pipe's time $= x$

First pipe's time $= \dfrac{5}{4}x$

Equation:

$$\frac{1}{x} + \frac{1}{\frac{5}{4}x} = \frac{1}{5}$$

$$5x\left(\frac{1}{x} + \frac{4}{5x}\right) = \left(\frac{1}{5}\right)5x$$

$$5 + 4 = x$$

$$9 \text{ hours} = x$$

$$11\frac{1}{4} \text{ hours} = \frac{45}{4} = \frac{5}{4}x$$

91. $y = \dfrac{87{,}709 - 1236(0)}{1000 - 93(0)} \approx 87.7$ $y = \dfrac{87{,}709 - 1236(3)}{1000 - 93(3)} \approx 116.5$

$y = \dfrac{87{,}709 - 1236(1)}{1000 - 93(1)} \approx 95.3$ $y = \dfrac{87{,}709 - 1236(4)}{1000 - 93(4)} \approx 131.8$

$y = \dfrac{87{,}709 - 1236(2)}{1000 - 93(2)} \approx 104.7$ $y = \dfrac{87{,}709 - 1236(5)}{1000 - 93(5)} \approx 152.4$

93. (a) Domain $= \{4, 6, 8, 10, \ldots\}$ (c) $135 = 43.4 + \dfrac{9353}{x^2}$

(b)

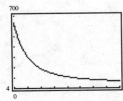

$$91.6 = \frac{9353}{x^2}$$

$$x^2 = \frac{9353}{91.6}$$

$$x \approx 10d$$

95. (d)
$$t(x) = \frac{10}{5 - x} + \frac{10}{5 + x}$$

$$6\frac{1}{4} = \frac{10}{5 - x} + \frac{10}{5 + x}$$

$$4(5 - x)(5 + x)\left(\frac{25}{4}\right) = \left(\frac{10}{5 - x} + \frac{10}{5 + x}\right)4(5 - x)(5 + x)$$

$$25(25 - x^2) = 40(5 + x) + 40(5 - x)$$

$$625 - 25x^2 = 200 + 40x + 200 - 40x$$

$$0 = 25x^2 - 225$$

$$0 = x^2 - 9$$

$$x = 3 \text{ miles per hour}$$

(e) $t(x) = \dfrac{10}{5 - 4} + \dfrac{10}{5 + 4}$

$t(x) = 10 + \dfrac{10}{9} = \dfrac{90}{9} + \dfrac{10}{9} = \dfrac{100}{9}$

$t(x) = 11\frac{1}{9}$ or 11.1 hours

Yes

97. Solve a rational equation by multiplying both sides of the equation by the lowest common denominator. Then solve the resulting equation, checking for any extraneous solutions.

99. (a) Simplify each side by removing symbols of grouping, combining like terms, and reducing fractions on one or both sides.

(b) Add (or subtract) the same quantity to (from) both sides of the equation.

(c) Multiply (or divide) both sides of the equation by the same nonzero real number.

(d) Interchange the two sides of the equation.

101. When the equation involves only two fractions, one on each side of the equation, the equation can be solved by cross-multiplication.

Review Exercises for Chapter 4

1. $(2^3 \cdot 3^2)^{-1} = (8 \cdot 9)^{-1}$

$= 72^{-1}$

$= \frac{1}{72}$

3. $\left(\frac{2}{5}\right)^{-3} = \left(\frac{5}{2}\right)^3$

$= \frac{125}{8}$

5. $(6 \times 10^3)^2 = 6^2 \times 10^6$

$= 36 \times 10^6$

$= 36,000,000$

7. $\dfrac{3.5 \times 10^7}{7 \times 10^4} = \dfrac{3.5}{7} \times 10^{7-4}$

$= 0.5 \times 10^3$

$= 5 \times 10^2$

$= 500$

9. $0.0000538 = 5.38 \times 10^{-5}$

11. $4.833 \times 10^8 = 483,300,000$

13. $(6y^4)(2y^{-3}) = 12y^{4+(-3)}$

$= 12y^1$

$= 12y$

15. $\dfrac{4x^{-2}}{2x} = 2x^{-2-1}$

$= 2x^{-3}$

$= \dfrac{2}{x^3}$

17. $(x^3 y^{-4})^2 = x^6 y^{-8}$

$= \dfrac{x^6}{y^8}$

19. $\dfrac{t^{-5}}{t^{-2}} = t^{(-5)-(-2)}$

$= t^{-5+2}$

$= t^{-3}$

$= \dfrac{1}{t^3}$

21. $\left(\dfrac{y}{3}\right)^{-3} = \left(\dfrac{3}{y}\right)^3$

$= \dfrac{27}{y^3}$

23. $y - 8 \neq 0$

$y \neq 8$

$D = (-\infty, 8) \cup (8, \infty)$

25. $u^2 - 7u + 6 \neq 0$

$(u - 6)(u - 1) \neq 0$

$u \neq 6, \quad u \neq 1$

$D = (-\infty, 1) \cup (1, 6) \cup (6, \infty)$

27. $\dfrac{6x^4y^2}{15xy^2} = \dfrac{2 \cdot 3x \cdot x^3 \cdot y^2}{5 \cdot 3x \cdot y^2}$

$= \dfrac{2x^3}{5}, \quad x \neq 0, y \neq 0$

29. $\dfrac{5b - 15}{30b - 120} = \dfrac{5(b - 3)}{30(b - 4)}$

$= \dfrac{5(b - 3)}{5 \cdot 6(b - 4)}$

$= \dfrac{b - 3}{6(b - 4)}$

31. $\dfrac{9x - 9y}{y - x} = \dfrac{9(x - y)}{-1(x - y)}$

$= -9, \quad x \neq y$

33. $\dfrac{x^2 - 5x}{2x^2 - 50} = \dfrac{x(x - 5)}{2(x^2 - 25)}$

$= \dfrac{x(x - 5)}{2(x - 5)(x + 5)}$

$= \dfrac{x}{2(x + 5)}, \quad x \neq 5$

35. $3x(x^2y)^2 = 3x(x^4y^2)$

$= 3x^5y^2$

37. $\dfrac{24x^4}{15x} = \dfrac{8x^3}{5}$

39. $\dfrac{7}{8} \cdot \dfrac{2x}{y} \cdot \dfrac{y^2}{14x^2} = \dfrac{7 \cdot 2 \cdot x \cdot y \cdot y}{2 \cdot 2 \cdot 2 \cdot y \cdot 7 \cdot 2 \cdot x \cdot x}$

$= \dfrac{y}{8x}, \quad y \neq 0$

41. $\dfrac{60z}{z + 6} \cdot \dfrac{z^2 - 36}{5} = \dfrac{5 \cdot 12z(z - 6)(z + 6)}{(z + 6)5}$

$= 12z(z - 6), \quad z \neq -6$

43. $\dfrac{u}{u - 3} \cdot \dfrac{3u - u^2}{4u^2} = \dfrac{u}{u - 3} \cdot \dfrac{-u(u - 3)}{4u^2}$

$= -\dfrac{1}{4}, \quad u \neq 0, u \neq 3$

45. $\dfrac{6/x}{2/x^3} = \dfrac{6}{x} \div \dfrac{2}{x^3}$

$= \dfrac{3 \cdot 2}{x} \cdot \dfrac{x \cdot x^2}{2}$

$= 3x^2, \quad x \neq 0$

47. $25y^2 \div \dfrac{xy}{5} = 25y \cdot y \cdot \dfrac{5}{xy}$

$= \dfrac{125y}{x}, \quad y \neq 0$

49. $\dfrac{x^2 - 7x}{x + 1} \div \dfrac{x^2 - 14x + 49}{x^2 - 1} = \dfrac{x(x - 7)}{x + 1} \cdot \dfrac{(x - 1)(x + 1)}{(x - 7)(x - 7)}$

$= \dfrac{x(x - 1)}{x - 7}, \quad x \neq -1, x \neq 1$

51. $\dfrac{\left(\dfrac{6x^2}{x^2+2x-35}\right)}{\left(\dfrac{x^3}{x^2-25}\right)} = \dfrac{\dfrac{6x^2}{(x+7)(x-5)}}{\dfrac{x^3}{(x-5)(x+5)}} \cdot \dfrac{(x+7)(x-5)(x+5)}{(x+7)(x-5)(x+5)}$

$\qquad = \dfrac{6x^2(x+5)}{x^3(x+7)}$

$\qquad = \dfrac{6(x+5)}{x(x+7)}, \quad x \neq 5, x \neq -5$

53. $\dfrac{4}{9} - \dfrac{11}{9} = \dfrac{4-11}{9} = -\dfrac{7}{9}$

55. $\dfrac{15}{16} - \dfrac{5}{24} - 1 = \dfrac{15(3)}{16(3)} - \dfrac{5(2)}{24(2)} - \dfrac{1(48)}{1(48)}$

$\qquad = \dfrac{45-10-48}{48}$

$\qquad = -\dfrac{13}{48}$

57. $\dfrac{1}{x+5} + \dfrac{3}{x-12} = \dfrac{1}{x+5}\left(\dfrac{x-12}{x-12}\right) + \dfrac{3}{x-12}\left(\dfrac{x+5}{x+5}\right)$

$\qquad = \dfrac{x-12}{(x+5)(x-12)} + \dfrac{3(x+5)}{(x-12)(x+5)}$

$\qquad = \dfrac{x-12+3x+15}{(x+5)(x-12)}$

$\qquad = \dfrac{4x+3}{(x+5)(x-12)}$

59. $5x + \dfrac{2}{x-3} - \dfrac{3}{x+2} = \dfrac{5x(x-3)(x+2)}{(x-3)(x+2)} + \dfrac{2}{(x-3)}\left(\dfrac{x+2}{x+2}\right) - \dfrac{3}{(x+2)}\left(\dfrac{x-3}{x-3}\right)$

$\qquad = \dfrac{5x^3 - 5x^2 - 30x + 2x + 4 - 3x + 9}{(x-3)(x+2)}$

$\qquad = \dfrac{5x^3 - 5x^2 - 31x + 13}{(x-3)(x+2)}$

61. $\dfrac{6}{x} - \dfrac{6x+1}{x^2+4} = \dfrac{6(x^2+4)}{x(x^2+4)} - \dfrac{6x-1(x)}{x^2+4(x)}$

$\qquad = \dfrac{6x^2 + 24 - 6x^2 + x}{x(x^2+4)}$

$\qquad = \dfrac{24+x}{x(x^2+4)}$

63. $\dfrac{5}{x+3} - \dfrac{4x}{(x+3)^2} - \dfrac{1}{x-3} = \dfrac{5}{x+3}\left(\dfrac{(x+3)(x-3)}{(x+3)(x-3)}\right) - \dfrac{4x}{(x+3)^2}\left(\dfrac{x-3}{x-3}\right) - \dfrac{1}{x-3}\left(\dfrac{(x+3)^2}{(x+3)^2}\right)$

$\qquad = \dfrac{5x^2 - 45 - 4x^2 + 12x - x^2 - 6x - 9}{(x+3)^2(x-3)}$

$\qquad = \dfrac{6x - 54}{(x+3)^2(x-3)}$

65. $\dfrac{3t}{\left(5 - \dfrac{2}{t}\right)} \cdot \dfrac{t}{t} = \dfrac{3t^2}{5t - 2}, t \neq 0$

67. $\dfrac{\left(\dfrac{1}{a^2 - 16} - \dfrac{1}{a}\right)}{\left(\dfrac{1}{a^2 + 4a} + 4\right)} \cdot \dfrac{a(a - 4)(a + 4)}{a(a - 4)(a + 4)} = \dfrac{a - (a - 4)(a + 4)}{a - 4 + 4a(a - 4)(a + 4)}$

$$= \dfrac{a - (a^2 - 16)}{a - 4 + 4a(a^2 - 16)}$$

$$= \dfrac{a - a^2 + 16}{a - 4 + 4a^3 - 64a}$$

$$= \dfrac{-a^2 + a + 16}{4a^3 - 63a - 4}, a \neq 0, a \neq -4$$

69. Keystrokes:

y_1 Y= (((X,T,θ x² + 6 X,T,θ + 9) ÷ X,T,θ x²) ×

((X,T,θ x² − 3 X,T,θ) ÷ (X,T,θ + 3))) ENTER

y_2 (X,T,θ x² − 9) ÷ X,T,θ GRAPH

$\dfrac{x^2 + 6x + 9}{x^2} \cdot \dfrac{x^2 - 3x}{x + 3} = \dfrac{(x + 3)(x + 3)x(x - 3)}{x^2(x + 3)} = \dfrac{x^2 - 9}{x}$

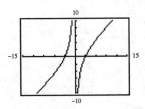

71. Keystrokes:

y_1 Y= (((1 ÷ X,T,θ) − (1 ÷ 2)) ÷ 2 X,T,θ ENTER

y_2 (2 − X,T,θ) ÷ 4 X,T,θ x² GRAPH

$\dfrac{\left(\dfrac{1}{x} - \dfrac{1}{2}\right)}{2x} \cdot \dfrac{2x}{2x} = \dfrac{2 - x}{4x^2}$

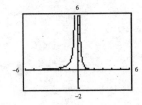

73. $(4x^3 - x) \div 2x = \dfrac{4x^3 - x}{2x}$

$$= \dfrac{4x^3}{2x} - \dfrac{x}{2x}$$

$$= 2x^2 - \dfrac{1}{2}, x \neq 0$$

75.
$$
\begin{array}{r}
2x^2 + \dfrac{4}{3}x - \dfrac{8}{9} + \dfrac{10}{9(3x - 1)} \\[4pt]
3x - 1 \overline{\smash{)}6x^3 + 2x^2 - 4x + 2} \\
\underline{6x^3 - 2x^2} \\
4x^2 - 4x \\
\underline{4x^2 - \dfrac{4}{3}x} \\
-\dfrac{8}{3}x + 2 \\
\underline{-\dfrac{8}{3}x + \dfrac{8}{9}} \\
\dfrac{10}{9}
\end{array}
$$

77.
$$
\begin{array}{r}
x^2 - 2 \\
x^2 - 1 \overline{\smash{)}x^4 + 0x^3 - 3x^2 + 2}, x \neq \pm 1 \\
\underline{x^4 \quad\ - \ x^2} \\
-2x^2 + 2 \\
\underline{-2x^2 + 2}
\end{array}
$$

79.

$$x^3 - 2x^2 + x - 1 \enclose{longdiv}{x^5 - 3x^4 + 0x^3 + x^2 + 0x + 6}$$

quotient: $x^2 - x - 3 + \dfrac{-3x^2 + 2x + 3}{x^3 - 2x^2 + x - 1}$

$$\underline{x^5 - 2x^4 + x^3 - x^2}$$
$$-x^4 - x^3 + 2x^2 + 0x$$
$$\underline{-x^4 + 2x^3 - x^2 + x}$$
$$-3x^3 + 3x^2 - x + 6$$
$$\underline{-3x^3 + 6x^2 - 3x + 3}$$
$$-3x^2 + 2x + 3$$

81. $\dfrac{x^3 + 7x^2 + 3x - 14}{x + 2} = x^2 + 5x - 7, \ x \neq -2$

$$\begin{array}{r|rrrr} -2 & 1 & 7 & 3 & -14 \\ & & -2 & -10 & 14 \\ \hline & 1 & 5 & -7 & 0 \end{array}$$

83. $(x^4 - 3x^2 - 25) \div (x - 3)$

$$= x^3 + 3x^2 + 6x + 18 + \dfrac{29}{x - 3}$$

$$\begin{array}{r|rrrrr} 3 & 1 & 0 & -3 & 0 & -25 \\ & & 3 & 9 & 18 & 54 \\ \hline & 1 & 3 & 6 & 18 & 29 \end{array}$$

85. $\dfrac{3x}{8} = -15 + \dfrac{x}{4}$

$$8\left(\dfrac{3}{8}x\right) = (-15)8 + \left(\dfrac{x}{4}\right)8$$

$$3x = -120 + 2x$$

$$x = -120$$

Check:

$$\dfrac{3(-120)}{8} \overset{?}{=} -15 + \dfrac{-120}{4}$$

$$\dfrac{-360}{8} \overset{?}{=} -15 + -30$$

$$-45 = -45$$

87. $(3t)\left(8 - \dfrac{12}{t}\right) = \dfrac{1}{3}(3t)$

$$24t - 36 = t$$

$$23t = 36$$

$$t = \dfrac{36}{23}$$

Check:

$$8 - \dfrac{12}{\left(\frac{36}{23}\right)} \overset{?}{=} \dfrac{1}{3}$$

$$8 - \dfrac{23}{3} \overset{?}{=} \dfrac{1}{3}$$

$$\dfrac{24}{3} - \dfrac{23}{3} \overset{?}{=} \dfrac{1}{3}$$

$$\dfrac{1}{3} = \dfrac{1}{3}$$

89. $\dfrac{2}{y} - \dfrac{1}{3y} = \dfrac{1}{3}$

$$3y\left(\dfrac{2}{y} - \dfrac{1}{3y}\right) = \left(\dfrac{1}{3}\right)3y$$

$$6 - 1 = y$$

$$5 = y$$

Check:

$$\dfrac{2}{5} - \dfrac{1}{3(5)} \overset{?}{=} \dfrac{1}{3}$$

$$\dfrac{2}{5} - \dfrac{1}{15} \overset{?}{=} \dfrac{1}{3}$$

$$\dfrac{6}{15} - \dfrac{1}{15} \overset{?}{=} \dfrac{1}{3}$$

$$\dfrac{5}{15} \overset{?}{=} \dfrac{1}{3}$$

$$\dfrac{1}{3} = \dfrac{1}{3}$$

91. $r = 2 + \dfrac{24}{r}$

$$r(r) = \left(2 + \dfrac{24}{r}\right)r$$

$$r^2 = 2r + 24$$

$$r^2 - 2r - 24 = 0$$

$$(r - 6)(r + 4) = 0$$

$$r = 6, \ r = -4$$

Check:

$$6 \overset{?}{=} 2 + \dfrac{24}{6}$$

$$6 \overset{?}{=} 2 + 4$$

$$6 = 6$$

Check:

$$-4 \overset{?}{=} 2 + \dfrac{24}{-4}$$

$$-4 \overset{?}{=} 2 - 6$$

$$-4 = -4$$

93.

$$8\left(\frac{6}{x} - \frac{1}{x+5}\right) = 15$$

$$\left(\frac{6}{x} - \frac{1}{x+5}\right) = \frac{15}{8}$$

$$8x(x+5)\left(\frac{6}{x} - \frac{1}{x+5}\right) = \left(\frac{15}{8}\right)8x(x+5)$$

$$48(x+5) - 8x = 15x(x+5)$$

$$48x + 240 - 8x = 15x^2 + 75x$$

$$240 + 40x = 15x^2 + 75x$$

$$0 = 15x^2 + 35x - 240$$

$$0 = 5(3x^2 + 7x - 48)$$

$$0 = 5(3x + 16)(x - 3)$$

$$3x + 16 = 0 \qquad x - 3 = 0$$

$$3x = -16 \qquad x = 3$$

$$x = -\frac{16}{3}$$

Check:

$$8\left(\frac{6}{-\frac{16}{3}} - \frac{1}{-\frac{16}{3} + 5}\right) \overset{?}{=} 15$$

$$8\left(-\frac{18}{16} - \frac{1}{-\frac{16}{3} + \frac{15}{3}}\right) \overset{?}{=} 15$$

$$8\left(-\frac{9}{8} - \frac{1}{-\frac{1}{3}}\right) \overset{?}{=} 15$$

$$8\left(-\frac{9}{8} + 3\right) \overset{?}{=} 15$$

$$8\left(-\frac{9}{8} + \frac{24}{8}\right) \overset{?}{=} 15$$

$$8\left(\frac{15}{8}\right) \overset{?}{=} 15$$

$$15 = 15$$

Check:

$$8\left(\frac{6}{3} - \frac{1}{3+5}\right) \overset{?}{=} 15$$

$$8\left(2 - \frac{1}{8}\right) \overset{?}{=} 15$$

$$8\left(\frac{16}{8} - \frac{1}{8}\right) \overset{?}{=} 15$$

$$8\left(\frac{15}{8}\right) \overset{?}{=} 15$$

$$15 = 15$$

95.

$$\frac{4x}{x-5} + \frac{2}{x} = -\frac{4}{x-5}$$

$$(x-5)\left(\frac{4x}{x-5} + \frac{2}{x}\right) = \left(-\frac{4}{x-5}\right)x(x-5)$$

$$4x^2 + 2(x-5) = -4x$$

$$4x^2 + 2x - 10 + 4x = 0$$

$$4x^2 + 6x - 10 = 0$$

$$2x^2 + 3x - 5 = 0$$

$$(2x + 5)(x - 1) = 0$$

$$x = -\frac{5}{2}, \; x = 1$$

Check:

$$\frac{4\left(-\frac{5}{2}\right)}{\left(-\frac{5}{2}\right) - 5} + \frac{2}{\left(-\frac{5}{2}\right)} \overset{?}{=} -\frac{4}{\left(-\frac{5}{2}\right) - 5}$$

$$\frac{-10}{-\frac{15}{2}} - \frac{4}{5} \overset{?}{=} -\frac{4}{-\frac{15}{2}}$$

$$\frac{20}{15} - \frac{12}{15} \overset{?}{=} \frac{8}{15}$$

$$\frac{8}{15} = \frac{8}{15}$$

Check:

$$\frac{4(1)}{1-5} + \frac{2}{1} \overset{?}{=} -\frac{4}{1-5}$$

$$\frac{4}{-4} + 2 \overset{?}{=} -\frac{4}{-4}$$

$$1 = 1$$

97.

$$\frac{12}{x^2 + x - 12} - \frac{1}{x-3} = -1$$

$$(x-3)(x+4)\left(\frac{12}{x^2 + x - 12} - \frac{1}{x-3}\right) = (-1)(x-3)(x+4)$$

$$12 - (x+4) = -1(x^2 + x - 12)$$

$$12 - x - 4 = -x^2 - x + 12$$

$$(x^2 - 4) = 0$$

$$(x-2)(x+2) = 0$$

$$x - 2 = 0 \qquad x + 2 = 0$$

$$x = 2 \qquad x = -2$$

99.
$$\frac{5}{x^2 - 4} - \frac{6}{x - 2} = -5$$

$$(x - 2)(x + 2)\left(\frac{5}{x^2 - 4} - \frac{6}{x - 2}\right) = (-5)(x - 2)(x + 2)$$

$$5 - 6(x + 2) = -5(x^2 - 4)$$

$$5 - 6x - 12 = -5x^2 + 20$$

$$5x^2 - 6x - 27 = 0$$

$$(5x + 9)(x - 3) = 0$$

$$5x + 9 = 0 \qquad x - 3 = 0$$

$$x = -\frac{9}{5} \qquad x = 3$$

101. *Keystrokes:*

Y= 1 ÷ X,T,θ − 1 ÷ (2 X,T,θ + 3) GRAPH

x-intercepts: $x = -3$

$$0 = \frac{1}{x} - \frac{1}{2x - 3}$$

$$0 = 2x + 3 - x$$

$$0 = x + 3$$

$$-3 = x$$

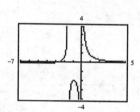

103. Domain: $(0, 6]$

$$P = 2\left(w + \frac{36}{w}\right), \quad w \neq 0$$

105. *Verbal Model:*

| Distance | = | Rate | · | Time |

| $\dfrac{\text{Original trip distance}}{\text{Rate}}$ | = | $\dfrac{\text{Return trip distance}}{\text{Rate}} + \dfrac{1}{6}$ |

Labels: Rate of original trip $= x$

Rate of return trip $= x + 8$

Equation:
$$\frac{56}{x} = \frac{56}{x + 8} + \frac{1}{6}$$

$$6x(x + 8)\left(\frac{56}{x}\right) = \left(\frac{56}{x + 8} + \frac{1}{6}\right)6x(x + 8)$$

$$336(x + 8) = 336x + x(x + 8)$$

$$336x + 2688 = 336x + x^2 + 8x$$

$$0 = x^2 + 8x - 2688$$

$$0 = (x - 48)(x + 56)$$

$$x = 48, \quad x = -56$$

$$x + 8 = 56 \text{ miles per hour}$$

107. *Verbal*
Model: $\boxed{\dfrac{\text{Hits}}{\text{At bats}}} = 0.400$

Label: Consecutive times $= x$

Equation: $\dfrac{45 + x}{150 + x} = 0.4$

$$(150 + x)\left(\frac{45 + x}{150 + x}\right) = 0.4(150 + x)$$

$$45 + x = 0.4(150 + x)$$

$$45 + x = 60 + 0.4x$$

$$45 + 0.6x = 60$$

$$0.6x = 15$$

$$x = \frac{15}{0.6}$$

$$x = 25$$

Thus, the player must hit safely 25 consecutive times to obtain a batting average of .400.

109. *Verbal*
Model: $\boxed{\begin{array}{c}\text{Share per}\\ \text{person now}\end{array}} = \boxed{\begin{array}{c}\text{Share per}\\ \text{person later}\end{array}} + 5000$

Labels: People presently in group $= x$
People in new group $= x + 2$

Equation: $\dfrac{60{,}000}{x} = \dfrac{60{,}000}{x + 2} + 5000$

$$x(x + 2)\left(\frac{60{,}000}{x}\right) = \left(\frac{60{,}000}{x + 2} + 5000\right)x(x + 2)$$

$$60{,}000(x + 2) = 60{,}000x + 5000x(x + 2)$$

$$60{,}000x + 120{,}00 = 60{,}000x + 5000x^2 + 10{,}000x$$

$$0 = 5000x^2 + 10{,}000x - 120{,}000$$

$$0 = x^2 + 2x - 24$$

$$0 = (x + 6)(x - 4)$$

$$x = -6, \quad x = 4 \text{ people}$$

111.

Verbal Model:

$$\boxed{\text{Rate of person 1}} + \boxed{\text{Rate of person 2}} = \boxed{\text{Rate together}}$$

Labels: Supervisor's time $= 12$

Your time $= 15$

Time together $= x$

Equation: $\dfrac{1}{12} + \dfrac{1}{15} = \dfrac{1}{x}$

$$60x\left(\dfrac{1}{12} + \dfrac{1}{15}\right) = \left(\dfrac{1}{x}\right)60x$$

$$5x + 4x = 60$$

$$9x = 60$$

$$x = \dfrac{60}{9}$$

$$x = \dfrac{20}{3} = 6\dfrac{2}{3} \text{ min or 6 min 40 sec}$$

113. (a) $N = \dfrac{20[4 + 3(5)]}{1 + 0.05(5)} = 304{,}000$

$\qquad N = \dfrac{20[4 + 3(10)]}{1 + 0.05(10)} \approx 453{,}333$

$\qquad N = \dfrac{20[4 + 3(25)]}{1 + 0.05(25)} \approx 702{,}222$

(b) $\qquad 752 = \dfrac{20(4 + 3t)}{1 + 0.05t}$

$\qquad 752(1 + 0.05t) = 20(4 + 3t)$

$\qquad 752 + 37.6t = 80 + 60t$

$\qquad 672 = 22.4t$

$\qquad 29.8 \text{ years} \approx t$

Chapter Test for Chapter 4

1. $2^{-2} + 2^{-3} = \dfrac{1}{2^2} + \dfrac{1}{2^3}$

$\qquad\qquad\quad = \dfrac{1}{4} + \dfrac{1}{8}$

$\qquad\qquad\quad = \dfrac{2}{8} + \dfrac{1}{8}$

$\qquad\qquad\quad = \dfrac{3}{8}$

2. $\dfrac{6.3 \times 10^{-3}}{2.1 \times 10^2} = 3 \times 10^{-3-2}$

$\qquad\qquad\qquad = 3 \times 10^{-5}$

3. $(5a^{-3})(2a^2) = 10a^{-3+2}$

$\qquad\qquad\quad = 10a^{-1}$

$\qquad\qquad\quad = \dfrac{10}{a}$

4. $\dfrac{r^2s^{-3}}{r^5s^2} = r^{2-5}s^{-3-2}$

$\qquad\quad = r^{-3}s^{-5}$

$\qquad\quad = \dfrac{1}{r^3s^5}$

5. $(x^2y^{-3})^4 = x^{2 \cdot 4}y^{-3 \cdot 4}$

$\qquad\qquad\quad = x^8y^{-12}$

$\qquad\qquad\quad = \dfrac{x^8}{y^{12}}$

6. $(3x^2y^2)^3(2x^{-2}y)^2 = (3^3x^6y^6)(2^2x^{-4}y^2)$

$\qquad\qquad\qquad\qquad = 27 \cdot 4x^{6+(-4)}y^{6+2}$

$\qquad\qquad\qquad\qquad = 108x^2y^8$

7. $0.000032 = 3.2 \times 10^{-5}$

8. $3.04 \times 10^7 = 30,400,000$

9.
$$y^2 - 25 \neq 0$$
$$(y - 5)(y + 5) \neq 0$$
$$y \neq 5, -5$$
$$D = (-\infty, -5) \cup (-5, 5) \cup (5, \infty)$$

10. Least common denominator: $x^3(x - 3)(x + 3)$

11. (a) $\dfrac{2 - x}{3x - 6} = \dfrac{2 - x}{-3(-x + 2)} = -\dfrac{1}{3}, \; x \neq 2$

(b) $\dfrac{2a^2 - 5a - 12}{5a - 20} = \dfrac{(2a + 3)(a - 4)}{5(a - 4)}$

$= \dfrac{2a + 3}{5}, \quad a \neq 4$

12. $\dfrac{4z^3}{5} \cdot \dfrac{25}{12z^2} = \dfrac{4 \cdot z^2 \cdot z \cdot 5 \cdot 5}{5 \cdot 4 \cdot 3 \cdot z^2} = \dfrac{5z}{3}, \quad z \neq 0$

13. $\dfrac{y^2 + 8y + 16}{2(y - 2)} \cdot \dfrac{8y - 16}{(y + 4)^3} = \dfrac{(y + 4)^2 \cdot 8(y - 2)}{2(y - 2)(y + 4)^2(y + 4)}$

$= \dfrac{4}{y + 4}, \quad y \neq 2$

14. $(4x^2 - 9) \cdot \dfrac{2x + 3}{2x^2 - x - 3} = \dfrac{(2x - 3)(2x + 3)(2x + 3)}{(2x - 3)(x + 1)}$

$= \dfrac{(2x + 3)^2}{x + 1}, \quad x \neq \dfrac{3}{2}$

15. $\dfrac{(2xy^2)^3}{15} \div \dfrac{12x^3}{21} = \dfrac{(2xy^2)^3}{15} \cdot \dfrac{21}{12x^3}$

$= \dfrac{8x^3y^6 \cdot 7 \cdot 3}{5 \cdot 3 \cdot 4 \cdot 3x^3}$

$= \dfrac{14y^6}{15}, \; x \neq 0$

16. $\dfrac{\left(\dfrac{3x}{x + 2}\right)}{\left(\dfrac{12}{x^3 + 2x^2}\right)} = \dfrac{3x}{x + 2} \div \dfrac{12}{x^3 + 2x^2}$

$= \dfrac{3x}{x + 2} \cdot \dfrac{x^2(x + 2)}{12}$

$= \dfrac{x^3}{4}, \; x \neq 0, -2$

17. $\dfrac{\left(9x - \dfrac{1}{x}\right)}{\left(\dfrac{1}{x} - 3\right)} = \dfrac{\left(9x - \dfrac{1}{x}\right)}{\left(\dfrac{1}{x} - 3\right)} \cdot \dfrac{x}{x}$

$= \dfrac{9x(x) - \dfrac{1}{x}(x)}{\dfrac{1}{x}(x) - 3(x)}$

$= \dfrac{9x^2 - 1}{1 - 3x}$

$= \dfrac{(3x - 1)(3x + 1)}{-1(-1 + 3x)}$

$= -(3x + 1), \quad x \neq 0, \dfrac{1}{3}$

18. $2x + \dfrac{1 - 4x^2}{x + 1} = 2x\left(\dfrac{x + 1}{x + 1}\right) + \dfrac{1 - 4x^2}{x + 1}$

$= \dfrac{2x^2 + 2x}{x + 1} + \dfrac{1 - 4x^2}{x + 1}$

$= \dfrac{-2x^2 + 2x + 1}{x + 1}$

19. $\dfrac{5x}{x+2} - \dfrac{2}{x^2-x-6} = \dfrac{5x}{x+2} - \dfrac{2}{(x-3)(x+2)}$

$$= \dfrac{5x}{x+2}\left(\dfrac{x-3}{x-3}\right) - \dfrac{2}{(x-3)(x+2)}$$

$$= \dfrac{5x^2 - 15x - 2}{(x+2)(x-3)}$$

20. $\dfrac{3}{x} - \dfrac{5}{x^2} + \dfrac{2x}{x^2+2x+1} = \dfrac{3}{x} - \dfrac{5}{x^2} + \dfrac{2x}{(x+1)^2}$

$$= \dfrac{3}{x}\left[\dfrac{x(x+1)^2}{x(x+1)^2}\right] - \dfrac{5}{x^2}\left[\dfrac{x(x+1)^2}{x(x+1)^2}\right] + \dfrac{2x}{(x+1)^2}\left(\dfrac{x^2}{x^2}\right)$$

$$= \dfrac{3x(x^2+2x+1) - 5(x^2+2x+1) + 2x^3}{x^2(x+1)^2}$$

$$= \dfrac{3x^3 + 6x^2 + 3x - 5x^2 - 10x - 5 + 2x^3}{x^2(x+1)^2}$$

$$= \dfrac{5x^3 + x^2 - 7x - 5}{x^2(x+1)^2}$$

21. $\dfrac{4}{x+1} + \dfrac{4x}{x+1} = \dfrac{4+4x}{x+1}$

$$= \dfrac{4(1+x)}{x+1}$$

$$= 4, \quad x \neq -1$$

22. $\dfrac{t^4+t^2-6t}{t^2-2} = t^2 - 2\overline{\smash{\big)}\ t^4 + 0t^3 + t^2 - 6t + 0}$

with quotient $t^2 \quad + 3 - \dfrac{6t-6}{t^2-2}$

$$\underline{t^4 \qquad\ -2t^2}$$
$$3t^2 - 6t$$
$$\underline{3t^2 \qquad -6}$$
$$-6t + 6$$

23. $\dfrac{2x^4 - 15x^2 - 7}{x-3}$

$$\begin{array}{r|rrrrr} 3 & 2 & 0 & -15 & 0 & -7 \\ & & 6 & 18 & 9 & 27 \\ \hline & 2 & 6 & 3 & 9 & 20 \end{array}$$

$$\dfrac{2x^4 - 15x^2 - 7}{x-3} = 2x^3 + 6x^2 + 3x + 9 + \dfrac{20}{x-3}$$

24. $\dfrac{3}{h+2} = \dfrac{1}{8}$

$$3(8) = h + 2$$
$$24 = h + 2$$
$$22 = h$$

Check:

$$\dfrac{3}{22+2} = \dfrac{1}{8}$$
$$\dfrac{3}{24} = \dfrac{1}{8}$$
$$\dfrac{1}{8} = \dfrac{1}{8}$$

25.
$$\frac{2}{x+5} - \frac{3}{x+3} = \frac{1}{x}$$

$$2x(x+3) - 3x(x+5) = (x+5)(x+3)$$

$$2x^2 + 6x - 3x^2 - 15x = x^2 + 3x + 5x + 15$$

$$-2x^2 - 17x - 15 = 0$$

$$(-2x - 15)(x+1) = 0$$

$$-2x - 15 = 0 \qquad x + 1 = 0$$

$$-2x = 15 \qquad x = -1$$

$$x = -\frac{15}{2}$$

Check:

$$\frac{2}{-\frac{15}{2}+5} - \frac{3}{-\frac{15}{2}+3} \overset{?}{=} \frac{1}{-\frac{15}{2}}$$

$$-\frac{12}{15} + \frac{10}{15} \overset{?}{=} -\frac{2}{15}$$

$$-\frac{2}{15} = -\frac{2}{15}$$

Check:

$$\frac{2}{-1+5} - \frac{3}{-1+3} \overset{?}{=} -\frac{1}{1}$$

$$\frac{2}{4} - \frac{3}{2} \overset{?}{=} 1$$

$$\frac{1}{2} - \frac{3}{2} \overset{?}{=} -1$$

$$-1 = -1$$

26. $\dfrac{1}{x+1} + \dfrac{1}{x-1} = \dfrac{2}{x^2-1}$

$$x - 1 + x + 1 = 2$$

$$2x = 2$$

$$x = 1$$

Division by zero is undefined. Solution is extraneous, so equation has no solution.

Check:

$$\frac{1}{1+1} + \frac{1}{1-1} \neq \frac{2}{1-1}$$

27. *Verbal Model:*

$$\boxed{\begin{array}{c}\text{Rate of}\\\text{painter 1}\end{array}} + \boxed{\begin{array}{c}\text{Rate of}\\\text{painter 2}\end{array}} = \boxed{\begin{array}{c}\text{Rate}\\\text{together}\end{array}}$$

Labels: Time of painter 1 = x

Time of painter 2 = $\dfrac{3}{2}x$

Equation:

$$\frac{1}{x} + \frac{1}{\frac{3}{2}x} = \frac{1}{4}$$

$$12x\left(\frac{1}{x} + \frac{2}{3x}\right) = \frac{1}{4}(12x)$$

$$12 + 8 = 3x$$

$$20 = 3x$$

$$\frac{20}{3} = 6\frac{2}{3} \text{ hours} = x$$

$$10 \text{ hours} = \frac{3}{2}x$$

CHAPTER 5
Radicals and Complex Numbers

CHAPTER 5
Radicals and Complex Numbers

Section 5.1 Radicals and Rational Exponents

Solutions to Odd-Numbered Exercises

1. $\sqrt{64} = 8$ because $8 \cdot 8 = 64$

3. $-\sqrt{49} = -7$ because $7 \cdot 7 = 49$

5. $\sqrt[3]{-8} = -2$ because $-2 \cdot -2 \cdot -2 = -8$

7. $\sqrt{-1}$ is not a real number because no real number multiplied by itself yields -1.

9. Because $7^2 = 49$, 7 is a square root of 49.

11. Because $4.2^3 = 74.088$, 4.2 is a cube root of 74.088.

13. Because $45^2 = 2025$, 45 is called the square root of 2025.

15. $\sqrt{8^2} = |8| = 8$

(index is even)

17. $\sqrt{(-10)^2} = |-10| = 10$

(index is even)

19. $\sqrt{-9^2} =$ not a real number

(even root of a negative number)

21. $-\sqrt{\left(\frac{2}{3}\right)^2} = -\frac{2}{3}$

(index is even)

23. $\sqrt{-\left(\frac{3}{10}\right)^2} =$ not a real number

(even root of a negative number)

25. $\left(\sqrt{5}\right)^2 = 5$

(inverse property of powers and roots)

27. $-\left(\sqrt{23}\right)^2 = -23$

(inverse property of powers and roots)

29. $\sqrt[3]{(5)^3} = 5$

(index is odd)

31. $\sqrt[3]{10^3} = 10$

(index is odd)

33. $-\sqrt[3]{(-6)^3} = 6$

(index is odd)

35. $\sqrt[3]{\left(-\frac{1}{4}\right)^3} = -\frac{1}{4}$

(index is odd)

37. $\left(\sqrt[3]{11}\right)^3 = 11$

(inverse property of powers and roots)

39. $\left(-\sqrt[3]{24}\right)^3 = -24$

(inverse property of powers and roots)

41. $\sqrt[4]{3^4} = 3$

(inverse property of powers and roots)

43. $-\sqrt[4]{-5^4} =$ not a real number

(even root of a negative number)

45. $\sqrt{6}$ is not rational because 6 is not a perfect square.

47. $\sqrt{900}$ is rational because $30 \cdot 30 = 900$, a perfect square.

49. *Radical Form*   *Rational Exponent Form*

$\sqrt{16} = 4$ $16^{1/2} = 4$

51. *Radical Form*   *Rational Exponent Form*

$\sqrt[3]{27^2} = 9$ $27^{2/3} = 9$

53. *Radical Form*   *Rational Exponent Form*

$\sqrt[4]{256^3} = 64$ $256^{3/4} = 64$

55. $25^{1/2} = \sqrt{25} = 5$

Root is 2. Power is 1.

57. $-36^{1/2} = -\sqrt{36} = -6$

Root is 2. Power is 1.

59. $-(16)^{3/4} = -\left(\sqrt[4]{16}\right)^3 = -8$

Root is 4. Power is 3.

61. $32^{-2/5} = \dfrac{1}{\left(\sqrt[5]{32}\right)^2} = \dfrac{1}{2^2} = \dfrac{1}{4}$

Root is 5. Power is 2.

63. $(-27)^{-2/3} = \dfrac{1}{(-27)^{2/3}} = \dfrac{1}{\left(\sqrt[3]{-27}\right)^2}$

$= \dfrac{1}{9}$

Root is 3. Power is 2.

65. $\left(\dfrac{8}{27}\right)^{2/3} = \left(\sqrt[3]{\dfrac{8}{27}}\right)^2 = \left(\dfrac{2}{3}\right)^2 = \dfrac{4}{9}$

Root is 3. Power is 2.

67. $\left(\dfrac{121}{9}\right)^{-1/2} = \left(\dfrac{9}{121}\right)^{1/2} = \sqrt{\dfrac{9}{121}} = \dfrac{3}{11}$

Root is 2. Power is 1.

69. $(3^3)^{2/3} = 3^{3 \cdot 2/3} = 3^2 = 9$

Root is 3. Power is 2.

71. $-(4^4)^{3/4} = -4^{4 \cdot 3/4} = -4^3 = -64$

Root is 4. Power is 3.

73. $\left(\dfrac{1}{5^3}\right)^{-2/3} = (5^3)^{2/3} = 5^{3 \cdot 2/3} = 5^2 = 25$

Root is 3. Power is 2.

75. $\sqrt{t} = t^{1/2}$

Root is 2. Power is 1.

77. $x\sqrt[4]{x^3} = x \cdot x^{3/4} = x^{1+3/4} = x^{7/4}$

Root is 4. Power is 3.

79. $u^2\sqrt[3]{u} = u^2 \cdot u^{1/3} = u^{2+1/3} = u^{7/3}$

Root is 3. Power is 1.

81. $s\sqrt[4]{s^5} = s^4 \cdot s^{5/2} = s^{4+5/2} = s^{13/2}$

Root is 2. Power is 5.

83. $\dfrac{\sqrt{x}}{\sqrt{x^3}} = \dfrac{x^{1/2}}{x^{3/2}} = x^{1/2 - 3/2} = x^{-1} = \dfrac{1}{x}$

85. $\dfrac{\sqrt[4]{t}}{\sqrt{t^5}} = \dfrac{t^{1/4}}{t^{5/2}} = t^{1/4 - 5/2}$

$= t^{1/4 - 10/4}$

$= t^{-9/4}$

$= \dfrac{1}{t^{9/4}}$

87. $\sqrt[3]{x^2} \cdot \sqrt[3]{x^7} = x^{2/3} \cdot x^{7/3} = x^{2/3 + 7/3} = x^{9/3}$

$= x^3$

89. $\sqrt[4]{y^3} \cdot \sqrt[3]{y} = y^{3/4} \cdot y^{1/3} = y^{3/4 + 1/3}$

$= y^{9/12 + 4/12} = y^{13/12}$

91. $\sqrt[4]{x^3 y} = (x^3 y)^{1/4}$

$= x^{3/4} y^{1/4}$

93. $z^2 \sqrt{y^5 z^4} = z^2 \cdot (y^5 z^4)^{1/2} = z^2 y^{5/2} z^2$

$= z^{2+2} y^{5/2} = z^4 y^{5/2}$

95. $3^{1/4} \cdot 3^{3/4} = 3^{1/4 + 3/4}$

$= 3^{4/4}$

$= 3^1$

97. $(2^{1/2})^{2/3} = 2^{1/2 \cdot 2/3}$

$= 2^{1/3}$

$= \sqrt[3]{2}$

99. $\dfrac{2^{1/5}}{2^{6/5}} = 2^{1/5 - 6/5}$

$= 2^{-5/5}$

$= 2^{-1} = \dfrac{1}{2}$

101. $(c^{3/2})^{1/3} = c^{3/2 \cdot 1/3}$

$= c^{1/2}$

$= \sqrt{c}$

103. $\dfrac{18y^{4/3}z^{-1/3}}{24y^{-2/3}z} = \dfrac{6 \cdot 3y^{4/3-(-2/3)}z^{-1/3-1}}{6 \cdot 4}$

$\qquad\qquad = \dfrac{3y^{6/3}z^{-4/3}}{4}$

$\qquad\qquad = \dfrac{3y^2}{4z^{4/3}}$

105. $(3x^{-1/3}y^{3/4})^2 = 3^2x^{-2/3}y^{3/2}$

$\qquad\qquad = \dfrac{9y^{3/2}}{x^{2/3}}$

107. $\left(\dfrac{x^{1/4}}{x^{1/6}}\right)^3 = (x^{1/4-1/6})^3$

$\qquad\qquad = (x^{3/12-2/12})^3$

$\qquad\qquad = (x^{1/12})^3$

$\qquad\qquad = x^{3/12}$

$\qquad\qquad = x^{1/4}$

109. $\sqrt{\sqrt[4]{y}} = (y^{1/4})^{1/2}$

$\qquad\qquad = y^{1/4 \cdot 1/2}$

$\qquad\qquad = y^{1/8}$

$\qquad\qquad = \sqrt[8]{y}$

111. $\sqrt[4]{\sqrt{x^3}} = \sqrt[4]{x^{3/2}}$

$\qquad\qquad = (x^{3/2})^{1/4}$

$\qquad\qquad = x^{3/2 \cdot 1/4}$

$\qquad\qquad = x^{3/8}$

113. $\dfrac{(x+y)^{3/4}}{\sqrt[4]{x+y}} = \dfrac{(x+y)^{3/4}}{(x+y)^{1/4}}$

$\qquad\qquad = (x+y)^{3/4-1/4}$

$\qquad\qquad = (x+y)^{2/4}$

$\qquad\qquad = (x+y)^{1/2}$

$\qquad\qquad = \sqrt{x+y}$

115. $\dfrac{(3u-2v)^{2/3}}{\sqrt{(3u-2v)^3}} = \dfrac{(3u-2v)^{2/3}}{(3u-2v)^{3/2}} = (3u-2v)^{2/3-3/2}$

$\qquad\qquad = (3u-2v)^{4/6-9/6}$

$\qquad\qquad = (3u-2v)^{-5/6}$

$\qquad\qquad = \dfrac{1}{(3u-2v)^{5/6}}$

117. $\sqrt{73} \approx 8.5440$

Scientific: 73 $\boxed{\sqrt{\;}}$

Graphing: $\boxed{\sqrt{\;}}$ 73 $\boxed{\text{ENTER}}$

119. $315^{2/5} = \left(\sqrt[5]{315}\right)^2 \approx 9.9845$

Scientific: 315 $\boxed{y^x}$ $\boxed{(}$ 2 $\boxed{\div}$ 5 $\boxed{)}$ $\boxed{=}$

Graphing: 315 $\boxed{\wedge}$ $\boxed{(}$ 2 $\boxed{\div}$ 5 $\boxed{)}$ $\boxed{\text{ENTER}}$

121. $1698^{-3/4} \approx 0.0038$

Scientific: 1698 $\boxed{y^x}$ $\boxed{(}$ 3 $\boxed{\div}$ 4 $\boxed{+/-}$ $\boxed{)}$ $\boxed{=}$

Graphing: 1698 $\boxed{\wedge}$ $\boxed{(}$ $\boxed{(-)}$ 3 $\boxed{\div}$ 4 $\boxed{)}$ $\boxed{\text{ENTER}}$

123. $\sqrt[4]{342} \approx 4.3004$

$\quad\sqrt[4]{342} = 342^{1/4}$

Scientific: 342 $\boxed{y^x}$ $\boxed{(}$ 1 $\boxed{\div}$ 4 $\boxed{)}$ $\boxed{=}$

Graphing: 342 $\boxed{\wedge}$ $\boxed{(}$ 1 $\boxed{\div}$ 4 $\boxed{)}$ $\boxed{\text{ENTER}}$

125. $\sqrt[3]{545^2} \approx 66.7213$

$\quad\sqrt[3]{545^2} = 545^{2/3}$

Scientific: 545 $\boxed{y^x}$ $\boxed{(}$ 2 $\boxed{\div}$ 3 $\boxed{)}$ $\boxed{=}$

Graphing: 545 $\boxed{\wedge}$ $\boxed{(}$ 2 $\boxed{\div}$ 3 $\boxed{)}$ $\boxed{\text{ENTER}}$

127. $\dfrac{8-\sqrt{35}}{2} \approx 1.0420$

Scientific: $\boxed{(}$ 8 $\boxed{-}$ 35 $\boxed{\sqrt{\;}}$ $\boxed{)}$ $\boxed{\div}$ 2 $\boxed{=}$

Graphing: $\boxed{(}$ 8 $\boxed{-}$ $\boxed{\sqrt{\;}}$ 35 $\boxed{)}$ $\boxed{\div}$ 2 $\boxed{\text{ENTER}}$

129. $\dfrac{3+\sqrt{17}}{9} \approx 0.7915$

Scientific: $\boxed{(}$ 3 $\boxed{+}$ 17 $\boxed{\sqrt{\;}}$ $\boxed{)}$ $\boxed{\div}$ 9 $\boxed{=}$

Graphing: $\boxed{(}$ 3 $\boxed{+}$ $\boxed{\sqrt{\;}}$ 17 $\boxed{)}$ $\boxed{\div}$ 9 $\boxed{\text{ENTER}}$

131. $f(x) = 3\sqrt{x}$, $x \geq 0$,

Domain $= [0, \infty)$

133. The domain of $g(x) = \dfrac{2}{\sqrt[4]{x}}$ is the set of all nonnegative real numbers or $(0, \infty)$.

135. $f(x) = \sqrt{-x}$, $-x \geq 0$

              $x \leq 0$

Domain $= (-\infty, 0]$

137. *Keystrokes:*

[Y=] 5 [÷] 4 [MATH 5] [X,T,θ] [MATH 3] [GRAPH]

Domain is $(0, \infty)$ so graphing utility did complete the graph.

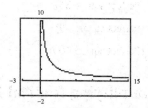

139. *Keystrokes:*

[Y=] 2 [X,T,θ] [^] [(] 3 [÷] 5 [)] [GRAPH]

Domain is $(-\infty, \infty)$ so graphing utility did complete the graph.

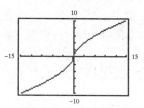

141. $x^{1/2}(2x - 3) = 2x^{3/2} - 3x^{1/2}$

143. $y^{-1/3}(y^{1/3} + 5y^{4/3}) = y^0 + 5y^{3/3}$

                           $= 1 + 5y$

145. $r = 1 - \left(\dfrac{25{,}000}{75{,}000}\right)^{1/8}$

   $= 1 - \left(\dfrac{1}{3}\right)^{1/8}$

   $\approx 0.128 \approx 12.8\%$

147. *Verbal Model:*   [Area] $=$ [side] $\cdot$ [side]

     Labels: Area $= 529$

                side $= x$

     Equation: $529 = x \cdot x$

                  $529 = x^2$

                $\sqrt{529} = x$

                   $23 = x$

     23 feet $\times$ 23 feet

149. $d = \sqrt{l^2 + w^2 + h^2}$

   $= \sqrt{9^2 + 5^2 + 2^2}$

   $= \sqrt{81 + 25 + 4}$

   $= \sqrt{110}$

   ≈ 10.49 cm

151. (a) $r = \sqrt{\dfrac{2v}{\pi l}}$

        $r = \sqrt{\dfrac{2(35{,}350)}{\pi(100)}}$

        $r \approx 15$ feet

   (b) $h = \sqrt{r^2 - \left(\dfrac{a}{2}\right)^2}$

        $h = \sqrt{15^2 - \left(\dfrac{a}{2}\right)^2}$

   (c) $h = \sqrt{15^2 - \left(\dfrac{25}{2}\right)^2}$

        $h = \sqrt{225 - 156.25}$

        $h = \sqrt{68.75}$

        $h \approx 8.29$ feet

   (d) $a = 2\sqrt{r^2 - h^2}$

        $a = 2\sqrt{15^2 - 8^2}$

        $= 2\sqrt{225 - 64}$

        $= 2\sqrt{161}$

        ≈ 25.38 feet

153. Given $\sqrt[n]{a}$, a is the radicand and n is the index.

155. No. $\sqrt{2}$ is an irrational number. Its decimal representation is a nonterminating, nonrepeating decimal.

157. (a) "Last digits:" 1 (Perfect square 81)

4 (Perfect square 64)

5 (Perfect square 25)

6 (Perfect square 36)

9 (Perfect square 49)

0 (Perfect square 100)

(b) Yes, 4,322,788,986 ends in a 6, but it is not a perfect square.

Section 5.2   Simplifying Radical Expressions

1. $\sqrt{20} = \sqrt{4 \cdot 5} = \sqrt{2^2 \cdot 5} = 2\sqrt{5}$

3. $\sqrt{50} = \sqrt{25 \cdot 2} = \sqrt{5^2 \cdot 2} = 5\sqrt{2}$

5. $\sqrt{96} = \sqrt{16 \cdot 6} = \sqrt{4^2 \cdot 6} = 4\sqrt{6}$

7. $\sqrt{216} = \sqrt{36 \cdot 6} = \sqrt{6^2 \cdot 6} = 6\sqrt{6}$

9. $\sqrt{1183} = \sqrt{169 \cdot 7} = \sqrt{13^2 \cdot 7} = 13\sqrt{7}$

11. $\sqrt{0.04} = \sqrt{4 \cdot 0.01} = \sqrt{4}\sqrt{0.01} = 2 \cdot 0.1 = 0.2$

13. $\sqrt{0.0072} = \sqrt{36 \cdot 2 \cdot 0.0001}$
$= \sqrt{36} \cdot \sqrt{2} \cdot \sqrt{0.0001}$
$= 6 \cdot 0.01\sqrt{2}$
$= 0.06\sqrt{2}$

15. $\sqrt{2.42} = \sqrt{121 \cdot 2 \cdot 0.01}$
$= \sqrt{121} \cdot \sqrt{2} \cdot \sqrt{0.01}$
$= 11 \cdot 0.1\sqrt{2}$
$= 1.1\sqrt{2}$

17. $\sqrt{\dfrac{15}{4}} = \dfrac{\sqrt{15}}{2}$

19. $\sqrt{\dfrac{13}{25}} = \dfrac{\sqrt{13}}{5}$

21. $\sqrt{9x^5} = \sqrt{3^2 x^4 \cdot x}$
$= 3 \cdot x^2 \cdot \sqrt{x}$
$= 3x^2\sqrt{x}$

23. $\sqrt{48y^4} = \sqrt{16 \cdot 3 \cdot y^4} = 4y^2\sqrt{3}$

25. $\sqrt{117y^6} = \sqrt{9 \cdot 13 \cdot y^6} = 3|y^3|\sqrt{13}$

27. $\sqrt{120x^2y^3} = \sqrt{4 \cdot 30 \cdot x^2 \cdot y^2 \cdot y} = 2|x|y\sqrt{30y}$

29. $\sqrt{192a^5b^7} = \sqrt{64 \cdot 3 \cdot a^4 \cdot a \cdot b^6 \cdot b}$
$= 8a^2b^3\sqrt{3ab}$

31. $\sqrt[3]{48} = \sqrt[3]{16 \cdot 3} = \sqrt[3]{2^4 \cdot 3} = 2\sqrt[3]{3 \cdot 2} = 2\sqrt[3]{6}$

33. $\sqrt[3]{112} = \sqrt[3]{8 \cdot 14}$
$= \sqrt[3]{8} \cdot \sqrt[3]{14}$
$= 2\sqrt[3]{14}$

35. $\sqrt[3]{40x^5} = \sqrt[3]{8 \cdot 5 \cdot x^3 \cdot x^2}$
$= 2x\sqrt[3]{5x^2}$

37. $\sqrt[4]{324y^6} = \sqrt[4]{81 \cdot 4 \cdot y^4 \cdot y^2}$
$= 3|y|\sqrt[4]{4y^2}$
$= 3|y|\sqrt[4]{2^2y^2}$
$= 3|y|\sqrt{2y}$

39. $\sqrt[3]{x^4y^3} = \sqrt[3]{x^3 \cdot x \cdot y^3} = xy\sqrt[3]{x}$

41. $\sqrt[4]{3x^4y^2} = \sqrt[4]{x^4} \cdot \sqrt[4]{3y^2}$
$= |x|\sqrt[4]{3y^2}$

43. $\sqrt[5]{32x^5y^6} = \sqrt[5]{2^5 \cdot x^5 \cdot y^5 \cdot y} = 2xy\sqrt[5]{y}$

45. $\sqrt[3]{\dfrac{35}{64}} = \dfrac{\sqrt[3]{35}}{4}$

47. $\sqrt[5]{\dfrac{15}{243}} = \dfrac{\sqrt[5]{15}}{3}$

49. $\sqrt[5]{\dfrac{32x^2}{y^5}} = \sqrt[5]{\dfrac{2^5 x^2}{y^5}}$

$\qquad\qquad = \dfrac{2}{y}\sqrt[5]{x^2}$

51. $\sqrt[3]{\dfrac{54a^4}{b^9}} = \sqrt[3]{\dfrac{3^3 \cdot 2 \cdot a^3 \cdot a}{b^9}} = \dfrac{3a}{b^3}\sqrt[3]{2a}$

53. $\sqrt{\dfrac{32a^4}{b^2}} = \dfrac{\sqrt{16 \cdot 2 \cdot a^4}}{\sqrt{b^2}} = \dfrac{4a^2\sqrt{2}}{|b|}$

55. $\sqrt[4]{(3x^2)^4} = 3x^2$

57. $\sqrt{\dfrac{1}{3}} = \dfrac{1}{\sqrt{3}} \cdot \dfrac{\sqrt{3}}{\sqrt{3}} = \dfrac{\sqrt{3}}{3}$

59. $\dfrac{1}{\sqrt{7}} = \dfrac{1}{\sqrt{7}} \cdot \dfrac{\sqrt{7}}{\sqrt{7}} = \dfrac{\sqrt{7}}{7}$

61. $\dfrac{12}{\sqrt{3}} = \dfrac{12}{\sqrt{3}} \cdot \dfrac{\sqrt{3}}{\sqrt{3}} = \dfrac{12\sqrt{3}}{3} = 4\sqrt{3}$

63. $\sqrt[4]{\dfrac{5}{4}} = \dfrac{\sqrt[4]{5}}{\sqrt[4]{2^2}} \cdot \dfrac{\sqrt[4]{2^2}}{\sqrt[4]{2^2}} = \dfrac{\sqrt[4]{5 \cdot 2^2}}{\sqrt[4]{2^4}} = \dfrac{\sqrt[4]{20}}{2}$

65. $\dfrac{6}{\sqrt[3]{32}} = \dfrac{6}{\sqrt[3]{2^3 \cdot 2^2}} = \dfrac{6}{2\sqrt[3]{2^2}} \cdot \dfrac{\sqrt[3]{2}}{\sqrt[3]{2}} = \dfrac{6\sqrt[3]{2}}{2\sqrt[3]{2^3}} = \dfrac{6\sqrt[3]{2}}{4} = \dfrac{3\sqrt[3]{2}}{2}$

67. $\dfrac{1}{\sqrt{y}} = \dfrac{1}{\sqrt{y}} \cdot \dfrac{\sqrt{y}}{\sqrt{y}} = \dfrac{\sqrt{y}}{\sqrt{y^2}} = \dfrac{\sqrt{y}}{y}$

69. $\sqrt{\dfrac{4}{x}} = \dfrac{\sqrt{4}}{\sqrt{x}} = \dfrac{2}{\sqrt{x}} \cdot \dfrac{\sqrt{x}}{\sqrt{x}} = \dfrac{2\sqrt{x}}{x}$

71. $\dfrac{1}{\sqrt{2x}} = \dfrac{1}{\sqrt{2x}} \cdot \dfrac{\sqrt{2x}}{\sqrt{2x}} = \dfrac{\sqrt{2x}}{2x}$

73. $\dfrac{6}{\sqrt{3b^3}} = \dfrac{6}{b\sqrt{3b}} \cdot \dfrac{\sqrt{3b}}{\sqrt{3b}} = \dfrac{6\sqrt{3b}}{3b^2} = \dfrac{2\sqrt{3b}}{b^2}$

75. $\sqrt[3]{\dfrac{2x}{3y}} = \dfrac{\sqrt[3]{2x}}{\sqrt[3]{3y}} \cdot \dfrac{\sqrt[3]{3^2 y^2}}{\sqrt[3]{3^2 y^2}} = \dfrac{\sqrt[3]{2x \cdot 3^2 y^2}}{\sqrt[3]{3^3 y^3}} = \dfrac{\sqrt[3]{18xy^2}}{3y}$

77. $\dfrac{a^3}{\sqrt[3]{ab^2}} = \dfrac{a^3}{\sqrt[3]{ab^2}} \cdot \dfrac{\sqrt[3]{a^2 b}}{\sqrt[3]{a^2 b}} = \dfrac{a^3\sqrt[3]{a^2 b}}{\sqrt[3]{a^3 b^3}} = \dfrac{a^3\sqrt[3]{a^2 b}}{ab} = \dfrac{a^2\sqrt[3]{a^2 b}}{b}$

79. $3\sqrt{2} - \sqrt{2} = 2\sqrt{2}$

81. $12\sqrt{8} - 3\sqrt[3]{8} = 12\sqrt{4 \cdot 2} - 3 \cdot 2 = 24\sqrt{2} - 6$

83. $\sqrt[4]{3} - 5\sqrt[4]{7} - 12\sqrt[4]{3} = -11\sqrt[4]{3} - 5\sqrt[4]{7}$

85. $2\sqrt[3]{54} + 12\sqrt[3]{16} = 2\sqrt[3]{27 \cdot 2} + 12\sqrt[3]{8 \cdot 2}$
$\qquad\qquad = 6\sqrt[3]{2} + 24\sqrt[3]{2} = 30\sqrt[3]{2}$

87. $5\sqrt{9x} - 3\sqrt{x} = 15\sqrt{x} - 3\sqrt{x} = 12\sqrt{x}$

89. $\sqrt{25y} + \sqrt{64y} = 5\sqrt{y} + 8\sqrt{y} = 13\sqrt{y}$

91. $10\sqrt[3]{z} - \sqrt[3]{z^4} = 10\sqrt[3]{z} - \sqrt[3]{z^3 \cdot z} = 10\sqrt[3]{z} - z\sqrt[3]{z}$
$\qquad\qquad\qquad = (10 - z)\sqrt[3]{z}$

93. $\sqrt{5} - \dfrac{3}{\sqrt{5}} = \sqrt{5} - \left(\dfrac{3}{\sqrt{5}} \cdot \dfrac{\sqrt{5}}{\sqrt{5}}\right) = \sqrt{5} - \dfrac{3\sqrt{5}}{5}$

$\qquad\qquad = \left(1 - \dfrac{3}{5}\right)\sqrt{5}$

$\qquad\qquad = \dfrac{2}{5}\sqrt{5}$

95. $\sqrt{20} - \sqrt{\dfrac{1}{5}} = \sqrt{4 \cdot 5} - \sqrt{\dfrac{1}{5}} \cdot \dfrac{\sqrt{5}}{\sqrt{5}} = 2\sqrt{5} - \dfrac{\sqrt{5}}{5}$

$\qquad\qquad = \left(2 - \dfrac{1}{5}\right)\sqrt{5}$

$\qquad\qquad = \dfrac{9}{5}\sqrt{5}$

97. $\sqrt{2x} - \dfrac{3}{\sqrt{2x}} = \sqrt{2x} - \left(\dfrac{3}{\sqrt{2x}} \cdot \dfrac{\sqrt{2x}}{\sqrt{2x}}\right) = \sqrt{2x} - \dfrac{3\sqrt{2x}}{2x}$

$\qquad\qquad = \dfrac{2x\sqrt{2x}}{2x} - \dfrac{3\sqrt{2x}}{2x}$

$\qquad\qquad = \dfrac{2x\sqrt{2x} - 3\sqrt{2x}}{2x}$

$\qquad\qquad = \dfrac{\sqrt{2x}(2x - 3)}{2x}$

99. $\sqrt{7} + \sqrt{18} > \sqrt{7 + 18}$

101. $5 > \sqrt{3^2 + 2^2}$

103. $c = \sqrt{a^2 + b^2}$

$= \sqrt{6^2 + 3^2}$

$= \sqrt{36 + 9} = \sqrt{45} = \sqrt{9 \cdot 5} = 3\sqrt{5}$

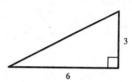

105. $c = \sqrt{a^2 + b^2}$

$= \sqrt{9^2 + 6^2}$

$= \sqrt{81 + 36}$

$= \sqrt{117}$

$= 3\sqrt{13}$

107. (a) $c = \sqrt{a^2 + b^2}$

$c = \sqrt{(15)^2 + (5)^2}$

$c = \sqrt{225 + 25}$

$c = \sqrt{250}$

$c = \sqrt{25 \cdot 10}$

$c = 5\sqrt{10}$

(b) Area of roof $= 2 \cdot$ Length $\cdot$ Width

$A = 2 \cdot 40 \cdot 5\sqrt{10}$

$A = 400\sqrt{10}$

Thus, the total area of the roof is $400\sqrt{10} \approx 1264.9$ square feet.

109. $f = \dfrac{1}{100}\sqrt{\dfrac{400 \times 10^6}{5}} \approx 8.9443 \times 10^1 \approx 89.443 \approx 89.44$ cycles per second

111. (a)

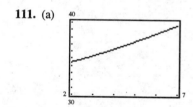

(b)

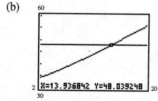

The average salary will reach \$48,000 after 14 years so $1990 + 14 = 2004$.

113. $\left(\dfrac{5}{\sqrt{3}}\right)^2 = \dfrac{5}{\sqrt{3}} \cdot \dfrac{5}{\sqrt{3}} = \dfrac{25}{3}$

No. When you rationalize the denominator, the value of the number is not changed.

$\dfrac{5}{\sqrt{3}} = \dfrac{5}{\sqrt{3}} \cdot \dfrac{\sqrt{3}}{\sqrt{3}} = \dfrac{5\sqrt{3}}{3} \neq \dfrac{25}{3}$

115. Example: $\sqrt{6} \cdot \sqrt{15} = \sqrt{6 \cdot 15} = \sqrt{3 \cdot 2 \cdot 3 \cdot 5} = 3\sqrt{10}$

117. $\sqrt{2} + \sqrt{18}$ is not in simplest form because $\sqrt{18}$ can be simplified to $3\sqrt{2}$ and then added to $\sqrt{2}$.

$\sqrt{2} + \sqrt{18} = \sqrt{2} + 3\sqrt{2} = 4\sqrt{2}$

119. $\sqrt{x^2} \neq x$ for all negative values of x.

Example: $\sqrt{(-8)^2} = \sqrt{64} = 8$

Section 5.3   Multiplying and Dividing Radical Expressions

1. $\sqrt{2} \cdot \sqrt{8} = \sqrt{2 \cdot 8}$
$= \sqrt{16}$
$= 4$

3. $\sqrt{3} \cdot \sqrt{6} = \sqrt{3 \cdot 6}$
$= \sqrt{18}$
$= \sqrt{9 \cdot 2}$
$= 3\sqrt{2}$

5. $\sqrt[3]{12} \cdot \sqrt[3]{6} = \sqrt[3]{12 \cdot 6}$
$= \sqrt[3]{8 \cdot 9}$
$= 2\sqrt[3]{9}$

7. $\sqrt[4]{8} \cdot \sqrt[4]{6} = \sqrt[4]{8 \cdot 6} = \sqrt[4]{2^4 \cdot 3}$
$= 2\sqrt[4]{3}$

9. $\sqrt{5}\left(2 - \sqrt{3}\right) = 2\sqrt{5} - \sqrt{5}\sqrt{3} = 2\sqrt{5} - \sqrt{15}$

11. $\sqrt{2}\left(\sqrt{20} + 8\right) = \sqrt{2}\sqrt{20} + 8\sqrt{2}$
$= \sqrt{40} + 8\sqrt{2}$
$= 2\sqrt{10} + 8\sqrt{2}$

13. $\sqrt{6}\left(\sqrt{12} - \sqrt{3}\right) = \sqrt{6}\sqrt{12} - \sqrt{6}\sqrt{3}$
$= \sqrt{72} - \sqrt{18}$
$= \sqrt{36 \cdot 2} - \sqrt{9 \cdot 2}$
$= 6\sqrt{2} - 3\sqrt{2}$
$= 3\sqrt{2}$

15. $\sqrt{2}\left(\sqrt{18} - \sqrt{10}\right) = \sqrt{2}\sqrt{18} - \sqrt{2}\sqrt{10}$
$= \sqrt{36} - \sqrt{20}$
$= 6 - \sqrt{4 \cdot 5}$
$= 6 - 2\sqrt{5}$

17. $\sqrt{y}\left(\sqrt{y} + 4\right) = \left(\sqrt{y}\right)^2 + 4\sqrt{y}$
$= y + 4\sqrt{y}$

19. $\sqrt{a}\left(4 - \sqrt{a}\right) = \sqrt{a} \cdot 4 - \sqrt{a}\sqrt{a}$
$= 4\sqrt{a} - a$

21. $\sqrt[3]{4}\left(\sqrt[3]{2} - 7\right) = \sqrt[3]{4}\sqrt[3]{2} - 7\sqrt[3]{4}$
$= \sqrt[3]{8} - 7\sqrt[3]{4}$
$= 2 - 7\sqrt[3]{4}$

23. $\left(\sqrt{3} + 2\right)\left(\sqrt{3} - 2\right) = \left(\sqrt{3}\right)^2 - 2^2$
$= 3 - 4$
$= -1$

25. $\left(\sqrt{5} + 3\right)\left(\sqrt{3} - 5\right) = \sqrt{15} - 5\sqrt{5} + 3\sqrt{3} - 15$

27. $\left(\sqrt{20} + 2\right)^2 = \left(\sqrt{20}\right)^2 + 2 \cdot \sqrt{20} \cdot 2 + 2^2$
$= 20 + 4\sqrt{20} + 4$
$= 24 + 4\sqrt{4 \cdot 5}$
$= 24 + 8\sqrt{5}$

29. $\left(\sqrt[3]{6} - 3\right)\left(\sqrt[3]{4} + 3\right) = \sqrt[3]{6}\sqrt[3]{4} + 3\sqrt[3]{6} - 3\sqrt[3]{4} - 9$
$= \sqrt[3]{24} + 3\sqrt[3]{6} - 3\sqrt[3]{4} - 9$
$= \sqrt[3]{8 \cdot 3} + 3\sqrt[3]{6} - 3\sqrt[3]{4} - 9$
$= 2\sqrt[3]{3} + 3\sqrt[3]{6} - 3\sqrt[3]{4} - 9$

31. $\left(10 + \sqrt{2x}\right)^2 = 10^2 + 2 \cdot 10 \cdot \sqrt{2x} + \left(\sqrt{2x}\right)^2$
$= 100 + 20\sqrt{2x} + 2x$

33. $\left(9\sqrt{x} + 2\right)\left(5\sqrt{x} - 3\right) = \left(9\sqrt{x}\right)\left(5\sqrt{x}\right) - 27\sqrt{x} + 10\sqrt{x} - 6$
$= 45x - 17\sqrt{x} - 6$

35. $\left(3\sqrt{x} - 5\right)\left(3\sqrt{x} + 5\right) = \left(3\sqrt{x}\right)^2 - 5^2$
$= 9x - 25$

37. $\left(\sqrt[3]{2x} + 5\right)^2 = \left(\sqrt[3]{2x}\right)^2 + 2 \cdot 5\sqrt[3]{2x} + 5^2$
$= \sqrt[3]{(2x)^2} + 10\sqrt[3]{2x} + 25$
$= \sqrt[3]{4x^2} + 10\sqrt[3]{2x} + 25$

39. $\left(\sqrt[3]{y} + 2\right)\left(\sqrt[3]{y^2} - 5\right) = \sqrt[3]{y} \cdot \sqrt[3]{y^2} - 5\sqrt[3]{y} + 2\sqrt[3]{y^2} - 10$

$\qquad = \sqrt[3]{y^3} - 5\sqrt[3]{y} + 2\sqrt[3]{y^2} - 10$

$\qquad = y - 5\sqrt[3]{y} + 2\sqrt[3]{y^2} - 10$

41. $\left(\sqrt[3]{t} + 1\right)\left(\sqrt[3]{t^2} + 4\sqrt[3]{t} - 3\right) = \sqrt[3]{t}\sqrt[3]{t^2} + \sqrt[3]{t} \cdot 4\sqrt[3]{t} - 3\sqrt[3]{t} + \sqrt[3]{t^2} + 4\sqrt[3]{t} - 3$

$\qquad = \sqrt[3]{t^3} + 4\sqrt[3]{t^2} - 3\sqrt[3]{t} + \sqrt[3]{t^2} + 4\sqrt[3]{t} - 3$

$\qquad = t + 5\sqrt[3]{t^2} + \sqrt[3]{t} - 3$

43. $5x\sqrt{3} + 15\sqrt{3} = 5\sqrt{3}(x + 3)$

45. $4\sqrt{12} - 2x\sqrt{27} = 4\sqrt{4 \cdot 3} - 2x\sqrt{9 \cdot 3}$

$\qquad = 8\sqrt{3} - 6x\sqrt{3}$

$\qquad = 2\sqrt{3}(4 - 3x)$

47. $6u^2 + \sqrt{18u^3} = 6u^2 + \sqrt{9 \cdot 2u^2 \cdot u}$

$\qquad = 6u^2 + 3u\sqrt{2u}$

$\qquad = 3u\left(2u + \sqrt{2u}\right)$

49. $2 + \sqrt{5}$, conjugate $= 2 - \sqrt{5}$

$\qquad$ product $= \left(2 + \sqrt{5}\right)\left(2 - \sqrt{5}\right)$

$\qquad = 2^2 - \left(\sqrt{5}\right)^2$

$\qquad = 4 - 5 = -1$

51. $\sqrt{11} - \sqrt{3}$, conjugate $= \sqrt{11} + \sqrt{3}$

$\qquad$ product $= \left(\sqrt{11} - \sqrt{3}\right)\left(\sqrt{11} + \sqrt{3}\right)$

$\qquad = \left(\sqrt{11}\right)^2 - \left(\sqrt{3}\right)^2$

$\qquad = 11 - 3 = 8$

53. $\sqrt{15} + 3$,

$\qquad$ conjugate $= \sqrt{15} - 3$

$\qquad$ product $= \left(\sqrt{15} + 3\right)\left(\sqrt{15} - 3\right)$

$\qquad = \sqrt{15} \cdot \sqrt{15} - 3\sqrt{15} + 3\sqrt{15} - 9$

$\qquad = 15 - 9 = 6$

55. $\sqrt{x} - 3$, conjugate $= \sqrt{x} + 3$

$\qquad$ product $= \left(\sqrt{x} - 3\right)\left(\sqrt{x} + 3\right)$

$\qquad = \left(\sqrt{x}\right)^2 - 3^2$

$\qquad = x - 9$

57. $\sqrt{2u} - \sqrt{3}$, conjugate $= \sqrt{2u} + \sqrt{3}$

$\qquad$ product $= \left(\sqrt{2u} - \sqrt{3}\right)\left(\sqrt{2u} + \sqrt{3}\right)$

$\qquad = \left(\sqrt{2u}\right)^2 - \left(\sqrt{3}\right)^2$

$\qquad = 2u - 3$

59. $2\sqrt{2} + \sqrt{4}$, conjugate $= 2\sqrt{2} - \sqrt{4}$

$\qquad$ product $= \left(2\sqrt{2} + \sqrt{4}\right)\left(2\sqrt{2} - \sqrt{4}\right)$

$\qquad = \left(2\sqrt{2}\right)^2 - \left(\sqrt{4}\right)^2$

$\qquad = 4 \cdot 2 - 4$

$\qquad = 8 - 4 = 4$

61. $\sqrt{x} + \sqrt{y}$, conjugate $= \sqrt{x} - \sqrt{y}$

$\qquad$ product $= \left(\sqrt{x} + \sqrt{y}\right)\left(\sqrt{x} - \sqrt{y}\right)$

$\qquad = \left(\sqrt{x}\right)^2 - \left(\sqrt{y}\right)^2$

$\qquad = x - y$

63. $\dfrac{4 - 8\sqrt{x}}{12} = \dfrac{4\left(1 - 2\sqrt{x}\right)}{12}$

$\qquad = \dfrac{1 - 2\sqrt{x}}{3}$

65. $\dfrac{-2y + \sqrt{12y^3}}{8y} = \dfrac{-2y + 2y\sqrt{3y}}{8y}$

$\qquad = \dfrac{2y\left(-1 + \sqrt{3y}\right)}{8y}$

$\qquad = \dfrac{-1 + \sqrt{3y}}{4}$

67. (a) $f(2 - \sqrt{3}) = (2 - \sqrt{3})^2 - 6(2 - \sqrt{3}) + 1$

$\qquad = 4 - 4\sqrt{3} + 3 - 12 + 6\sqrt{3} + 1$

$\qquad = 2\sqrt{3} - 4$

(b) $f(3 - 2\sqrt{2}) = (3 - 2\sqrt{2})^2 - 6(3 - 2\sqrt{2}) + 1$

$\qquad = 9 - 12\sqrt{2} + 8 - 18 + 12\sqrt{2} + 1$

$\qquad = 0$

69. (a) $f(1 + \sqrt{2}) = (1 + \sqrt{2})^2 - 2(1 + \sqrt{2}) - 1$

$\qquad = 1 + 2\sqrt{2} + 2 - 2 - 2\sqrt{2} - 1$

$\qquad = 0$

(b) $f(\sqrt{4}) = (\sqrt{4})^2 - 2\sqrt{4} - 1$

$\qquad = 4 - 4 - 1$

$\qquad = -1$

71. $\dfrac{6}{\sqrt{2} - 2} = \dfrac{6}{\sqrt{2} - 2} \cdot \dfrac{\sqrt{2} + 2}{\sqrt{2} + 2} = \dfrac{6(\sqrt{2} + 2)}{(\sqrt{2})^2 - 2^2} = \dfrac{6(\sqrt{2} + 2)}{2 - 4} = \dfrac{6(\sqrt{2} + 2)}{-2} = -3(\sqrt{2} + 2)$

73. $\dfrac{7}{\sqrt{3} + 5} = \dfrac{7}{\sqrt{3} + 5} \cdot \dfrac{\sqrt{3} - 5}{\sqrt{3} - 5} = \dfrac{7(\sqrt{3} - 5)}{(\sqrt{3})^2 - 5^2} = \dfrac{7(\sqrt{3} - 5)}{3 - 25} = \dfrac{7(\sqrt{3} - 5)}{-22} = \dfrac{7(5 - \sqrt{3})}{22}$

75. $\dfrac{3}{2\sqrt{10} - 5} = \dfrac{3}{2\sqrt{10} - 5} \cdot \dfrac{2\sqrt{10} + 5}{2\sqrt{10} + 5}$

$\qquad = \dfrac{3(2\sqrt{10} + 5)}{(2\sqrt{10})^2 - 5^2}$

$\qquad = \dfrac{3(2\sqrt{10} + 5)}{40 - 25}$

$\qquad = \dfrac{3(2\sqrt{10} + 5)}{15}$

$\qquad = \dfrac{2\sqrt{10} + 5}{5}$

77. $\dfrac{2}{\sqrt{6} + \sqrt{2}} = \dfrac{2}{\sqrt{6} + \sqrt{2}} \cdot \dfrac{\sqrt{6} - \sqrt{2}}{\sqrt{6} - \sqrt{2}} = \dfrac{2(\sqrt{6} - \sqrt{2})}{6 - 2}$

$\qquad = \dfrac{2(\sqrt{6} - \sqrt{2})}{4}$

$\qquad = \dfrac{\sqrt{6} - \sqrt{2}}{2}$

79. $\dfrac{9}{\sqrt{3} - \sqrt{7}} = \dfrac{9}{\sqrt{3} - \sqrt{7}} \cdot \dfrac{\sqrt{3} + \sqrt{7}}{\sqrt{3} + \sqrt{7}} = \dfrac{9(\sqrt{3} + \sqrt{7})}{(\sqrt{3})^2 - (\sqrt{7})^2} = \dfrac{9(\sqrt{3} + \sqrt{7})}{3 - 7} = \dfrac{9(\sqrt{3} + \sqrt{7})}{-4} = \dfrac{-9(\sqrt{3} + \sqrt{7})}{4}$

81. $(\sqrt{7} + 2) \div (\sqrt{7} - 2) = \dfrac{\sqrt{7} + 2}{\sqrt{7} - 2} \cdot \dfrac{\sqrt{7} + 2}{\sqrt{7} + 2} = \dfrac{(\sqrt{7})^2 + 2\sqrt{7} + 2\sqrt{7} + 4}{(\sqrt{7})^2 - 2^2} = \dfrac{7 + 4\sqrt{7} + 4}{7 - 4} = \dfrac{11 + 4\sqrt{7}}{3}$

83. $(\sqrt{x} - 5) \div (2\sqrt{x} - 1) = \dfrac{\sqrt{x} - 5}{2\sqrt{x} - 1} \cdot \dfrac{2\sqrt{x} + 1}{2\sqrt{x} + 1} = \dfrac{2x + \sqrt{x} - 10\sqrt{x} - 5}{(2\sqrt{x})^2 - 1^2} = \dfrac{2x - 9\sqrt{x} - 5}{4x - 1}$

85. $\dfrac{3x}{\sqrt{15} - \sqrt{3}} = \dfrac{3x}{\sqrt{15} - \sqrt{3}} \cdot \dfrac{\sqrt{15} + \sqrt{3}}{\sqrt{15} + \sqrt{3}} = \dfrac{3x(\sqrt{15} + \sqrt{3})}{(\sqrt{15})^2 - (\sqrt{3})^2} = \dfrac{3x(\sqrt{15} + \sqrt{3})}{15 - 3}$

$\qquad = \dfrac{3x(\sqrt{15} + \sqrt{3})}{12} = \dfrac{x\sqrt{15} + x\sqrt{3}}{4}$

87. $\dfrac{2t^2}{\sqrt{5} - \sqrt{t}} = \dfrac{2t^2}{\sqrt{5} - \sqrt{t}} \cdot \dfrac{\sqrt{5} + \sqrt{t}}{\sqrt{5} + \sqrt{t}} = \dfrac{2t^2(\sqrt{5} + \sqrt{t})}{(\sqrt{5})^2 - (\sqrt{t})^2} = \dfrac{2t^2(\sqrt{5} + \sqrt{t})}{5 - t} = \dfrac{2t^2(\sqrt{5} + \sqrt{t})}{5 - t}$

89. $\dfrac{8a}{\sqrt{3a} + \sqrt{a}} = \dfrac{8a}{\sqrt{3a} + \sqrt{a}} \cdot \dfrac{\sqrt{3a} - \sqrt{a}}{\sqrt{3a} - \sqrt{a}} = \dfrac{8a(\sqrt{3a} - \sqrt{a})}{(\sqrt{3a})^2 - (\sqrt{a})^2} = \dfrac{8a(\sqrt{3a} - \sqrt{a})}{3a - a} = \dfrac{8a(\sqrt{3a} - \sqrt{a})}{2a} = 4(\sqrt{3a} - \sqrt{a})$

91. $\dfrac{3(x-4)}{x^2-\sqrt{x}} = \dfrac{3(x-4)}{x^2-\sqrt{x}} \cdot \dfrac{x^2+\sqrt{x}}{x^2+\sqrt{x}} = \dfrac{3(x-4)(x^2+\sqrt{x})}{(x^2)^2-(\sqrt{x})^2} = \dfrac{3(x-4)(x^2+\sqrt{x})}{x^4-x}$

$\qquad = \dfrac{3(x-4)(x^2+\sqrt{x})}{x(x^3-1)} = \dfrac{3(x-4)(x^2+\sqrt{x})}{x(x-1)(x^2+x+1)}$

93. $\dfrac{\sqrt{u+v}}{\sqrt{u-v}-\sqrt{u}} = \dfrac{\sqrt{u+v}}{\sqrt{u-v}-\sqrt{u}} \cdot \dfrac{\sqrt{u-v}+\sqrt{u}}{\sqrt{u-v}+\sqrt{u}} = \dfrac{\sqrt{u+v}\left(\sqrt{u-v}+\sqrt{u}\right)}{u-v-u}$

$\qquad = \dfrac{\sqrt{u+v}\left(\sqrt{u-v}+\sqrt{u}\right)}{-v} = \dfrac{-\sqrt{u+v}\left(\sqrt{u-v}+\sqrt{u}\right)}{v}$

95. *Keystrokes:*

y_1 [Y=] 10 ÷ (([√] [X,T,θ] [+] 1) [ENTER]

y_2 (10 ([√] [X,T,θ] [−] 1)) ÷ (([X,T,θ] [−] 1) [GRAPH]

$y_1 = y_2$, except at $x = 1$

$\dfrac{10}{\sqrt{x}+1} = \dfrac{10}{\sqrt{x}+1} \cdot \dfrac{\sqrt{x}-1}{\sqrt{x}-1} = \dfrac{10(\sqrt{x}-1)}{x-1},\ x \neq 1$

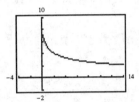

97. *Keystrokes:*

y_1 [Y=] 2 [√] [X,T,θ] ÷ (2 [−] [√] [X,T,θ]) [ENTER]

y_2 2 (2 [√] [X,T,θ] [+] [X,T,θ]) ÷ ((4 [−] [X,T,θ]) [GRAPH]

$y_1 = y_2$

$\dfrac{2\sqrt{x}}{2-\sqrt{x}} = \dfrac{2\sqrt{x}}{2-\sqrt{x}} \cdot \dfrac{2+\sqrt{x}}{2+\sqrt{x}}$

$\qquad = \dfrac{2\sqrt{x}(2+\sqrt{x})}{2^2-(\sqrt{x})^2}$

$\qquad = \dfrac{2\sqrt{x}(2+\sqrt{x})}{4-x}$

$\qquad = \dfrac{2(2\sqrt{x}+x)}{4-x}$

99. $\dfrac{\sqrt{2}}{7} = \dfrac{\sqrt{2}}{7} \cdot \dfrac{\sqrt{2}}{\sqrt{2}} = \dfrac{2}{7\sqrt{2}}$

101. $\dfrac{\sqrt{7}+\sqrt{3}}{5} = \dfrac{\sqrt{7}+\sqrt{3}}{5} \cdot \dfrac{\sqrt{7}-\sqrt{3}}{\sqrt{7}-\sqrt{3}}$

$\qquad = \dfrac{(\sqrt{7})^2 - (\sqrt{3})^2}{5(\sqrt{7}-\sqrt{3})}$

$\qquad = \dfrac{7-3}{5(\sqrt{7}-\sqrt{3})}$

$\qquad = \dfrac{4}{5(\sqrt{7}-\sqrt{3})}$

103. Area $= h \cdot w$

$\qquad = \sqrt{24^2 - (8\sqrt{3})^2} \cdot 8\sqrt{3}$

$\qquad = \sqrt{576 - 192} \cdot 8\sqrt{3}$

$\qquad = \sqrt{384} \cdot 8\sqrt{3}$

$\qquad = 8\sqrt{1152}$

$\qquad = 8\sqrt{2^7 \cdot 3^2}$

$\qquad = 8 \cdot 2^3 \cdot 3\sqrt{2}$

$\qquad = 192\sqrt{2}$ square inches

105. $\dfrac{500k}{\dfrac{1}{\sqrt{k^2+1}} + \dfrac{k^2}{\sqrt{k^2+1}}} = \dfrac{500k}{\dfrac{1+k^2}{\sqrt{k^2+1}}}$

$\qquad\qquad\qquad\qquad = \dfrac{500k\sqrt{k^2+1}}{1+k^2}$

107. $\sqrt{3}\left(1-\sqrt{6}\right) = \sqrt{3} - \sqrt{3}\cdot\sqrt{6}$

$\qquad$ Distributive Property

$\qquad = \sqrt{3} - \sqrt{9\cdot2}$

$\qquad$ Multiplication Property of Radicals

$\qquad = \sqrt{3} - 3\sqrt{2}$

$\qquad$ Simplify radicals.

109. $\left(3-\sqrt{2}\right)\left(3+\sqrt{2}\right) = 9 - 2 = 7$

Multilpying the number by its conjugate yields the difference of two squares. Squaring a square root eliminates the radical.

Mid-Chapter Quiz for Chapter 5

1. $\sqrt{225} = 15$ because $15\cdot15 = 225$

2. $\sqrt[4]{\dfrac{81}{16}} = \dfrac{3}{2}$ because $\dfrac{3}{2}\cdot\dfrac{3}{2}\cdot\dfrac{3}{2}\cdot\dfrac{3}{2} = \dfrac{81}{16}$

3. $64^{1/2} = \sqrt{64} = 8$ because $8\cdot8 = 64$

4. $(-27)^{2/3} = \sqrt[3]{(-27)^2} = \left(\sqrt[3]{-27}\right)^2 = (-3)^2 = 9$

5. $\sqrt{27x^2} = \sqrt{9\cdot3\cdot x^2} = 3|x|\sqrt{3}$

6. $\sqrt[4]{81x^6} = \sqrt[4]{81\cdot x^4\cdot x^2} = 3|x|\sqrt[4]{x^2}$

$\qquad\qquad\qquad\qquad\qquad\quad = 3|x|\sqrt{x}$

7. $\sqrt{\dfrac{4u^3}{9}} = \dfrac{\sqrt{4\cdot u^2\cdot u}}{\sqrt{9}} = \dfrac{2|u|\sqrt{u}}{3}$

8. $\sqrt[3]{\dfrac{16}{u^6}} = \dfrac{\sqrt[3]{16}}{\sqrt[3]{u^6}} = \dfrac{\sqrt[3]{16}}{u^2} = \dfrac{\sqrt[3]{8\cdot2}}{u^2} = \dfrac{2\sqrt[3]{2}}{u^2}$

9. $\sqrt{200y} - 3\sqrt{8y} = \sqrt{100\cdot2y} - 3\sqrt{4\cdot2y}$

$\qquad\qquad\qquad\quad = 10\sqrt{2y} - 6\sqrt{2y}$

$\qquad\qquad\qquad\quad = 4\sqrt{2y}$

10. $6x\sqrt[3]{5x^2} + 2\sqrt[3]{40x^4} = 6x\sqrt[3]{5x^2} + 2\sqrt[3]{8\cdot5\cdot x^3\cdot x}$

$\qquad\qquad\qquad\qquad\qquad = 6x\sqrt[3]{5x^2} + 4x\sqrt[3]{5x}$

11. $\sqrt{8}\left(3+\sqrt{32}\right) = 3\sqrt{8} + \sqrt{256}$

$\qquad\qquad\qquad\quad = 3\sqrt{4\cdot2} + \sqrt{2^8}$

$\qquad\qquad\qquad\quad = 6\sqrt{2} + 2^4$

$\qquad\qquad\qquad\quad = 6\sqrt{2} + 16$

12. $\left(\sqrt{50} - 4\right)\sqrt{2} = \sqrt{100} - 4\sqrt{2}$

$\qquad\qquad\qquad\quad = \sqrt{10^2} - 4\sqrt{2}$

$\qquad\qquad\qquad\quad = 10 - 4\sqrt{2}$

13. $\left(\sqrt{6}+3\right)\left(4\sqrt{6}-7\right) = \sqrt{6}\cdot4\sqrt{6} - 7\sqrt{6} + 12\sqrt{6} - 21$

$\qquad\qquad\qquad\qquad\qquad = 24 + 5\sqrt{6} - 21$

$\qquad\qquad\qquad\qquad\qquad = 3 + 5\sqrt{6}$

14. $\left(9+2\sqrt{3}\right)\left(2+7\sqrt{3}\right) = 18 + 63\sqrt{3} + 4\sqrt{3} + 2\sqrt{3}\cdot7\sqrt{3}$

$\qquad\qquad\qquad\qquad\qquad = 18 + 67\sqrt{3} + 14(3)$

$\qquad\qquad\qquad\qquad\qquad = 18 + 67\sqrt{3} + 42$

$\qquad\qquad\qquad\qquad\qquad = 60 + 67\sqrt{3}$

15. $\dfrac{\sqrt{7}}{1+\sqrt{3}} \cdot \dfrac{1-\sqrt{3}}{1-\sqrt{3}} = \dfrac{\sqrt{7}(1-\sqrt{3})}{1-(\sqrt{3})^2} = \dfrac{\sqrt{7}(1-\sqrt{3})}{1-3} = \dfrac{\sqrt{7}(1-\sqrt{3})}{-2}$

$\qquad = \dfrac{\sqrt{7}-\sqrt{21}}{-2} = \dfrac{\sqrt{21}-\sqrt{7}}{2}$

16. $\dfrac{6\sqrt{2}}{2\sqrt{2}-4} \cdot \dfrac{2\sqrt{2}+4}{2\sqrt{2}+4} = \dfrac{6\sqrt{2}(2\sqrt{2}+4)}{(2\sqrt{2})^2-4^2} = \dfrac{12(\sqrt{2})^2+24\sqrt{2}}{8-16}$

$\qquad = \dfrac{24+24\sqrt{2}}{-8} = \dfrac{24(1+\sqrt{2})}{-8} = -3(1+\sqrt{2})$

$\qquad\qquad = -3-3\sqrt{2}$

17. $4 \div (\sqrt{6}+3) = \dfrac{4}{\sqrt{6}+3} \cdot \dfrac{\sqrt{6}-3}{\sqrt{6}-3} = \dfrac{4(\sqrt{6}-3)}{(\sqrt{6})^2-3^2} = \dfrac{4(\sqrt{6}-3)}{6-9}$

$\qquad = \dfrac{4(\sqrt{6}-3)}{-3}$

$\qquad = \dfrac{4}{3}(3-\sqrt{6})$

18. $(4\sqrt{2}-2\sqrt{3}) \div (\sqrt{2}+\sqrt{6}) = \dfrac{4\sqrt{2}-2\sqrt{3}}{\sqrt{2}+\sqrt{6}} \cdot \dfrac{\sqrt{2}-\sqrt{6}}{\sqrt{2}-\sqrt{6}} = \dfrac{4\sqrt{2}\cdot\sqrt{2}-4\sqrt{2}\cdot\sqrt{6}-2\sqrt{3}\cdot\sqrt{2}+2\sqrt{3}\cdot\sqrt{6}}{(\sqrt{2})^2-(\sqrt{6})^2}$

$= \dfrac{4(2)-4\sqrt{12}-2\sqrt{6}+2\sqrt{18}}{2-6} = \dfrac{8-4\sqrt{4\cdot3}-2\sqrt{6}+2\sqrt{9\cdot2}}{-4} = \dfrac{8-8\sqrt{3}-2\sqrt{6}+6\sqrt{2}}{-4}$

$= \dfrac{2(4-4\sqrt{3}-\sqrt{6}+3\sqrt{2})}{-4} = \dfrac{4-4\sqrt{3}-\sqrt{6}+3\sqrt{2}}{-2} = \dfrac{1}{2}(4\sqrt{3}+\sqrt{6}-3\sqrt{2}-4)$

19. $1+\sqrt{4}$, conjugate $= 1-\sqrt{4}$

$\qquad$ product $= (1+\sqrt{4})(1-\sqrt{4})$

$\qquad\qquad = 1^2-(\sqrt{4})^2$

$\qquad\qquad = 1-4$

$\qquad\qquad = -3$

20. $\sqrt{10}-5$, conjugate $= \sqrt{10}+5$

$\qquad$ product $= (\sqrt{10}-5)(\sqrt{10}+5)$

$\qquad\qquad = (\sqrt{10})^2-5^2$

$\qquad\qquad = 10-25$

$\qquad\qquad = -15$

21. $\sqrt{5^2+12^2} = \sqrt{25+144}$

$\qquad = \sqrt{169}$

$\qquad = 13$

$\qquad 13 \neq 17$

$\qquad \sqrt{5^2+12^2} \neq 17$

22. $C = \sqrt{2^2+2^2}$

$\qquad = \sqrt{4+4} = \sqrt{8}$

Equation:

$P = 2(7)+2(4\tfrac{1}{2})+4(\sqrt{8})$

$\qquad = 14+9+8\sqrt{2}$

$\qquad = 23+8\sqrt{2}$ inches

Section 5.4   Solving Radical Equations

1. (a) $x=-4$ $\qquad \sqrt{-4}-10 \neq 0$ $\qquad$ Not a solution

$\quad$ (b) $x=-100$ $\quad \sqrt{-100}-10 \neq 0$ $\quad$ Not a solution

$\quad$ (c) $x=\sqrt{10}$ $\quad \sqrt{\sqrt{10}}-10 \neq 0$ $\quad$ Not a solution

$\quad$ (d) $x=100$ $\qquad \sqrt{100}-10=0$ $\qquad$ A solution

3. (a) $x=-60$ $\qquad \sqrt[3]{-60-4} \neq 4$ $\qquad$ Not a solution

$\quad$ (b) $x=68$ $\qquad \sqrt[3]{68-4}=4$ $\qquad$ A solution

$\quad$ (c) $x=20$ $\qquad \sqrt[3]{20-4} \neq 4$ $\qquad$ Not a solution

$\quad$ (d) $x=0$ $\qquad \sqrt[3]{0-4} \neq 4$ $\qquad$ Not a solution

5. $\sqrt{x} = 20$ **Check:** $\sqrt{400} \overset{?}{=} 20$

$(\sqrt{x})^2 = 20^2$ $20 = 20$

$x = 400$

7. $\sqrt{x} = 3$ **Check:** $\sqrt{9} \overset{?}{=} 3$

$(\sqrt{x})^2 = 3^2$ $3 = 3$

$x = 9$

9. $\sqrt[3]{z} = 3$ **Check:** $\sqrt[3]{27} \overset{?}{=} 3$

$(\sqrt[3]{z})^3 = 3^3$ $3 = 3$

$z = 27$

11. $\sqrt{y} - 7 = 0$ **Check:** $\sqrt{49} - 7 \overset{?}{=} 0$

$\sqrt{y} = 7$ $7 - 7 \overset{?}{=} 0$

$(\sqrt{y})^2 = 7^2$ $0 = 0$

$y = 49$

13. $\sqrt{u} + 13 = 0$ **Check:** $\sqrt{169} + 13 \overset{?}{=} 0$

$\sqrt{u} = -13$ $13 + 13 \ne 0$

$(\sqrt{u})^2 = (-13)^2$ No solution

$u = 169$

15. $\sqrt{x} - 8 = 0$ **Check:** $\sqrt{64} - 8 \overset{?}{=} 0$

$\sqrt{x} = 8$ $8 - 8 \overset{?}{=} 0$

$(\sqrt{x})^2 = 8^2$ $0 = 0$

$x = 64$

17. $\sqrt{10x} = 30$ **Check:** $\sqrt{10 \cdot 90} \overset{?}{=} 30$

$(\sqrt{10x})^2 = 30^2$ $\sqrt{900} \overset{?}{=} 30$

$10x = 900$ $30 = 30$

$x = 90$

19. $\sqrt{-3x} = 9$ **Check:** $\sqrt{-3(-27)} \overset{?}{=} 9$

$(\sqrt{-3x})^2 = 9^2$ $\sqrt{81} \overset{?}{=} 9$

$-3x = 81$ $9 = 9$

$x = -27$

21. $\sqrt{5t} - 2 = 0$ **Check:** $\sqrt{5\left(\frac{4}{5}\right)} - 2 \overset{?}{=} 0$

$\sqrt{5t} = 2$ $\sqrt{4} - 2 \overset{?}{=} 0$

$(\sqrt{5t})^2 = 2^2$ $2 - 2 \overset{?}{=} 0$

$5t = 4$ $0 = 0$

$t = \frac{4}{5}$

23. $\sqrt{3y + 1} = 4$ **Check:** $\sqrt{3(5) + 1} \overset{?}{=} 4$

$(\sqrt{3y + 1})^2 = 4^2$ $\sqrt{16} \overset{?}{=} 4$

$3y + 1 = 16$ $4 = 4$

$3y = 15$

$y = 5$

25. $\sqrt{4 - 5x} = -3$ **Check:** $\sqrt{4 - 5(-1)} \overset{?}{=} -3$

$(\sqrt{4 - 5x})^2 = (-3)^2$ $\sqrt{9} \overset{?}{=} -3$

$4 - 5x = 9$ $3 \ne -3$

$-5x = 5$ No solution

$x = -1$

27. $\sqrt{3y + 5} - 3 = 4$ **Check:** $\sqrt{3\left(\frac{44}{3}\right) + 5} - 3 \overset{?}{=} 4$

$\sqrt{3y + 5} = 7$ $\sqrt{49} - 3 \overset{?}{=} 4$

$(\sqrt{3y + 5})^2 = 7^2$ $7 - 3 \overset{?}{=} 4$

$3y + 5 = 49$ $4 = 4$

$3y = 44$

$y = \frac{44}{3}$

29. $5\sqrt{x + 2} = 8$ **Check:** $5\sqrt{\frac{14}{25} + 2} \overset{?}{=} 8$

$(5\sqrt{x + 2})^2 = 8^2$ $5\sqrt{\frac{64}{25}} \overset{?}{=} 8$

$25(x + 2) = 64$ $5 \cdot \frac{8}{5} \overset{?}{=} 8$

$25x + 50 = 64$ $8 = 8$

$25x = 14$

$x = \frac{14}{25}$

31. $\sqrt{3x + 2} + 5 = 0$ **Check:** $\sqrt{3\left(\frac{23}{3}\right) + 2} + 5 \overset{?}{=} 0$

$\sqrt{3x + 2} = -5$ $\sqrt{23 + 2} + 5 \overset{?}{=} 0$

$(\sqrt{3x + 2})^2 = (-5)^2$ $\sqrt{25} + 5 \overset{?}{=} 0$

$3x + 2 = 25$ $5 + 5 \overset{?}{=} 0$

$3x = 23$ $10 \ne 0$

$x = \frac{23}{3}$ No solution

33. $\sqrt{x+3} = \sqrt{2x-1}$

$\left(\sqrt{x+3}\right)^2 = \left(\sqrt{2x-1}\right)^2$

$x + 3 = 2x - 1$

$4 = x$

Check: $\sqrt{4+3} \overset{?}{=} \sqrt{2(4)-1}$

$\sqrt{7} = \sqrt{7}$

35. $\sqrt{3y-5} - 3\sqrt{y} = 0$

$\sqrt{3y-5} = 3\sqrt{y}$

$\left(\sqrt{3y-5}\right)^2 = \left(3\sqrt{y}\right)^2$

$3y - 5 = 9y$

$-5 = 6y$

$-\frac{5}{6} = y$

Check: $\sqrt{3\left(-\frac{5}{6}\right)-5} - 3\sqrt{-\frac{5}{6}} \overset{?}{=} 0$

No solution

37. $\sqrt[3]{3x-4} = \sqrt[3]{x+10}$

$\left(\sqrt[3]{3x-4}\right)^3 = \left(\sqrt[3]{x+10}\right)^3$

$3x - 4 = x + 10$

$2x = 14$

$x = 7$

Check: $\sqrt[3]{3(7)-4} \overset{?}{=} \sqrt[3]{7+10}$

$\sqrt[3]{17} = \sqrt[3]{17}$

39. $\sqrt[3]{2x+15} - \sqrt[3]{x} = 0$

$\sqrt[3]{2x+15} = \sqrt[3]{x}$

$\left(\sqrt[3]{2x+15}\right)^3 = \left(\sqrt[3]{x}\right)^3$

$2x + 15 = x$

$x = -15$

Check: $\sqrt[3]{2(-15)+15} - \sqrt[3]{-15} \overset{?}{=} 0$

$\sqrt[3]{-15} - \sqrt[3]{-15} \overset{?}{=} 0$

$0 = 0$

41. $\sqrt{x^2+5} = x + 3$

$\left(\sqrt{x^2+5}\right)^2 = (x+3)^2$

$x^2 + 5 = x^2 + 6x + 9$

$-4 = 6x$

$-\frac{4}{6} = x$

$-\frac{2}{3} = x$

Check: $\sqrt{\left(-\frac{2}{3}\right)^2+5} \overset{?}{=} -\frac{2}{3} + 3$

$\sqrt{\frac{4}{9} + \frac{45}{9}} \overset{?}{=} -\frac{2}{3} + \frac{9}{3}$

$\sqrt{\frac{49}{9}} \overset{?}{=} \frac{7}{3}$

$\frac{7}{3} = \frac{7}{3}$

43. $\sqrt{2x} = x - 4$

$\left(\sqrt{2x}\right)^2 = (x-4)^2$

$2x = x^2 - 8x + 16$

$0 = x^2 - 10x + 16$

$0 = (x-8)(x-2)$

$8 = x, x = 2$

Not a solution

Check: $\sqrt{2(8)} \overset{?}{=} 8 - 4$

$\sqrt{16} \overset{?}{=} 4$

$4 = 4$

$\sqrt{2(2)} \overset{?}{=} 2 - 4$

$\sqrt{4} \overset{?}{=} -2$

$2 \neq -2$

45.
$$\sqrt{8x + 1} = x + 2$$
$$\left(\sqrt{8x + 1}\right)^2 = (x + 2)^2$$
$$8x + 1 = x^2 + 4x + 4$$
$$0 = x^2 - 4x + 3$$
$$0 = (x - 3)(x - 1)$$
$$3 = x, \qquad x = 1$$

Check: $\sqrt{8(3) + 1} \stackrel{?}{=} 3 + 2$
$$\sqrt{25} \stackrel{?}{=} 5$$
$$5 = 5$$
$$\sqrt{8(1) + 1} \stackrel{?}{=} 1 + 2$$
$$\sqrt{9} \stackrel{?}{=} 3$$
$$3 = 3$$

47.
$$\sqrt{z + 2} = 1 + \sqrt{2}$$
$$\left(\sqrt{z + 2}\right)^2 = \left(1 + \sqrt{z}\right)^2$$
$$z + 2 = 1 + 2\sqrt{z} + z$$
$$1 = 2\sqrt{z}$$
$$1^2 = \left(2\sqrt{z}\right)^2$$
$$1 = 4z$$
$$\tfrac{1}{4} = z$$

Check: $\sqrt{\tfrac{1}{4} + 2} \stackrel{?}{=} 1 + \sqrt{\tfrac{1}{4}}$
$$\sqrt{\tfrac{9}{4}} \stackrel{?}{=} 1 + \tfrac{1}{2}$$
$$\tfrac{3}{2} = \tfrac{3}{2}$$

49.
$$\sqrt{2t + 3} = 3 - \sqrt{2t}$$
$$\left(\sqrt{2t + 3}\right)^2 = \left(3 - \sqrt{2t}\right)^2$$
$$2t + 3 = 9 - 6\sqrt{2t} + 2t$$
$$-6 = -6\sqrt{2t}$$
$$1 = \sqrt{2t}$$
$$1^2 = \left(\sqrt{2t}\right)^2$$
$$1 = 2t$$
$$\tfrac{1}{2} = t$$

Check: $\sqrt{2\left(\tfrac{1}{2}\right) + 3} \stackrel{?}{=} 3 - \sqrt{2\left(\tfrac{1}{2}\right)}$
$$\sqrt{1 + 3} \stackrel{?}{=} 3 - \sqrt{1}$$
$$\sqrt{4} \stackrel{?}{=} 3 - 1$$
$$2 = 2$$

51.
$$\sqrt{x + 5} - \sqrt{x} = 1$$
$$\sqrt{x + 5} = 1 + \sqrt{x}$$
$$\left(\sqrt{x + 5}\right)^2 = \left(1 + \sqrt{x}\right)^2$$
$$x + 5 = 1 + 2\sqrt{x} + x$$
$$4 = 2\sqrt{x}$$
$$2 = \sqrt{x}$$
$$2^2 = \left(\sqrt{x}\right)^2$$
$$4 = x$$

Check: $\sqrt{4 + 5} - \sqrt{4} \stackrel{?}{=} 1$
$$\sqrt{9} - \sqrt{4} \stackrel{?}{=} 1$$
$$3 - 2 \stackrel{?}{=} 1$$
$$1 = 1$$

53.
$$t^{3/2} = 8$$
$$\sqrt{t^3} = 8$$
$$\left(\sqrt{t^3}\right)^2 = 8^2$$
$$t^3 = 64$$
$$t = 4$$

Check: $4^{3/2} \stackrel{?}{=} 8$
$$\left(\sqrt{4}\right)^3 \stackrel{?}{=} 8$$
$$2^3 \stackrel{?}{=} 8$$
$$8 = 8$$

55. $3y^{1/3} = 18$

$y^{1/3} = 6$

$\sqrt[3]{y} = 6$

$\left(\sqrt[3]{y}\right)^3 = 6^3$

$y = 216$

Check: $3(216)^{1/3} \overset{?}{=} 18$

$3\sqrt[3]{216} \overset{?}{=} 18$

$3 \cdot 6 \overset{?}{=} 18$

$18 = 18$

57. $(x + 4)^{2/3} = 4$

$\sqrt[3]{(x + 4)^2} = 4$

$\left(\sqrt[3]{(x + 4)^2}\right)^3 = (4)^3$

$(x + 4)^2 = 64$

$x + 4 = \pm\sqrt{64}$

$x = -4 \pm 8$

$= 4, -12$

Check: $(4 + 4)^{2/3} \overset{?}{=} 4$

$8^{2/3} \overset{?}{=} 4$

$2^2 = 4$

$(-12 + 4)^{2/3} \overset{?}{=} 4$

$(-8)^{2/3} \overset{?}{=} 4$

$(-2)^2 = 4$

59. $(2x + 5)^{1/3} + 3 = 0$

$\sqrt[3]{(2x + 5)} = -3$

$\left(\sqrt[3]{2x + 5}\right)^3 = (-3)^3$

$2x + 5 = -27$

$2x = -32$

$x = -16$

Check: $(2(-16) + 5)^{1/3} + 3 \overset{?}{=} 0$

$(-32 + 5)^{1/3} + 3 \overset{?}{=} 0$

$(-27)^{1/3} + 3 \overset{?}{=} 0$

$-3 + 3 \overset{?}{=} 0$

$0 = 0$

61. *Keystrokes:*

y_1 [Y=] [√] [X,T,θ] [ENTER]

y_2 2 [(] 2 [−] [X,T,θ] [)] [GRAPH]

Approximate solution: $x \approx 1.407$

Check algebraically: $\sqrt{1.407} \overset{?}{=} 2(2 - 1.407)$

$1.186 = 1.186$

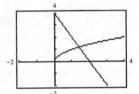

63. *Keystrokes:*

y_1 [Y=] [√] [(] [X,T,θ] [x^2] [+] 1 [)] [ENTER]

y_2 5 [−] 2 [X,T,θ] [GRAPH]

Approximate solution: $x \approx 1.569$

Check algebraically: $\sqrt{1.569^2 + 1} \overset{?}{=} 5 - 2(1.569)$

$1.86 = 1.86$

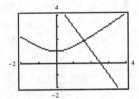

65. *Keystrokes:*

y_1 [Y=] [√] [(] [X,T,θ] [+] 3 [)] [ENTER]

y_2 5 [−] [√] [X,T,θ] [GRAPH]

Approximate solution: $x \approx 4.840$

Check algebraically: $\sqrt{4.840 + 3} \overset{?}{=} 5 - \sqrt{4.840}$

$2.8 = 2.8$

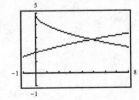

67. *Keystrokes:*

y_1 [Y=] 4 [MATH 4] [X,T,θ] [ENTER]

y_2 7 [−] [X,T,θ] [GRAPH]

Approximate solution: $x \approx 1.978$

Check algebraically: $4\sqrt[3]{1.978} \overset{?}{=} 7 - 1.978$

$$5.02 = 5.02$$

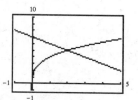

69. *Keystrokes:*

y_1 [Y=] [$\sqrt{\ }$] [(] 15 [−] 4 [X,T,θ] [)] [ENTER]

y_2 2 [X,T,θ] [GRAPH]

Solution: $x = 1.5$

Check algebraically: $\sqrt{15 - 4(1.5)} \overset{?}{=} 2(1.5)$

$$\sqrt{9} \overset{?}{=} 3$$

$$3 = 3$$

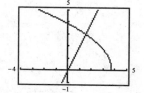

71. (c) graph is shifted down 1 unit

73. (d) graph is shifted left 3 units and upward 1 unit

75. (f) graph is shifted down 1 unit

77.
$$15^2 = x^2 + 12^2$$
$$225 = x^2 + 144$$
$$81 = x^2$$
$$\sqrt{81} = x^2$$
$$9 = x$$

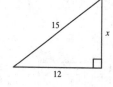

79.
$$c^2 = a^2 + b^2$$
$$13^2 = x^2 + 5^2$$
$$169 = x^2 + 25$$
$$144 = x^2$$
$$\sqrt{144} = x$$
$$12 = x$$

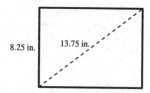

81.
$$13.75^2 = 8.25^2 + x^2$$
$$x^2 = 13.75^2 - 8.25^2$$
$$x = \sqrt{121}$$
$$x = 11 \text{ inches}$$

83. $c = \sqrt{32^2 + 26^2}$

$ = \sqrt{1024 + 676}$

$ = \sqrt{1700}$

$ = 10\sqrt{17}$

$ \approx 41.23$ feet

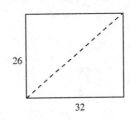

85. $17^2 = x^2 + 8^2$

$ x^2 = 17^2 - 8^2$

$ x = \sqrt{289 - 64}$

$ x = \sqrt{225}$

$ x = 15$ feet

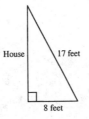

87. $ P = 2l + 2w$

$ 92 = 2l + 2w$

$ 46 = l + w$

$ 46 - w = l$

$34^2 = w^2 + (46 - w)^2$

$1156 = w^2 + 2116 - 92w + w^2$

$0 = 2w^2 - 92w + 960$

$0 = w^2 - 46w + 480$

$0 = (w - 30)(w - 16)$

$w = 30 \qquad w = 16$

$l = 16 \qquad l = 30$

30 inches $\times$ 16 inches

89. $ S = \pi r \sqrt{r^2 + h^2}$

$ \dfrac{S}{\pi r} = \sqrt{r^2 + h^2}$

$ \left(\dfrac{S}{\pi r}\right)^2 = \left(\sqrt{r^2 + h^2}\right)^2$

$ \dfrac{S^2}{\pi^2 r^2} = r^2 + h^2$

$ \dfrac{S^2}{\pi^2 r^2} - r^2 = h^2$

$ \dfrac{S^2 - \pi^2 r^4}{\pi^2 r^2} = h^2$

$\sqrt{\dfrac{S^2 - \pi^2 r^4}{\pi^2 r^2}} = h$

$ \dfrac{\sqrt{S^2 - \pi^2 r^4}}{\pi r} = h$

91. $ 2 = \sqrt{\dfrac{d}{16}}$

$ 2^2 = \left(\sqrt{\dfrac{d}{16}}\right)^2$

$ 4 = \dfrac{d}{16}$

64 feet $= d$

93. $v = \sqrt{2(32)50}$

$ v = \sqrt{3200}$

$ v = 40\sqrt{2}$

$ v \approx 56.57$ feet per second

95. $ 60 = \sqrt{2(32)h}$

$ 60^2 = \left(\sqrt{64h}\right)^2$

$ 3600 = 64h$

$ \dfrac{3600}{64} = h$

56.25 feet $= h$

97.
$$1.5 = 2\pi\sqrt{\frac{L}{32}}$$

$$\left(\frac{1.5}{2\pi}\right)^2 = \left(\sqrt{\frac{L}{32}}\right)^2$$

$$\frac{2.25}{4\pi^2} = \frac{L}{32}$$

$$\frac{2.25}{4\pi^2}(32) = L$$

$$1.82 \text{ feet} \approx L$$

99.
$$30.02 = 50 - \sqrt{0.8(x-1)}$$

$$\sqrt{0.8(x-1)} = 19.98$$

$$\left(\sqrt{0.8(x-1)}\right)^2 = (19.98)^2$$

$$0.8(x-1) = 399.2004$$

$$0.8x - 0.8 = 399.2004$$

$$0.8x = 400.0004$$

$$x = 500.0005$$

$$\approx 500 \text{ units}$$

101. (a) *Keystrokes:*

y_1 Y= 133.5 + 9.3 X,T,θ + 18 √ X,T,θ GRAPH

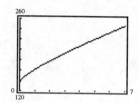

(b)
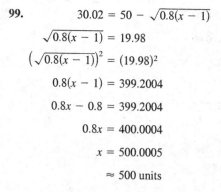

$$\approx 5 \text{ years from } 1990 \approx 1995$$

103.
$$R = \left(\frac{A}{P}\right)^{1/n} - 1$$

$$0.07 = \left(\frac{25,000}{P}\right)^{1/10} - 1$$

$$1.07 = \left(\frac{25,000}{P}\right)^{1/10}$$

$$1.07 = \sqrt[10]{\frac{25,000}{P}}$$

$$1.07^{10} = \left(\sqrt[10]{\frac{25,000}{P}}\right)^{10}$$

$$1.07^{10} = \frac{25,000}{P}$$

$$P = \frac{25,000}{1.07^{10}}$$

$$P \approx \$12,708.73$$

105. No. It is not an operation that necessarily yields an equivalent equation. There may be extraneous solutions.

107. $\left(\sqrt{x} + \sqrt{6}\right)^2 \neq \left(\sqrt{x}\right)^2 + \left(\sqrt{6}\right)^2$

$\left(\sqrt{x} + \sqrt{6}\right)^2$ must be multiplied by FOIL.

Section 5.5   Complex Numbers

1. $\sqrt{-4} = \sqrt{-1 \cdot 4}$
$= \sqrt{-1} \cdot \sqrt{4}$
$= 2i$

3. $-\sqrt{-144} = -\sqrt{144 \cdot -1}$
$= -\sqrt{144} \cdot \sqrt{-1}$
$= -12i$

5. $\sqrt{\dfrac{-4}{25}} = \sqrt{\dfrac{4}{25} \cdot -1}$
$= \sqrt{\dfrac{4}{25}} \cdot \sqrt{-1}$
$= \dfrac{2}{5}i$

7. $\sqrt{-0.09} = \sqrt{0.09 \cdot -1}$

$\phantom{\sqrt{-0.09}} = \sqrt{0.09} \cdot \sqrt{-1}$

$\phantom{\sqrt{-0.09}} = 0.3i$

9. $\sqrt{-8} = \sqrt{4 \cdot 2 \cdot -1}$

$\phantom{\sqrt{-8}} = \sqrt{4} \cdot \sqrt{2} \cdot \sqrt{-1}$

$\phantom{\sqrt{-8}} = 2i\sqrt{2}$

11. $\sqrt{-27} = \sqrt{-1 \cdot 9 \cdot 3}$

$\phantom{\sqrt{-27}} = \sqrt{-1} \cdot \sqrt{9} \cdot \sqrt{3}$

$\phantom{\sqrt{-27}} = 3i\sqrt{3}$

13. $\sqrt{-7} = \sqrt{7 \cdot -1}$

$\phantom{\sqrt{-7}} = \sqrt{7} \cdot \sqrt{-1}$

$\phantom{\sqrt{-7}} = i\sqrt{7}$

15. $\dfrac{\sqrt{-12}}{\sqrt{-3}} = \dfrac{\sqrt{4 \cdot 3 \cdot -1}}{\sqrt{3 \cdot -1}}$

$\phantom{\dfrac{\sqrt{-12}}{\sqrt{-3}}} = \dfrac{\sqrt{4} \cdot \sqrt{3} \cdot \sqrt{-1}}{\sqrt{3} \cdot \sqrt{-1}}$

$\phantom{\dfrac{\sqrt{-12}}{\sqrt{-3}}} = \sqrt{4} = 2$

or

$$\dfrac{\sqrt{-12}}{\sqrt{-3}} = \sqrt{\dfrac{-12}{-3}} = \sqrt{4} = 2$$

17. $\dfrac{\sqrt{-20}}{\sqrt{4}} = \sqrt{\dfrac{-20}{4}}$

$\phantom{\dfrac{\sqrt{-20}}{\sqrt{4}}} = \sqrt{-5}$

$\phantom{\dfrac{\sqrt{-20}}{\sqrt{4}}} = \sqrt{5} \cdot \sqrt{-1}$

$\phantom{\dfrac{\sqrt{-20}}{\sqrt{4}}} = i\sqrt{5}$

19. $\sqrt{\dfrac{-18}{64}} = \sqrt{\dfrac{-1 \cdot 9 \cdot 2}{64}}$

$\phantom{\sqrt{\dfrac{-18}{64}}} = \dfrac{3i}{8}\sqrt{2}$

21. $\sqrt{-16} + \sqrt{-36} = 4i + 6i$

$\phantom{\sqrt{-16} + \sqrt{-36}} = (4 + 6)i$

$\phantom{\sqrt{-16} + \sqrt{-36}} = 10i$

23. $\sqrt{-50} - \sqrt{-8} = 5i\sqrt{2} - 2i\sqrt{2}$

$\phantom{\sqrt{-50} - \sqrt{-8}} = \left(5\sqrt{2} - 2\sqrt{2}\right)i$

$\phantom{\sqrt{-50} - \sqrt{-8}} = 3\sqrt{2}i$

25. $\sqrt{-48} + \sqrt{-12} - \sqrt{-27} = \sqrt{16 \cdot 3 \cdot -1} + \sqrt{4 \cdot 3 \cdot -1} - \sqrt{9 \cdot 3 \cdot -1}$

$\phantom{\sqrt{-48} + \sqrt{-12} - \sqrt{-27}} = 4i\sqrt{3} + 2i\sqrt{3} - 3i\sqrt{3}$

$\phantom{\sqrt{-48} + \sqrt{-12} - \sqrt{-27}} = (4i + 2i - 3i)\sqrt{3}$

$\phantom{\sqrt{-48} + \sqrt{-12} - \sqrt{-27}} = 3i\sqrt{3}$

27. $\sqrt{-8}\sqrt{-2} = \left(2i\sqrt{2}\right)\left(i\sqrt{2}\right)$

$\phantom{\sqrt{-8}\sqrt{-2}} = 2 \cdot 2 \cdot i^2$

$\phantom{\sqrt{-8}\sqrt{-2}} = 4(-1) = -4$

29. $\sqrt{-18}\sqrt{-3} = \left(3i\sqrt{2}\right)\left(i\sqrt{3}\right)$

$\phantom{\sqrt{-18}\sqrt{-3}} = 3\sqrt{6} \cdot i^2$

$\phantom{\sqrt{-18}\sqrt{-3}} = -3\sqrt{6}$

31. $\sqrt{-0.16}\sqrt{-1.21} = (0.4i)(1.1i) = 0.44i^2 = -0.44$

33. $\sqrt{-3}\left(\sqrt{-3} + \sqrt{-4}\right) = i\sqrt{3}\left(i\sqrt{3} + 2i\right)$

$\phantom{\sqrt{-3}\left(\sqrt{-3} + \sqrt{-4}\right)} = \left(i\sqrt{3}\right)^2 + 2\sqrt{3}i^2$

$\phantom{\sqrt{-3}\left(\sqrt{-3} + \sqrt{-4}\right)} = -3 - 2\sqrt{3}$

35. $\sqrt{-5}\left(\sqrt{-16} - \sqrt{-10}\right) = i\sqrt{5}\left(4i - i\sqrt{10}\right)$

$\phantom{\sqrt{-5}\left(\sqrt{-16} - \sqrt{-10}\right)} = i^2 4\sqrt{5} - i^2\sqrt{50}$

$\phantom{\sqrt{-5}\left(\sqrt{-16} - \sqrt{-10}\right)} = -4\sqrt{5} + 5\sqrt{2}$

$\phantom{\sqrt{-5}\left(\sqrt{-16} - \sqrt{-10}\right)} = 5\sqrt{2} - 4\sqrt{5}$

37. $\sqrt{-2}\left(3 - \sqrt{-8}\right) = i\sqrt{2}\left(3 - 2i\sqrt{2}\right)$

$\phantom{\sqrt{-2}\left(3 - \sqrt{-8}\right)} = 3\sqrt{2}i - 2i^2(2)$

$\phantom{\sqrt{-2}\left(3 - \sqrt{-8}\right)} = 3\sqrt{2}i + 4$

39. $\left(\sqrt{-16}\right)^2 = (4i)^2$

$\phantom{\left(\sqrt{-16}\right)^2} = 16i^2$

$\phantom{\left(\sqrt{-16}\right)^2} = -16$

41. $\left(\sqrt{-4}\right)^3 = (2i)^3$

$\phantom{\left(\sqrt{-4}\right)^3} = 8i^3$

$\phantom{\left(\sqrt{-4}\right)^3} = -8i$

43. $3 - 4i = a + bi$

$ a = 3 \qquad b = -4$

45. $5 - 4i = (a + 3) + (b - 1)i$

$a + 3 = 5 \qquad b - 1 = -4$

$a = 2 \qquad\quad b = -3$

47. $-4 - \sqrt{-8} = a + bi$

$-4 - 2i\sqrt{2} = a + bi$

$-4 = a \qquad -2i\sqrt{2} = bi$

$-2\sqrt{2} = b$

49. $(a + 5) + (b - 1)i = 7 - 3i$

$a + 5 = 7 \qquad b - 1 = -3$

$a = 2 \qquad\quad b = -2$

51. $(4 - 3i) + (6 + 7i) = (4 + 6) + (-3 + 7)i$

$= 10 + 4i$

53. $(-4 - 7i) + (-10 - 33i) = (-4 - 10) + (-7 - 33)i$

$= -14 - 40i$

55. $13i - (14 - 7i) = (-14) + (13 + 7)i$

$= -14 + 20i$

57. $(30 - i) - (18 + 6i) + 3i^2 = 30 - i - 18 - 6i - 3$

$= 9 - 7i$

59. $6 - (3 - 4i) + 2i = 6 - 3 + 4i + 2i$

$= 3 + 6i$

61. $\left(\frac{4}{3} + \frac{1}{3}i\right) + \left(\frac{5}{6} + \frac{7}{6}i\right) = \left(\frac{4}{3} + \frac{5}{6}\right) + \left(\frac{1}{3} + \frac{7}{6}\right)i$

$= \left(\frac{8}{6} + \frac{5}{6}\right) + \left(\frac{2}{6} + \frac{7}{6}\right)i$

$= \frac{13}{6} + \frac{9}{6}i$

$= \frac{13}{6} + \frac{3}{2}i$

63. $15i - (3 - 25i) + \sqrt{-81} = 15i - 3 + 25i + 9i$

$= -3 + (15 + 25 + 9)i$

$= -3 + 49i$

65. $8 - \left(5 - \sqrt{-63}\right) + (4 - 5i) = 8 - 5 + 3i\sqrt{7} + 4 - 5i$

$= 7 + \left(3\sqrt{7} - 5\right)i$

67. $(3i)(12i) = 36i^2$

$= -36$

69. $(3i)(-8i) = -24i^2$

$= -24(-1)$

$= 24$

71. $(-6i)(-i)(6i) = 36i^3 = -36i$

73. $(-3i)^3 = -27i^3 = 27i$

75. $(-3i)^2 = 9i^2$

$= 9(-1)$

$= -9$

77. $-5(13 + 2i) = -65 - 10i$

79. $4i(-3 - 5i) = -12i - 20i^2 = 20 - 12i$

81. $(9 - 2i)\left(\sqrt{-4}\right) = (9 - 2i)(2i)$

$= 18i - 4i^2$

$= 18i + 4$

$= 4 + 18i$

83. $\sqrt{-20}\left(6 + 2\sqrt{5}i\right) = 2i\sqrt{5}\left(6 + 2\sqrt{5}i\right)$

$= 12i\sqrt{5} + 4i^2(5)$

$= -20 + 12i\sqrt{5}$

85. $(4 + 3i)(-7 + 4i) = -28 + 16i - 21i + 12i^2$

$= -28 - 12 - 5i$

$= -40 - 5i$

87. $(-7 + 7i)(4 - 2i) = -28 + 14i + 28i - 14i^2$

$$= -28 + 42i + 14$$

$$= -14 + 42i$$

89. $\left(-2 + \sqrt{-5}\right)\left(-2 - \sqrt{-5}\right) = \left(-2 + i\sqrt{5}\right)\left(-2 - i\sqrt{5}\right)$

$$= 4 + 2i\sqrt{5} - 2i\sqrt{5} - 5i^2$$

$$= 4 + 5$$

$$= 9$$

91. $(3 - 4i)^2 = 3^2 - 2(3)(4i) + (4i)^2$

$$= 9 - 24i + 16i^2$$

$$= 9 - 16 - 24i$$

$$= -7 - 24i$$

93. $(2 + 5i)^2 = 2^2 + 2(2)(5i) + (5i)^2$

$$= 4 + 20i + 25i^2$$

$$= 4 - 25 + 20i$$

$$= -21 + 20i$$

95. $(2 + i)^3 = (2 + i)(2 + i)(2 + i)$

$$= (4 + 2(2)i + i^2)(2 + i)$$

$$= (4 + 4i - 1)(2 + i)$$

$$= (3 + 4i)(2 + i)$$

$$= 6 + 3i + 8i + 4i^2$$

$$= 6 + 3i + 8i - 4$$

$$= 2 + 11i$$

97. $2 + i$, conjugate $= 2 - i$

$$\text{product} = (2 + i)(2 - i)$$

$$= 2^2 - i^2$$

$$= 4 + 1$$

$$= 5$$

99. $-2 - 8i$, conjugate $= -2 + 8i$

$$\text{product} = (-2 - 8i)(-2 + 8i)$$

$$= (-2)^2 - (8i)^2$$

$$= 4 - 64i^2 = 4 + 64 = 68$$

101. $5 - \sqrt{6}i$, conjugate $= 5 + \sqrt{6}i$

$$\text{product} = \left(5 - \sqrt{6}i\right)\left(5 + \sqrt{6}i\right)$$

$$= 5^2 - \left(\sqrt{6}i\right)^2$$

$$= 25 - 6i^2 = 25 + 6 = 31$$

103. $10i$, conjugate $= -10i$

$$\text{product} = (10i)(-10i)$$

$$= -(10i)^2$$

$$= -100i^2$$

$$= 100$$

105. $1 + \sqrt{-3} = 1 + i\sqrt{3}$, conjugate $= 1 - i\sqrt{3}$

$$\text{product} = \left(1 + i\sqrt{3}\right)\left(1 - i\sqrt{3}\right)$$

$$= 1^2 - \left(i\sqrt{3}\right)^2$$

$$= 1 - 3i^2$$

$$= 1 + 3$$

$$= 4$$

107. $1.5 + \sqrt{-0.25}$, conjugate $= 1.5 - \sqrt{-0.25}$

$$\text{product} = (1.5 + 0.5i)(1.5 - 0.5i)$$
$$= 1.5^2 - (0.5i)^2$$
$$= 2.25 + 0.25$$
$$= 2.5$$

109. $\dfrac{20}{2i} = \dfrac{10}{i} \cdot \dfrac{-i}{-i} = \dfrac{-10i}{1}$

$$= 0 - 10i$$

111. $\dfrac{4}{1-i} = \dfrac{4}{1-i} \cdot \dfrac{1+i}{1+i} = \dfrac{4(1+i)}{1+1}$

$$= \dfrac{4(1+i)}{2}$$
$$= 2(1+i)$$
$$= 2 + 2i$$

113. $\dfrac{-12}{2+7i} = \dfrac{-12}{2+7i} \cdot \dfrac{2-7i}{2-7i} = \dfrac{-12(2-7i)}{4+49}$

$$= \dfrac{-12(2-7i)}{53}$$
$$= \dfrac{-24 + 84i}{53}$$
$$= \dfrac{-24}{53} + \dfrac{84}{53}i$$

115. $\dfrac{4i}{1-3i} = \dfrac{4i}{1-3i} \cdot \dfrac{1+3i}{1+3i} = \dfrac{4i(1+3i)}{1+9}$

$$= \dfrac{4i + 12i^2}{10}$$
$$= \dfrac{-12 + 4i}{10} = \dfrac{4(-3+i)}{10}$$
$$= \dfrac{2(-3+i)}{5} = \dfrac{-6+2i}{5}$$
$$= -\dfrac{6}{5} + \dfrac{2}{5}i$$

117. $\dfrac{2+3i}{1+2i} = \dfrac{2+3i}{1+2i} \cdot \dfrac{1-2i}{1-2i} = \dfrac{2 - 4i + 3i - 6i^2}{1+4}$

$$= \dfrac{2 + 6 - i}{5}$$
$$= \dfrac{8 - i}{5}$$
$$= \dfrac{8}{5} - \dfrac{1}{5}i$$

119. $\dfrac{1}{1-2i} + \dfrac{4}{1+2i} = \dfrac{1}{1-2i} \cdot \dfrac{1+2i}{1+2i} + \dfrac{4}{1+2i} \cdot \dfrac{1-2i}{1-2i}$

$$= \dfrac{1+2i}{1+4} + \dfrac{4-8i}{1+4} = \dfrac{1+2i}{5} + \dfrac{4-8i}{5}$$
$$= \dfrac{(1+4) + (2-8)i}{5} = \dfrac{5 - 6i}{5}$$
$$= 1 - \dfrac{6}{5}i$$

121. $\dfrac{i}{4-3i} - \dfrac{5}{2+i} = \dfrac{i}{4-3i} \cdot \dfrac{4+3i}{4+3i} - \dfrac{5}{2+i} \cdot \dfrac{2-i}{2-i}$

$$= \dfrac{4i + 3i^2}{16+9} - \dfrac{10 - 5i}{4+1} = \dfrac{-3 + 4i}{25} - \dfrac{10 - 5i}{5} \cdot \dfrac{5}{5}$$
$$= \dfrac{-3 + 4i}{25} - \dfrac{50 - 25i}{25} = \dfrac{(-3 - 50) + (4 + 25)i}{25}$$
$$= \dfrac{-53 + 29i}{25} = \dfrac{-53}{25} + \dfrac{29}{25}i$$

123. (a) $x = -1 + 2i$

$$(-1 + 2i)^2 + 2(-1 + 2i) + 5 \overset{?}{=} 0$$

$$1 - 4i + 4i^2 - 2 + 4i + 5 \overset{?}{=} 0$$

$$1 - 4 - 2 + 5 \overset{?}{=} 0$$

$$0 = 0 \text{ Solution}$$

(b) $x = -1 - 2i$

$$(-1 - 2i)^2 + 2(-1 - 2i) + 5 \overset{?}{=} 0$$

$$1 + 4i + 4i^2 - 2 - 4i + 5 \overset{?}{=} 0$$

$$1 - 4 - 2 + 5 \overset{?}{=} 0$$

$$0 = 0 \text{ Solution}$$

125. (a) $x = -4$

$$(-4)^3 + 4(-4)^2 + 9(-4) + 36 \overset{?}{=} 0$$

$$-64 + 64 - 36 + 36 \overset{?}{=} 0$$

$$0 = 0 \text{ Solution}$$

(b) $x = -3i$

$$(-3i)^3 + 4(-3i)^2 + 9(-3i) + 36 \overset{?}{=} 0$$

$$-27i^3 + 36i^2 - 27i + 36 \overset{?}{=} 0$$

$$27i - 36 - 27i + 36 \overset{?}{=} 0$$

$$0 = 0 \text{ Solution}$$

127. (a) $\left(\dfrac{-5 + 5\sqrt{3}i}{2}\right)^3 = \left(\dfrac{-5}{2} + \dfrac{5}{2}\sqrt{3}i\right)^2 \left(\dfrac{-5}{2} + \dfrac{5}{2}\sqrt{3}i\right)$

$$= \left(\frac{25}{4} - \frac{25}{2}\sqrt{3}i + \frac{25}{4}(3)i^2\right)\left(\frac{-5}{2} + \frac{5}{2}\sqrt{3}i\right)$$

$$= \left(\frac{25}{4} - \frac{25}{2}\sqrt{3}i - \frac{75}{4}\right)\left(\frac{-5}{2} + \frac{5}{2}\sqrt{3}i\right)$$

$$= \left(\frac{-50}{4} - \frac{25}{2}\sqrt{3}i\right)\left(\frac{-5}{2} + \frac{5}{2}\sqrt{3}i\right)$$

$$= \left(\frac{-25}{2} - \frac{25}{2}\sqrt{3}i\right)\left(\frac{-5}{2} + \frac{5}{2}\sqrt{3}i\right)$$

$$= \frac{125}{4} - \frac{125}{4}\sqrt{3}i + \frac{125}{4}\sqrt{3}i - \frac{125}{4}(3)i^2$$

$$= \frac{125}{4} + \frac{375}{4}$$

$$= \frac{500}{4} = 125$$

(b) use same method as part (a)

129. (a) $1, \dfrac{-1 + \sqrt{3}i}{2}, \dfrac{-1 - \sqrt{3}i}{2}$

(b) $2, \dfrac{-2 + 2\sqrt{3}i}{2} = -1 + \sqrt{3}i, \dfrac{-2 - 2\sqrt{3}i}{2} = -1 - \sqrt{3}i$

(c) $4, \dfrac{-4 + 4\sqrt{3}i}{2} = -2 + 2\sqrt{3}i, \dfrac{-4 - 4\sqrt{3}i}{2} = -2 - 2\sqrt{3}i$

131. $(a + bi) + (a - bi) = (a + a) + (b - b)i$

$$= 2a + 0i$$

133. $(a + bi) - (a - bi) = (a - a) + (b + b)i$

$$= 0 + 2bi$$

135. $i = \sqrt{-1}$

137. $\sqrt{-3}\sqrt{-3} = \sqrt{(-3)(-3)} = \sqrt{9} = 3$

The product rule for radicals does not hold if both radicands are negative.

$\sqrt{-3}\sqrt{-3} = i\sqrt{3} \cdot i\sqrt{3} = i^2(3) = -3$

139. $3 - 2i$, conjugate $= 3 + 2i$

product $= (3 - 2i)(3 + 2i)$

$= 3^2 - (2i)^2$

$= 9 + 4$

$= 13$

Review Exercises for Chapter 5

1. $\sqrt{49} = 7$ because $7 \cdot 7 = 49$

3. $-\sqrt{81} = -9$ because $9 \cdot 9 = 81$

5. $\sqrt[3]{-8} = -2$ because $-2 \cdot -2 \cdot -2 = -8$

7. $-\sqrt[3]{64} = -4$ because $4 \cdot 4 \cdot 4 = 64$

9. $\sqrt{(1.2)^2} = 1.2$ (inverse property of powers and roots)

11. $\sqrt{\left(\frac{5}{6}\right)^2} = \frac{5}{6}$ (inverse property of powers and roots)

13. $\sqrt[3]{-\left(\frac{1}{5}\right)^3} = -\frac{1}{5}$ (inverse property of powers and roots)

15. $\sqrt{-2^2} = 2i$

17. $49^{1/2} = 7$

19. $\sqrt[3]{216} = 6$

21. $27^{4/3} = \left(\sqrt[3]{27}\right)^4 = 3^4 = 81$

23. $-(5^2)^{3/2} = -\left(\sqrt{25}\right)^3 = -5^3 = -125$

25. $8^{-4/3} = \frac{1}{8^{4/3}} = \frac{1}{\left(\sqrt[3]{8}\right)^4} = \frac{1}{2^4} = \frac{1}{16}$

27. $-\left(\frac{27}{64}\right)^{2/3} = -\left(\sqrt[3]{\frac{27}{64}}\right)^2$

$= -\left(\frac{3}{4}\right)^2$

$= -\frac{9}{16}$

29. $x^{3/4} \cdot x^{-1/6} = x^{3/4 + (-1/6)}$

$= x^{9/12 + (-2)/12}$

$= x^{7/12}$

31. $z\sqrt[3]{z^2} = z \cdot z^{2/3}$

$= z^{1 + 2/3}$

$= z^{5/3}$

33. $\frac{\sqrt[4]{x^3}}{\sqrt{x^4}} = \frac{x^{3/4}}{x^{4/2}} = x^{3/4 - 2} = x^{3/4 - 8/4} = x^{-5/4} = \frac{1}{x^{5/4}}$

35. $\sqrt[3]{a^3 b^2} = a\sqrt[3]{b^2}$

37. $\sqrt[4]{\sqrt{x}} = \sqrt[4]{x^{1/2}} = (x^{1/2})^{1/4} = x^{1/8} = \sqrt[8]{x}$

39. $\frac{(3x + 2)^{2/3}}{\sqrt[3]{3x + 2}} = \frac{(3x + 2)^{2/3}}{(3x + 2)^{1/3}}$

$= (3x + 2)^{2/3 - 1/3}$

$= (3x + 2)^{1/3}$

$= \sqrt[3]{3x + 2}$

41. $75^{-3/4} = 0.0392377 \approx 0.04$

43. $\sqrt{13^2 - 4(2)(7)} = 10.630146 \approx 10.63$

45. *Keystrokes:*

$\boxed{Y=}\ 3\ \boxed{\sqrt[3]{\ }}\ 2\ \boxed{X,T,\theta}\ \boxed{GRAPH}$

Domain $= (-\infty, \infty)$

47. *Keystrokes:*

$\boxed{Y=}\ 4\ \boxed{X,T,\theta}\ \boxed{\wedge}\ .75\ \boxed{GRAPH}$

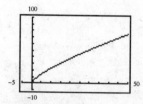

Domain $= [0, \infty)$

49. $\sqrt{360} = \sqrt{36 \cdot 10}$
$\quad\quad = 6\sqrt{10}$

51. $\sqrt{75u^5v^4} = \sqrt{25 \cdot 3 \cdot u^4 \cdot u \cdot v^4}$
$\quad\quad\quad\quad = 5u^2v^2\sqrt{3u}$

53. $\sqrt{0.25x^4y} = \sqrt{25 \times 10^{-2}x^4y}$
$\quad\quad\quad\quad = 5 \times 10^{-1}x^2\sqrt{y}$
$\quad\quad\quad\quad = 0.5x^2\sqrt{y}$

55. $\sqrt[4]{64a^2b^5} = \sqrt[4]{16 \cdot 4 \cdot a^2 \cdot b^4 \cdot b}$
$\quad\quad\quad\quad = 2b\sqrt[4]{4a^2b}$

57. $\sqrt[3]{48a^3b^4} = \sqrt[3]{8 \cdot 6a^3b^3b}$
$\quad\quad\quad\quad = 2ab\sqrt[3]{6b}$

59. $\sqrt{\dfrac{5}{6}} = \sqrt{\dfrac{5}{6}} \cdot \dfrac{\sqrt{6}}{\sqrt{6}} = \dfrac{\sqrt{30}}{6}$

61. $\dfrac{3}{\sqrt{12x}} = \dfrac{3}{\sqrt{4 \cdot 3x}} = \dfrac{3}{2\sqrt{3x}} \cdot \dfrac{\sqrt{3x}}{\sqrt{3x}} = \dfrac{3\sqrt{3x}}{6x} = \dfrac{\sqrt{3x}}{2x}$

63. $\dfrac{2}{\sqrt[3]{2x}} = \dfrac{2}{\sqrt[3]{2x}} \cdot \dfrac{\sqrt[3]{2^2x^2}}{\sqrt[3]{2^2x^2}} = \dfrac{2\sqrt[3]{4x^2}}{\sqrt[3]{8x^3}} = \dfrac{2\sqrt[3]{4x^2}}{2x} = \dfrac{\sqrt[3]{4x^2}}{x}$

65. $2\sqrt{7} - 5\sqrt{7} + 4\sqrt{7} = \sqrt{7}(2 - 5 + 4)$
$\quad\quad\quad\quad\quad\quad\quad\quad = \sqrt{7}$

67. $3\sqrt{40} - 10\sqrt{90} = 3\sqrt{4 \cdot 10} - 10\sqrt{9 \cdot 10}$
$\quad\quad\quad\quad\quad\quad\quad = 6\sqrt{10} - 30\sqrt{10}$
$\quad\quad\quad\quad\quad\quad\quad = -24\sqrt{10}$

69. $5\sqrt{x} - \sqrt[3]{x} + 9\sqrt{x} - 8\sqrt[3]{x} = 5\sqrt{x} + 9\sqrt{x} - \sqrt[3]{x} - 8\sqrt[3]{x}$
$\quad\quad\quad\quad\quad\quad\quad\quad\quad\quad\quad\quad = (5 + 9)\sqrt{x} + (-1 - 8)\sqrt[3]{x}$
$\quad\quad\quad\quad\quad\quad\quad\quad\quad\quad\quad\quad = 14\sqrt{x} - 9\sqrt[3]{x}$

71. $10\sqrt[4]{y + 3} - 3\sqrt[4]{y + 3} = (10 - 3)\sqrt[4]{y + 3}$
$\quad\quad\quad\quad\quad\quad\quad\quad\quad\quad = 7\sqrt[4]{y + 3}$

73. $\sqrt{25x} + \sqrt{49x} - \sqrt[3]{8x} = 5\sqrt{x} + 7\sqrt{x} - 2\sqrt[3]{x}$
$\quad\quad\quad\quad\quad\quad\quad\quad\quad\quad = 12\sqrt{x} - 2\sqrt[3]{x}$

75. $\sqrt{5} - \dfrac{3}{\sqrt{5}} = \sqrt{5} - \dfrac{3}{\sqrt{5}} \cdot \dfrac{\sqrt{5}}{\sqrt{5}}$
$\quad\quad\quad\quad\quad = \sqrt{5} - \dfrac{3\sqrt{5}}{5}$
$\quad\quad\quad\quad\quad = \sqrt{5} \cdot \dfrac{5}{5} - \dfrac{3\sqrt{5}}{5}$
$\quad\quad\quad\quad\quad = \dfrac{5\sqrt{5}}{5} - \dfrac{3\sqrt{5}}{5}$
$\quad\quad\quad\quad\quad = \dfrac{2\sqrt{5}}{5}$

77. $\sqrt{15} \cdot \sqrt{20} = \sqrt{15 \cdot 20}$
$\quad\quad\quad\quad\quad = \sqrt{300}$
$\quad\quad\quad\quad\quad = \sqrt{100 \cdot 3}$
$\quad\quad\quad\quad\quad = 10\sqrt{3}$

79. $\sqrt{5}(\sqrt{10} + 3) = \sqrt{5}\sqrt{10} + \sqrt{5} \cdot 3$
$\quad\quad\quad\quad\quad\quad = \sqrt{50} + 3\sqrt{5}$
$\quad\quad\quad\quad\quad\quad = \sqrt{25 \cdot 2} + 3\sqrt{5}$
$\quad\quad\quad\quad\quad\quad = 5\sqrt{2} + 3\sqrt{5}$

81. $\sqrt{10}(\sqrt{2} + \sqrt{5}) = \sqrt{10}\sqrt{2} + \sqrt{10}\sqrt{5}$
$\quad\quad\quad\quad\quad\quad\quad = \sqrt{20} + \sqrt{50}$
$\quad\quad\quad\quad\quad\quad\quad = \sqrt{4 \cdot 5} + \sqrt{25 \cdot 2}$
$\quad\quad\quad\quad\quad\quad\quad = 2\sqrt{5} + 5\sqrt{2}$

83. $(2\sqrt{3} + 7)(\sqrt{6} - 2) = 2\sqrt{3}\sqrt{6} - 4\sqrt{3} + 7\sqrt{6} - 14$
$\quad\quad\quad\quad\quad\quad\quad\quad\quad = 2\sqrt{18} - 4\sqrt{3} + 7\sqrt{6} - 14$
$\quad\quad\quad\quad\quad\quad\quad\quad\quad = 6\sqrt{2} - 4\sqrt{3} + 7\sqrt{6} - 14$

85. $(\sqrt{5} + 6)^2 = (\sqrt{5})^2 + 2(6)\sqrt{5} + 6^2 = 5 + 12\sqrt{5} + 36 = 41 + 12\sqrt{5}$

87. $(\sqrt{3} - \sqrt{x})(\sqrt{3} + \sqrt{x}) = 3 - \sqrt{3x} + \sqrt{3x} - x = 3 - x$

89. $\dfrac{3}{1 - \sqrt{2}} \cdot \dfrac{1 + \sqrt{2}}{1 + \sqrt{2}} = \dfrac{3(1 + \sqrt{2})}{1^2 - (\sqrt{2})^2}$

$ = \dfrac{3(1 + \sqrt{2})}{1 - 2}$

$ = \dfrac{3(1 + \sqrt{2})}{-1}$

$ = -3(1 + \sqrt{2})$

91. $\dfrac{3\sqrt{8}}{2\sqrt{2} + \sqrt{3}} \cdot \dfrac{2\sqrt{2} - \sqrt{3}}{2\sqrt{2} - \sqrt{3}} = \dfrac{6\sqrt{16} - 3\sqrt{24}}{(2\sqrt{2})^2 - (\sqrt{3})^2}$

$ = \dfrac{24 - 6\sqrt{6}}{8 - 3}$

$ = \dfrac{24 - 6\sqrt{6}}{5}$

93. $\dfrac{\sqrt{2} - 1}{\sqrt{3} - 4} = \dfrac{\sqrt{2} - 1}{\sqrt{3} - 4} \cdot \dfrac{\sqrt{3} + 4}{\sqrt{3} + 4}$

$ = \dfrac{\sqrt{6} + 4\sqrt{2} - \sqrt{3} - 4}{(\sqrt{3})^2 - 4^2}$

$ = \dfrac{\sqrt{6} + 4\sqrt{2} - \sqrt{3} - 4}{3 - 16}$

$ = \dfrac{\sqrt{6} + 4\sqrt{2} - \sqrt{3} - 4}{-13}$

$ = -\dfrac{\sqrt{6} + 4\sqrt{2} - \sqrt{3} - 4}{13}$

95. $\dfrac{\sqrt{x} + 10}{\sqrt{x} - 10} = \dfrac{\sqrt{x} + 10}{\sqrt{x} - 10} \cdot \dfrac{\sqrt{x} + 10}{\sqrt{x} + 10}$

$ = \dfrac{x + 10\sqrt{x} + 10\sqrt{x} + 100}{(\sqrt{x})^2 - 10^2}$

$ = \dfrac{x + 20\sqrt{x} + 100}{x - 100}$

97. *Keystrokes:*

y_1 $\boxed{Y=}$ $\boxed{\sqrt{}}$ $\boxed{(}$ $\boxed{(}$ 5 $\boxed{\div}$ $\boxed{(}$ 2 $\boxed{X,T,\theta}$ $\boxed{)}$ $\boxed{)}$ $\boxed{)}$ $\boxed{ENTER}$

y_2 $\boxed{\sqrt{}}$ $\boxed{(}$ 10 $\boxed{X,T,\theta}$ $\boxed{)}$ $\boxed{\div}$ $\boxed{(}$ 2 $\boxed{X,T,\theta}$ $\boxed{)}$ $\boxed{GRAPH}$

$\sqrt{\dfrac{5}{2x}} = \sqrt{\dfrac{5}{2x}} \cdot \dfrac{\sqrt{2x}}{\sqrt{2x}} = \dfrac{\sqrt{10x}}{2x}$

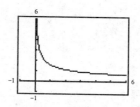

99. *Keystrokes:*

y_1 $\boxed{Y=}$ 5 $\boxed{\sqrt{}}$ $\boxed{X,T,\theta}$ $\boxed{-}$ 2 $\boxed{\sqrt{}}$ $\boxed{X,T,\theta}$ $\boxed{ENTER}$

y_2 3 $\boxed{\sqrt{}}$ $\boxed{X,T,\theta}$ $\boxed{GRAPH}$

$5\sqrt{x} - 2\sqrt{x} = (5 - 2)\sqrt{x} = 3\sqrt{x}$

101. $\sqrt{y} = 15$ **Check:** $\sqrt{225} \stackrel{?}{=} 15$

$(\sqrt{y})^2 = (15)^2$ $\qquad\qquad$ $15 = 15$

$y = 225$

103. $\sqrt{3x} + 9 = 0$ **Check:** $\sqrt{3 \cdot 27} + 9 \stackrel{?}{=} 0$

$\sqrt{3} = -9$ $\qquad\qquad$ $\sqrt{81} + 9 \stackrel{?}{=} 0$

$(\sqrt{3x})^2 = (-9)^2$ $\qquad$ $9 + 9 \stackrel{?}{=} 0$

$3x = 81$ $\qquad\qquad\qquad$ $18 \neq 0$

$x = \dfrac{81}{3}$ $\qquad\qquad$ No real solution

$x = 27$

105. $\sqrt{2(a - 7)} = 14$ **Check:** $\sqrt{2(105 - 7)} \stackrel{?}{=} 14$

$(\sqrt{2(a - 7)})^2 = (14)^2$ $\qquad\qquad$ $\sqrt{196} \stackrel{?}{=} 14$

$2(a - 7) = 196$ $\qquad\qquad\qquad$ $14 = 14$

$2a - 14 = 196$

$2a = 210$

$a = 105$

107. $\sqrt[3]{5x - 7} - 3 = -1$ **Check:** $\sqrt[3]{5(3) - 7} - 3 \stackrel{?}{=} -1$

$\sqrt[3]{5x - 7} = 2$ $\qquad\qquad$ $\sqrt[3]{8} - 3 \stackrel{?}{=} -1$

$(\sqrt[3]{5x - 7})^3 = 2^3$ $\qquad\qquad$ $2 - 3 \stackrel{?}{=} -1$

$5x - 7 = 8$ $\qquad\qquad\qquad$ $-1 = -1$

$5x = 15$

$x = 3$

109. $\sqrt[3]{5x + 2} - \sqrt[3]{7x - 8} = 0$

$$\sqrt[3]{5x + 2} = \sqrt[3]{7x - 8}$$

$$\left(\sqrt[3]{5x + 2}\right)^3 = \left(\sqrt[3]{7x - 8}\right)^3$$

$$5x + 2 = 7x - 8$$

$$10 = 2x$$

$$5 = x$$

Check: $\sqrt[3]{5(5) + 2} - \sqrt[3]{7(5) - 8} \overset{?}{=} 0$

$$\sqrt[3]{27} - \sqrt[3]{27} \overset{?}{=} 0$$

$$0 = 0$$

111. $\sqrt{2(x + 5)} = x + 5$

$$\left(\sqrt{2(x + 5)}\right)^2 = (x + 5)^2$$

$$2(x + 5) = x^2 + 10x + 25$$

$$2x + 10 = x^2 + 10x + 25$$

$$0 = x^2 + 8x + 15$$

$$0 = (x + 5)(x + 3)$$

$$-5 = x, \qquad x = -3$$

Check: $\sqrt{2(-5 + 5)} \overset{?}{=} -5 + 5$

$$\sqrt{0} \overset{?}{=} 0$$

$$0 = 0$$

$$\sqrt{2(-3 + 5)} \overset{?}{=} -3 + 5$$

$$\sqrt{4} \overset{?}{=} 2$$

$$2 = 2$$

113. $\sqrt{v - 6} = 6 - v$

$$\left(\sqrt{v - 6}\right)^2 = (6 - v)^2$$

$$v - 6 = 36 - 12v + v^2$$

$$0 = v^2 - 13v + 42$$

$$0 = (v - 6)(v - 7)$$

$$v = 6, \qquad v = 7$$

Check: $\sqrt{6 - 6} \overset{?}{=} 6 - 6$

$$0 = 0$$

$$\sqrt{7 - 6} \overset{?}{=} 6 - 7$$

$$1 \neq -1$$

not a solution

115. $\sqrt{1 + 6x} = 2 - \sqrt{6x}$

$$\left(\sqrt{1 + 6x}\right)^2 = \left(2 - \sqrt{6x}\right)^2$$

$$1 + 6x = 4 - 4\sqrt{6x} + 6x$$

$$1 = 4 - 4\sqrt{6x}$$

$$-3 = -4\sqrt{6x}$$

$$(3)^2 = \left(4\sqrt{6x}\right)^2$$

$$9 = 16(6x)$$

$$\frac{9}{96} = x$$

$$\frac{3}{32} = x$$

Check: $\sqrt{1 + 6\left(\dfrac{3}{32}\right)} \overset{?}{=} 2 - \sqrt{6\left(\dfrac{3}{32}\right)}$

$$\sqrt{\frac{32}{32} + \frac{18}{32}} \overset{?}{=} 2 - \sqrt{\frac{18}{32}}$$

$$\sqrt{\frac{50}{32}} \overset{?}{=} 2 - \sqrt{\frac{9 \cdot 2}{16 \cdot 2}}$$

$$\sqrt{\frac{25 \cdot 2}{16 \cdot 2}} \overset{?}{=} 2 - \sqrt{\frac{9 \cdot 2}{16 \cdot 2}}$$

$$\sqrt{\frac{25}{16}} \overset{?}{=} 2 - \sqrt{\frac{9}{16}}$$

$$\frac{5}{4} \overset{?}{=} 2 - \frac{3}{4}$$

$$\frac{5}{4} \overset{?}{=} \frac{8}{4} - \frac{3}{4}$$

$$\frac{5}{4} = \frac{5}{4}$$

117. $\sqrt{-48} = \sqrt{16 \cdot 3 \cdot -1} = 4i\sqrt{3}$

119. $10 - 3\sqrt{-27} = 10 - 3\sqrt{-1 \cdot 9 \cdot 3}$

$$= 10 - 3\sqrt{-1} \cdot \sqrt{9} \cdot \sqrt{3}$$

$$= 10 - 9i\sqrt{3}$$

121. $\frac{3}{4} - 5\sqrt{-\frac{3}{25}} = \frac{3}{4} - 5\sqrt{\frac{3}{25} \cdot -1}$

$\qquad\qquad = \frac{3}{4} - \frac{5}{5}i\sqrt{3}$

$\qquad\qquad = \frac{3}{4} - i\sqrt{3}$

123. $\sqrt{-81} + \sqrt{-36} = 9i + 6i$

$\qquad\qquad\quad = 15i$

125. $\sqrt{-121} - \sqrt{-84} = 11i - 2i\sqrt{21}$

127. $\sqrt{-5}\sqrt{-5} = i\sqrt{5} \cdot i\sqrt{5} = i^2 \cdot 5 = -5$

129. $\sqrt{-10}\left(\sqrt{-4} - \sqrt{-7}\right) = i\sqrt{10}\left(2i - i\sqrt{7}\right)$

$\qquad\qquad\qquad\qquad = 2i^2\sqrt{10} - i^2\sqrt{70}$

$\qquad\qquad\qquad\qquad = -2\sqrt{10} + \sqrt{70}$

131. $4x - \sqrt{-36} = 8 - 2yi$

$\qquad 4x - 6i = 8 - 2yi$

$\qquad\quad 4x = 8 \qquad -6 = -2y$

$\qquad\qquad x = 2 \qquad\; 3 = y$

133. $24 + \sqrt{-5y} = 6x + 25i$

$\qquad 24 + i\sqrt{5y} = 6x + 25i$

$\qquad\quad 24 = 6x \qquad \sqrt{5y} = 25$

$\qquad\qquad 4 = x \qquad\;\; 5y = 625$

$\qquad\qquad\qquad\qquad\quad y = 125$

135. $(-4 + 5i) - (-12 + 8i) = (-4 + 12) + (5 - 8)i$

$\qquad\qquad\qquad\qquad\qquad = 8 - 3i$

137. $(3 - 8i) + (5 + 12i) = 3 - 8i + 5 + 12i$

$\qquad\qquad\qquad\qquad = (3 + 5) + (-8 + 12)i$

$\qquad\qquad\qquad\qquad = 8 + 4i$

139. $(4 - 3i)(4 + 3i) = 4^2 - (3i)^2$

$\qquad\qquad\qquad\quad = 16 + 9$

$\qquad\qquad\qquad\quad = 25$

141. $(6 - 5i)^2 = 6^2 - 2(6)(5i) + (5i)^2$

$\qquad\qquad = 36 - 60i - 25$

$\qquad\qquad = 11 - 60i$

143. $\dfrac{7}{3i} = \dfrac{7}{3i} \cdot \dfrac{-i}{-i} = \dfrac{-7i}{-3i^2} = \dfrac{-7i}{3}$

145. $\dfrac{4i}{2 - 8i} = \dfrac{4i}{2 - 8i} \cdot \dfrac{2 + 8i}{2 + 8i}$

$\qquad\quad = \dfrac{8i + 32i^2}{2^2 - (8i)^2}$

$\qquad\quad = \dfrac{8i - 32}{4 + 64}$

$\qquad\quad = \dfrac{8i - 32}{68}$

$\qquad\quad = \dfrac{-8 + 2i}{17}$

$\qquad\quad = \dfrac{-8}{17} + \dfrac{2}{17}i$

147. $\dfrac{3 - 5i}{6 + i} = \dfrac{3 - 5i}{6 + i} \cdot \dfrac{6 - i}{6 - i}$

$\qquad\quad = \dfrac{18 - 3i - 30i + 5i^2}{6^2 - i^2}$

$\qquad\quad = \dfrac{18 - 33i - 5}{36 + 1}$

$\qquad\quad = \dfrac{13 - 33i}{37}$

$\qquad\quad = \dfrac{13}{37} - \dfrac{33}{37}i$

149. $c = \sqrt{3^2 + 3^2} = \sqrt{9 + 9} = \sqrt{18}$

Equation: $P = 2(8) + 2\left(2\frac{1}{2}\right) + 4\left(\sqrt{18}\right)$

$\qquad\qquad = 16 + 5 + 12\sqrt{2}$

$\qquad\qquad = 21 + 12\sqrt{2}$ inches

151.

$$1.3 = 2\pi\sqrt{\frac{L}{32}}$$

$$\frac{1.3}{2\pi} = \sqrt{\frac{L}{32}}$$

$$\left(\frac{1.3}{2\pi}\right)^2 = \left(\sqrt{\frac{L}{32}}\right)^2$$

$$\frac{1.69}{4\pi^2} = \frac{L}{32}$$

$$\frac{1.69}{4\pi^2}(32) = L$$

$$1.3698624 = L \approx 1.37 \text{ feet}$$

153.

$$I = \sqrt{\frac{P}{R}}$$

$$5 = \sqrt{\frac{P}{20}}$$

$$5^2 = \left(\sqrt{\frac{P}{20}}\right)^2$$

$$25 = \frac{P}{20}$$

$$500 \text{ watts} = P$$

155.

$$I = \sqrt{\frac{P}{R}}$$

$$15 = \sqrt{\frac{P}{40}}$$

$$15^2 = \left(\sqrt{\frac{P}{40}}\right)^2$$

$$225 = \frac{P}{40}$$

$$9000 \text{ watts} = P$$

157.

$$v = \sqrt{2gh}$$

$$25 = \sqrt{2(32)h}$$

$$25^2 = \left(\sqrt{2(32)h}\right)^2$$

$$625 = 2(32)h$$

$$9.77 \text{ feet} \approx h$$

Chapter Test for Chapter 5

1. (a) $16^{3/2} = \left(\sqrt{16}\right)^3$

$\qquad\quad = 4^3$

$\qquad\quad = 64$

(b) $\sqrt{5}\sqrt{20} = \sqrt{5 \cdot 20}$

$\qquad\qquad = \sqrt{100}$

$\qquad\qquad = 10$

2. (a) $27^{-2/3} = \dfrac{1}{27^{2/3}}$

$\qquad\qquad = \dfrac{1}{9}$

(b) $\sqrt{2}\sqrt{18} = \sqrt{2 \cdot 18}$

$\qquad\qquad = \sqrt{36}$

$\qquad\qquad = 6$

3. (a) $\left(\dfrac{x^{1/2}}{x^{1/3}}\right)^2 = \dfrac{x}{x^{2/3}}$

$\qquad\qquad\quad = x^{1-2/3} = x^{1/3}$

(b) $5^{1/4} \cdot 5^{7/4} = 5^{1/4 + 7/4}$

$\qquad\qquad\quad = 5^{8/4} = 5^2 = 25$

4. (a) $\sqrt{\dfrac{32}{9}} = \sqrt{\dfrac{16 \cdot 2}{9}} = \dfrac{4}{3}\sqrt{2}$

(b) $\sqrt[3]{24} = \sqrt[3]{8 \cdot 3} = 2\sqrt[3]{3}$

5. (a) $\sqrt{24x^3} = \sqrt{4 \cdot 6 \cdot x^2 \cdot x}$

$= 2x\sqrt{6x}$

(b) $\sqrt[4]{16x^5y^8} = \sqrt[4]{16x^4xy^8}$

$= 2xy^2\sqrt[4]{x}$

6. $\dfrac{3}{\sqrt{6}} = \dfrac{3}{\sqrt{6}} \cdot \dfrac{\sqrt{6}}{\sqrt{6}} = \dfrac{3\sqrt{6}}{6} = \dfrac{\sqrt{6}}{2}$

Multiply the numerator and denominator of a fraction by a factor such that no radical contains a fraction and no denominator of a fraction contains a radical.

7. $5\sqrt{3x} - 3\sqrt{75x} = 5\sqrt{3x} - 3\sqrt{25 \cdot 3x}$

$= 5\sqrt{3x} - 15\sqrt{3x}$

$= -10\sqrt{3x}$

8. $\sqrt{5}\left(\sqrt{15x} + 3\right) = \sqrt{75x} + 3\sqrt{5}$

$= \sqrt{25 \cdot 3x} + 3\sqrt{5}$

$= 5\sqrt{3x} + 3\sqrt{5}$

9. $\left(4 - \sqrt{2x}\right)^2 = 16 - 8\sqrt{2x} + 2x$

10. $7\sqrt{27} + 14y\sqrt{12} = 7\sqrt{9 \cdot 3} + 14y\sqrt{4 \cdot 3}$

$= 21\sqrt{3} + 28y\sqrt{3}$

$= 7\sqrt{3}(3 + 4y)$

11. $\sqrt{3y} - 6 = 3$

$\sqrt{3y} = 9$

$\left(\sqrt{3y}\right)^2 = 9^2$

$3y = 81$

$y = 27$

Check: $\sqrt{3(27)} - 6 \overset{?}{=} 3$

$\sqrt{81} - 6 \overset{?}{=} 3$

$9 - 6 \overset{?}{=} 3$

$3 = 3$

12. $\sqrt{x^2 - 1} = x - 2$

$\left(\sqrt{x^2 - 1}\right)^2 = (x - 2)^2$

$x^2 - 1 = x^2 - 4x + 4$

$4x = 5$

$x = \dfrac{5}{4}$

No solution

Check: $\sqrt{\left(\frac{5}{4}\right)^2 - 1} \overset{?}{=} \dfrac{5}{4} - 2$

$\sqrt{\dfrac{25}{16} - \dfrac{16}{16}} \overset{?}{=} \dfrac{5}{4} - \dfrac{8}{4}$

$\sqrt{\dfrac{9}{16}} \overset{?}{=} -\dfrac{3}{4}$

$\dfrac{3}{4} \neq -\dfrac{3}{4}$

13. $\sqrt{x} - x + 6 = 0$

$\left(\sqrt{x}\right)^2 = (x - 6)^2$

$x = x^2 - 12x + 36$

$0 = x^2 - 13x + 36$

$0 = (x - 9)(x - 4)$

$0 = x - 9 \qquad 0 = x - 4$

$9 = x \qquad\qquad 4 = x$

Not a solution

Check: $\sqrt{9} - 9 + 6 \overset{?}{=} 0$

$3 - 9 + 6 \overset{?}{=} 0$

$0 = 0$

$\sqrt{4} - 4 + 6 \overset{?}{=} 0$

$2 - 4 + 6 \overset{?}{=} 0$

$4 \neq 0$

14. $3x + \sqrt{-4y} = 12 + 40i$

$3x + 2\sqrt{y}i = 12 + 40i$

$3x = 12 \qquad 2\sqrt{y} = 40$

$x = 4 \qquad\quad \sqrt{y} = 20$

$y = 400$

15. $27 - \sqrt{-16y} = 9x - 4i$

$27 - 4\sqrt{y}i = 9x - 4i$

$27 = 9x \qquad -4\sqrt{y} = -4$

$3 = x \qquad\quad \sqrt{y} = 1$

$y = 1$

16. $(2 + 3i) - \sqrt{-25} = 2 + 3i - 5i = 2 - 2i$

17. $(2 - 3i)^2 = (2 - 3i)(2 - 3i)$

$= 4 - 6i - 6i + 9i^2$

$= 4 - 12i - 9$

$= -5 - 12i$

18. $\sqrt{-16}\left(1 + \sqrt{4}\right) = 4i(1 + 2i)$

$= 4i + 8i^2$

$= -8 + 4i$

19. $(3 - 2i)(1 + 5i) = 3 + 13i - 10i^2$

$= 3 + 13i + 10$

$= 13 + 13i$

20. $\dfrac{5 - 2i}{i} = \dfrac{5 - 2i}{i} \cdot \dfrac{-i}{-i} = \dfrac{-5i + 2i^2}{-i^2} = -2 - 5i$

21. $v = \sqrt{2gh}$

$80 = \sqrt{2(32)h}$

$80 = \sqrt{64h}$

$80^2 = \left(\sqrt{64h}\right)^2$

$6400 = 64h$

$100 \text{ feet} = h$

CHAPTER 6
Quadratic Equations and Inequalities

CHAPTER 6
Quadratic Equations and Inequalities

Section 6.1   Factoring and Extracting Square Roots

Solutions to Odd-Numbered Exercises

1. $x^2 - 12x + 35 = 0$

$(x - 5)(x - 7) = 0$

$x = 5 \quad x = 7$

3. $x^2 + x - 72 = 0$

$(x + 9)(x - 8) = 0$

$x = -9 \quad x = 8$

5. $\qquad x^2 + 4x = 45$

$x^2 + 4x - 45 = 0$

$(x + 9)(x - 5) = 0$

$x = -9 \quad x = 5$

7. $x^2 - 12x + 36 = 0$

$(x - 6)(x - 6) = 0$

$x - 6 = 0 \quad x - 6 = 0$

$x = 6 \qquad x = 6$

9. $9x^2 + 24x + 16 = 0$

$(3x + 4)(3x + 4) = 0$

$3x + 4 = 0 \qquad 3x + 4 = 0$

$3x = -4 \qquad 3x = -4$

$x = -\frac{4}{3} \qquad x = -\frac{4}{3}$

11. $4x^2 - 12x = 0$

$4x(x - 3) = 0$

$4x = 0 \quad x - 3 = 0$

$x = 0 \qquad x = 3$

13. $u(u - 9) - 12(u - 9) = 0$

$(u - 9)(u - 12) = 0$

$u - 9 = 0 \quad u - 12 = 0$

$u = 9 \qquad u = 12$

15. $3x(x - 6) - 5(x - 6) = 0$

$(x - 6)(3x - 5) = 0$

$x - 6 = 0 \quad 3x - 5 = 0$

$x = 6 \qquad x = \frac{5}{3}$

17. $\qquad (y - 4)(y - 3) = 6$

$y^2 - 7y + 12 - 6 = 0$

$y^2 - 7y + 6 = 0$

$(y - 6)(y - 1) = 0$

$y - 6 = 0 \quad y - 1 = 0$

$y = 6 \qquad y = 1$

19. $\qquad 2x(3x + 2) = 5 - 6x^2$

$6x^2 + 4x = 5 - 6x^2$

$12x^2 + 4x - 5 = 0$

$(6x + 5)(2x - 1) = 0$

$6x + 5 = 0 \qquad 2x - 1 = 0$

$x = -\frac{5}{6} \qquad x = \frac{1}{2}$

21. $x^2 = 64$

$x = \pm\sqrt{64}$

$x = \pm 8$

23. $6x^2 = 54$

$x^2 = 9$

$x = \pm\sqrt{9}$

$x = \pm 3$

25. $25x^2 = 16$

$x^2 = \frac{16}{25}$

$x = \pm\sqrt{\frac{16}{25}}$

$x = \pm\frac{4}{5}$

27. $\frac{1}{2}y^2 = 32$

$y^2 = 64$

$y = \pm\sqrt{64}$

$y = \pm 8$

29. $4x^2 - 25 = 0$

$4x^2 = 25$

$x^2 = \frac{25}{4}$

$x = \pm\sqrt{\frac{25}{4}}$

$x = \pm\frac{5}{2}$

31. $4u^2 - 225 = 0$

$u^2 = \frac{225}{4}$

$u = \pm\sqrt{\frac{225}{4}}$

$u = \pm\frac{15}{2}$

33. $(x + 4)^2 = 169$

$x + 4 = \pm\sqrt{169}$

$x = -4 \pm 13$

$x = 9, -17$

35. $(x - 3)^2 = 0.25$

$x - 3 = \pm\sqrt{0.25}$

$x = 3 \pm 0.5$

$x = 3.5, 2.5$

37. $(x - 2)^2 = 7$

$x - 2 = \pm\sqrt{7}$

$x = 2 \pm \sqrt{7}$

39. $(2x + 1)^2 = 50$

$2x + 1 = \pm\sqrt{50}$

$2x = -1 \pm 5\sqrt{2}$

$x = \dfrac{-1 \pm 5\sqrt{2}}{2}$

41. $(4x - 3)^2 - 98 = 0$

$(4x - 3)^2 = 98$

$4x - 3 = \pm\sqrt{98}$

$4x = 3 \pm 7\sqrt{2}$

$x = \dfrac{3 \pm 7\sqrt{2}}{4}$

43. $z^2 = -36$

$z = \pm\sqrt{-36}$

$z = \pm 6i$

45. $x^2 + 4 = 0$

$x^2 = -4$

$x = \pm\sqrt{-4}$

$x = \pm 2i$

47. $9u^2 + 17 = 0$

$9u^2 = -17$

$u = \pm\sqrt{-\dfrac{17}{9}}$

$= \pm i\dfrac{\sqrt{17}}{3}$

49. $(t - 3)^2 = -25$

$t - 3 = \pm\sqrt{-25}$

$t = 3 \pm 5i$

51. $(3z + 4)^2 + 144 = 0$

$(3z + 4)^2 = -144$

$3z + 4 = \pm\sqrt{-144}$

$3z + 4 = \pm 12i$

$3z = -4 \pm 12i$

$z = \dfrac{-4 \pm 12i}{3}$

$z = -\dfrac{4}{3} \pm 4i$

53. $(2x + 3)^2 = -54$

$2x + 3 = \pm\sqrt{-54}$

$2x = -3 \pm 3i\sqrt{6}$

$x = -\dfrac{3}{2} \pm \dfrac{3i\sqrt{6}}{2}$

55. $9(x + 6)^2 = -121$

$(x + 6)^2 = \dfrac{-121}{9}$

$x + 6 = \pm\sqrt{\dfrac{-121}{9}}$

$x = -6 \pm \dfrac{11}{3}i$

57. $(x - 1)^2 = -27$

$x - 1 = \pm\sqrt{-27}$

$x = 1 \pm 3i\sqrt{3}$

59. $(x + 1)^2 + 0.04 = 0$

$(x + 1)^2 = -0.04$

$x + 1 = \pm\sqrt{-0.04}$

$x = -1 \pm 0.2i$

61. $\left(c - \dfrac{2}{3}\right)^2 + \dfrac{1}{9} = 0$

$\left(c - \dfrac{2}{3}\right)^2 = -\dfrac{1}{9}$

$c - \dfrac{2}{3} = \pm\sqrt{-\dfrac{1}{9}}$

$c = \dfrac{2}{3} \pm \dfrac{1}{3}i$

63. $\left(x + \dfrac{7}{3}\right)^2 = -\dfrac{38}{9}$

$x + \dfrac{7}{3} = \pm\sqrt{-\dfrac{38}{9}}$

$x = -\dfrac{7}{3} \pm \dfrac{i}{3}\sqrt{38}$

65. $2x^2 - 5x = 0$

$x(2x - 5) = 0$

$x = 0 \qquad 2x - 5 = 0$

$x = \dfrac{5}{2}$

67. $2x^2 + 5x - 12 = 0$

$(2x - 3)(x + 4) = 0$

$x = \dfrac{3}{2} \qquad x = -4$

69. $x^2 - 900 = 0$

$x^2 = 900$

$x = \pm 30$

71. $x^2 + 900 = 0$

$x^2 = -900$

$x = \pm\sqrt{-900}$

$x = \pm 30i$

73. $\frac{2}{3}x^2 = 6$

$\frac{3}{2} \cdot \frac{2}{3}x^2 = 6 \cdot \frac{3}{2}$

$x^2 = 9$

$x = \pm 3$

75. $(x - 5)^2 - 100 = 0$

$(x - 5)^2 = 100$

$x - 5 = \pm 10$

$x = 15, -5$

77. $(x - 5)^2 + 100 = 0$

let $u = (x - 5)$

$u^2 + 100 = 0$

$(u + 10i)(u - 10i) = 0$

$u + 10i = 0 \qquad\qquad u - 10i = 0$

$u = -10i \qquad\qquad u = 10i$

$x - 5 = -10i \qquad\quad x - 5 = 10i$

$x = 5 - 10i \qquad\quad x = 5 + 10i$

79. $(x + 2)^2 + 18 = 0$

$(x + 2)^2 = -18$

$x + 2 = \pm\sqrt{-18}$

$x = -2 \pm 3i\sqrt{2}$

81. *Keystrokes:*

$\boxed{Y=}\ \boxed{X,T,\theta}\ \boxed{x^2}\ \boxed{-}\ 9\ \boxed{\text{GRAPH}}$

x-intercepts are -3 and 3.

$0 = x^2 - 9$

$\quad = (x - 3)(x + 3)$

$x - 3 = 0 \qquad x + 3 = 0$

$\quad x = 3 \qquad\quad x = -3$

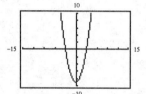

83. *Keystrokes:*

$\boxed{Y=}\ \boxed{X,T,\theta}\ \boxed{x^2}\ \boxed{-}\ 2\ \boxed{X,T,\theta}\ \boxed{-}\ 15\ \boxed{\text{GRAPH}}$

x-intercepts are -3 and 5.

$0 = x^2 - 2x - 15$

$0 = (x - 5)(x + 3)$

$x - 5 = 0 \qquad x + 3 = 0$

$\quad x = 5 \qquad\quad x = -3$

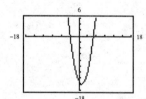

85. *Keystrokes:*

$\boxed{Y=}\ 4\ \boxed{-}\ \boxed{(}\ \boxed{X,T,\theta}\ \boxed{-}\ 3\ \boxed{)}\ \boxed{x^2}\ \boxed{\text{GRAPH}}$

x-intercepts are 1 and 5.

$0 = 4 - (x - 3)^2$

$(x - 3)^2 = 4$

$x - 3 = \pm 2$

$x = 5, 1$

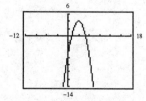

87. *Keystrokes:*

$\boxed{Y=}$ 2 $\boxed{X,T,\theta}$ $\boxed{x^2}$ $\boxed{-}$ $\boxed{X,T,\theta}$ $\boxed{-}$ 6 $\boxed{GRAPH}$

x-intercepts are $-\frac{3}{2}$ and 2.

$0 = 2x^2 - x - 6$

$0 = (2x + 3)(x - 2)$

$x = -\frac{3}{2} \qquad x = 2$

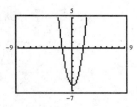

89. *Keystrokes:*

$\boxed{Y=}$ 3 $\boxed{X,T,\theta}$ $\boxed{x^2}$ $\boxed{-}$ 8 $\boxed{X,T,\theta}$ $\boxed{-}$ 16 $\boxed{GRAPH}$

x-intercepts are $-\frac{4}{3}$ and 4.

$0 = 3x^2 - 8x - 16$

$0 = (3x + 4)(x - 14)$

$x = -\frac{4}{3} \qquad x = 4$

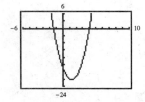

91. *Keystrokes:*

$\boxed{Y=}$ $\boxed{X,T,\theta}$ $\boxed{x^2}$ $\boxed{+}$ 7 $\boxed{GRAPH}$

$0 = x^2 + 7$

$-7 = x^2$

$\pm\sqrt{-7} = x$

$\pm i\sqrt{7} = x$

The equation has complex roots.

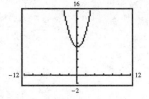

93. *Keystrokes:*

$\boxed{Y=}$ $\boxed{(}$ $\boxed{X,T,\theta}$ $\boxed{-}$ 1 $\boxed{)}$ $\boxed{x^2}$ $\boxed{+}$ 1 $\boxed{GRAPH}$

$0 = (x - 1)^2 + 1$

$-1 = (x - 1)^2$

$\pm i = x - 1$

$1 \pm i = x$

The equation has complex roots.

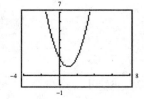

95. *Keystrokes:*

$\boxed{Y=}$ $\boxed{(}$ $\boxed{X,T,\theta}$ $\boxed{+}$ 3 $\boxed{)}$ $\boxed{x^2}$ $\boxed{+}$ 5 $\boxed{GRAPH}$

$0 = (x + 3)^2 + 5$

$-5 = (x + 3)^2$

$\pm\sqrt{-5} = x + 3$

$\pm\sqrt{5}i = x + 3$

$-3 \pm \sqrt{5}i = x$

The equation has complex roots.

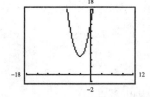

97. $x^2 + y^2 = 4$

$y^2 = 4 - x^2$

$y = \pm\sqrt{4 - x^2}$

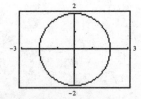

99. $x^2 + 4y^2 = 4$

$$4y^2 = 4 - x^2$$

$$y^2 = \frac{4 - x^2}{4}$$

$$y = \pm\sqrt{\frac{4 - x^2}{4}} = \pm\frac{\sqrt{4 - x^2}}{2}$$

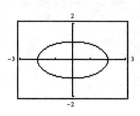

101. $\qquad x^4 - 5x^2 + 4 = 0$

$$(x^2 - 4)(x^2 - 1) = 0$$

$$(x - 2)(x + 2)(x - 1)(x + 1) = 0$$

$x - 2 = 0 \qquad x + 2 = 0 \qquad x - 1 = 0 \qquad x + 1 = 0$

$\qquad x = 2 \qquad\qquad x = -2 \qquad\qquad x = 1 \qquad\qquad x = -1$

103. $\qquad x^4 - 5x^2 + 6 = 0$

$$(x^2 - 3)(x^2 - 2) = 0$$

$x^2 - 3 = 0 \qquad x^2 - 2 = 0$

$\quad x^2 = 3 \qquad\qquad x^2 = 2$

$\quad x = \pm\sqrt{3} \qquad\quad x = \pm\sqrt{2}$

105. $\qquad x^4 - 3x^2 - 4 = 0$

$$(x^2 - 4)(x^2 + 1) = 0$$

$x^2 - 4 = 0 \qquad x^2 + 1 = 0$

$\quad x^2 = 4 \qquad\qquad x^2 = -1$

$\quad x = \pm 2 \qquad\qquad x = \pm i$

107. $\qquad (x^2 - 4)^2 + 2(x^2 - 4) - 3 = 0$

$$\left[(x^2 - 4) + 3\right]\left[(x^2 - 4) - 1\right] = 0$$

$$(x^2 - 1)(x^2 - 5) = 0$$

$x^2 - 1 = 0 \qquad x^2 - 5 = 0$

$\quad x^2 = 1 \qquad\qquad x^2 = 5$

$\quad x = \pm 1 \qquad\qquad x = \pm\sqrt{5}$

109. $\qquad x - 7\sqrt{x} + 10 = 0$

let $u = \sqrt{x}$

$$\left(\sqrt{x}\right)^2 - 7\left(\sqrt{x}\right) + 10 = 0$$

$$u^2 - 7u + 10 = 0$$

$$(u - 5)(u - 2) = 0$$

$u = 5 \qquad u = 2$

$\sqrt{x} = 5 \qquad \sqrt{x} = 2$

$\quad x = 25 \qquad\quad x = 4$

Check: $25 - 7\sqrt{25} + 10 \overset{?}{=} 0$

$\qquad\qquad 25 - 35 + 10 \overset{?}{=} 0$

$\qquad\qquad\qquad\qquad 0 = 0$

Check: $\quad 4 - 7\sqrt{4} + 10 \overset{?}{=} 0$

$\qquad\qquad 4 - 14 + 10 \overset{?}{=} 0$

$\qquad\qquad\qquad\qquad 0 = 0$

111. $\qquad x^{2/3} - x^{1/3} - 6 = 0$

$$(x^{1/3} - 3)(x^{1/3} + 2) = 0$$

$x^{1/3} - 3 = 0 \qquad x^{1/3} + 2 = 0$

$\quad x^{1/3} = 3 \qquad\qquad x^{1/3} = -2$

$\quad x = 27 \qquad\qquad x = -8$

113. $2x^{2/3} - 7x^{1/3} + 5 = 0$

let $u = x^{1/3}$

$2(x^{1/3})^2 - 7x^{1/3} + 5 = 0$

$2u^2 - 7u + 5 = 0$

$(2u - 5)(u - 1) = 0$

$2u - 5 = 0 \qquad u - 1 = 0$

$2u = 5 \qquad\qquad u = 1$

$u = \frac{5}{2} \qquad\qquad x^{1/3} = 1$

$x^{1/3} = \frac{5}{2} \qquad (x^{1/3}) = 1^3$

$(x^{1/3}) = \left(\frac{5}{2}\right)^3 \qquad x = 1$

$x = \frac{125}{8}$

115. $x^{2/5} - 3x^{1/5} + 2 = 0$

$(x^{1/5} - 2)(x^{1/5} - 1) = 0$

$x^{1/5} = 2 \qquad x^{1/5} = 1$

$x = 2^5 \qquad\quad x = 1^5$

$x = 32 \qquad\quad x = 1$

117. $2x^{2/5} - 7x^{1/5} + 3 = 0$

$(2x^{1/5} - 1)(x^{1/5} - 3) = 0$

$x^{1/5} = \frac{1}{2} \qquad x^{1/5} = 3$

$x = \left(\frac{1}{2}\right)^5 \qquad x = 3^5$

$x = \frac{1}{32} \qquad\quad x = 243$

119. $\frac{1}{x^2} - \frac{3}{x} + 2 = 0$

$1 - 3x + 2x^2 = 0$

$2x^2 - 3x + 1 = 0$

$(2x - 1)(x - 1) = 0$

$2x - 1 = 0 \qquad x - 1 = 0$

$x = \frac{1}{2} \qquad\qquad x = 1$

121. $(x - 5)(x - (-2)) = 0$

$(x - 5)(x + 2) = 0$

$x^2 - 5x + 2x - 10 = 0$

$x^2 - 3x - 10 = 0$

123. $\left[x - \left(1 + \sqrt{2}\right)\right]\left[x - \left(1 - \sqrt{2}\right)\right] = 0$

$\left[(x - 1) - \sqrt{2}\right]\left[(x - 1) + \sqrt{2}\right] = 0$

$(x - 1)^2 - \left(\sqrt{2}\right)^2 = 0$

$x^2 - 2x + 1 - 2 = 0$

$x^2 - 2x - 1 = 0$

125. $(x - 5i)(x - (-5i)) = 0$

$(x - 5i)(x + 5i) = 0$

$x^2 - 25i^2 = 0$

$x^2 + 25 = 0$

127. $0 = -16t^2 + 256$

$16t^2 = 256$

$t^2 = 16$

$t = 4 \text{ seconds}$

129. $0 = -16t^2 + 128$

$16t^2 = 128$

$t^2 = 8$

$t = \pm\sqrt{8}$

$t = \pm 2\sqrt{2}$

$t = 2\sqrt{2} \approx 2.828 \text{ seconds}$

131. $0 = 144 + 128 - 16^2$

$0 = -16t^2 + 128t + 144$

$0 = -16(t^2 - 8t - 9)$

$0 = -16(t - 9)(t + 1)$

$t - 9 = 0 \qquad t + 1 = 0$

$t = 9 \text{ seconds} \qquad \bowtie$

133. $1685.40 = 1500(1 + r)^2$

$1.1236 = (1 + r)^2$

$1.06 = 1 + r$

$.06 = r$

$6\% = r$

135.
$$892 = (26.6 + t)^2$$
$$\sqrt{892} = 26.6 + t$$
$$\sqrt{892} - 26.6 = t$$
$$3 \approx t$$

Year 1993

137. (a) $h_0 = 100$ feet $v_0 = 0$ feet/sec $h = 0$

$$0 = 16t^2 + 0 \cdot t + 100$$
$$16t^2 = 100$$
$$t^2 = 6.25$$
$$t = \sqrt{6.25}$$
$$t = 2.5 \text{ seconds}$$

Extracting the roots method was used because the quadratic equation did not have a linear term.

(b) $h_0 = 100$ feet $v_0 = 32$ feet/sec $h = 100$ feet

$$100 = -16t^2 + 32t + 100$$
$$0 = -16t^2 + 32t$$
$$0 = -16t(t - 2)$$
$$-16t = 0 \qquad\qquad t - 2 = 0$$
$$t = 0 \text{ seconds} \qquad t = 2 \text{ seconds}$$

Factoring method was used because the quadratic equation did not have a constant term.

139. Factoring and the Zero-Factor Property allow you to solve a quadratic equation by converting it into two linear equations that you already know how to solve.

143. To solve an equation of quadratic form, determine an algebraic expression u such that substitution yields the quadratic equation $au^2 + bu + c = 0$. Solve this quadratic equation for u and then, through back-substitution, find the solution of the original equation.

141. False. The solutions are $x = 5$ and $x = -5$.

Section 6.2   Completing the Square

1. $x^2 + 8x + 16$ $\left[16 = \left(\dfrac{8}{2}\right)^2\right]$

3. $y^2 - 20y + 100$ $\left[100 = \left(-\dfrac{20}{2}\right)^2\right]$

5. $x^2 - 16x + 64$ $\left[64 = \left(-\dfrac{16}{2}\right)^2\right]$

7. $t^2 + 5t + \dfrac{25}{4}$ $\left[\dfrac{25}{4} = \left(\dfrac{5}{2}\right)^2\right]$

9. $x^2 - 9x + \dfrac{81}{4}$ $\left[\dfrac{81}{4} = \left(-\dfrac{9}{2}\right)^2\right]$

11. $a^2 - \dfrac{1}{3}a + \dfrac{1}{36}$ $\left[\dfrac{1}{36} = \left[\left(-\dfrac{1}{3}\right)\left(\dfrac{1}{2}\right)\right]^2\right]$

13. $y^2 - \dfrac{3}{5}y + \dfrac{9}{100}$ $\left[\dfrac{9}{100} = \left[\left(-\dfrac{3}{5}\right)\left(\dfrac{1}{2}\right)\right]^2\right]$

15. $r^2 - 0.4r + 0.04$ $\left[0.04 = \left(-\dfrac{0.4}{2}\right)^2\right]$

17. (a) $x^2 - 20x + 100 = 100$

$$(x - 10)^2 = 100$$
$$x - 10 = \pm 10$$
$$x = 10 \pm 10$$
$$x = 20, 0$$

(b) $x^2 - 20x = 0$

$$x(x - 20) = 0$$
$$x = 0 \qquad x = 20$$

19. (a) $x^2 + 6x + 9 = 0 + 9$

$$(x + 3)^2 = 9$$
$$x + 3 = \pm 3$$
$$x = -3 \pm 3$$
$$x = -6, 0$$

(b) $x^2 + 6x = 0$

$$x(x + 6) = 0$$
$$x = 0 \qquad x + 6 = 0$$
$$x = -6, 0$$

21. (a)
$$y^2 - 5y = 0$$
$$y^2 - 5y + \tfrac{25}{4} = \tfrac{25}{4}$$
$$\left(y - \tfrac{5}{2}\right)^2 = \tfrac{25}{4}$$
$$y - \tfrac{5}{2} = \pm\tfrac{5}{2}$$
$$y = \tfrac{5}{2} \pm \tfrac{5}{2}$$
$$= 0, 5$$

(b)
$$y^2 - 5y = 0$$
$$y(y - 5) = 0$$
$$y = 0 \qquad y - 5 = 0$$
$$y = 5$$

23. (a)
$$t^2 - 8t + 16 = -7 + 16$$
$$(t - 4)^2 = 9$$
$$t - 4 = \pm 3$$
$$t = 4 \pm 3$$
$$t = 7, 1$$

(b)
$$t^2 - 8t + 7 = 0$$
$$(t - 7)(t - 1) = 0$$
$$t = 7 \qquad t = 1$$

25. (a)
$$x^2 + 2x + 1 = 24 + 1$$
$$(x + 1)^2 = 25$$
$$x + 1 = \pm 5$$
$$x = -1 \pm 5$$
$$x = 4, -6$$

(b)
$$x^2 + 2x - 24 = 0$$
$$(x + 6)(x - 4) = 0$$
$$x = -6 \qquad x = 4$$

27. (a)
$$x^2 + 7x + \tfrac{49}{4} = -12 + \tfrac{49}{4}$$
$$\left(x + \tfrac{7}{2}\right)^2 = \tfrac{1}{4}$$
$$x + \tfrac{7}{2} = \pm\tfrac{1}{2}$$
$$x = -\tfrac{7}{2} \pm \tfrac{1}{2}$$
$$x = -\tfrac{6}{2}, -\tfrac{8}{2}$$
$$x = -3, -4$$

(b)
$$x^2 + 7x + 12 = 0$$
$$(x + 4)(x + 3) = 0$$
$$x = -4 \qquad x = -3$$

29. (a)
$$x^2 - 3x + \tfrac{9}{4} = 18 + \tfrac{9}{4}$$
$$\left(x - \tfrac{3}{2}\right)^2 = \tfrac{81}{4}$$
$$x - \tfrac{3}{2} = \pm\tfrac{9}{2}$$
$$x = \tfrac{3}{2} \pm \tfrac{9}{2}$$
$$x = \tfrac{12}{2}, -\tfrac{6}{2}$$
$$x = 6, -3$$

(b)
$$x^2 - 3x - 18 = 0$$
$$(x - 6)(x + 3) = 0$$
$$x = 6 \qquad x = -3$$

31. (a)
$$2x^2 - 14x + 12 = 0$$
$$x^2 - 7x + 6 = 0$$
$$x^2 - 7x = -6$$
$$x^2 - 7x + \tfrac{49}{4} = -6 + \tfrac{49}{4}$$
$$\left(x - \tfrac{7}{2}\right)^2 = -\tfrac{24}{4} + \tfrac{49}{4}$$
$$\left(x - \tfrac{7}{2}\right)^2 = \tfrac{25}{4}$$
$$x - \tfrac{7}{2} = \pm\tfrac{5}{2}$$
$$x = \tfrac{7}{2} \pm \tfrac{5}{2}$$
$$x = \tfrac{12}{2}, \tfrac{2}{2}$$
$$x = 6, 1$$

(b)
$$2x^2 - 14x + 12 = 0$$
$$x^2 - 7x + 6 = 0$$
$$(x - 6)(x - 1) = 0$$
$$x = 6 \qquad x = 1$$

33. (a) $4x^2 + 4x - 15 = 0$

$x^2 + x - \frac{15}{4} = 0$

$x^2 + x = \frac{15}{4}$

$x^2 + x + \frac{1}{4} = \frac{15}{4} + \frac{1}{4}$

$\left(x + \frac{1}{2}\right)^2 = \frac{16}{4}$

$x + \frac{1}{2} = \pm\sqrt{4}$

$x = -\frac{1}{2} \pm 2$

$x = \frac{3}{2}, -\frac{5}{2}$

(b) $4x^2 + 4x - 15 = 0$

$(2x - 3)(2x + 5) = 0$

$x = \frac{3}{2} \qquad x = -\frac{5}{2}$

35. $x^2 - 4x - 3 = 0$

$x^2 - 4x + 4 = 3 + 4$

$(x - 2)^2 = 7$

$x - 2 = \pm\sqrt{7}$

$x = 2 \pm \sqrt{7}$

$x \approx 4.65, -0.65$

37. $x^2 + 4x - 3 = 0$

$x^2 + 4x + 4 = 3 + 4$

$(x + 2)^2 = 7$

$x + 2 = \pm\sqrt{7}$

$x = -2 \pm \sqrt{7}$

$x \approx 0.65, -4.65$

39. $u^2 - 4u + 1 = 0$

$u^2 - 4u + 4 = -1 + 4$

$(u - 2)^2 = 3$

$u - 2 = \pm\sqrt{3}$

$u = 2 \pm \sqrt{3}$

$u \approx 3.73, 0.27$

41. $x^2 + 2x + 3 = 0$

$x^2 + 2x + 1 = -3 + 1$

$(x + 1)^2 = -2$

$x + 1 = \pm\sqrt{-2}$

$x = -1 \pm i\sqrt{2}$

$x \approx -1 + 1.41i$

$x \approx -1 - 1.41i$

43. $x^2 - 10x - 2 = 0$

$x^2 - 10x + 25 = 2 + 25$

$(x - 5)^2 = 27$

$x - 5 = \pm\sqrt{27}$

$x = 5 \pm 3\sqrt{3}$

$x \approx 10.20, -0.20$

45. $y^2 + 20y + 10 = 0$

$y^2 + 20y + 100 = -10 + 100$

$(y + 10)^2 = 90$

$y + 10 = \pm\sqrt{90}$

$y = -10 \pm 3\sqrt{10}$

$y \approx -0.51, -19.49$

47. $t^2 + 5t + 3 = 0$

$t^2 + 5t + \frac{25}{4} = -3 + \frac{25}{4}$

$\left(t + \frac{5}{2}\right)^2 = \frac{13}{4}$

$t + \frac{5}{2} = \pm\sqrt{\frac{13}{4}}$

$t = -\frac{5}{2} \pm \frac{\sqrt{13}}{2}$

$t = \frac{-5 \pm \sqrt{13}}{2}$

$t \approx -0.70, -4.30$

49. $v^2 + 3v - 2 = 0$

$v^2 + 3v + \frac{9}{4} = 2 + \frac{9}{4}$

$\left(v + \frac{3}{2}\right)^2 = \frac{17}{4}$

$v + \frac{3}{2} = \pm\sqrt{\frac{17}{4}}$

$v = -\frac{3}{2} \pm \sqrt{\frac{17}{4}}$

$v = -\frac{3}{2} \pm \frac{\sqrt{17}}{2}$

$v = \frac{-3 \pm \sqrt{17}}{2}$

$v \approx 0.56, -3.56$

51. $-x^2 + x - 1 = 0$

$x^2 - x + 1 = 0$

$x^2 - x + \dfrac{1}{4} = -1 + \dfrac{1}{4}$

$\left(x - \dfrac{1}{2}\right)^2 = -\dfrac{3}{4}$

$x - \dfrac{1}{2} = \pm\sqrt{-\dfrac{3}{4}}$

$x = \dfrac{1}{2} \pm \dfrac{i\sqrt{3}}{2}$

$x = \dfrac{1 \pm i\sqrt{3}}{2}$

$x \approx 0.5 + 0.87i$

$x \approx 0.5 - 0.87i$

53. $x^2 - 7x + 12 = 0$

$x^2 - 7x + \dfrac{49}{4} = -12 + \dfrac{49}{4}$

$\left(x - \dfrac{7}{2}\right)^2 = \dfrac{-48}{4} + \dfrac{49}{4}$

$\left(x - \dfrac{7}{2}\right)^2 = \dfrac{1}{4}$

$x - \dfrac{7}{2} = \pm\sqrt{\dfrac{1}{4}}$

$x = \dfrac{7}{2} \pm \dfrac{1}{2}$

$x = 4, 3$

55. $x^2 - \dfrac{2}{3}x - 3 = 0$

$x^2 - \dfrac{2}{3}x + \dfrac{1}{9} = 3 + \dfrac{1}{9}$

$\left(x - \dfrac{1}{3}\right)^2 = \dfrac{28}{9}$

$x - \dfrac{1}{3} = \pm\sqrt{\dfrac{28}{9}}$

$x = \dfrac{1}{3} \pm \dfrac{2}{3}\sqrt{7}$

$x = \dfrac{1 \pm 2\sqrt{7}}{3}$

$x \approx 2.10, -1.43$

57. $v^2 + \dfrac{3}{4}v - 2 = 0$

$v^2 + \dfrac{3}{4}v + \dfrac{9}{64} = 2 + \dfrac{9}{64}$

$\left(v + \dfrac{3}{8}\right)^2 = \dfrac{128}{64} + \dfrac{9}{64}$

$\left(v + \dfrac{3}{8}\right)^2 = \dfrac{137}{64}$

$v + \dfrac{3}{8} = \pm\sqrt{\dfrac{137}{64}}$

$v = -\dfrac{3}{8} \pm \dfrac{\sqrt{137}}{8}$

$v \approx 1.09, -1.84$

59. $2x^2 + 8x + 3 = 0$

$x^2 + 4x + 4 = -\dfrac{3}{2} + 4$

$(x + 2)^2 = \dfrac{5}{2}$

$x + 2 = \pm\sqrt{\dfrac{5}{2}} \cdot \dfrac{\sqrt{2}}{\sqrt{2}}$

$x = -2 \pm \dfrac{\sqrt{10}}{2}$

$x \approx -0.42, -3.58$

61. $3x^2 + 9x + 5 = 0$

$x^2 + 3x + \dfrac{9}{4} = -\dfrac{5}{3} + \dfrac{9}{4}$

$\left(x + \dfrac{3}{2}\right)^2 = \dfrac{-20 + 27}{12}$

$\left(x + \dfrac{3}{2}\right)^2 = \dfrac{7}{12}$

$x + \dfrac{3}{2} = \pm\sqrt{\dfrac{7}{12}} \cdot \dfrac{\sqrt{3}}{\sqrt{3}}$

$x = -\dfrac{3}{2} \pm \dfrac{\sqrt{21}}{6}$

$x = \dfrac{-9 \pm \sqrt{21}}{6}$

$x \approx -0.74, -2.26$

63. $4y^2 + 4y - 9 = 0$

$$y^2 + y + \frac{1}{4} = \frac{9}{4} + \frac{1}{4}$$

$$\left(y + \frac{1}{2}\right)^2 = \frac{10}{4}$$

$$y + \frac{1}{2} = \pm\sqrt{\frac{10}{4}}$$

$$y = -\frac{1}{2} \pm \frac{\sqrt{10}}{2}$$

$$y = \frac{-1 \pm \sqrt{10}}{2}$$

$$y \approx 1.08, -2.08$$

65. $5x^2 - 3x + 10 = 0$

$$x^2 - \frac{3}{5}x = -2$$

$$x^2 - \frac{3}{5}x + \frac{9}{100} = -2 + \frac{9}{100}$$

$$\left(x - \frac{3}{10}\right)^2 = \frac{-200}{100} + \frac{9}{100}$$

$$\left(x - \frac{3}{10}\right)^2 = -\frac{191}{100}$$

$$x - \frac{3}{10} = \pm\sqrt{-\frac{191}{100}}$$

$$x = \frac{3}{10} \pm \frac{\sqrt{191}}{10}i$$

$$x \approx 0.30 + 1.38i, 0.30 - 1.38i$$

67. $x(x - 7) = 2$

$$x^2 - 7x + \frac{49}{4} = 2 + \frac{49}{4}$$

$$\left(x - \frac{7}{2}\right)^2 = \frac{8 + 49}{4}$$

$$\left(x - \frac{7}{2}\right)^2 = \frac{57}{4}$$

$$x - \frac{7}{2} = \pm\sqrt{\frac{57}{4}}$$

$$x = \frac{7}{2} \pm \frac{\sqrt{57}}{2}$$

$$x = \frac{7 \pm \sqrt{57}}{2}$$

$$x \approx 7.27, -0.27$$

69. $0.5t^2 + t + 2 = 0$

$$t^2 + 2t = -4$$

$$t^2 + 2t + 1 = -4 + 1$$

$$(t + 1)^2 = -3$$

$$t + 1 = \pm\sqrt{-3}$$

$$t + 1 = \pm\sqrt{3}i$$

$$t = -1 \pm \sqrt{3}i$$

$$t \approx -1 + 1.73i, -1 - 1.73i$$

71. $0.1x^2 + 0.2x + 0.5 = 0$

$$x^2 + 2x + 5 = 0$$

$$x^2 + 2x + 1 = -5 + 1$$

$$(x + 1)^2 = -4$$

$$x + 1 = \pm\sqrt{-4}$$

$$x = -1 \pm 2i$$

73. $\dfrac{x}{2} - \dfrac{1}{x} = 1$

$$2x\left(\frac{x}{2} - \frac{1}{x}\right) = (1)2x$$

$$x^2 - 2 = 2x$$

$$x^2 - 2x + 1 = 2 + 1$$

$$(x - 1)^2 = 3$$

$$x - 1 = \pm\sqrt{3}$$

$$x = 1 \pm \sqrt{3}$$

75.
$$\frac{x^2}{4} = \frac{x+1}{2}$$
$$2x^2 = 4x + 4$$
$$2x^2 - 4x - 4 = 0$$
$$x^2 - 2x - 2 = 0$$
$$x^2 - 2x + 1 = 2 + 1$$
$$(x - 1)^2 = 3$$
$$x - 1 = \pm\sqrt{3}$$
$$x = 1 \pm \sqrt{3}$$

77.
$$\sqrt{2x + 1} = x - 3$$
$$\left(\sqrt{2x + 1}\right)^2 = (x - 3)^2$$
$$2x + 1 = x^2 - 6x + 9$$
$$0 = x^2 - 8x + 8$$
$$+16 - 8 = x^2 - 8x + 16$$
$$8 = (x - 4)^2$$
$$\pm\sqrt{8} = x - 4$$
$$4 \pm \sqrt{8} = x$$
$$4 \pm 2\sqrt{2} = x$$

79. *Keystrokes:*

$\boxed{Y=}\ \boxed{X,T,\theta}\ \boxed{x^2}\ \boxed{+}\ 4\ \boxed{X,T,\theta}\ \boxed{-}\ 1\ \boxed{GRAPH}$

$$0 = x^2 + 4x - 1$$
$$1 = x^2 + 4x$$
$$1 + 4 = x^2 + 4x + 4$$
$$5 = (x + 2)^2$$
$$\pm\sqrt{5} = x + 2$$
$$-2 \pm \sqrt{5} = x$$
$$x \approx .236$$
$$x \approx -4.236$$

81. *Keystrokes:*

$\boxed{Y=}\ \boxed{X,T,\theta}\ \boxed{x^2}\ \boxed{-}\ 2\ \boxed{X,T,\theta}\ \boxed{-}\ 5\ \boxed{GRAPH}$

$$0 = x^2 - 2x - 5$$
$$5 = x^2 - 2x$$
$$1 + 5 = x^2 - 2x + 1$$
$$6 = (x - 1)^2$$
$$\pm\sqrt{6} = x - 1$$
$$1 \pm \sqrt{6} = x$$
$$x \approx 3.449$$
$$x \approx -1.449$$

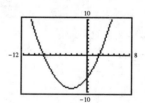

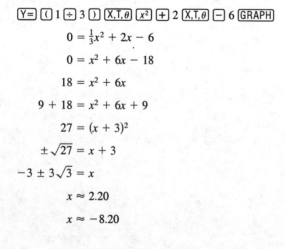

83. *Keystrokes:*

$\boxed{Y=}\ \boxed{(}\ 1\ \boxed{\div}\ 3\ \boxed{)}\ \boxed{X,T,\theta}\ \boxed{x^2}\ \boxed{+}\ 2\ \boxed{X,T,\theta}\ \boxed{-}\ 6\ \boxed{GRAPH}$

$$0 = \tfrac{1}{3}x^2 + 2x - 6$$
$$0 = x^2 + 6x - 18$$
$$18 = x^2 + 6x$$
$$9 + 18 = x^2 + 6x + 9$$
$$27 = (x + 3)^2$$
$$\pm\sqrt{27} = x + 3$$
$$-3 \pm 3\sqrt{3} = x$$
$$x \approx 2.20$$
$$x \approx -8.20$$

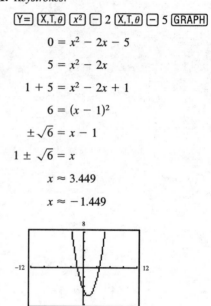

85. *Keystrokes:*

$\boxed{Y=}\ \boxed{(-)}\ \boxed{X,T,\theta}\ \boxed{x^2}\ \boxed{-}\ \boxed{X,T,\theta}\ \boxed{+}\ 3\ \boxed{GRAPH}$

$$-x^2 - x + 3 = 0$$

$$x^2 + x - 3 = 0$$

$$x^2 + x = 3$$

$$x^2 + x + \frac{1}{4} = 3 + \frac{1}{4}$$

$$\left(x + \frac{1}{2}\right)^2 = \frac{13}{4}$$

$$x + \frac{1}{2} = \pm\frac{\sqrt{13}}{2}$$

$$x = -\frac{1}{2} \pm \frac{\sqrt{13}}{2}$$

$$x \approx 1.30, -2.30$$

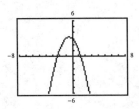

87. (a) Area of square $= x \cdot x = x^2$

Area of vertical rectangle $= 4 \cdot x = 4x$

Area of horizontal rectangle $= 4 \cdot x = 4x$

Total area $= x^2 + 4x + 4x = x^2 + 8x$

(b) Area of small square $= 4 \cdot 4 = 16$

Total area $= x^2 + 8x + 16$

(c) $(x + 4)(x + 4) = x^2 + 8x + 16$

89. *Verbal model:* $\boxed{\text{Area}} = \frac{1}{2} \cdot \boxed{\text{Base}} \cdot \boxed{\text{Height}}$

Labels: Base $= x$

Height $= x + 2$

Equation: $12 = \frac{1}{2}x(x + 2)$

$24 = x^2 + 2x$

$0 = x^2 + 2x - 24$

$0 = (x + 6)(x - 4)$

$x = -6 \qquad\qquad x = 4$ cm base

not a solution $\qquad x + 2 = 6$ cm height

91. *Verbal model:* $\boxed{\text{Area}} = \boxed{\text{Length}} \cdot \boxed{\text{Width}}$

Labels: Length $= x$

Width $= \dfrac{200 - 4x}{3}$

Equation:

$$1400 = 2\left[x \cdot \left(\frac{200 - 4x}{3}\right)\right]$$

$$1400 = 2\left[\frac{200}{3}x - \frac{4x^2}{3}\right]$$

$$1400 = \frac{400x}{3} - \frac{8x^2}{3}$$

$$4200 = 400x - 8x^2$$

$$8x^2 - 400x + 4200 = 0$$

$$x^2 - 50x + 525 = 0$$

$$(x - 35)(x - 15) = 0$$

$$x - 35 = 0 \qquad\qquad x - 15 = 0$$

$$x = 35 \text{ ft.} \qquad\qquad x = 15 \text{ ft.}$$

$$\frac{200 - 4x}{3} = 20 \text{ ft.} \qquad \frac{200 - 4x}{3} = 46\frac{2}{3}\text{ ft.}$$

93. *Verbal model:* $\boxed{\text{side 1}}^2 + \boxed{\text{side 2}}^2 = \boxed{\text{Hypotenuse}}^2$

Labels: side 1 $= x$

side 2 $= 400 - x$

Equation:

$$x^2 + (400 - x)^2 = 300^2$$

$$x^2 + 160,000 - 2(400)x + x^2 = 90,000$$

$$x^2 + 160,000 - 800x + x^2 = 90,000$$

$$2x^2 - 800x + 70,000 = 0$$

$$x^2 - 400x + 35,000 = 0$$

$$x^2 - 400x = -35,000$$

$$x^2 - 400x + 40,000 = -35,000 + 40,000$$

$$(x - 200)^2 = 5000$$

$$x - 200 = \pm\sqrt{5000}$$

$$x - 200 = \pm 50\sqrt{2}$$

$$x = 200 \pm 50\sqrt{2}$$

$$x = 200 \pm 50\sqrt{2} \text{ meters}$$

$$x \approx 270.71 \text{ meters and } 129.29 \text{ meters}$$

95. *Equation:*

$$12,000 = x\left(100 - \tfrac{1}{10}x\right)$$

$$12,000 = 100x - \tfrac{1}{10}x^2$$

$$120,000 = 1000x - x^2$$

$$x^2 - 1000x + 120,000 = 0$$

$$x^2 - 1000x = -120,000$$

$$x^2 - 1000x + 250,000 = -120,000 + 250,000$$

$$(x - 500)^2 = 130,000$$

$$x - 500 = \pm\sqrt{130,000}$$

$$x - 500 = \pm 100\sqrt{13}$$

$$x = 500 \pm 100\sqrt{13}$$

$$x \approx 860.56,\ 139.44$$

Thus, 139 or 861 units must be sold.

97. $\frac{25}{4}$. Divide the coefficient of the first-degree term by 2, and square the result to obtain $\left(\frac{5}{2}\right)^2 = \frac{25}{4}$.

99. Yes. $x^2 + 1 = 0$

101. True. Given the solutions $x = r_1$ and $x = r_2$, the quadratic equation can be written as $(x - r_1)(x - r_2) = 0$.

Section 6.3   The Quadratic Formula

1.
$$2x^2 = 7 - 2x$$
$$2x^2 + 2x - 7 = 0$$

3.
$$x(10 - x) = 5$$
$$10x - x^2 = 5$$
$$-x^2 + 10x - 5 = 0$$
$$x^2 - 10x + 5 = 0$$

5. (a) $x = \dfrac{11 \pm \sqrt{11^2 - 4(1)(28)}}{2(1)}$

$x = \dfrac{11 \pm \sqrt{121 - 112}}{2}$

$x = \dfrac{11 \pm \sqrt{9}}{2}$

$x = \dfrac{11 \pm 3}{2}$

$x = 7, 4$

(b) $(x - 7)(x - 4) = 0$

$x - 7 = 0 \qquad x - 4 = 0$

$\qquad x = 7 \qquad\qquad x = 4$

7. (a) $x = \dfrac{-6 \pm \sqrt{6^2 - 4(1)(8)}}{2(1)}$

$x = \dfrac{6 \pm \sqrt{36 - 32}}{2}$

$x = \dfrac{-6 \pm \sqrt{4}}{2}$

$x = \dfrac{-6 \pm 2}{2} \qquad x = -2, -4$

(b) $(x + 4)(x + 2) = 0$

$x + 4 = 0 \qquad\qquad x + 2 = 0$

$\quad x = -4 \qquad\qquad\qquad x = -2$

9. (a) $x = \dfrac{-4 \pm \sqrt{4^2 - 4(4)(1)}}{2(4)}$

$x = \dfrac{-4 \pm \sqrt{16 - 16}}{8}$

$x = \dfrac{-4}{8} = \dfrac{-1}{2}$

(b) $(2x + 1)(2x + 1) = 0$

$2x + 1 = 0 \qquad\qquad 2x + 1 = 0$

$\quad x = -\dfrac{1}{2} \qquad\qquad\qquad x = -\dfrac{1}{2}$

11. (a) $x = \dfrac{-12 \pm \sqrt{12^2 - 4(4)(9)}}{2(4)}$

$x = \dfrac{-12 \pm \sqrt{144 - 144}}{8}$

$x = \dfrac{-12 \pm 0}{8}$

$x = -\dfrac{12}{8} = -\dfrac{3}{2}$

(b) $(2x + 3)(2x + 3) = 0$

$2x + 3 = 0 \quad 2x + 3 = 0$

$\quad x = -\dfrac{3}{2} \qquad\qquad x = -\dfrac{3}{2}$

13. (a) $x = \dfrac{1 \pm \sqrt{(-1)^2 - 4(6)(-2)}}{2(6)}$

$x = \dfrac{1 \pm \sqrt{1 + 48}}{12}$

$x = \dfrac{1 \pm \sqrt{49}}{12}$

$x = \dfrac{1 \pm 7}{12}$

$x = \dfrac{8}{12}, -\dfrac{6}{12} = \dfrac{2}{3}, -\dfrac{1}{2}$

(b) $(3x - 2)(2x + 1) = 0$

$3x - 2 = 0 \qquad\qquad 2x + 1 = 0$

$\quad x = \dfrac{2}{3} \qquad\qquad\qquad x = -\dfrac{1}{2}$

15. (a) $x = \dfrac{-(-5) \pm \sqrt{(-5)^2 - 4(1)(-300)}}{2(1)}$

$x = \dfrac{5 \pm \sqrt{25 + 1200}}{2}$

$x = \dfrac{5 \pm \sqrt{1225}}{2}$

$x = \dfrac{5 \pm 35}{2}$

$x = 20, -15$

(b) $(x - 20)(x + 15) = 0$

$x - 20 = 0 \qquad x + 15 = 0$

$x = 20 \qquad\qquad x = -15$

17. $x = \dfrac{-(-2) \pm \sqrt{(-2)^2 - 4(1)(-4)}}{2(1)}$

$x = \dfrac{2 \pm \sqrt{4 + 16}}{2}$

$x = \dfrac{2 \pm \sqrt{20}}{2}$

$x = \dfrac{2 \pm 2\sqrt{5}}{2}$

$x = \dfrac{2(1 \pm \sqrt{5})}{2}$

$x = 1 \pm \sqrt{5}$

19. $t = \dfrac{-4 \pm \sqrt{4^2 - 4(1)(1)}}{2(1)}$

$t = \dfrac{-4 \pm \sqrt{16 - 4}}{2}$

$t = \dfrac{4 \pm \sqrt{12}}{2}$

$t = \dfrac{-4 \pm 2\sqrt{3}}{2}$

$t = \dfrac{2(-2 \pm \sqrt{3})}{2}$

$t = -2 \pm \sqrt{3}$

21. $x = \dfrac{-6 \pm \sqrt{6^2 - 4(1)(-3)}}{2(1)}$

$x = \dfrac{-6 \pm \sqrt{36 + 12}}{2}$

$x = \dfrac{-6 \pm \sqrt{48}}{2}$

$x = \dfrac{-6 \pm 4\sqrt{3}}{2}$

$x = \dfrac{2(-3 \pm 2\sqrt{3})}{2}$

$x = -3 \pm 2\sqrt{3}$

23. $x = \dfrac{-(-10) \pm \sqrt{(-10)^2 - 4(1)(23)}}{2(1)}$

$x = \dfrac{10 \pm \sqrt{100 - 92}}{2}$

$x = \dfrac{10 \pm \sqrt{8}}{2}$

$x = \dfrac{10 \pm 2\sqrt{2}}{2}$

$x = \dfrac{2(5 \pm \sqrt{2})}{2}$

$x = 5 \pm \sqrt{2}$

25. $x = \dfrac{-3 \pm \sqrt{3^2 - 4(2)(3)}}{2(2)}$

$x = \dfrac{-3 \pm \sqrt{9 - 24}}{4}$

$x = \dfrac{-3 \pm \sqrt{-15}}{4}$

$x = \dfrac{-3 \pm i\sqrt{15}}{4}$

$x = \dfrac{-3}{4} \pm \dfrac{\sqrt{15}}{4}i$

27. $v = \dfrac{-(-2) \pm \sqrt{(-2)^2 - 4(3)(-1)}}{2(3)}$

$v = \dfrac{2 \pm \sqrt{4 + 12}}{6}$

$v = \dfrac{2 \pm \sqrt{16}}{6}$

$v = \dfrac{2 \pm 4}{6}$

$v = \dfrac{6}{6}, \dfrac{-2}{6}$

$v = 1, -\dfrac{1}{3}$

29. $x = \dfrac{-4 \pm \sqrt{4^2 - 4(2)(-3)}}{2(2)}$

$x = \dfrac{-4 \pm \sqrt{16 + 24}}{4}$

$x = \dfrac{-4 \pm \sqrt{40}}{4}$

$x = \dfrac{-4 \pm 2\sqrt{10}}{4}$

$x = \dfrac{2(-2 \pm \sqrt{10})}{4}$

$x = \dfrac{-2 \pm \sqrt{10}}{2}$

31. $z = \dfrac{-6 \pm \sqrt{6^2 - 4(9)(-4)}}{2(9)}$

$z = \dfrac{-6 \pm \sqrt{36 + 144}}{18}$

$z = \dfrac{-6 \pm \sqrt{180}}{18}$

$z = \dfrac{-6 \pm 6\sqrt{5}}{18}$

$z = \dfrac{6(-1 \pm \sqrt{5})}{18}$

$z = \dfrac{-1 \pm \sqrt{5}}{3}$

33. $x = \dfrac{-(-6) \pm \sqrt{(-6)^2 - 4(-4)(3)}}{2(-4)}$

$x = \dfrac{6 \pm \sqrt{36 + 48}}{-8}$

$x = \dfrac{6 \pm \sqrt{84}}{-8}$

$x = \dfrac{6 \pm 2\sqrt{21}}{-8}$

$x = \dfrac{-3 \pm \sqrt{21}}{4}$

35. $4x^2 - 3x + 1 = 0$

$x = \dfrac{-(-3) \pm \sqrt{(-3)^2 - 4(4)(1)}}{2(4)}$

$x = \dfrac{3 \pm \sqrt{9 - 16}}{8}$

$x = \dfrac{3 \pm \sqrt{-7}}{8} = \dfrac{3}{8} \pm \dfrac{\sqrt{7}}{8} i$

37. $2x^2 - 5x - 6 = 0$

$x = \dfrac{-(-5) \pm \sqrt{(-5)^2 - 4(2)(-6)}}{2(2)}$

$x = \dfrac{5 \pm \sqrt{25 + 48}}{4}$

$x = \dfrac{5 \pm \sqrt{73}}{4}$

39. $\qquad 9x^2 = 1 + 9x$

$9x^2 - 9x - 1 = 0$

$x = \dfrac{-(-9) \pm \sqrt{(-9)^2 - 4(9)(-1)}}{2(9)}$

$x = \dfrac{9 \pm \sqrt{81 + 36}}{18}$

$x = \dfrac{9 \pm \sqrt{117}}{18}$

$x = \dfrac{9}{18} \pm \dfrac{3\sqrt{13}}{18}$

$x = \dfrac{1}{2} \pm \dfrac{\sqrt{13}}{6} \text{ or } \dfrac{3 \pm \sqrt{13}}{6}$

41. $3x - 2x^2 - 4 + 5x^2 = 0$

$\qquad 3x^2 + 3x - 4 = 0$

$x = \dfrac{-3 \pm \sqrt{3^2 - 4(3)(-4)}}{2(3)}$

$x = \dfrac{-3 \pm \sqrt{9 + 48}}{6}$

$x = \dfrac{-3 \pm \sqrt{57}}{6}$

43. $x = \dfrac{-(-0.4) \pm \sqrt{(-0.4)^2 - 4(1)(-0.16)}}{2(1)}$

$x = \dfrac{0.4 \pm \sqrt{0.16 + 0.64}}{2}$

$x = \dfrac{0.4 \pm \sqrt{0.80}}{2}$

$x = \dfrac{0.4 \pm 2\sqrt{0.2}}{2}$

$x = 0.2 \pm \sqrt{0.2}$ or $\dfrac{1 \pm \sqrt{5}}{5}$

45. $x = \dfrac{-1 \pm \sqrt{1^2 - 4(2.5)(-0.9)}}{2(2.5)}$

$x = \dfrac{-1 \pm \sqrt{1 + 9}}{5}$

$x = \dfrac{-1 \pm \sqrt{10}}{5}$

47. $b^2 - 4ac = 1^2 - 4(1)(1)$

$\qquad = 1 - 4$

$\qquad = -3$

2 distinct imaginary solutions

49. $b^2 - 4ac = (-5)^2 - 4(2)(-4)$

$\qquad = 25 + 32$

$\qquad = 57$

2 distinct irrational solutions

51. $b^2 - 4ac = 7^2 - 4(5)(3)$

$\qquad = 49 - 60$

$\qquad = -11$

2 distinct imaginary solutions

53. $b^2 - 4ac = (-12)^2 - 4(4)(9)$

$\qquad = 144 - 144$

$\qquad = 0$

1 rational repeated solution

55. $b^2 - 4ac = (-1)^2 - 4(3)(2)$

$\qquad = 1 - 24$

$\qquad = -23$

2 distinct imaginary solutions

57. $z^2 - 169 = 0$

$z^2 = 169$

$z = \pm 13$

59. $5y^2 + 15y = 0$

$5y(y + 3) = 0$

$5y = 0 \qquad y + 3 = 0$

$y = 0 \qquad y = -3$

61. $25(x - 3)^2 - 36 = 0$

$(x - 3)^2 = \dfrac{36}{25}$

$x - 3 = \pm\sqrt{\dfrac{36}{25}}$

$x = 3 \pm \dfrac{6}{5}$

$x = \dfrac{15}{5} \pm \dfrac{6}{5}$

$x = \dfrac{21}{5}, \dfrac{9}{5}$

63. $2y(y - 18) + 3(y - 18) = 0$

$(y - 18)(2y + 3) = 0$

$y - 18 = 0 \qquad 2y + 3 = 0$

$y = 18 \qquad 2y = -3$

$\qquad\qquad y = -\dfrac{3}{2}$

65. $x^2 + 8x + 25 = 0$

$x^2 + 8x + 16 = -25 + 16$

$(x + 4)^2 = -9$

$x + 4 = \pm\sqrt{-9}$

$x = -4 \pm 3i$

67. $x^2 - 24x + 128 = 0$

$x^2 - 24x + 144 = -128 + 144$

$(x - 12)^2 = 16$

$x - 12 = \pm\sqrt{16}$

$x = 12 \pm 4$

$x = 16, 8$

69. $x = \dfrac{-(-13) \pm \sqrt{(-13)^2 - 4(3)(169)}}{2(3)}$

$x = \dfrac{13 \pm \sqrt{169 - 2028}}{6}$

$x = \dfrac{13 \pm \sqrt{-1859}}{6}$

$x = \dfrac{13}{6} \pm \dfrac{13\sqrt{11}}{6}i$

71. $x = \dfrac{-15 \pm \sqrt{15^2 - 4(18)(-50)}}{2(18)}$

$x = \dfrac{-15 \pm \sqrt{225 + 3600}}{36}$

$x = \dfrac{-15 \pm \sqrt{3825}}{36}$

$x = \dfrac{-15 \pm 15\sqrt{17}}{36}$

$x = \dfrac{-5 \pm 5\sqrt{17}}{12}$

73. $1.2x^2 - 0.8x - 5.5 = 0$

$12x^2 - 8x - 55 = 0$

$(6x + 11)(2x - 5) = 0$

$6x + 11 = 0 \qquad 2x - 5 = 0$

$6x = -11 \qquad 2x = 5$

$x = -\frac{11}{6} \qquad\quad x = \frac{5}{2}$

75. *Keystrokes:*

$\boxed{Y=}\ 3\ \boxed{X,T,\theta}\ \boxed{x^2}\ \boxed{-}\ 6\ \boxed{X,T,\theta}\ \boxed{+}\ 1\ \boxed{GRAPH}$

$0 = 3x^2 - 6x + 1$

$x = \dfrac{-(-6) \pm \sqrt{(-6)^2 - 4(3)(1)}}{2(3)}$

$x = \dfrac{6 \pm \sqrt{36 - 12}}{6}$

$x = \dfrac{6 \pm \sqrt{24}}{6}$

$x \approx 1.82, 0.18$

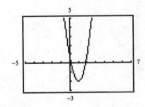

77. *Keystrokes:*

$\boxed{Y=}\ \boxed{(-)}\ \boxed{(}\ 4\ \boxed{X,T,\theta}\ \boxed{x^2}\ \boxed{-}\ 20\ \boxed{X,T,\theta}\ \boxed{+}\ 25\ \boxed{)}\ \boxed{GRAPH}$

$0 = -(4x^2 - 20x + 25)$

$= 4x^2 - 20x + 25$

$x = \dfrac{-(-20) \pm \sqrt{(-20)^2 - 4(4)(25)}}{2(4)}$

$x = \dfrac{20 \pm \sqrt{400 - 400}}{8}$

$x = \dfrac{20}{8} = \dfrac{5}{2} = 2.50$

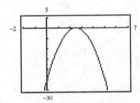

79. *Keystrokes:*

$\boxed{Y=}$ 5 $\boxed{X,T,\theta}$ $\boxed{x^2}$ $\boxed{-}$ 18 $\boxed{X,T,\theta}$ $\boxed{+}$ 6 $\boxed{GRAPH}$

$$x = \frac{-(-18) \pm \sqrt{(-18)^2 - 4(5)(6)}}{2(5)}$$

$$x = \frac{18 \pm \sqrt{324 - 120}}{10}$$

$$x = \frac{18 \pm \sqrt{204}}{10}$$

$$x = \frac{18 \pm 2\sqrt{51}}{10}$$

$$x = \frac{2(9 \pm \sqrt{51})}{10}$$

$$x = \frac{9 \pm \sqrt{51}}{5}$$

$$x \approx 3.23, 0.37$$

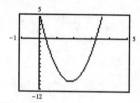

81. *Keystrokes:*

$\boxed{Y=}$ $\boxed{(-)}$ .04 $\boxed{X,T,\theta}$ $\boxed{x^2}$ $\boxed{+}$ 4 $\boxed{X,T,\theta}$ $\boxed{-}$ .8 $\boxed{GRAPH}$

$$x = \frac{-4 \pm \sqrt{4^2 - 4(-0.04)(-0.8)}}{2(-0.04)}$$

$$x = \frac{-4 \pm \sqrt{16 - 0.128}}{-0.08}$$

$$x = \frac{-4 \pm \sqrt{15.872}}{-0.08}$$

$$x = \frac{-4 \pm 16\sqrt{0.062}}{-0.08}$$

$$x = \frac{4(-1 \pm 4\sqrt{0.062})}{-0.08}$$

$$x = \frac{-1 \pm 4\sqrt{0.062}}{-0.02}$$

$$x \approx 0.20, 99.80$$

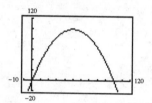

83. *Keystrokes:*

$\boxed{Y=}$ 2 $\boxed{X,T,\theta}$ $\boxed{x^2}$ $\boxed{-}$ 5 $\boxed{X,T,\theta}$ $\boxed{+}$ 5 $\boxed{GRAPH}$

$$b^2 - 4ac = (-5)^2 - 4(2)(5)$$

$$= 25 - 40$$

$$= -15$$

No real solutions

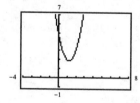

85. *Keystrokes:*

$\boxed{Y=}$ $\boxed{X,T,\theta}$ $\boxed{x^2}$ $\boxed{+}$ 6 $\boxed{X,T,\theta}$ $\boxed{-}$ 40 $\boxed{GRAPH}$

$$b^2 - 4ac = 6^2 - 4(1)(-40)$$

$$= 36 + 160$$

$$= 196$$

Two real solutions

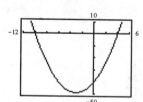

87. $\dfrac{2x^2}{5} - \dfrac{x}{2} = 1$

$10\left(\dfrac{2x^2}{5} - \dfrac{x}{2}\right) = (1)10$

$4x^2 - 5x = 10$

$4x^2 - 5x - 10 = 0$

$x = \dfrac{-(-5) \pm \sqrt{(-5)^2 - 4(4)(-10)}}{2(4)}$

$x = \dfrac{5 \pm \sqrt{25 + 160}}{8}$

$x = \dfrac{5 \pm \sqrt{185}}{8}$

89. $\sqrt{x + 3} = x - 1$

$\left(\sqrt{x + 3}\right)^2 = (x - 1)^2$

$x + 3 = x^2 - 2x + 1$

$0 = x^2 - 3x - 2$

$x = \dfrac{-(-3) \pm \sqrt{(-3)^2 - 4(1)(-2)}}{2(1)}$

$x = \dfrac{3 \pm \sqrt{9 + 8}}{2}$

$x = \dfrac{3 \pm \sqrt{17}}{2}$

$x = \dfrac{3 + \sqrt{17}}{2}$

$x = \dfrac{3 - \sqrt{17}}{2}$ does not check.

91. (a) $b^2 - 4ac > 0$

$(-6)^2 - 4(1)c > 0$

$36 - 4c > 0$

$-4c > -36$

$c < 9$

(b) $b^2 - 4ac = 0$

$(-6)^2 - 4(1)c = 0$

$36 - 4c = 0$

$-4c = -36$

$c = 9$

(c) $b^2 - 4ac < 0$

$(-6)^2 - 4(1)c < 0$

$36 - 4c < 0$

$-4c < -36$

$c > 9$

93. (a) $b^2 - 4ac > 0$

$8^2 - 4(1)c > 0$

$64 - 4c > 0$

$-4c > -64$

$c < 16$

(b) $b^2 - 4ac = 0$

$8^2 - 4(1)c = 0$

$64 - 4c = 0$

$-4c = -64$

$c = 16$

(c) $b^2 - 4ac < 0$

$8^2 - 4(1)c < 0$

$64 - 4c < 0$

$-4c < -64$

$c > 16$

95. *Verbal model:* | Area | $=$ | Length | $\cdot$ | Width |

Labels: Length $= x + 6.3$

Width $= x$

Equation: $58.14 = (x + 6.3) \cdot x$

$58.14 = x^2 + 6.3x$

$0 = x^2 + 6.3x - 58.14$

$x = \dfrac{-6.3 \pm \sqrt{6.3^2 - 4(1)(-58.14)}}{2(1)}$

$x = \dfrac{-6.3 \pm \sqrt{39.69 + 232.56}}{2}$

$x = \dfrac{-6.3 \pm \sqrt{272.25}}{2}$

$x \approx 5.1$ inches

$x + 6.3 \approx 11.4$ inches

97. (a) $50 = -16t^2 + 40t + 50$

$0 = -16t^2 + 40t$

$0 = -8(2t^2 - 5t)$

$0 = 2t^2 - 5t$

$0 = t(2t - 5)$

$0 = t \qquad 2t - 5 = 0$

$t = \dfrac{5}{2} = 2.5$ seconds

(b) $0 = -16t^2 + 40t + 50$

$0 = -2(8t^2 - 20t - 25)$

$t = \dfrac{-(-20) \pm \sqrt{(-20)^2 - 4(8)(-25)}}{2(8)}$

$t = \dfrac{20 \pm \sqrt{400 + 800}}{16}$

$t = \dfrac{20 \pm \sqrt{1200}}{16}$

$t = \dfrac{20 \pm 20\sqrt{3}}{16}$

$t = \dfrac{4\left(5 \pm 5\sqrt{3}\right)}{16}$

$t = \dfrac{5 + 5\sqrt{3}}{4}, \dfrac{5 - 5\sqrt{3}}{4}$ reject

$t \approx 3.4$ seconds

99. (a) *Keystrokes:*

$\boxed{Y=}$ 831.3 $\boxed{-}$ 85.71 $\boxed{X,T,\theta}$ $\boxed{+}$ 3.452 $\boxed{X,T,\theta}$ $\boxed{x^2}$ $\boxed{\text{GRAPH}}$

(b) $750 = 831.3 - 85.71t + 3.452t^2$

$0 = 3.452t^2 - 85.71t + 81.3$

$t = \dfrac{-(-85.71) \pm \sqrt{(-85.71)^2 - 4(3.452)(81.3)}}{2(3.452)}$

$t = \dfrac{85.71 \pm \sqrt{6223.6137}}{6.904} = \dfrac{85.71 \pm 78.89}{6.904}$

$t \approx .9879$ year 1991

(c) $y = 831.3 - 85.71(7) + 3.452(7)^2$

$y = 400,500$

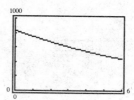

101.

	x_1, x_2	$x_1 + x_2$	$x_1 \cdot x_2$
(a) $x^2 - x - 6 = 0$	$3, -2$	1	-6
(b) $2x^2 + 5x - 3 = 0$	$\frac{1}{2}, -3$	$-\frac{5}{2}$	$-\frac{3}{2}$
(c) $4x^2 - 9 = 0$	$\frac{3}{2}, -\frac{3}{2}$	0	$-\frac{9}{4}$
(d) $x^2 - 10x + 34 = 0$	$5 + 3i, 5 - 3i$	10	34

(a) $x^2 - x - 6 = 0$

$(x - 3)(x + 2) = 0$

$x = 3 \qquad x = -2$

(b) $2x^2 + 5x - 3 = 0$

$(2x - 1)(x + 3) = 0$

$x = \frac{1}{2} \qquad x = -3$

(c) $4x^2 - 9 = 0$

$(2x - 3)(2x + 3)$

$x = \frac{3}{2} \qquad x = -\frac{3}{2}$

(d) $x^2 - 10x + 34 = 0$

$x^2 - 10x + 25 = -34 + 25$

$(x - 5)^2 = -9$

$x - 5 = \pm\sqrt{-9}$

$x = 5 \pm 3i$

103. (c) $\quad h = -16t^2 + v_0t + h_0 \qquad\qquad v_0 = 32$ feet/sec

$\qquad\qquad 50 = -16t^2 + 32t + 100 \qquad\quad h = 50$ feet

$\qquad\qquad 0 = -16t^2 + 32t + 50$

$\qquad\qquad 0 = 8t^2 - 16t - 25 \qquad$ (Divide by -2)

$\qquad\qquad t = \dfrac{-(-16) \pm \sqrt{(-16)^2 - 4(8)(-25)}}{2(8)}$

$\qquad\qquad t = \dfrac{16 \pm \sqrt{256 + 800}}{16}$

$\qquad\qquad t = \dfrac{16 \pm \sqrt{1056}}{16} = \dfrac{16 \pm 4\sqrt{66}}{16} = \dfrac{4 \pm \sqrt{66}}{4} \approx 3.0$ seconds

$\qquad$ Quadratic formula method was used because the numbers were large and equation would not factor.

(d) $\quad 0 = -16t^2 + 32t + 100 \qquad\qquad\qquad 0 = -16t^2 + 32t + 84$

$\qquad\quad 0 = 4t^2 - 8t - 25 \qquad\qquad\qquad\qquad 0 = 4t^2 - 8t - 21$

$\qquad\quad t = \dfrac{-(-8) \pm \sqrt{(-8)^2 - 4(4)(-25)}}{2(4)} \qquad t = \dfrac{-(-8) \pm \sqrt{(-8)^2 - 4(4)(-21)}}{2(4)}$

$\qquad\quad t = \dfrac{8 \pm \sqrt{64 + 400}}{8} \qquad\qquad\qquad\quad t = \dfrac{8 \pm \sqrt{64 + 336}}{8}$

$\qquad\quad t = \dfrac{8 \pm \sqrt{464}}{8} \qquad\qquad\qquad\qquad\quad t = \dfrac{8 \pm \sqrt{400}}{8}$

$\qquad\quad t \approx 3.7$ seconds $\qquad\qquad\qquad\qquad\quad t \approx 3.5$ seconds

105. $b^2 - 4ac$. If the discriminant is positive, the quadratic equation has two real solutions; if it is zero, the equation has one (repeated) real solution; and if it is negative, the equation has no real solutions.

107. The four methods are factoring, extracting square roots, completing the square, and the Quadratic Formula.

Mid-Chapter Quiz for Chapter 6

1. $\qquad 2x^2 - 72 = 0$

$\qquad\quad 2(x^2 - 36) = 0$

$\qquad 2(x - 6)(x + 6) = 0$

$\quad x - 6 = 0 \qquad x + 6 = 0$

$\qquad\quad x = 6 \qquad\qquad x = -6$

2. $\quad 2x^2 + 3x - 20 = 0$

$\qquad (2x - 5)(x + 4) = 0$

$\quad 2x - 5 = 0 \qquad x + 4 = 0$

$\qquad x = \frac{5}{2} \qquad\qquad x = -4$

3. $t^2 = 12$

$\quad t = \pm\sqrt{12}$

$\quad t = \pm 2\sqrt{3}$

4. $(u - 3)^2 - 16 = 0$

$\qquad (u - 3)^2 = 16$

$\qquad\quad u - 3 = \pm 4$

$\qquad\qquad u = 3 \pm 4 = 7, -1$

5. $\quad s^2 + 10s + 1 = 0$

$\qquad\quad s^2 + 10s = -1$

$\quad s^2 + 10s + 25 = -1 + 25$

$\qquad\quad (s + 5)^2 = 24$

$\qquad\quad s + 5 = \pm\sqrt{24}$

$\qquad\qquad\quad s = -5 \pm 2\sqrt{6}$

6. $2y^2 + 6y - 5 = 0$

$\qquad y^2 + 3y = \dfrac{5}{2}$

$\quad y^2 + 3y + \dfrac{9}{4} = \dfrac{5}{2} + \dfrac{9}{4}$

$\qquad \left(y + \dfrac{3}{2}\right)^2 = \dfrac{10}{4} + \dfrac{9}{4}$

$\qquad \left(y + \dfrac{3}{2}\right)^2 = \dfrac{19}{4}$

$\qquad\quad y + \dfrac{3}{2} = \pm\dfrac{\sqrt{19}}{2}$

$\qquad\qquad\quad y = -\dfrac{3}{2} \pm \dfrac{\sqrt{19}}{2}$

7. $x = \dfrac{-4 \pm \sqrt{4^2 - 4(1)(-6)}}{2(1)}$

$x = \dfrac{-4 \pm \sqrt{16 + 24}}{2}$

$x = \dfrac{-4 \pm \sqrt{40}}{2}$

$x = \dfrac{-4 \pm 2\sqrt{10}}{2} = -2 \pm \sqrt{10}$

8. $v = \dfrac{-(-3) \pm \sqrt{(-3)^2 - 4(6)(-4)}}{2(6)}$

$v = \dfrac{3 \pm \sqrt{9 + 96}}{12}$

$v = \dfrac{3 \pm \sqrt{105}}{12}$

9. $x = \dfrac{-5 \pm \sqrt{5^2 - 4(1)(7)}}{2(1)}$

$x = \dfrac{-5 \pm \sqrt{25 - 28}}{2}$

$x = \dfrac{-5 \pm \sqrt{-3}}{2}$

$x = \dfrac{-5 \pm i\sqrt{3}}{2} = -\dfrac{5}{2} \pm \dfrac{\sqrt{3}}{2}i$

10. $\quad 36 = (t - 4)^2$

$\pm 6 = t - 4$

$4 \pm 6 = t$

$10, -2 = t$

11. $(x - 10)(x + 3) = 0$

$\quad (x - 10) = 0 \qquad x + 3 = 0$

$\qquad x = 10 \qquad\qquad x = -3$

12. $\quad x^2 - 3x - 10 = 0$

$(x - 5)(x + 2) = 0$

$x - 5 = 0 \qquad x + 2 = 0$

$x = 5 \qquad\quad x = -2$

13. $(2b - 3)(2b - 3) = 0$

$2b - 3 = 0 \qquad 2b - 3 = 0$

$\qquad b = \dfrac{3}{2} \qquad\qquad b = \dfrac{3}{2}$

14. $m = \dfrac{-10 \pm \sqrt{10^2 - 4(3)(5)}}{2(3)}$

$m = \dfrac{-10 \pm \sqrt{100 - 60}}{6}$

$m = \dfrac{-10 \pm \sqrt{40}}{6}$

$m = \dfrac{-10 \pm 2\sqrt{10}}{6}$

$m = \dfrac{-5 \pm \sqrt{10}}{3}$

15. $\quad x - 2\sqrt{x} - 24 = 0$

$\qquad\qquad \text{let } u = \sqrt{x}$

$\left(\sqrt{x}\right)^2 - 2\sqrt{x} - 24 = 0$

$\quad u^2 - 2u - 24 = 0$

$\quad (u - 6)(u + 4) = 0$

$\quad u = 6 \qquad\quad u = -4$

$\quad \sqrt{x} = 6 \qquad\quad \sqrt{x} = -4$

$\quad x = 6^2 \qquad\quad x = (-4)^2$

$\quad x = 36 \qquad\quad x = 16$

Check:

$36 - 2\sqrt{36} - 24 \overset{?}{=} 0$

$36 - 12 - 24 \overset{?}{=} 0$

$0 = 0$

Not a solution

$16 - 2\sqrt{16} - 24 \overset{?}{=} 0$

$16 - 8 - 24 \overset{?}{=} 0$

$-16 \neq 0$

16. $\quad x^4 + 7x^2 + 12 = 0$

$(x^2 + 4)(x^2 + 3) = 0$

$x^2 = -4 \qquad\quad x^2 = -3$

$x = \pm\sqrt{-4} \qquad x = \pm\sqrt{-3}$

$x = \pm 2i \qquad\quad x = \pm\sqrt{3}i$

17. *Keystrokes:*

$\boxed{Y=}$ .5 $\boxed{X,T,\theta}$ $\boxed{x^2}$ $\boxed{-}$ 3 $\boxed{X,T,\theta}$ $\boxed{-}$ 1 $\boxed{GRAPH}$

$0 = .5x^2 - 3x - 1$

$0 = x^2 - 6x - 2$

$x = \dfrac{-(-6) \pm \sqrt{(-6)^2 - 4(1)(-2)}}{2(1)}$

$x = \dfrac{6 \pm \sqrt{36 + 8}}{2}$

$x = \dfrac{6 \pm \sqrt{44}}{2}$

$x = \dfrac{6 \pm 2\sqrt{11}}{2}$

$x = 3 \pm \sqrt{11}$

$x \approx 6.32$ and -0.32

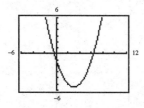

18. *Keystrokes:*

$\boxed{Y=}$ $\boxed{X,T,\theta}$ $\boxed{x^2}$ $\boxed{+}$ .045 $\boxed{X,T,\theta}$ $\boxed{-}$ 4 $\boxed{GRAPH}$

$0 = x^2 + 0.45x - 4$

$x = \dfrac{-0.45 \pm \sqrt{(0.45)^2 - 4(1)(-4)}}{2(1)}$

$x = \dfrac{-0.45 \pm \sqrt{0.2025 + 16}}{2}$

$x = \dfrac{-0.45 \pm \sqrt{16.2025}}{2}$

$x \approx 1.79$ and -2.24

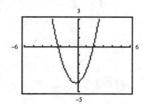

19.

$$500 = x(20 - 0.2x)$$
$$= 20x - 0.2x^2$$
$$0.2x^2 - 20x + 500 = 0$$
$$x^2 - 100x + 2500 = 0$$

$$x = \frac{-(-100) \pm \sqrt{(-100)^2 - 4(1)(2500)}}{2(1)}$$

$$x = \frac{100 \pm \sqrt{10,000 - 10,000}}{2}$$

$$x = \frac{100 \pm \sqrt{0}}{2} = 50 \text{ units}$$

20. *Verbal model:* $\boxed{\text{Area}} = \boxed{\text{Length}} \cdot \boxed{\text{Width}}$

Equation:

$$2275 = x \cdot (100 - x)$$
$$2275 = 100x - x^2$$
$$0 = x^2 - 100x + 2275$$
$$0 = (x - 35)(x - 65)$$

$x - 35 = 0 \qquad\qquad x - 65 = 0$

$\quad x = 35 \text{ meters} \qquad\qquad x = 65 \text{ meters}$

35 meters $\times$ 65 meters

Section 6.4   Applications of Quadratic Equations

1. *Verbal model:* $\boxed{\begin{array}{c}\text{Selling price}\\\text{per doz eggs}\end{array}} = \boxed{\begin{array}{c}\text{Cost per}\\\text{doz eggs}\end{array}} + \boxed{\begin{array}{c}\text{Profit per}\\\text{doz eggs}\end{array}}$

Equation: $\dfrac{21.60}{x} = \dfrac{21.60}{x+6} + 0.30$

Labels: Number eggs sold $= x$

Number eggs purchased $= x + 6$

$$21.60(x+6) = 21.60x + 0.30x(x+6)$$
$$21.6x + 129.6 = 21.6x + 0.3x^2 + 1.8x$$
$$0 = 0.3x^2 + 1.8x - 129.6$$
$$0 = 3x^2 + 18x - 1296$$
$$0 = x^2 + 6x - 432$$
$$0 = (x+24)(x-18)$$
$$x = -24 \quad x = 18 \text{ dozen}$$

Selling price $= \dfrac{21.60}{18} = \$1.20$ per dozen

3. *Verbal model:* $\boxed{\begin{array}{c}\text{Selling price}\\\text{per video}\end{array}} = \boxed{\begin{array}{c}\text{Cost per}\\\text{video}\end{array}} + \boxed{\begin{array}{c}\text{Profit per}\\\text{video}\end{array}}$

Labels: Number videos sold $= x$

Number videos purchased $= x + 8$

Equation: $\dfrac{480}{x} = \dfrac{480}{x+8} + 10$

$$480(x+8) = 480x + 10x(x+8)$$
$$480x + 3840 = 480x + 10x^2 + 80x$$
$$0 = 10x^2 + 80x - 3840$$
$$0 = x^2 + 8x - 384$$
$$0 = (x+24)(x-16)$$
$$x = -24 \quad x = 16 \text{ videos}$$

Selling price $= \dfrac{480}{16} = \$30$

5. *Verbal model:* $2\boxed{\text{Length}} + 2\boxed{\text{Width}} = \boxed{\text{Perimeter}}$

Labels: Length $= l$

Width $= 0.75\, l$

Equation: $2l + 2(0.75l) = 42$

$$2l + 1.5l = 42$$
$$3.5l = 42$$
$$l = 12 \text{ inches}$$

$w = 0.75\, l = 9$ inches

Verbal model: $\boxed{\text{Length}} \cdot \boxed{\text{Width}} = \boxed{\text{Area}}$

Equation: $12 \cdot 9 = A$

108 square inches $= A$

7. *Verbal model:* $\boxed{\text{Area}} = \boxed{\text{Length}} \cdot \boxed{\text{Width}}$

Labels: Length $= 2.5w$

Width $= w$

Equation: $250 = 2.5w \cdot w$

$$250 = 2.5w^2$$
$$100 = w^2$$
$$10 = w$$
$$25 = 2.5w$$

Verbal model: $2\boxed{\text{Length}} + 2\boxed{\text{Width}} = \boxed{\text{Perimeter}}$

Equation: $2(25) + 2(10) = P$

70 feet $= P$

9. *Verbal model:* | Length | · | Width | = | Area |

Labels: Length = l

Width = $\frac{1}{3}l$

Equation: $l \cdot \frac{1}{3}l = 192$

$\frac{1}{3}l^2 = 192$

$l^2 = 576$

$l = 24$ inches

$w = \frac{1}{3}l = 8$ inches

Verbal model: 2 | Length | + 2 | Width | = | Perimeter |

Equation: $2(24) + 2(8) = P$

$48 + 16 = P$

64 inches $= P$

11. *Verbal model:* 2 | Length | + 2 | Width | = | Perimeter |

Labels: Length = $w + 3$

Width = w

Equation: $2(w + 3) + 2w = 54$

$2w + 6 + 2w = 54$

$4w = 48$

$w = 12$ km

$l = w + 3 = 15$ km

Verbal model: | Length | · | Width | = | Area |

Equation: $15 \cdot 12 = 180$ square kilometers $= A$

13. *Verbal model:* | Length | · | Width | = | Area |

Labels: Length = l

Width = $l - 20$

Equation: $l \cdot (l - 20) = 12{,}000$

$l^2 - 20l = 12{,}000$

$l^2 - 20l + 100 = 12{,}000 + 100$

$(l - 10)^2 = 12{,}100$

$l - 10 = \pm\sqrt{12{,}100}$

$l = 10 + 110 = 120$ meters

$w = l - 20 = 100$ meters

Verbal model: 2 | Length | + 2 | Width | = | Perimeter |

Equation: $2(120) + 2(100) = 440$ meters $= P$

15. *Verbal model:* | Area | = | Length | · | Width |

Labels: Length = $x + 4$

Width = x

Equation: $192 = (x + 4)x$

$192 = x^2 + 4x$

$0 = x^2 + 4x - 192$

$0 = (x + 16)(x - 12)$

$x = -16 \quad x = 12$ inches

$x + 4 = 16$ inches

17. *Verbal model:* | Area | = $\frac{1}{2}$ · | Height | · | Base |

Labels: Height = $x - 8$

Base = x

Equation: $192 = \frac{1}{2}(x - 8)x$

$384 = x^2 - 8x$

$0 = x^2 - 8x - 384$

$0 = (x - 24)(x + 16)$

$x = 24$ inches   reject $x = -16$

$x - 8 = 16$ inches

19. *Verbal model:* | Length | · | Width | = | Area |

Labels: Length = $350 - 2x$

Width = x

Equation: $(350 - 2x) \cdot x = 12{,}500$

$350x - 2x^2 = 12{,}500$

$2x^2 - 350x + 12{,}500 = 0$

$x^2 - 175x + 6{,}250 = 0$

$x = \dfrac{175 \pm \sqrt{175^2 - 4(1)(6{,}250)}}{2(1)}$

$x = \dfrac{175 \pm \sqrt{5625}}{2} = \dfrac{175 \pm 75}{2}$

$x = 125, 50$

$350 - 2x = 100, 250$

100 ft $\times$ 125 ft. or 50 ft $\times$ 250 ft.

21. *Verbal model:* | Side 1 | + | Side 2 | + | Side 3 | = 550

Equation: $x + x + b = 550$

$2x + b = 550$

$b = 550 - 2x$

Verbal model: | $\frac{1}{2}$ | · | Height | (| Base 1 | + | Base 2 |) | = | Area |

Labels: Height = x

Base 1 = x

Base 2 = 6

Equation: $\frac{1}{2}x(x + b) = 43{,}560$

$\frac{1}{2}x(x + 550 - 2x) = 43{,}560$

$\frac{1}{2}x(-x + 550) = 43{,}560$

$-\frac{1}{2}x^2 + 275x = 43{,}560$

$-x^2 + 550x = 87{,}120$

$0 = x^2 - 550x + 87{,}120$

This has no real solution, so it would be impossible to have an area of 43,560 square feet.

23. *Verbal model:* | Height | · | Width | = | Area |

Labels: Height = x

Width = $48 - 2x$

Equation: $x \cdot (48 - 2x) = 288$

$2x^2 - 48x + 288 = 0$

$x^2 - 24x + 144 = 0$

$(x - 12)(x - 12) = 0$

$x = 12$

height = 12 inches

width = $48 - 2(12)$

$= 48 - 24 = 24$ inches

25. $A = P(1 + r)^2$

$3499.20 = 3000(1 + r)^2$

$1.1664 = (1 + r)^2$

$1.08 = 1 + r$

$0.08 = r$ or 8%

27. $A = P(1 + r)^2$

$280.90 = 250.00(1 + r)^2$

$\dfrac{280.90}{250.00} = (1 + r)^2$

$1.1236 = (1 + r)^2$

$1.06 = 1 + r$

$.06 = r$

$6\% = r$

29. $A = P(1 + r)^2$

$8420.20 = 8000.00(1 + r)^2$

$1.052525 = (1 + r)^2$

$1.0259 \approx 1 + r$

$.0259 \approx r$ or 2.59%

31. *Verbal model:* $\boxed{\begin{array}{c}\text{Cost per}\\ \text{member}\end{array}} \cdot \boxed{\begin{array}{c}\text{Number of}\\ \text{members}\end{array}} = \boxed{\$240}$

Labels: Number of members $= x$

Number going to game $= x + 8$

Equation: $\left(\dfrac{240}{x} - 1\right) \cdot (x + 8) = 240$

$\left(\dfrac{240 - x}{x}\right)(x + 8) = 240$

$(240 - x)(x + 8) = 240x$

$240x + 1920 - x^2 - 8x = 240x$

$-x^2 - 8x + 1920 = 0$

$x^2 + 8x - 1920 = 0$

$(x + 48)(x - 40) = 0$

$x = -48 \quad x = 40$

$x + 8 = 48$

33. *Verbal model:* $\boxed{\begin{array}{c}\text{Investment per}\\ \text{person; current group}\end{array}} - \boxed{\begin{array}{c}\text{Investment per}\\ \text{person; new group}\end{array}} = \boxed{6000}$

Labels: Number in current group $= x$

Number in new group $= x + 3$

Equation: $\dfrac{80,000}{x} - \dfrac{80,000}{x + 3} = 6000$

$x(x + 3)\left(\dfrac{80,000}{x} - \dfrac{80,000}{x + 3}\right) = (6000)x(x + 3)$

$80,000(x + 3) - 80,000x = 6000(x^2 + 3x)$

$80,000x + 240,000 - 80,000x = 6000x^2 + 18,000x$

$0 = 6000x^2 + 18,000x - 240,000$

$0 = x^2 + 3x - 40$

$0 = (x + 8)(x - 5)$

$x + 8 = 0 \qquad x - 5 = 0$

$\cancel{x = -8} \qquad x = 5$ investors

35. *Common Formula:* $a^2 + b^2 = c^2$

Equation: $x^2 + (18 - x)^2 = 16^2$

$x^2 + 324 - 36x + x^2 = 256$

$2x^2 - 36x + 68 = 0$

$x^2 - 18x + 34 = 0$

$x = \dfrac{18 \pm \sqrt{18^2 - 4(1)(34)}}{2(1)}$

$x = \dfrac{18 \pm \sqrt{324 - 136}}{2} = \dfrac{18 \pm \sqrt{188}}{2}$

$x = 15.855655, \quad$ reject 2.1443454

≈ 15.86 miles

37. (a) $d = \sqrt{(3 + x)^2 + (4 + x)^2}$

Keystrokes:

$\boxed{Y=}$ $\boxed{\sqrt{}}$ $\boxed{(}$ $\boxed{(}$ $\boxed{3}$ $\boxed{+}$ $\boxed{X,T,\theta}$ $\boxed{)}$ $\boxed{x^2}$ $\boxed{+}$ $\boxed{(}$ $\boxed{4}$ $\boxed{+}$ $\boxed{X,T,\theta}$ $\boxed{)}$ $\boxed{x^2}$ $\boxed{)}$ $\boxed{\text{GRAPH}}$

Approximate value of $x \approx 3.55$ when $d = 10$.

(b) $10 = \sqrt{(3 + x)^2 + (4 + x)^2}$

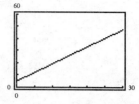

$100 = (3 + x)^2 + (4 + x)^2$

$ = 9 + 6x + x^2 + 16 + 8x + x^2$

$0 = 2x^2 + 14x - 75$

$x = \dfrac{-14 \pm \sqrt{14^2 - 4(2)(-75)}}{2(2)}$

$x = \dfrac{-14 \pm \sqrt{196 + 600}}{4}$

$x = \dfrac{-14 \pm \sqrt{796}}{4}$

$x = \dfrac{14 \pm 2\sqrt{199}}{4}$

$x = \dfrac{-7 \pm \sqrt{199}}{2} \approx 3.55$ meters

39. *Verbal model:* $\boxed{\begin{array}{c}\text{Work done by}\\\text{Person 1}\end{array}}$ $+$ $\boxed{\begin{array}{c}\text{Work done by}\\\text{Person 2}\end{array}}$ $=$ $\boxed{\text{One complete job}}$

Labels: Time to do job by Person 1 $= x$

Time to do job by Person 2 $= x + 2$

Equation: $\dfrac{1}{x}(5) + \dfrac{1}{x + 2}(5) = 1$

$x(x + 2)\left[(5)\left(\dfrac{1}{x} + \dfrac{1}{x + 2}\right) = 1\right]x(x + 2)$

$5(x + 2) + 5x = x(x + 2)$

$5x + 10 + 5x = x^2 + 2x$

$-x^2 + 8x + 10 = 0$

$x^2 - 8x - 10 = 0$

$x = \dfrac{8 \pm \sqrt{(-8)^2 - 4(1)(-10)}}{2(1)}$

$x = \dfrac{8 \pm \sqrt{64 + 40}}{2}$

$x = \dfrac{8 \pm \sqrt{104}}{2}$

$x \approx 9.1$ hours,   reject -1.1

$x + 2 \approx 11.1$ hours

41. *Verbal model:* | Rate Company A | + | Rate Company B | = | Rate together |

Labels: Time Company A $= x + 3$

                Time Company B $= x$

Equation:
$$\frac{1}{x+3} + \frac{1}{x} = \frac{1}{4}$$

$$4x(x+3)\left(\frac{1}{x+3} + \frac{1}{x}\right) = \left(\frac{1}{4}\right)4x(x+3)$$

$$4x + 4(x+3) = x(x+3)$$

$$4x + 4x + 12 = x^2 + 3x$$

$$0 = x^2 - 5x - 12$$

$$x = \frac{-(-5) \pm \sqrt{(-5)^2 - 4(1)(-12)}}{2(1)}$$

$$x = \frac{5 \pm \sqrt{25 + 48}}{2}$$

$$x = \frac{5 \pm \sqrt{73}}{2}$$

$$x \approx 6.8 \text{ days} \quad \cancel{x \approx 1.8}$$

$$x + 3 \approx 9.8$$

43.
$$h = h_0 - 16t^2$$

$$0 = 144 - 16t^2$$

$$16t^2 = 144$$

$$t^2 = 9$$

$$t = 3 \text{ seconds}$$

45.
$$h = h_0 - 16t^2$$

$$0 = 1454 - 16t^2$$

$$16t^2 = 1454$$

$$t^2 = 90.875$$

$$t = 9.532838 \text{ seconds} \approx 9.5 \text{ seconds}$$

47.
$$h = 3 + 75t - 16t^2$$

$$0 = 3 + 75t - 16t^2$$

$$0 = 16t^2 - 75t - 3$$

$$t = \frac{75 \pm \sqrt{(-75)^2 - 4(16)(-3)}}{2(16)}$$

$$t = \frac{75 \pm \sqrt{5625 + 192}}{32}$$

$$t = \frac{75 \pm \sqrt{5817}}{32}$$

$$t = \frac{75 \pm 76.26926}{32}$$

$$t = 4.7271644, \quad \text{reject} -0.0396644$$

$$\approx 4.7 \text{ seconds}$$

49. (a)
$$336 = -16t^2 + 160t$$

$$0 = -16t^2 + 160t - 336$$

$$0 = t^2 - 10t + 21$$

$$0 = (t - 7)(t - 3)$$

at 3 seconds and at 7 seconds

(b)
$$0 = -16t^2 + 160t$$

$$0 = -16t(t - 10)$$

$$t = 0, 10$$

after 10 seconds.

51. *Verbal model:* ┌ Integer ┐ · ┌ Integer ┐ = ┌ Product ┐

Labels: First integer = n

Second integer = $n + 1$

Equation:
$$n \cdot (n + 1) = 240$$
$$n^2 + n + \frac{1}{4} = 240 + \frac{1}{4}$$
$$\left(n + \frac{1}{2}\right)^2 = \frac{960 + 1}{4}$$
$$n + \frac{1}{2} = \pm\sqrt{\frac{961}{4}}$$
$$n = -\frac{1}{2} \pm \frac{\sqrt{961}}{2}$$
$$n = \frac{-1 \pm 31}{2}$$

$n = 15 \qquad n = -16$

$n + 1 = 16 \qquad n + 1 = 2 - 15$ } reject

53. *Verbal model:* ┌ Even integer ┐ · ┌ Even integer ┐ = ┌ Product ┐

Labels: First even integer = $2n$

Second even integer = $2n + 2$

Equation:
$$2n \cdot (2n + 2) = 224$$
$$4n^2 + 4n = 224$$
$$n^2 + n = 56$$
$$n^2 + n - 56 = 0$$
$$(n + 8)(n - 7) = 0$$

$n + 8 = 0 \qquad n - 7 = 0$

$n = -8 \cdot \qquad n = 7$

reject { $2n = -16 \qquad 2n = 14$

$2n + 2 = -14 \qquad 2n + 2 = 16$

55. *Verbal model:* ┌ Odd integer ┐ · ┌ Odd integer ┐ = ┌ Product ┐

Labels: First odd integer = $2n + 1$

Second odd integer = $2n + 3$

Equation:
$$(2n + 1) \cdot (2n + 3) = 483$$
$$4n^2 + 8n + 3 = 483$$
$$4n^2 + 8n - 480 = 0$$
$$n^2 + 2n - 120 = 0$$
$$(n + 12)(n - 10) = 0$$

$n + 12 = 0 \qquad n - 10 = 0$

~~$n = -12$~~ $\qquad n = 10$

$\qquad\qquad\qquad 2n + 1 = 21$

$\qquad\qquad\qquad 2n + 3 = 23$

57. *Verbal model:* ┌ Original time ┐ = ┌ New time ┐ + ┌ $\frac{1}{5}$ ┐

Labels: Speed = x

Increased speed = $x + 40$

Equation:
$$\frac{720}{x} = \frac{720}{x + 40} + \frac{1}{5}$$
$$720(5)(x + 40) = 720(5x) + x(x + 40)$$
$$3600x + 144{,}000 = 3600x + x^2 + 40x$$
$$0 = x^2 + 40x - 144{,}000$$
$$x = \frac{-40 \pm \sqrt{40^2 - 4(1)(-144{,}000)}}{2(1)}$$
$$x = \frac{40 \pm \sqrt{1600 + 576{,}000}}{2}$$
$$x = \frac{-40 \pm 760}{2}$$
$$x = 360, \; \cancel{-400}$$
$$x + 40 = 400 \text{ miles per hour}$$

59. *Verbal model:* | Total Cost | = | Wage Cost | + | Fuel Cost |

Label: Time $= x$

Equation:

$$20.39 = 5x + x = \left[\frac{\left(\frac{110}{x} \right)^2}{600} \right]$$

$$20.39 = 5x + \frac{121}{6x}$$

$$122.34x = 30x^2 + 121$$

$$0 = 30x^2 - 122.34x + 121$$

$$x = \frac{-(-122.34) \pm \sqrt{(-122.34)^2 - 4(30)(121)}}{2(30)}$$

$$x = \frac{122.34 \pm \sqrt{477.0756}}{60}$$

$$x \approx 2.39, \ 1.67$$

$$v = \frac{110}{2.39} \approx 46 \ \text{mi/hr}$$

or

$$v = \frac{110}{1.67} \approx 65 \ \text{mi/hr}$$

61. (a) $a + b = 20$ $A = \pi ab$

  $b = 20 - a$ $A = \pi a(20 - a)$

(b)

a	4	7	10	13	16
A	201.1	285.9	314.2	285.9	201.1

$A = \pi(4)(20 - 4)$ $A = \pi(7)(20 - 7)$ $A = \pi(10)(20 - 10)$

  $= \pi(4)(16)$ $= \pi(7)(13)$ $= \pi(10)(10)$

  $= 64\pi$ $= 91\pi$ $= 100\pi$

  ≈ 201.1 ≈ 285.9 ≈ 314.2

$A = \pi(13)(20 - 13)$ $A = \pi(16)(20 - 16)$

  $= \pi(13)(7)$ $= \pi(16)(4)$

  $= 91\pi$ $= 64\pi$

  ≈ 285.9 ≈ 201.1

(c) $300 = \pi a(20 - a)$

  $0 = 20\pi a - \pi a^2 - 300$

  $0 = \pi a^2 - 20\pi a + 300$

  $a = \dfrac{-(-20\pi) \pm \sqrt{(-20\pi)^2 - 4(\pi)(300)}}{2(\pi)}$

  $a = \dfrac{20\pi \pm \sqrt{177.9305761}}{2\pi}$

  $a \approx 12.1, \ 7.9$

(d) $A = \pi a(20 - a)$

Keystrokes:

Y= π X,T,θ (20 − X,T,θ) GRAPH

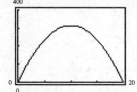

63. Guidelines for solving word problems:

   (a) Write a verbal model that will describe what you need to know.

   (b) Assign labels to each part of the verbal model—numbers to the known quantities and letters to the variable quantities.

   (c) Use the labels to write an algebraic model based on the verbal model.

   (d) Solve the resulting algebraic equation and check your solution.

65. Unit Analysis

$$\frac{9\text{ dollars}}{\text{hour}} \cdot (20 \text{ hours}) = 180 \text{ dollars}$$

67. An example of a quadratic equation that has only one repeated solution is $(x + 4)^2 = 0$. Any equation of the form $(x - c)^2 = 0$, where c is a constant will have only one repeated solution.

Section 6.5   Quadratic and Rational Inequalities

1. $x(2x - 5) = 0$

   $x = 0 \quad 2x - 5 = 0$

   $\qquad\qquad x = \frac{5}{2}$

   Critical numbers $= 0, \frac{5}{2}$

3. $4x^2 - 81 = 0$

   $x^2 = \frac{81}{4}$

   $x = \pm\frac{9}{2}$

   Critical numbers: $\frac{9}{2}, -\frac{9}{2}$

5. $x(x + 3) - 5(x + 3) = 0$

   $(x - 5)(x + 3) = 0$

   $x = 5 \quad x = -3$

   Critical numbers: $5, -3$

7. $x^2 - 4x + 3 = 0$

   $(x - 3)(x - 1) = 0$

   $x = 3 \quad x = 1$

   Critical numbers $= 3, 1$

9. $4x^2 - 20x + 25 = 0$

   $(2x - 5)^2 = 0$

   $2x - 5 = 0$

   $x = \frac{5}{2}$

   Critical number: $\frac{5}{2}$

11. Negative: $(-\infty, 4)$

   Positive: $(4, \infty)$

   Choose a test value from each interval.

   $(-\infty, 4) \Rightarrow x = 0 \Rightarrow 0 - 4 = -4 < 0$

   $(4, \infty) \Rightarrow x = 5 \Rightarrow 5 - 4 = 1 > 0$

13. Negative: $(6, \infty)$

   Positive: $(-\infty, 6)$

   Choose a test value from each interval.

   $(-\infty, 6) \Rightarrow x = 0 \Rightarrow 3 - \frac{1}{2}(0) = 3 > 0$

   $(6, \infty) \Rightarrow x = 8 \Rightarrow 3 - \frac{1}{2}(8) = -1 < 0$

15. Positive: $(-\infty, 0)$

   Negative: $(0, 4)$

   Positive: $(4, \infty)$

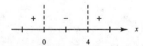

   Choose a test value from each interval.

   $(-\infty, 0) \Rightarrow x = -1 \Rightarrow 2(-1)(-1 - 4) = 10 > 0$

   $(0, 4) \Rightarrow x = 1 \Rightarrow 2(1)(1 - 4) = -6 < 0$

   $(4, \infty) \Rightarrow x = 5 \Rightarrow 2(5)(5 - 4) = 10 > 0$

17. $4 - x^2 = (2 - x)(2 + x)$

Negative: $(-\infty, -2) \cup (2, \infty)$

Positive: $(-2, 2)$

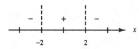

Choose a test value from each interval.

$(-\infty, -2) \Rightarrow x = -3 \Rightarrow (2-3)(2 + -3) = -5 < 0$

$(-2, 2) \Rightarrow x = 0 \Rightarrow (2 - 0)(2 + 0) = 4 > 0$

$(2, \infty) \Rightarrow x = 3 \Rightarrow (2 - 3)(2 + 3) = -5 < 0$

19. $(x - 5)(x + 1)$

Positive: $(-\infty, -1)$

Negative: $(-1, 5)$

Positive: $(5, \infty)$

Choose a test value from each interval.

$(-\infty, -1) \Rightarrow x = -2 \Rightarrow (-2 - 5)(-2 + 1) = 7 > 0$

$(-1, 5) \Rightarrow x = 0 \Rightarrow (0 - 5)(0 + 1) = -5 < 0$

$(5, \infty) \Rightarrow x = 6 \Rightarrow (6 - 5)(6 + 1) = 7 > 0$

21. $2(x + 3) \geq 0$

Critical number: $x = -3$

Test intervals:

Negative: $(-\infty, -3]$

Positive: $[-3, \infty)$

Solution: $[-3, \infty)$

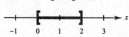

23. $-\dfrac{3}{4}x + 6 < 0$

Critical number: $x = 8$

Test intervals:

Negative: $(8, \infty)$

Positive: $(-\infty, 8)$

Solution: $(8, \infty)$

25. $3x(x - 2) < 0$

Critical number: $x = 0, 2$

Test intervals:

Positive: $(-\infty, 0)$

Negative: $(0, 2)$

Positive: $(2, \infty)$

Solution: $(0, 2)$

27. $3x(2 - x) \geq 0$

Critical numbers: $x = 0, 2$

Test intervals:

Negative: $(-\infty, 0]$

Positive: $[0, 2]$

Negative: $[2, \infty)$

Solution: $[0, 2]$

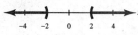

29. $x^2 > 4$

$x^2 - 4 > 0$

$(x - 2)(x + 2) > 0$

Critical numbers: $x = 2, -2$

Test intervals:

Positive: $(-\infty, 2)$

Negative: $(-2, 2)$

Positive: $(2, \infty)$

Solution: $(-\infty, -2) \cup (2, \infty)$

31. $x^2 + 3x - 10 \leq 0$

$(x + 5)(x - 2) \leq 0$

Critical number: $x = -5, 2$

Test intervals:

Positive: $(-\infty, -5]$

Negative: $[-5, 2]$

Positive: $[2, \infty)$

Solution: $[-5, 2]$

33. $u^2 + 2u - 2 > 1$

$u^2 + 2u - 3 > 0$

$(u + 3)(u - 1) > 0$

Critical numbers: $u = -3, 1$

Test intervals:

Positive: $(-\infty, -3)$

Negative: $(-3, 1)$

Positive: $(1, \infty)$

Solution: $(-\infty, -3) \cup (1, \infty)$

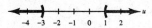

35. $x^2 + 4x + 5 < 0$

$x = \dfrac{-4 \pm \sqrt{16 - 20}}{2}$

No critical numbers

$x^2 + 4x + 5$ is not less than zero for any value of x.

Solution: none

37. $(x + 1)^2 \geq 0$

$(x + 1)^2 \geq 0$ for all real numbers

Solution: $(-\infty, \infty)$

39. $x^2 - 4x + 2 > 0$

$$x = \frac{4 \pm \sqrt{16 - 8}}{2}$$

$$= \frac{4 \pm \sqrt{8}}{2} = \frac{4 \pm 2\sqrt{2}}{2}$$

$$= 2 \pm \sqrt{2}$$

Critical numbers: $x = 2 + \sqrt{2}, 2 - \sqrt{2}$

Test intervals:

Positive: $\left(-\infty, 2 - \sqrt{2}\right)$

Negative: $\left(2 - \sqrt{2}, 2 + \sqrt{2}\right)$

Positive: $\left(2 + \sqrt{2}, \infty\right)$

Solution: $\left(-\infty, 2 - \sqrt{2}\right) \cup \left(2 + \sqrt{2}, \infty\right)$

41. $x^2 - 6x + 9 \geq 0$

$$(x - 3)^2 \geq 0$$

$(x - 3)^2 \geq 0$ for all real numbers

43. $u^2 - 10u + 25 < 0$

$$(u - 5)(u - 5) < 0$$

Critical number: $u = 5$

Test intervals:

Positive: $(-\infty, 5)$

Positive: $(5, \infty)$

Solution: none

45. $3x^2 + 2x - 8 \leq 0$

$$(3x - 4)(x + 2) \leq 0$$

Critical numbers: $x = \frac{4}{3}, -2$

Test intervals:

Positive: $(-\infty, -2]$

Negative: $\left[-2, \frac{4}{3}\right]$

Positive: $\left[\frac{4}{3}, \infty\right)$

Solution: $\left[-2, \frac{4}{3}\right]$

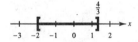

47. $-6u^2 + 19u - 10 > 0$

$$6u^2 - 19u + 10 < 0 \quad \text{(Multiply by } -1\text{)}$$

$$(3u - 2)(2u - 5) < 0$$

Critical numbers: $u = \frac{2}{3}, \frac{5}{2}$

Test intervals:

Positive: $\left(-\infty, \frac{2}{3}\right)$

Negative: $\left(\frac{2}{3}, \frac{5}{2}\right)$

Positive: $\left(\frac{5}{2}, \infty\right)$

Solution: $\left(\frac{2}{3}, \frac{5}{2}\right)$

49. $2u^2 - 7u - 4 > 0$

$$(2u + 1)(u - 4) > 0$$

Critical numbers: $u = -\frac{1}{2}, 4$

Test intervals:

Positive: $\left(-\infty, -\frac{1}{2}\right)$

Negative: $\left(-\frac{1}{2}, 4\right)$

Positive: $(4, \infty)$

Solution: $\left(-\infty, -\frac{1}{2}\right) \cup (4, \infty)$

51. $4x^2 + 28x + 49 \le 0$

$(2x + 7)(2x + 7) \le 0$

Critical number: $x = \frac{-7}{2}$

Test intervals:

Positive: $\left(-\infty, -\frac{7}{2}\right)$

Positive: $\left(-\frac{7}{2}, \infty\right)$

Solution: $-\frac{7}{2}$

$\begin{array}{c} -\frac{7}{2} \\ \end{array}$

-5 -4 -3 -2 -1   0

53. $(x - 5)^2 > 0$ for all real numbers except 5.

Solution: none

55. $6 - (x^2 - 10x + 25) < 0$

$6 - x^2 + 10x - 25 < 0$

$x^2 - 10x + 19 > 0$

$x = \dfrac{10 \pm \sqrt{100 - 76}}{2}$

$= \dfrac{10 \pm \sqrt{24}}{2} = \dfrac{10 \pm 2\sqrt{6}}{2}$

$= 5 \pm \sqrt{6}$

Critical numbers: $x = 5 + \sqrt{6}, 5 - \sqrt{6}$

Test intervals:

Positive: $\left(-\infty, 5 - \sqrt{6}\right)$

Negative: $\left(5 - \sqrt{6}, 5 + \sqrt{6}\right)$

Positive: $\left(5 + \sqrt{6}, \infty\right)$

Solution: $\left(-\infty, 5 - \sqrt{6}\right) \cup \left(5 + \sqrt{6}, \infty\right)$

$\begin{array}{cc} 5 - \sqrt{6} & 5 + \sqrt{6} \end{array}$

0   2   4   6   8   10

57.
$$16 \le (u + 5)^2$$
$$(u + 5)^2 \ge 16$$
$$u^2 + 10u + 25 - 16 \ge 0$$
$$u^2 + 10u + 9 \ge 0$$
$$(u + 9)(u + 1) \ge 0$$

Critical numbers: $x = -9, -1$

Test intervals:

Positive: $(-\infty, -9]$

Negative: $(-9, -1]$

Positive: $[-1, \infty)$

Solution: $(-\infty, -9] \cup [-1, \infty)$

$\begin{array}{cc} -9 & -1 \end{array}$

-10 -8 -6 -4 -2   0

59. $x(x - 2)(x + 2) > 0$

Critical numbers: $x = 0, 2, -2$

Test intervals:

Negative: $(-\infty, -2)$

Positive: $(-2, 0)$

Negative: $(0, 2)$

Positive: $(2, \infty)$

Solution: $(-2, 0) \cup (2, \infty)$

-3 -2 -1   0   1   2   3

61. *Keystrokes:*

$\boxed{Y=}$ $\boxed{X,T,\theta}$ $\boxed{x^2}$ $\boxed{-}$ 6 $\boxed{X,T,\theta}$ $\boxed{GRAPH}$

$(0, 6)$

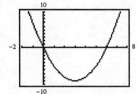

63. *Keystrokes:*

$\boxed{\text{Y=}}$ 0.5 $\boxed{\text{X,T,}\theta}$ $\boxed{x^2}$ $\boxed{+}$ 1.25 $\boxed{\text{X,T,}\theta}$ $\boxed{-}$ 3 $\boxed{\text{GRAPH}}$

$(-\infty, -4) \cup \left(\frac{3}{2}, \infty\right)$

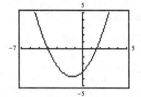

65. *Keystrokes:*

y_1 $\boxed{\text{Y=}}$ $\boxed{\text{X,T,}\theta}$ $\boxed{x^2}$ $\boxed{+}$ 4 $\boxed{\text{X,T,}\theta}$ $\boxed{+}$ 4 $\boxed{\text{ENTER}}$

y_2 9 $\boxed{\text{GRAPH}}$

$(-\infty, -5] \cup [1, \infty)$

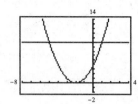

67. *Keystrokes:*

y_1 $\boxed{\text{Y=}}$ 9 $\boxed{-}$ 0.2 $\boxed{(}$ $\boxed{\text{X,T,}\theta}$ $\boxed{-}$ 2 $\boxed{)}$ $\boxed{x^2}$

y_2 4 $\boxed{\text{GRAPH}}$

$(-\infty, -3) \cup (7, \infty)$

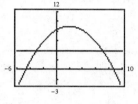

69. Critical number: $x = 3$

71. Critical numbers: $x = 0, -5$

73. $\dfrac{5}{x - 3} > 0$

Critical number: $x = 3$

Test intervals:

Negative: $(-\infty, 3)$

Positive: $(3, \infty)$

Solution: $(3, \infty)$

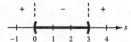

75. $\dfrac{-5}{x - 3} > 0$

Critical number: $x = 3$

Test intervals:

Positive: $(-\infty, 3)$

Negative: $(3, \infty)$

Solution: $(-\infty, 3)$

77. $\dfrac{x}{x - 3} < 0$

Critical numbers: $x = 0, 3$

Test intervals:

Positive: $(-\infty, 0)$

Negative: $(0, 3)$

Positive: $(3, \infty)$

Solution: $(0, 3)$

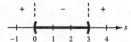

79. $\dfrac{x + 3}{x - 4} \le 0$

Critical numbers: $x = -3, 4$

Test intervals:

Positive: $(-\infty, -3]$

Negative: $[-3, 4)$

Positive: $(4, \infty)$

Solution: $[-3, 4)$

81. $\dfrac{y-4}{y+6} < 0$

Critical numbers: $y = 4, -6$

Test intervals:

Positive: $(-\infty, -6)$

Negative: $(-6, 4)$

Positive: $(4, \infty)$

Solution: $(-6, 4)$

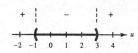

83. $\dfrac{y-3}{y-11} \geq 0$

Critical numbers: $y = 3, \dfrac{11}{2}$

Test intervals:

Positive: $(-\infty, 3]$

Negative: $\left[3, \dfrac{11}{2}\right)$

Positive: $\left(\dfrac{11}{2}, \infty\right)$

Solution: $(-\infty, 3] \cup \left(\dfrac{11}{2}, \infty\right)$

85. $\dfrac{x+2}{4x+6} \leq 0$

Critical numbers: $x = -2, -\dfrac{3}{2}$

Test intervals:

Positive: $(-\infty, -2]$

Negative: $\left[-2, -\dfrac{3}{2}\right)$

Positive: $\left(-\dfrac{3}{2}, \infty\right)$

Solution: $\left[-2, -\dfrac{3}{2}\right)$

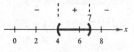

87. $\dfrac{3(u-3)}{u+1} < 0$

Critical numbers: $u = 3, -1$

Test intervals:

Positive: $(-\infty, -1)$

Negative: $(-1, 3)$

Positive: $(3, \infty)$

Solution: $(-1, 3)$

89. $\dfrac{6}{x-4} > 2$

$\dfrac{6}{x-4} - 2 > 0$

$\dfrac{6 - 2(x-4)}{x-4} > 0$

$\dfrac{6 - 2x + 8}{x-4} > 0$

$\dfrac{14 - 2x}{x-4} > 0$

$\dfrac{-2(-7+x)}{x-4} > 0$

Critical numbers: $x = 7, 4$

Test intervals:

Negative: $(-\infty, 4)$

Positive: $(4, 7)$

Negative: $(7, \infty)$

Solution: $(4, 7)$

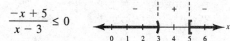

91. $\dfrac{4x}{x+2} < -1$

$\dfrac{4x}{x+2} + 1 < 0$

$\dfrac{4x + (x+2)}{x+2} < 0$

$\dfrac{5x+2}{x+2} < 0$

Critical numbers: $x = -\dfrac{2}{5}, -2$

Test intervals:

Positive: $(-\infty, -2)$

Negative: $\left(-2, -\dfrac{2}{5}\right)$

Positive: $\left(-\dfrac{2}{5}, \infty\right)$

Solution: $\left(-2, -\dfrac{2}{5}\right)$

93. $\dfrac{x-1}{x-3} \leq 2$

$\dfrac{x-1}{x-3} - 2 \leq 0$

$\dfrac{x - 1 - 2(x-3)}{x-3} \leq 0$

$\dfrac{x - 1 - 2x + 6}{x-3} \leq 0$

$\dfrac{-x+5}{x-3} \leq 0$

Critical numbers: $x = 5, 3$

Test intervals:

Negative: $(-\infty, 3)$

Positive: $(3, 5]$

Negative: $[5, \infty)$

Solution: $(-\infty, 3) \cup [5, \infty)$

95. *Keystrokes:*

$\boxed{Y=}$ 1 $\boxed{\div}$ $\boxed{X,T,\theta}$ $\boxed{-}$ $\boxed{X,T,\theta}$ $\boxed{GRAPH}$

Solution: $(-\infty, -1) \cup (0, 1)$

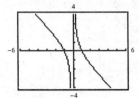

97. *Keystrokes:*

$\boxed{Y=}$ $\boxed{(}$ $\boxed{X,T,\theta}$ $\boxed{+}$ 6 $\boxed{)}$ $\boxed{\div}$ $\boxed{(}$ $\boxed{X,T,\theta}$ $\boxed{+}$ 1 $\boxed{)}$ $\boxed{-}$ 2 $\boxed{GRAPH}$

Solution: $(-\infty, -1) \cup (4, \infty)$

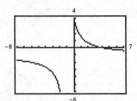

99. *Keystrokes:*

y_1 $\boxed{Y=}$ $\boxed{(}$ 6 $\boxed{X,T,\theta}$ $\boxed{-}$ 3 $\boxed{)}$ $\boxed{\div}$ $\boxed{(}$ $\boxed{X,T,\theta}$ $\boxed{+}$ 5 $\boxed{)}$ $\boxed{ENTER}$

y_2 2 $\boxed{GRAPH}$

Solution: $(-5, 3.25)$

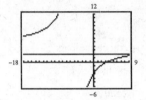

101. *Keystrokes:*

y_1 $\boxed{Y=}$ $\boxed{X,T,\theta}$ $\boxed{+}$ 1 $\boxed{\div}$ $\boxed{X,T,\theta}$ $\boxed{ENTER}$

y_2 3 $\boxed{GRAPH}$

Solution: $(0, 0.382) \cup (2.618, \infty)$

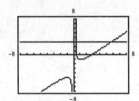

103. *Keystrokes:*

$\boxed{Y=}$ 3 $\boxed{X,T,\theta}$ $\boxed{\div}$ $\boxed{(}$ $\boxed{X,T,\theta}$ $\boxed{-}$ 2 $\boxed{GRAPH}$

(a) Solution $[0, 2)$

   (Look at x-axis and vertical asymptote $x = 2$)

(b) $(2, 4]$

   (Graph $y = 6$ as y_2 and find the intersection.)

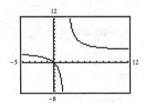

105. *Keystrokes:*

$\boxed{Y=}$ 2 $\boxed{X,T,\theta}$ $\boxed{x^2}$ $\boxed{\div}$ $\boxed{(}$ $\boxed{X,T,\theta}$ $\boxed{x^2}$ $\boxed{+}$ 4 $\boxed{)}$ $\boxed{GRAPH}$

(a) Solution: $(-\infty, -2] \cup [2, \infty)$

   (Graph $y = 1$ as y_2 and find the intersection.)

(b) Solution $(-\infty, \infty)$

   (Notice graph stays below line $y = 2$.)

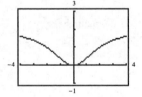

107.

$$\text{height} > 240$$
$$-16t^2 + 128t > 240$$
$$-16t^2 + 128t - 240 > 0$$
$$t^2 - 8t + 15 < 0$$
$$(t - 3)(t - 5) < 0$$

Critical numbers: $x = 3, 5$

Test intervals:

Positive: $(-\infty, 3)$

Negative: $(3, 5)$

Positive: $(5, \infty)$

Solution: $(3, 5)$

109.
$$1000(1 + r)^2 > 1150$$
$$1000(1 + 2r + r^2) > 1150$$
$$1000 + 2000r + 1000r^2 > 1150$$
$$1000r^2 + 2000r - 150 > 0$$
$$20r^2 + 40r - 3 > 0$$

Critical numbers: $r = \dfrac{-40 + \sqrt{1840}}{40}, \dfrac{-40 - \sqrt{1840}}{40}$

r cannot be negative.

Test intervals:

Negative: $\left(0, \dfrac{-40 + \sqrt{1840}}{40}\right)$

Positive: $\left(\dfrac{-40 + \sqrt{1840}}{40}, \infty\right)$

Solution: $\left(\dfrac{-40 + \sqrt{1840}}{40}, \infty\right)$

$(0.0724, \infty), \quad r > 7.24\%$

111. *Verbal model:* $\boxed{\text{Profit}} > 1{,}650{,}000$

$$\boxed{\text{Revenue}} - \boxed{\text{Cost}} = \text{Profit} > 1{,}650{,}000$$
$$x(50 - 0.0002x) - [12x + 150{,}000] > 1{,}650{,}000$$
$$50x - 0.0002x^2 - 12x - 150{,}000 > 1{,}650{,}000$$
$$-0.0002x^2 + 38x - 150{,}000 > 1{,}650{,}000$$
$$0 > 0.0002x^2 - 38x + 1{,}800{,}000$$
$$0 > (0.0002x - 20)(x - 90{,}000)$$

Critical numbers: 90,000, 100,000
Test intervals:
Positive: (0, 90,000)
Negative: (90,000, 100,000)
Positive: (100,000, ∞)
Solution: (90,000, 100,000)
$90{,}000 \le x \le 100{,}000$ units

113.
$$\text{Area} > 240$$
$$l(32 - l) > 240$$
$$32l - l^2 > 240$$
$$-l^2 + 32l - 240 > 0$$
$$l^2 - 32l + 240 < 0$$
$$(l - 20)(l - 12) < 0$$

Critical numbers: $l = 20, 12$
Test intervals:
Positive: $(-\infty, 12)$
Negative: (12, 20)
Positive: $(20, \infty)$
Solution: (12, 20)

115. (a) *Keystrokes:*

$\boxed{\text{Y=}}$ $\boxed{(}$ $\boxed{(}$ 244.20 $\boxed{-}$ 13.23 $\boxed{\text{X,T,}\theta}$ $\boxed{)}$ $\boxed{\div}$ $\boxed{(}$ 1 $\boxed{-}$ .13 $\boxed{\text{X,T,}\theta}$ $\boxed{+}$ .005 $\boxed{\text{X,T,}\theta}$ $\boxed{x^2}$ $\boxed{)}$ $\boxed{\text{GRAPH}}$

(b) Let $y_2 = 400$ and find the intersection of the graphs.

Solution: $[5.7, 13.7], \; 5.7 \le t \le 13 \cdot 7$

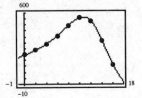

117. The direction of the inequality is reversed, when both sides are multiplied by a negative real number.

119. A polynomial can change signs only at the *x*-values that make the polynomial zero. The zeros of the polynomial are called the ciritical numbers, and they are used ro determine the test intervals in solving polynomial inequalities.

121. $x^2 + 1 < 0$ is one example of a quadratic inequality that has no real solution. Any inequality of the form $x^2 + c < 0$, c any positive constant or $-x^2 - c > 0$, c any positive constant will not have a real solution.

Review Exercises for Chapter 6

1. $x^2 + 12x = 0$

$x(x + 12) = 0$

$x = 0 \qquad x + 12 = 0$

$x = 0 \qquad\qquad x = -12$

3. $\qquad 4y^2 - 1 = 0$

$(2y - 1)(2y + 1) = 0$

$2y - 1 = 0 \qquad 2y + 1 = 0$

$y = \frac{1}{2} \qquad\qquad y = -\frac{1}{2}$

5. $4y^2 + 20y + 25 = 0$

$(2y + 5)(2y + 5) = 0$

$2y + 5 = 0 \qquad 2y + 5 = 0$

$2y = -5 \qquad\qquad 2y = -5$

$y = -\frac{5}{2} \qquad\qquad y = -\frac{5}{2}$

7. $2x^2 - 2x - 180 = 0$

$2(x^2 - x - 90) = 0$

$2(x - 10)(x + 9) = 0$

$x - 10 = 0 \qquad x + 9 = 0$

$x = 10 \qquad\qquad x = -9$

9. $\qquad 6x^2 - 12x = 4x^2 - 3x + 18$

$2x^2 - 9x - 18 = 0$

$(2x + 3)(x - 6) = 0$

$x = -\frac{3}{2} \qquad x = 6$

11. $4x^2 = 10{,}000$

$x^2 = 2500$

$x = \pm\sqrt{2500}$

$x = \pm 50$

13. $y^2 - 12 = 0$

$y^2 = 12$

$y = \pm\sqrt{12}$

$y = \pm 2\sqrt{3}$

15. $(x - 16)^2 = 400$

$x - 16 = \pm\sqrt{400}$

$x = 16 \pm 20$

$x = 36, -4$

17. $z^2 = -121$

$z = \pm\sqrt{-121}$

$z = \pm 11i$

19. $y^2 + 50 = 0$

$y^2 = -50$

$y = \pm\sqrt{-50}$

$y = \pm 5\sqrt{2}i$

21. $(y + 4)^2 + 18 = 0$

$(y + 4)^2 = -18$

$y + 4 = \pm\sqrt{-18}$

$y = -4 \pm 3\sqrt{2}i$

23. $\qquad x^4 - 4x^2 - 5 = 0$

$(x^2 - 5)(x^2 + 1) = 0$

$\qquad\qquad x^2 + 1 = 0$

$x^2 - 5 = 0 \qquad x^2 = -1$

$\qquad x^2 = 5 \qquad x = \pm\sqrt{-1}$

$\qquad x = \pm\sqrt{5} \qquad x = \pm i$

25. $\qquad x - 4\sqrt{x} + 3 = 0$

$\left(\sqrt{x} - 3\right)\left(\sqrt{x} - 1\right) = 0$

$\left(\sqrt{x} - 3\right) = 0 \qquad \left(\sqrt{x} - 1\right) = 0$

$\sqrt{x} = 3 \qquad\qquad \sqrt{x} = 1$

$\left(\sqrt{x}\right)^2 = 3^2 \qquad\qquad \left(\sqrt{x}\right)^2 = 1^2$

$x = 9 \qquad\qquad\qquad x = 1$

Check: $\qquad\qquad\qquad$ **Check:**

$9 - 4\sqrt{9} + 3 \overset{?}{=} 0 \qquad 1 - 4\sqrt{1} + 3 \overset{?}{=} 0$

$9 - 12 + 3 \overset{?}{=} 0 \qquad 1 - 4 + 3 \overset{?}{=} 0$

$0 = 0 \qquad\qquad\qquad 0 = 0$

27. $(x^2 - 2x)^2 - 4(x^2 - 2x) - 5 = 0$

$[(x^2 - 2x) - 5][(x^2 - 2x) + 1] = 0$

$(x^2 - 2x - 5)(x^2 - 2x + 1) = 0$

$x = \dfrac{-(-2) \pm \sqrt{(-2)^2 - 4(1)(-5)}}{2(1)}$

$x = \dfrac{2 \pm \sqrt{4 + 20}}{2}$

$x = \dfrac{2 \pm \sqrt{24}}{2}$

$x = \dfrac{2 \pm 2\sqrt{6}}{2}$ $(x - 1)^2 = 0$

$x = 1 \pm \sqrt{6}$ $x = 1$

29. $x^{2/3} + 3x^{1/3} - 28 = 0$

$(x^{1/3} + 7)(x^{1/3} - 4) = 0$

$x^{1/3} + 7 = 0$ $x^{1/3} - 4 = 0$

$x^{1/3} = -7$ $x^{1/3} = 4$

$\sqrt[3]{x} = -7$ $\sqrt[3]{x} = 4$

$\left(\sqrt[3]{x}\right)^3 = (-7)^3$ $\left(\sqrt[3]{x}\right)^3 = 4^3$

$x = -343$ $x = 64$

31. $x^2 - 6x - 3 = 0$

$x^2 - 6x + 9 = 3 + 9$

$(x - 3)^2 = 12$

$x - 3 = \pm\sqrt{12}$

$x = 3 \pm 2\sqrt{3}$

33. $x^2 - 3x + 3 = 0$

$x^2 - 3x + \dfrac{9}{4} = -3 + \dfrac{9}{4}$

$\left(x - \dfrac{3}{2}\right)^2 = \dfrac{-12 + 9}{4}$

$\left(x - \dfrac{3}{2}\right)^2 = -\dfrac{3}{4}$

$x - \dfrac{3}{2} = \pm\sqrt{-\dfrac{3}{4}}$

$x = \dfrac{3}{2} \pm \dfrac{i\sqrt{3}}{2}$

35. $y^2 - \dfrac{2}{3}y + 2 = 0$

$y^2 - \dfrac{2}{3}y = -2$

$y^2 - \dfrac{2}{3}y + \dfrac{1}{9} = -2 + \dfrac{1}{9}$

$\left(y - \dfrac{1}{3}\right)^2 = \dfrac{-17}{9}$

$y - \dfrac{1}{3} = \pm\sqrt{\dfrac{-17}{9}}$

$y = \dfrac{1}{3} \pm \dfrac{\sqrt{17}i}{3}$

37. $2y^2 + 10y + 3 = 0$

$y^2 + 5y + \dfrac{25}{4} = -\dfrac{3}{2} + \dfrac{25}{4}$

$\left(y + \dfrac{5}{2}\right)^2 = \dfrac{-6 + 25}{4}$

$\left(y + \dfrac{5}{2}\right)^2 = \dfrac{19}{4}$

$y + \dfrac{5}{2} = \pm\sqrt{\dfrac{19}{4}}$

$y = -\dfrac{5}{2} \pm \dfrac{\sqrt{19}}{2}$

39. $y^2 + y - 30 = 0$

$$y = \frac{-1 \pm \sqrt{1^2 - 4(1)(-30)}}{2(1)}$$

$$y = \frac{-1 \pm \sqrt{1 + 120}}{2}$$

$$y = \frac{-1 \pm \sqrt{121}}{2}$$

$$y = \frac{-1 \pm 11}{2}$$

$$y = 5, -6$$

41. $2y^2 + y - 21 = 0$

$$y = \frac{-1 \pm \sqrt{1^2 - 4(2)(-21)}}{2(2)}$$

$$y = \frac{-1 \pm \sqrt{1 + 168}}{4}$$

$$y = \frac{-1 \pm \sqrt{169}}{4}$$

$$y = \frac{-1 \pm 13}{4}$$

$$y = 3, -\frac{7}{2}$$

43. $5x^2 - 16x + 2 = 0$

$$x = \frac{-(-16) \pm \sqrt{(-16)^2 - 4(5)(2)}}{2(5)}$$

$$x = \frac{16 \pm \sqrt{256 - 40}}{10}$$

$$x = \frac{16 \pm \sqrt{216}}{10}$$

$$x = \frac{16 \pm 6\sqrt{6}}{10}$$

$$x = \frac{8 \pm 3\sqrt{6}}{5}$$

45. $0.3t^2 - 2t + 5 = 0$

$$t = \frac{-(-2) \pm \sqrt{(-2)^2 - 4(0.3)(5)}}{2(0.3)}$$

$$t = \frac{2 \pm \sqrt{4 - 6}}{0.6}$$

$$t = \frac{2 \pm \sqrt{-2}}{0.6}$$

$$t = \frac{2 \pm i\sqrt{2}}{0.6}$$

$$t = \frac{20 \pm 10\sqrt{2}i}{6} = \frac{10}{3} \pm \frac{5\sqrt{2}i}{3}$$

47. $x^2 + 4x + 4 = 0$

$$b^2 - 4ac = 4^2 - 4(1)(4)$$

$$= 16 - 16$$

$$= 0$$

One repeated rational solution.

49. $s^2 - s - 20 = 10$

$$b^2 - 4ac = (-1)^2 - 4(1)(-20)$$

$$= 1 + 80$$

$$= 81$$

Two distinct rational solutions.

51. $3t^2 + 17t + 10 = 0$

$$b^2 - 4ac = 17^2 - 4(3)(10)$$

$$= 289 - 120$$

$$= 169$$

Two distinct rational solutions.

53. $v^2 - 6v + 21 = 0$

$$b^2 - 4ac = (-6)^2 - 4(1)(21)$$

$$= 36 - 84$$

$$= -48$$

Two distinct imaginary solutions.

55. $5x(7 - x) > 0$

Critical numbers: $x = 0, 7$

Test intervals:

Negative: $(-\infty, 0)$

Positive: $(0, 7)$

Negative: $(7, \infty)$

Solution: $(0, 7)$

57. $16 - (x - 2)^2 \le 0$

$(4 - x + 2)(4 + x - 2) \le 0$

$(6 - x)(2 + x) \le 0$

Critical numbers: $x = -2, 6$

Test intervals:

Negative: $(-\infty, 2]$

Positive: $[-2, 6]$

Negative: $[6, \infty)$

Solution: $(-\infty, -2] \cup [6, \infty)$

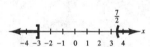

59. $2x^2 + 3x - 20 < 0$

$(2x - 5)(x + 4) < 0$

Critical numbers: $x = -4, \frac{5}{2}$

Test intervals:

Positive: $(-\infty, -4)$

Negative: $\left(-4, \frac{5}{2}\right)$

Positive: $\left(\frac{5}{2}, \infty\right)$

Solution: $\left(-4, \frac{5}{2}\right)$

61. $\dfrac{x + 3}{2x - 7} \ge 0$

Critical numbers: $x = -3, \frac{7}{2}$

Test intervals:

Positive: $(-\infty, -3]$

Negative: $\left[-3, \frac{7}{2}\right]$

Positive: $\left(\frac{7}{2}, \infty\right)$

Solution: $\left[-\infty, -3\right] \cup \left(\frac{7}{2}, \infty\right)$

63. $\dfrac{2x - 2}{x + 6} + 2 < 0$

$\dfrac{2x - 2 + 2(x + 6)}{x + 6} < 0$

$\dfrac{2x - 2 + 2x + 12}{x + 6} < 0$

$\dfrac{4x + 10}{x + 6} < 0$

Critical numbers: $x = -6, -\frac{5}{2}$

Test intervals:

Positive: $(-\infty, -6)$

Negative: $\left(-6, -\frac{5}{2}\right)$

Positive: $\left(-\frac{5}{2}, \infty\right)$

Solution: $\left(-6, -\frac{5}{2}\right)$

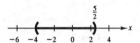

65. *Verbal model:* | Selling price per car | = | Cost per car | + | Profit per car |

Labels: Number cars sold $= x$

Number cars purchased $= x + 4$

Equation: $\dfrac{80,000}{x} = \dfrac{80,000}{x + 4} + 1,000$

$x(x + 4)\left(\dfrac{80,000}{x}\right) = \left(\dfrac{80,000}{x + 4} + 1,000\right)x(x + 4)$

$80,000(x + 4) = 80,000x + 1,000x(x + 4)$

$80,000x + 320,000 = 80,000x + 1,000x^2 + 4,000x$

$0 = 1,000x^2 + 4,000x - 320,000$

$0 = x^2 + 4x - 320$

$0 = (x + 20)(x - 16)$

reject $x = -20$ $x = 16$ cars

Average price per car $= \dfrac{80,000}{16} = \$5,000$

67. *Verbal model:* | Area | = | Length | · | Width |

Labels: Width = x

Length = $x + 12$

Equation: $108 = (x + 12)x$

$0 = x^2 + 12x - 108$

$0 = (x + 18)(x - 6)$

reject $x = -18$ $x = 6$ inches

$x + 12 = 18$ inches

69. Formula: $A = P(1 + r)^2$

$21,424.50 = 20,000(1 + r)^2$

$1.071225 = (1 + r)^2$

$1.035 = 1 + r$

$.035 = r$ or 3.5%

71. *Verbal model:* | Cost per person Current Group | − | Cost per person New Group | = | $1.50 |

Labels: Number in Current Group = x

Number in New Group = $x + 8$

Equation: $\dfrac{360}{x} - \dfrac{360}{x + 8} = 1.50$

$[x(x + 8)]\left(\dfrac{360}{x} - \dfrac{360}{x + 8}\right) = (1.50)[x(x + 8)]$

$360(x + 8) - 360x = 1.50(x^2 + 8x)$

$360x + 2880 - 360x = 1.50x^2 + 12x$

$0 = 1.5x^2 + 12x - 2880$

$0 = x^2 + 8x - 1920$

$0 = (x + 48)(x - 40)$

$x + 48 = 0$ $x - 40 = 0$

$\cancel{x = -48}$ $x = 40$

$x + 8 = 48$

73. *Verbal model:* | Cost per ticket | · | Number of tickets | = | $96 |

Labels: Number in team = x

Number going to game = $x + 3$

Equation: $\left(\dfrac{96}{x} - 1.60\right)(x + 3) = 96$

$\left(\dfrac{96 - 1.60x}{x}\right)(x + 3) = 96$

$(96 - 1.6x)(x + 3) = 96x$

$96x - 1.6x^2 - 4.8x + 288 = 96x$

$1.6x^2 + 4.8x - 288 = 0$

$x^2 + 3x - 180 = 0$

$(x - 12)(x + 15) = 0$

$x - 12 = 0$ $x + 15 = 0$

$x = 12$ $x = -15$ reject

$x + 3 = 15$

75. *Formula:* $c^2 = a^2 + b^2$ $a + b = 140$

Labels: $c = 100$ $x + b = 140$

$a = x$ $b = 140 - x$

$b = 140 - x$

Equation: $100^2 = x^2 + (140 - x)^2$

$10,000 = x^2 + 19,600 - 280x + x^2$

$0 = 2x^2 - 280x + 9,600$

$0 = x^2 - 140x + 4800$

$0 = (x - 60)(x - 80)$

$x = 60$ $x = 80$

$140 - x = 80$ $140 - x = 60$

60 feet and 80 feet

77. *Verbal model:* $\boxed{\begin{array}{c}\text{Work done}\\\text{by Person 1}\end{array}}$ + $\boxed{\begin{array}{c}\text{Work done}\\\text{by Person 2}\end{array}}$ = $\boxed{\text{One complete job}}$

Labels: Time Person 1 = x

Labels: Time Person 2 = $x + 2$

Equation:

$$\frac{1}{x}(10) + \frac{1}{x+2}(10) = 1$$

$$x(x+2)\left[10\left(\frac{1}{x} + \frac{1}{x+2}\right)\right] = [1]x(x+2)$$

$$10(x+2) + 10x = x(x+2)$$

$$10x + 20 + 10x = x^2 + 2x$$

$$0 = x^2 - 18x - 20$$

$$x = \frac{-(-18) \pm \sqrt{(-18)^2 - 4(1)(-20)}}{2(1)}$$

$$x = \frac{18 \pm \sqrt{324 + 80}}{2}$$

$$x = \frac{18 \pm \sqrt{404}}{2}$$

$$x = \frac{18 \pm 2\sqrt{101}}{2}$$

$$x = 9 \pm \sqrt{101}$$

$$x \approx 19$$

$$x + 2 \approx 21$$

19 hours, 21 hours

79. (a) $256 = -16t^2 + 64t + 192$

$0 = -16t^2 + 64t - 64$

$0 = t^2 - 4t + 4$

$0 = (t-2)^2$

$t = 2$ seconds

(b) $0 = -16t^2 + 64t + 192$

$0 = -16(t^2 - 4t - 12)$

$0 = -16(t+2)(t-6)$

$t + 2 = 0 \qquad t - 6 = 0$

discard $t = -2 \qquad t = 6$ seconds

81. $\overline{C} = \dfrac{C}{x} = \dfrac{50{,}000 + 1.2x}{x} = \dfrac{50{,}000}{x} + 1.2$

$\overline{C} < 5$

$\dfrac{50{,}000}{x} + 1.2 < 5$

$\dfrac{50{,}000}{x} - 3.8 < 0$

$\dfrac{50{,}000 - 3.8x}{x} < 0$

Critical numbers: $x = 0, 13158$

Test intervals:

x must be positive

Positive: $(0, 13{,}158)$

Negative: $(13{,}158, \infty)$

Solution: $(13{,}158, \infty)$

83. $h = -16t^2 + 312t$

$$-16t^2 + 312\,t > 1200$$

$$-16t^2 + 312t - 1200 > 0 \qquad \text{(Divide by } -16\text{)}$$

$$t^2 - 19.5t + 75 < 0$$

$$t = \frac{-(-19.5) \pm \sqrt{(-19.5)^2 - 4(1)(75)}}{2(1)}$$

$$t = \frac{19.5 \pm \sqrt{80.25}}{2}$$

$$t \approx 14.2,\ 5.3$$

Critical numbers: $t = 14.2,\ 5.3$

Test intervals:

Positive: $(-\infty, 5.3)$

Negative: $(5.3, 14.2)$

Positive: $(14.2, \infty)$

Solution: $(5.3, 14.2)$

$5.3 < t < 14.2$

Chapter Test for Chapter 6

1. $x(x + 5) - 10(x + 5) = 0$

$\qquad (x + 5)(x - 10) = 0$

$x + 5 = 0 \qquad x - 10 = 0$

$\qquad x = -5 \qquad\quad x = 10$

2. $8x^2 - 21x - 9 = 0$

$\qquad (8x + 3)(x - 3) = 0$

$8x + 3 = 0 \qquad x - 3 = 0$

$\qquad x = -\frac{3}{8} \qquad\quad x = 3$

3. $(x - 2)^2 = 0.09$

$\quad x - 2 = \pm 0.3$

$\qquad x = 2 \pm 0.3$

$\qquad x = 2.3,\ 1.7$

4. $(x + 3)^2 + 81 = 0$

$\qquad (x + 3)^2 = -81$

$\qquad x + 3 = \pm\sqrt{-81}$

$\qquad\quad x = -3 \pm 9i$

5. $2x^2 - 6x + 3 = 0$

$$x^2 - 3x + \frac{9}{4} = -\frac{3}{2} + \frac{9}{4}$$

$$\left(x - \frac{3}{2}\right)^2 = \frac{-6 + 9}{4}$$

$$\left(x - \frac{3}{2}\right)^2 = \frac{3}{4}$$

$$x - \frac{3}{2} = \pm\sqrt{\frac{3}{4}}$$

$$x = \frac{3}{2} \pm \frac{\sqrt{3}}{2}$$

6. $2y(y - 2) = 7$

$2y^2 - 4y - 7 = 0$

$$y = \frac{-(-4) \pm \sqrt{(-4)^2 - 4(2)(-7)}}{2(2)}$$

$$y = \frac{4 \pm \sqrt{16 + 56}}{4}$$

$$y = \frac{4 \pm \sqrt{72}}{4}$$

$$y = \frac{4 \pm 6\sqrt{2}}{4}$$

$$y = \frac{2 \pm 3\sqrt{2}}{2} \approx 7.41 \text{ and } -0.41$$

7. $x - 5\sqrt{x} + 4 = 0$

$\left(\sqrt{x} - 4\right)\left(\sqrt{x} - 1\right) = 0$

$\sqrt{x} - 4 = 0 \qquad \sqrt{x} - 1 = 0$

$\sqrt{x} = 4 \qquad\quad \sqrt{x} = 1$

$\left(\sqrt{x}\right)^2 = 4^2 \qquad \left(\sqrt{x}\right)^2 = 1^2$

$x = 16 \qquad\quad x = 1$

Check: **Check:**

$16 - 5\sqrt{16} + 4 \overset{?}{=} 0 \qquad 1 - 5\sqrt{1} + 4 \overset{?}{=} 0$

$16 - 20 + 4 \overset{?}{=} 0 \qquad\quad 1 - 5 + 4 \overset{?}{=} 0$

$0 = 0 \qquad\qquad\qquad 0 = 0$

$5x^2 - 12x + 10 = 0$

8. $x^4 + 6x^2 - 16 = 0$

$(x^2 + 8)(x^2 - 2) = 0$

$x^2 + 8 = 0 \qquad\qquad x^2 - 2 = 0$

$x^2 = -8 \qquad\qquad\quad x^2 = 2$

$x = \pm\sqrt{-8} \qquad\qquad x = \pm\sqrt{2}$

$x = \pm 2\sqrt{2}\,i$

9. $b^2 - 4ac = (-12)^2 - 4(5)(10)$

$= 144 - 200$

$= -56$

2 imaginary solutions.

10. $(x - (-4))(x - 5) = 0$

$(x + 4)(x - 5) = 0$

$x^2 - x - 20 = 0$

11. $16 \le (x - 2)^2$

$(x - 2)^2 \ge 16$

$x^2 - 4x + 4 \ge 16$

$x^2 - 4x - 12 \ge 0$

$(x - 6)(x + 2) \ge 0$

Critical numbers: $x = -2, 6$

Test intervals:

Positive: $(-\infty, -2]$

Negative: $[-2, 6]$

Positive: $[6, \infty)$

Solution: $(-\infty, -2] \cup [6, \infty)$

12. $2x(x - 3) < 0$

Critical numbers: $x = 0, 3$

Test intervals:

Positive: $(-\infty, 0)$

Negative: $(0, 3)$

Positive: $(3, \infty)$

Solution: $(0, 3)$

13.

$$\frac{3u + 2}{u - 3} \leq 2$$

$$\frac{3u + 2}{u - 3} - \frac{2(u - 3)}{u - 3} \leq 0$$

$$\frac{3u + 2 - 2u + 6}{u - 3} \leq 0$$

$$\frac{u + 8}{u - 3} \leq 0$$

Critical numbers: $u = -8, 3$

Test intervals:

Positive: $(-\infty, -8]$

Negative: $[-8, 3)$

Positive: $(3, \infty)$

Soluton: $[-8, 3)$

14.

$$\frac{3}{x - 2} > 4$$

$$\frac{3}{x - 2} - 4 > 0$$

$$\frac{3 - 4(x - 2)}{x - 2} > 0$$

$$\frac{3 - 4x + 8}{x - 2} > 0$$

$$\frac{11 - 4x}{x - 2} > 0$$

$$\frac{-1(4x - 11)}{x - 2} > 0$$

Critical numbers: $x = \frac{11}{4}, 2$

Test intervals:

Negative: $(-\infty, 2)$

Positive: $\left(2, \frac{11}{4}\right)$

Negative: $\left(\frac{11}{4}, \infty\right)$

Soluton: $\left(2, \frac{11}{4}\right)$

15. *Verbal model:*   Area = Length · Width

Labels: Length = l

               Width = $l - 8$

Equation: $240 = l \cdot (l - 8)$

               $0 = l^2 - 8l - 240$

               $0 = (l - 20)(l + 12)$

               $0 = l - 20$ $0 = l + 12$

               20 feet = l $-12 = l$ reject

               12 feet = $l - 8$

16. *Verbal model:*   Cost per person Current Group − Cost per person New Group = 6.25

Labels: Number Current Group = x

               Number New Group = $x + 10$

Equation:

$$\frac{1250}{x} - \frac{1250}{x + 10} = 6.25$$

$$x(x + 10)\left(\frac{1250}{x} - \frac{1250}{x + 10}\right) = (6.25)x(x + 10)$$

$$1250(x + 10) - 1250x = 6.25x(x + 10)$$

$$1250x + 12500 - 1250x = 6.25x^2 + 62.5x$$

$$0 = 6.25x^2 + 62.5x - 12500$$

$$0 = x^2 + 10x - 2000$$

$$0 = (x + 50)(x - 40)$$

reject $x = -50$ $x = 40$ club members

17. $35 = -16t^2 + 75$

$16t^2 = 40$

$t^2 = \dfrac{40}{16} = \dfrac{5}{2}$

$t = \sqrt{\dfrac{5}{2}}$

$t = \dfrac{\sqrt{10}}{2} \approx 1.5811388$

$t \approx 1.58$ seconds

18. $R = -\dfrac{1}{20}(n^2 - 240n),\ 80 \le n \le 160$

$R = -\dfrac{1}{20}(n^2 - 240n + 14{,}400) + 720$

$R = -\dfrac{1}{20}(n - 120)^2 + 720$

$n = 120$ passengers will produce a maximum revenue

19. $h = -16t^2 + 288t$

$-16t^2 + 288t > 1040$

$-16t^2 + 288t - 1040 > 0$ (Divide by -16)

$t^2 - 18t + 65 < 0$

$(t - 5)(t - 13) < 0$

Critical numbers: $t = 5, 13$

Test intervals:

t must be positive

Positive: $(0, 5)$

Negative: $(5, 13)$

Positive: $(13, \infty)$

Solution: $(5, 13)$

$5 < t < 13$ seconds

Cumulative Test for Chapters 4–6

1. $\left(\dfrac{2x^{-4}y^3}{3x^5y^{-3}z^0}\right)^{-2} = \left(\dfrac{2x^{(-4)+(-5)}y^{3+(3)}}{3}\right)^{-2}$

$= \left(\dfrac{2x^{-9}y^6}{3}\right)^{-2} = \left(\dfrac{2y^6}{3x^9}\right)^{-2} = \left(\dfrac{3x^9}{2y^6}\right)^2$

$= \dfrac{9x^{18}}{4y^{12}}$

2. $(4 \times 10^3)^2 = 4^2 \times 10^6 = 16 \times 10^6 = 1.6 \times 10^7$

3.

$$2x - 1\ )\overline{\ 4x^4 - 6x^3 + 0x^2 + x - \quad 4\ } \quad\ 2x^3 - 2x^2 - x + \dfrac{-4}{2x - 1}$$

$\underline{4x^4 - 2x^3}$

$-4x^3 + 0x^2$

$\underline{-4x^3 + 2x^2}$

$-2x^2 + x$

$\underline{-2x^2 + x}$

-4

4. $\dfrac{x^2 + 8x + 16}{18x^2} \cdot \dfrac{2x^4 + 4x^3}{x^2 - 16} = \dfrac{(x + 4)^2}{18x^2} \cdot \dfrac{2x^3(x + 2)}{(x - 4)(x + 4)} = \dfrac{x(x + 4)(x + 2)}{9(x - 4)}$

5. $\dfrac{2}{x} - \dfrac{x}{x^3 + 3x^2} + \dfrac{1}{x + 3} = \dfrac{2}{x} - \dfrac{x}{x^2(x + 3)} + \dfrac{1}{x + 3}$

$\qquad\qquad = \dfrac{2}{x} - \dfrac{1}{x(x + 3)} + \dfrac{1}{x + 3}$

$\qquad\qquad = \dfrac{2}{x}\!\left(\dfrac{x + 3}{x + 3}\right) - \dfrac{1}{x(x + 3)}\!\left(\dfrac{1}{1}\right) + \dfrac{1}{x + 3}\!\left(\dfrac{x}{x}\right)$

$\qquad\qquad = \dfrac{2x + 6}{x(x + 3)} - \dfrac{1}{x(x + 3)} + \dfrac{x}{x(x + 3)}$

$\qquad\qquad = \dfrac{2x + 6 - 1 + x}{x(x + 3)}$

$\qquad\qquad = \dfrac{3x + 5}{x(x + 3)}$

6. $\dfrac{\left(\dfrac{x}{y} - \dfrac{y}{x}\right)}{\left(\dfrac{x - y}{xy}\right)} = \dfrac{\left(\dfrac{x}{y} - \dfrac{y}{x}\right)}{\left(\dfrac{x - y}{xy}\right)} \cdot \dfrac{xy}{xy}$

$\qquad = \dfrac{x^2 - y^2}{x - y}$

$\qquad = \dfrac{(x - y)(x + y)}{x - y}$

$\qquad = x + y$

7. $\sqrt{-2}\left(\sqrt{-8} + 3\right) = i\sqrt{2}\left(2i\sqrt{2} + 3\right)$

$\qquad\qquad = 2i^2 \cdot 2 + 3i\sqrt{2}$

$\qquad\qquad = -4 + 3i\sqrt{2}$

8. $(3 - 4i)^2 = 3^2 + 2(3)(-4i) + (4i)^2$

$\qquad\quad = 9 - 24i + 16i^2$

$\qquad\quad = 9 - 16 - 24i$

$\qquad\quad = -7 - 24i$

9. $\left(\dfrac{t^{1/2}}{t^{1/4}}\right)^2 = \dfrac{t}{t^{1/2}} = t^{1 - 1/2}$

$\qquad\qquad = t^{1/2}$

10. $10\sqrt{20x} + 3\sqrt{125x} = 10\sqrt{4 \cdot 5x} + 3\sqrt{25 \cdot 5x}$

$\qquad\qquad\qquad = 20\sqrt{5x} + 15\sqrt{5x}$

$\qquad\qquad\qquad = 35\sqrt{5x}$

11. $\left(\sqrt{2x} - 3\right)^2 = 2x - 6\sqrt{2x} + 9$

12. $\dfrac{6}{\sqrt{10} - 2} = \dfrac{6}{\sqrt{10} - 2} \cdot \dfrac{\sqrt{10} + 2}{\sqrt{10} + 2}$

$\qquad = \dfrac{6\left(\sqrt{10} + 2\right)}{10 - 4}$

$\qquad = \dfrac{6\left(\sqrt{10} + 2\right)}{6}$

$\qquad = \sqrt{10} + 2$

13. $\dfrac{1 - 2i}{4 + i} = \dfrac{1 - 2i}{4 + i} \cdot \dfrac{4 - i}{4 - i}$

$\qquad = \dfrac{4 - i - 8i + 2i^2}{16 - i^2} = \dfrac{4 - 9i - 2}{16 + 1}$

$\qquad = \dfrac{2 - 9i}{17} = \dfrac{2}{17} - \dfrac{9}{17}i$

14.
$$\frac{1}{x} + \frac{4}{10-x} = 1$$

$$x(10-x)\left(\frac{1}{x} + \frac{4}{10-x}\right) = (1)x(10-x)$$

$$10 - x + 4x = 10x - x^2$$

$$x^2 - 7x + 10 = 0$$

$$(x-5)(x-2) = 0$$

$$x = 5 \qquad x = 2$$

Check: $\dfrac{1}{5} + \dfrac{4}{10-5} \stackrel{?}{=} 1$

$$\frac{1}{5} + \frac{4}{5} \stackrel{?}{=} 1$$

$$\frac{5}{5} \stackrel{?}{=} 1$$

$$1 = 1$$

$\dfrac{1}{2} + \dfrac{4}{10-2} \stackrel{?}{=} 1$

$$\frac{1}{2} + \frac{4}{8} \stackrel{?}{=} 1$$

$$\frac{1}{2} + \frac{1}{2} \stackrel{?}{=} 1$$

$$1 = 1$$

15.
$$\frac{x-3}{x} + 1 = \frac{x-4}{x-6}$$

$$x(x-6)\left(\frac{x-3}{x} + 1\right) = \left(\frac{x-4}{x-6}\right)x(x-6)$$

$$(x-6)(x-3) + x(x-6) = x(x-4)$$

$$x^2 - 9x + 18 + x^2 - 6x = x^2 - 4x$$

$$x^2 - 11x + 18 = 0$$

$$(x-9)(x-2) = 0$$

$$x = 9 \qquad x = 2$$

Check: $\dfrac{9-3}{9} + 1 \stackrel{?}{=} \dfrac{9-4}{9-6}$

$$\frac{6}{9} + 1 \stackrel{?}{=} \frac{5}{3}$$

$$\frac{2}{3} + \frac{3}{3} \stackrel{?}{=} \frac{5}{3}$$

$$\frac{5}{3} = \frac{5}{3}$$

$\dfrac{2-3}{2} + 1 \stackrel{?}{=} \dfrac{2-4}{2-6}$

$$\frac{-1}{2} + \frac{2}{2} \stackrel{?}{=} \frac{-2}{-4}$$

$$\frac{1}{2} = \frac{1}{2}$$

16. $\sqrt{x} - x + 12 = 0$

$$\sqrt{x} = x - 12$$

$$\left(\sqrt{x}\right)^2 = (x-12)^2$$

$$x = x^2 - 24x + 144$$

$$0 = x^2 - 25x + 144$$

$$0 = (x-16)(x-9)$$

$$x = 16 \qquad x = 9$$

Check: $\sqrt{16} - 16 + 12 \stackrel{?}{=} 0$

$$4 - 16 + 12 \stackrel{?}{=} 0$$

$$0 = 0$$

$\sqrt{9} - 9 + 12 \stackrel{?}{=} 0$

$$3 - 9 + 12 \stackrel{?}{=} 0$$

$$6 \neq 0$$

Not a solution

17. $\sqrt{5-x} + 10 = 11$

$$\sqrt{5-x} = 1$$

$$\left(\sqrt{5-x}\right)^2 = 1^2$$

$$5 - x = 1$$

$$-x = -4$$

$$x = 4$$

Check: $\sqrt{5-4} + 10 \stackrel{?}{=} 11$

$$\sqrt{1} + 10 \stackrel{?}{=} 11$$

$$11 = 11$$

18. $(x - 5)^2 + 50 = 0$

$$(x - 5)^2 = -50$$

$$x - 5 = \pm\sqrt{-50}$$

$$x = 5 \pm 5i\sqrt{2}$$

19. $3x^2 + 6x + 2 = 0$

$$x^2 + 2x + 1 = -\frac{2}{3} + 1$$

$$(x + 1)^2 = \frac{1}{3}$$

$$x + 1 = \pm\sqrt{\frac{1}{3}}$$

$$x = -1 \pm \frac{\sqrt{3}}{3} = \frac{-3 \pm \sqrt{3}}{3}$$

20. $\pi r_2^2(5) = \pi r_1^2(3)$

$$r_2^2 = \frac{3}{5}r_1^2$$

$$r_2 = \sqrt{\frac{3r_1^2}{5}}$$

$$r_2 = \frac{\sqrt{15r_1^2}}{5}$$

$$r_2 = r_1\frac{\sqrt{15}}{5}$$

21. $c = \sqrt{4^2 + 4^2}$

$$= \sqrt{32}$$

$$P = 4(4) + 4\left(\sqrt{32}\right)$$

$$P = 16 + 16\sqrt{2} \text{ inches}$$

$$P \approx 38.6 \text{ inches}$$

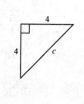

22. $y = x^2 - 6x - 8$

Keystrokes:

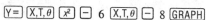

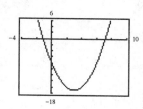

Estimate of x-intercepts ≈ -1.12 and 7.12

$x^2 - 6x - 8 = 0$

$$x = \frac{-(-6) \pm \sqrt{(-6)^2 - 4(1)(-8)}}{2(1)}$$

$$x = \frac{6 \pm \sqrt{36 + 32}}{2}$$

$$x = \frac{6 \pm \sqrt{68}}{2}$$

$$x \approx -1.12 \text{ and } 7.12$$

23. $x = -2$ and $x = 6$

$$(x + 2) = 0 \quad (x - 6) = 0$$

$$(x + 2)(x - 6) = 0$$

$$x^2 - 6x + 2x - 12 = 0$$

$$x^2 - 4x - 12 = 0$$

C H A P T E R 7
Linear Models and Graphs of Nonlinear Models

C H A P T E R 7
Linear Models and Graphs of Nonlinear Models

Section 7.1   Variation

Solutions to Odd-Numbered Exercises

1. $l = kV$

3. $V = kt$

5. $u = kv^2$

7. $p = \dfrac{k}{d}$

9. $P = \dfrac{k}{\sqrt{1+r}}$

11. $A = klw$

13. $P = \dfrac{k}{V}$

15. The area of a triangle varies jointly as the base and height.

17. The area of a rectangle varies jointly as the length and the width.

19. The volume of a right circular cylinder varies jointly as the square of the radius and the height.

21. The average speed varies directly as the distance and inversely as the time.

23. $s = kt$
$20 = k(4)$
$5 = k$
$s = 5t$

25. $F = kx^2$
$500 = k(40)^2$
$\dfrac{500}{1600} = k$
$\dfrac{5}{16} = k$
$F = \dfrac{5}{16}x^2$

27. $H = ku$
$100 = k(40)$
$\dfrac{100}{40} = k$
$\dfrac{5}{2} = k$
$H = \dfrac{5}{2}u$

29. $n = \dfrac{k}{m}$
$32 = \dfrac{k}{1.5}$
$48 = k$
$n = \dfrac{48}{m}$

31. $g = \dfrac{k}{\sqrt{z}}$
$\dfrac{4}{5} = \dfrac{k}{\sqrt{25}}$
$4 = k$
$g = \dfrac{4}{\sqrt{z}}$

33. $F = kxy$
$500 = k(15)(8)$
$\dfrac{500}{120} = k$
$\dfrac{25}{6} = k$
$F = \dfrac{25}{6}xy$

35. $d = k\left(\dfrac{x^2}{r}\right)$
$3000 = k\left(\dfrac{10^2}{4}\right)$
$3000 = k(25)$
$120 = k$
$d = \dfrac{120x^2}{r}$

37. (a) $R = kx$
$3875 = k(500)$
$7.75 = k$
$R = 7.75x$
$R = 7.75(635)$
$R = \$4921.25$

(b) Price per unit

39. (a) $d = kF$ $d = \dfrac{1}{10}F$

$\qquad\quad 5 = k(50)$

$\qquad\quad \dfrac{5}{50} = k$ $d = \dfrac{1}{10}(20)$

$\qquad\qquad\qquad\qquad d = 2$ inches

$\qquad\quad \dfrac{1}{10} = k$

(b) $\qquad d = \dfrac{1}{10}F$

$\qquad\quad 1.5 = \dfrac{1}{10}F$

$\qquad$ 15 pounds $= F$

41. $\qquad\quad d = kF$

$\qquad\quad 7 = k(10.5)$

$\qquad\quad \dfrac{7}{10.5} = k$

$\qquad\quad \dfrac{70}{105} = k$

$\qquad\quad \dfrac{2}{3} = k$

$\qquad\quad 12 = \dfrac{2}{3}F$

$\qquad$ 18 pounds $= F$

43. $v = kt$

$\quad 96 = k(3)$

$\quad 32 = k$

$\quad$ acceleration $= 32$ ft/sec^2

45. $d = ks^2$

$\quad 75 = k(30)^2$

$\quad \dfrac{75}{900} = k$

$\quad \dfrac{1}{12} = k$

$\quad d = \dfrac{1}{12}(50)^2$

$\quad d = 208.\overline{3}$ feet

47. $F = ks^2$

$\quad F = k(2s)^2$

$\quad F = 4ks^2$

$\quad F = 4(ks^2)$

$\quad F$ will change by a factor of 4.

49. $p = kA$

9-inch: $6.78 = k(\pi)(4.5)^2$

$\qquad\quad 6.78 = 20.25\pi k$

$\qquad\quad \dfrac{6.78}{20.25\pi} = k$

$\qquad\quad 0.106575 \approx k$

12-inch: $9.78 = k(\pi)(6)^2$

$\qquad\qquad 9.78 = 36\pi k$

$\qquad\qquad \dfrac{9.78}{36\pi} = k$

$\qquad\qquad 0.0864745 \approx k$

15-inch: $12.18 = k(\pi)(7.5)^2$

$\qquad\qquad 12.18 = 56.25\pi k$

$\qquad\qquad \dfrac{12.18}{56.25\pi} = k$

$\qquad\qquad 0.068923 \approx k$

No, the price of the pizza is not directly proportional to its area. The 15-inch pizza at \$12.18 is the best buy.

51. $x = \dfrac{k}{p}$

$\quad 800 = \dfrac{k}{5}$

$\quad 4000 = k$

$\quad x = \dfrac{4000}{6}$

$\quad x = 666.\overline{6} \approx 667$ units

53. $W_m = k \cdot W_e$ $W_m = \dfrac{1}{6} \cdot W_e$

$\qquad 60 = k \cdot 360$ $54 = \dfrac{1}{6} \cdot x$

$\qquad\quad k = \dfrac{1}{6}$ $\quad x = 324$ pounds

55. $I = \dfrac{k}{d^2}$

$I = \dfrac{k}{18^2}$ $I = \dfrac{k}{36^2}$

$I = \dfrac{k}{324}$ $I = \dfrac{k}{1296}$

I will change by a factor of $\frac{324}{1296}$ or $\frac{1}{4}$.

57. $p = \dfrac{k}{t}$

$38 = \dfrac{k}{3}$

$114 = k$

So, $p = \dfrac{114}{t}$.

$p = \dfrac{114}{6.5}$

$p = 17.5\%$

59. (a) $I = Krt$

$202.50 = K(0.09)(3)$ $I = 750rt$

$202.50 = K(0.27)$ $I = 750(0.09)(4)$

$750 = K$ $I = \$270$

(b) *K* is the principal or the amount of investment.

61.

x	2	4	6	8	10
$y = kx^2$	4	16	36	64	100

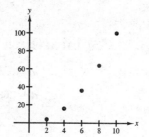

63.

x	2	4	6	8	10
$y = kx^2$	2	8	18	32	50

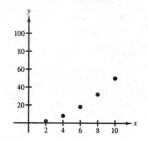

65.

x	2	4	6	8	10
$y = \dfrac{k}{x^2}$	$\frac{1}{2}$	$\frac{1}{8}$	$\frac{1}{18}$	$\frac{1}{32}$	$\frac{1}{50}$

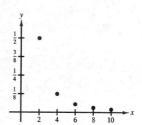

67.

x	2	4	6	8	10
$y = \dfrac{k}{x^2}$	$\frac{5}{2}$	$\frac{5}{8}$	$\frac{5}{18}$	$\frac{5}{32}$	$\frac{1}{10}$

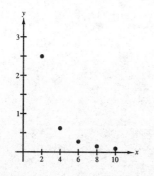

69.

x	10	20	30	40	50
y	$\frac{2}{5}$	$\frac{1}{5}$	$\frac{2}{15}$	$\frac{1}{10}$	$\frac{2}{25}$

$\dfrac{2}{5} = \dfrac{k}{10}$ $\dfrac{1}{5} = \dfrac{k}{20}$

$4 = k$ $4 = k$

Using any two pairs of numbers, *k* is 4.

71.

x	10	20	30	40	50
y	-3	-6	-9	-12	-15

$$-3 = k \cdot 10 \qquad -6 = k \cdot 20$$

$$-\frac{3}{10} = k \qquad -\frac{6}{20} = k$$

$$-\frac{3}{10} = k$$

Using any two pairs of numbers, k is $-\frac{3}{10}$.

75. $y = kx^2$

$y = k(2x)^2$

$y = k(4x^2)$

$y = 4kx^2$

y will quadruple.

Section 7.2   Graphs of Linear Inequalities

1. $x - 2y < 4$

(a) $0 - 2(0) \overset{?}{<} 4$

$0 < 4$

$(0, 0)$ is a solution.

(b) $2 - 2(-1) \overset{?}{<} 4$

$2 + 2 < 4$

$4 \not< 4$

$(2, -1)$ is not a solution.

(c) $3 - 2(4) \overset{?}{<} 4$

$3 - 8 < 4$

$-5 < 4$

$(3, 4)$ is a solution.

(d) $5 - 2(1) \overset{?}{<} 4$

$5 - 2 < 4$

$3 < 4$

$(5, 1)$ is a solution.

3. $3x + y \geq 10$

(a) $3(1) + 3 \overset{?}{\geq} 10$

$9 \not\geq 10$

$(1, 3)$ is not a solution.

(b) $3(-3) + 1 \overset{?}{\geq} 10$

$-8 \not\geq 10$

$(-3, 1)$ is not a solution.

(c) $3(3) + 1 \overset{?}{\geq} 10$

$10 \geq 10$

$(3, 1)$ is a solution.

(d) $3(2) + 15 \overset{?}{\geq} 10$

$21 \geq 10$

$(2, 15)$ is a solution.

5. $y > 0.2x - 1$

(a) $2 \overset{?}{>} 0.2(0) - 1$

$2 > -1$

$(0, 2)$ is a solution.

(b) $0 \overset{?}{>} 0.2(6) - 1$

$0 \not> 0.2$

$(6, 0)$ is not a solution.

(c) $-1 \overset{?}{>} 0.2(4) - 1$

$-1 \not> -0.2$

$(4, -1)$ is not a solution.

(d) $7 \overset{?}{>} 0.2(-2) - 1$

$7 > -1.4$

$(-2, 7)$ is a solution.

7. $y \le 3 - |x|$

(a) $4 \overset{?}{\le} 3 - |-1|$

$4 \not\le 3 - 1$

$(-1, 4)$ is not a solution.

(b) $-2 \overset{?}{\le} 3 - |2|$

$-2 \le 3 - 2$

$(2, -2)$ is a solution.

(c) $0 \overset{?}{\le} 3 - |6|$

$0 \le 3 - 6$

$0 \not\le -3$

$(6, 0)$ is not a solution.

(d) $-2 \overset{?}{\le} 3 - |5|$

$-2 \le 3 - 5$

$-2 \le -2$

$(5, -2)$ is a solution.

9. $y \ge -2$ (b)

11. $3x - 2y < 0$ (d)

13. $x + y < 4$ (f)

15. $x \ge 2$

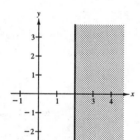

17. $y < 5$

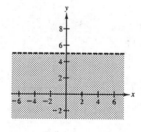

19. $y > \frac{1}{2}x$

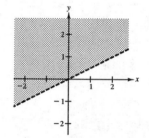

21. $y \ge 5 - x$

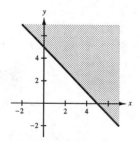

23. $y \le x + 2$

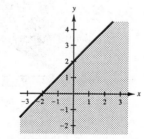

25. $x + y \ge 4$

$y \ge -x + 4$

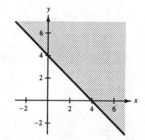

27. $x - 2y \geq 6$

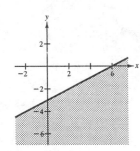

29. $3x + 2y \geq 2$

$2y \geq -3x + 2$

$y \geq -\frac{3}{2}x + 1$

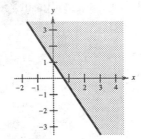

31. $3x - 2y \geq 4$

$-2y \geq -3x + 4$

$y \leq \frac{3}{2}x - 2$

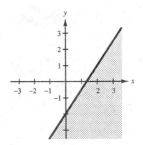

33. $0.2x + 0.3y < 2$ or $y < -\frac{2}{3}x + \frac{20}{3}$

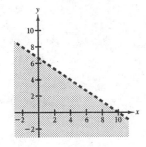

35. $y - 1 > -\frac{1}{2}(x - 2)$

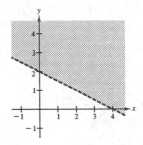

37. $\frac{x}{3} + \frac{y}{4} \leq 1$ or $y \leq -\frac{4}{3}x + 4$

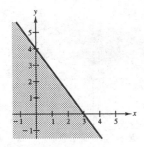

39. $y \geq \frac{3}{4}x - 1$

Keystrokes:

[Y=] .75 [X,T,θ] [−] 1

[DRAW] 7 [(] [Y-VARS] 1   1 [,] 10 [)] [ENTER]

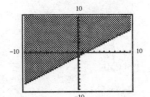

41. $y \leq -\frac{2}{3}x + 6$

Keystrokes:

[Y=] [(] [(−)] 2 [÷] 3 [)] [X,T,θ] [+] 6

[DRAW] 7 [(] [(−)] 10 [,] [Y-VARS] 1   1 [)] [ENTER]

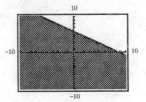

43. $x - 2y - 4 \geq 0$

$$-2y \geq -x + 4$$

$$y \leq \tfrac{1}{2}x - 2$$

Keystrokes:

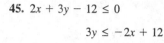

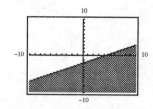

45. $2x + 3y - 12 \leq 0$

$$3y \leq -2x + 12$$

$$y \leq -\tfrac{2}{3}x + 4$$

Keystrokes:

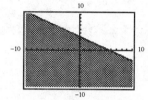

47. $m = \dfrac{2 - 5}{3 + 1} = -\dfrac{3}{4}$ $y - 2 > -\dfrac{3}{4}(x - 3)$

$$4y - 8 > -3x + 9$$

$$3x + 4y > 17$$

49. $y < 2$

51. $m = \dfrac{1 - 0}{2 - 0} = \dfrac{1}{2}$ $y > \dfrac{1}{2}x$

$$2y > x$$

$$-x + 2y > 0$$

$$x - 2y < 0$$

53. $P = 2x + 2y$

$2x + 2y \leq 500$

or

$0 \leq x + y \leq 250$

or

$y \leq -x + 250$

(*Note:* x and y cannot be negative.)

Keystrokes:

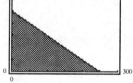

55. $10x + 15y \leq 1000$ (*Note:* x and y cannot be negative.)

$$15y \leq -10x + 1000$$

$$y \leq -\tfrac{2}{3}x + \tfrac{200}{3}$$

(*Note:* x and y cannot be negative.)

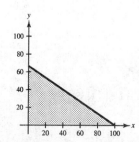

57. (12, 220) yes

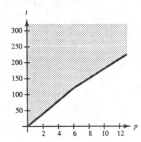

59. *Verbal model:*

| Cost of cheese pizzas | + | Cost for extra toppings | + | Cost for drinks | ≤ 48 |

Labels:

Cost of cheese pizzas = $3(9) = \$27$

Cost for extra toppings = $1.00x$ (dollars)

Cost for drinks = $1.50y$ (dollars)

Inequality:

$27 + 1.00x + 1.50y \leq 48$

$1.00x + 1.50y \leq 21$

$x + 1.5y \leq 21$

(*Note:* x and y cannot be negative.)

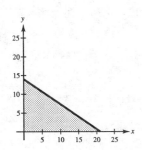

$$(6, 8)$$

$$6 + 1.5(8) \overset{?}{\leq} 21$$

$$6 + 12 \overset{?}{\leq} 21$$

$$18 \leq 21 \quad \text{yes}$$

61. $9x + 6y \geq 150$ (*Note:* x and y cannot be negative.)

$$6y \geq -9x + 150$$

$$y \geq -\tfrac{3}{2}x + 25$$

Here are some examples of ordered pairs that are solutions. Note that there are other correct answers.

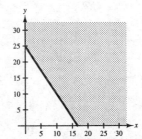

(2, 22)   (4, 21)

(10, 10)   (20, 1)

(12, 7)   (22, 0)

63. $r = 0.75(220 - A)$

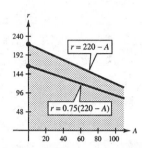

65. (x_1, y_1) is a solution of a linear inequality in x and y means the inequality is true when x_1 and y_1 are substituted for x and y respectively.

67. The solution of $x - y > 1$ does not include the points on the line $x - y = 1$. The solution of $x - y \geq 1$ does include the points on the line $x - y = 1$.

69. On the real number line, the solution of $x \leq 3$ is an unbounded interval.

On a rectangular coordinate system, the solution of $x \leq 3$ is a half-plane.

Section 7.3   Graphs of Quadratic Functions

1. $y = 4 - 2x$ (e)

3. $y = x^2 - 3$ (b)

5. $y = (x - 2)^2$ (d)

7. $y = x^2 + 2 = (x - 0)^2 + 2$

  vertex $(0, 2)$

9. $y = x^2 - 4x + 7$

  $= (x^2 - 4x + 4) + 7 - 4$

  $= (x - 2)^2 + 3$

  vertex $= (2, 3)$

11. $y = x^2 + 6x + 5$

  $y = (x^2 + 6x + 9) + 5 - 9$

  $y = (x + 3)^2 - 4$

  vertex $= (-3, -4)$

13. $y = -x^2 + 6x - 10$

  $y = -1(x^2 - 6x) - 10$

  $y = -1(x^2 - 6x + 9) - 10 + 9$

  $y = -1(x - 3)^2 - 1$

  vertex $(3, -1)$

15. $y = -x^2 + 2x - 7$

  $= -1(x^2 - 2x + 1) - 7 + 1$

  $= -1(x - 1)^2 - 6$

  vertex $= (1, -6)$

17. $y = 2x^2 + 6x + 2$

  $= 2\left(x^2 + 3x + \dfrac{9}{4}\right) + 2 - \dfrac{9}{2}$

  $= 2\left(x + \dfrac{3}{2}\right)^2 - \dfrac{5}{2}$

  vertex $= \left(-\dfrac{3}{2}, -\dfrac{5}{2}\right)$

19. $f(x) = x^2 - 8x + 15$

  $a = 1$ $b = -8$

  $x = \dfrac{-b}{2a} = \dfrac{-(-8)}{2(1)} = 4$

  $f\left(-\dfrac{b}{2a}\right) = 4^2 - 8(4) + 15$

  $= 16 - 32 + 15$

  $= -1$

  vertex $= (4, -1)$

21. $g(x) = -x^2 - 2x + 1$

  $a = -1$ $b = -2$

  $x = \dfrac{-b}{2a} = \dfrac{-(-2)}{2(-1)} = -1$

  $g\left(\dfrac{-b}{2a}\right) = -(-1)^2 - 2(-1) + 1$

  $= -1 + 2 + 1$

  $= 2$

  vertex $= (-1, 2)$

23. $y = 4x^2 + 4x + 4$

  $a = 4$ $b = 4$

  $x = \dfrac{-b}{2a} = \dfrac{-4}{2(4)} = \dfrac{-1}{2}$

  $y = 4\left(-\dfrac{1}{2}\right)^2 + 4\left(-\dfrac{1}{2}\right) + 4$

  $= 4\left(\dfrac{1}{4}\right) - 2 + 4$

  $= 1 - 2 + 4$

  $= 3$

  vertex $= \left(-\dfrac{1}{2}, 3\right)$

25. $2 > 0$ opens upward

vertex $= (0, 2)$

27. $-1 < 0$ opens downward

vertex $= (10, 4)$

29. $1 > 0$ opens upward

vertex $= (0, -6)$

31. $-1 < 0$ opens downward

vertex $= (3, 0)$

33. $y = 25 - x^2$

$0 = 25 - x^2$

$x^2 = 25$

$x = \pm 5$

$(5, 0), (-5, 0)$

$y = 25 - x^2$

$y = 25 - 0^2$

$y = 25$

$(0, 25)$

35. $y = x^2 - 9x$

$0 = x^2 - 9x$

$0 = x(x - 9)$

$(0, 0), (9, 0)$

$y = x^2 - 9x$

$y = 0^2 - 9(0)$

$y = 0$

$(0, 0)$

37. $y = 4x^2 - 12x + 9$

$0 = 4x^2 - 12x + 9$

$0 = (2x - 3)^2$

$0 = 2x - 3$

$\dfrac{3}{2} = x$

$\left(\dfrac{3}{2}, 0\right)$

$y = 4x^2 - 12x + 9$

$y = 4(0)^2 - 12(0) + 9$

$y = 9$

$(0, 9)$

39. $y = x^2 - 3x + 3$

$0 = x^2 - 3x + 3$

$x = \dfrac{3 \pm \sqrt{9 - 12}}{2}$

$= \dfrac{3 \pm \sqrt{-3}}{2}$

no x-intercepts

$y = x^2 - 3x + 3$

$y = 0^2 - 3(0) + 3$

$y = 3$

$(0, 3)$

41. $g(x) = x^2 - 4$

x-intercepts

$0 = x^2 - 4$

$0 = (x - 2)(x + 2)$

$x = 2 \quad x = -2$

vertex

$g(x) = (x - 0)^2 - 4$

$(0, -4)$

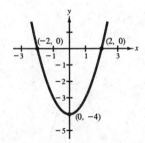

43. $f(x) = -x^2 + 4$

x-intercepts

$0 = -x^2 + 4$

$x^2 = 4$

$x = \pm 2$

vertex

$f(x) = -(x - 0)^2 + 4$

$(0, 4)$

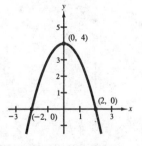

45. $f(x) = x^2 - 3x$

x-intercepts

$0 = x^2 - 3x$

$0 = x(x - 3)$

$0 = x$ $x = 3$

vertex

$f(x) = \left(x^2 - 3x + \frac{9}{4}\right) - \frac{9}{4}$

$f(x) = \left(x - \frac{3}{2}\right)^2 - \frac{9}{4}$

$\left(\frac{3}{2}, -\frac{9}{4}\right)$

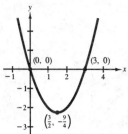

47. $f(x) = -x^2 + 3x$

x-intercepts

$0 = -x^2 + 3x$

$0 = -x(x - 3)$

$0 = x$ $x = 3$

vertex

$y = -1\left(x^2 - 3x + \frac{9}{4}\right) + \frac{9}{4}$

$= -1\left(x - \frac{3}{2}\right)^2 + \frac{9}{4}$

$\left(\frac{3}{2}, \frac{9}{4}\right)$

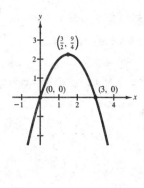

49. $f(x) = (x - 4)^2$

x-intercepts

$0 = (x - 4)^2$

$0 = x - 4$

$4 = x$

vertex

$y = (x - 4)^2 + 0$

$(4, 0)$

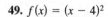

51. $f(x) = x^2 - 8x + 15$

x-intercepts

$0 = x^2 - 8x + 15$

$0 = (x - 5)(x - 3)$

$5 = x$ $x = 3$

vertex

$y = (x^2 - 8x + 16) + 15 - 16$

$= (x - 4)^2 - 1$

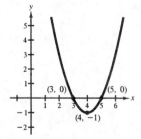

53. $f(x) = -(x^2 + 6x + 5)$

x-intercepts

$0 = x^2 + 6x + 5$

$0 = (x + 5)(x + 1)$

$-5 = x$ $x = -1$

vertex

$y = -(x^2 + 6x + 9) - 5 + 9$

$y = -(x + 3)^2 + 4$

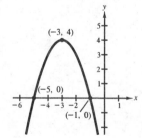

55. $g(x) = -x^2 + 6x - 7$

x-intercepts

$0 = -x^2 + 6x - 7$

$x = \dfrac{-6 \pm \sqrt{6^2 - 4(-1)(-7)}}{2(-1)}$

$x = \dfrac{-6 \pm \sqrt{36 - 28}}{-2}$

$x = \dfrac{-6 \pm \sqrt{8}}{-2}$

$x = \dfrac{-6 \pm 2\sqrt{2}}{2}$

$x = -3 \pm \sqrt{2}$

vertex

$q(x) = -x^2 + 6x - 7$

$q(x) = -(x^2 - 6x) - 7$

$q(x) = -(x^2 - 6x + 9 - 9) - 7$

$q(x) = -(x^2 - 6x + 9) + 9 - 7$

$q(x) = -(x - 3)^2 + 2$

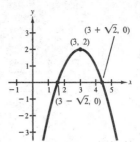

57. $f(x) = 2(x^2 + 6x + 8)$

vertex

$y = 2(x^2 + 6x + 9) + 16 - 18$

$y = 2(x + 3)^2 - 2$

x-intercepts

$0 = x^2 + 6x + 8$

$0 = (x + 4)(x + 2)$

$-4 = x \quad x = -2$

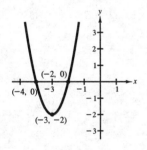

59. $f(x) = \frac{1}{2}(x^2 - 2x - 3)$

vertex

$y = \frac{1}{2}(x^2 - 2x + 1) - \frac{3}{2} - \frac{1}{2}$

$y = \frac{1}{2}(x - 1)^2 - 2$

x-intercepts

$0 = x^2 - 2x - 3$

$0 = (x - 3)(x + 1)$

$3 = x \quad x = -1$

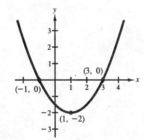

61. $y = \dfrac{1}{5}(3x^2 - 24x + 38)$

$y = \dfrac{3}{5}(x^2 - 8x + 16) + \dfrac{38}{5} - \dfrac{48}{5}$

$y = \dfrac{3}{5}(x - 4)^2 - 2$

$0 = 3x^2 - 24x + 38$

$x = \dfrac{24 \pm \sqrt{576 - 456}}{6}$

$x = \dfrac{24 \pm \sqrt{120}}{6} = \dfrac{12 \pm \sqrt{30}}{3}$

$\approx 5.83, 2.17$

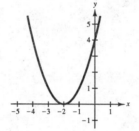

63. $f(x) = 5 - \dfrac{1}{3}x^2$

$f(x) = -\dfrac{1}{3}x^2 + 5$

$f(x) = -\dfrac{1}{3}(x - 0)^2 + 5$

$0 = -\dfrac{1}{3}x^2 + 5$

$\dfrac{1}{3}x^2 = 5$

$x^2 = 15$

$x = \pm\sqrt{15}$

$x \approx 3.87, -3.87$

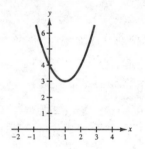

65. $h(x) = x^2 + 2$

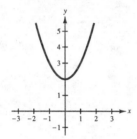

Vertical shift 2 units up.

67. $h(x) = (x + 2)^2$

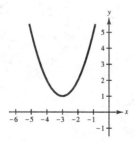

Horizontal shift 2 units left.

69. $h(x) = (x - 1)^2 + 3$

Horizontal shift 1 unit right.
Vertical shift 3 units up.

71. $h(x) = (x + 3)^2 + 1$

Horizontal shift 3 units left.
Vertical shift 1 unit up.

73. $y = \dfrac{1}{6}(2x^2 - 8x + 11)$

Keystrokes:

$\boxed{\text{Y=}}\ \boxed{(}\ 1\ \boxed{\div}\ 6\ \boxed{)}\ \boxed{(}\ 2\ \boxed{\text{X,T,}\theta}\ \boxed{x^2}\ \boxed{-}\ 8\ \boxed{\text{X,T,}\theta}\ \boxed{+}\ 11\ \boxed{)}\ \boxed{\text{GRAPH}}$

vertex $= (2, 0.5)$

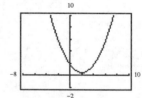

75. $y = -0.7x^2 - 2.7x + 2.3$

Keystrokes:

$\boxed{\text{Y=}}\ \boxed{(-)}\ .7\ \boxed{\text{X,T,}\theta}\ \boxed{x^2}\ \boxed{(-)}\ 2.7\ \boxed{\text{X,T,}\theta}\ \boxed{+}\ 2.3\ \boxed{\text{GRAPH}}$

vertex $= (-1.9, 4.9)$

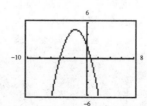

77. vertex $= (0, 4)$ point $= (-2, 0)$

$y = a(x - 0)^2 + 4$ $y = -1(x - 0)^2 + 4$

$0 = a(-2 - 0)^2 + 4$ $y = -x^2 + 4$

$0 = 4a + 4$

$-4 = 4a$

$-1 = a$

79. vertex $= (-2, 2)$ point $= (0, 2)$

$y = a(x - (-2))^2 + (-2)$ $y = 1(x + 2)^2 - 2$

$y = a(x + 2)^2 - 2$ $y = (x + 2)^2 - 2$

$2 = a(0 + 2)^2 - 2$ $y = x^2 + 4x + 4 - 2$

$2 = 4a - 2$ $y = x^2 + 4x + 2$

$4 = 4a$

$1 = a$

81. vertex $= (2, 6)$ point $= (0, 4)$

$y = a(x - 2)^2 + 6$ $y = -\frac{1}{2}(x - 2)^2 + 6$

$4 = a(0 - 2)^2 + 6$ $y = -\frac{1}{2}(x^2 - 4x + 4) + 6$

$4 = a(4) + 6$ $y = -\frac{1}{2}x^2 + 2x - 2 + 6$

$-2 = a(4)$ $y = -\frac{1}{2}x^2 + 2x + 4$

$-\frac{2}{4} = a$

83. vertex $= (2, 1)$ $a = 1$

$y = 1(x - 2)^2 + 1 = x^2 - 4x + 5$

85. vertex $= (2, -4)$ point $= (0, 0)$

$0 = a(0 - 2)^2 - 4$

$4 = a(4)$

$1 = a$

$y = 1(x - 2)^2 - 4 = x^2 - 4x$

87. vertex $= (3, 2)$ point $= (1, 4)$

$4 = a(1 - 3)^2 + 2$

$2 = a(4)$

$\frac{1}{2} = a$

$y = \frac{1}{2}(x - 3)^2 + 2 = \frac{1}{2}x^2 - 3x + \frac{13}{2}$

89. vertex $= (-1, 5)$ point $= (0, 1)$

$1 = a(0 - (-1))^2 + 5$ $y = -4(x + 1)^2 + 5$

$1 = a(1) + 5$ $y = -4(x^2 + 2x + 1) + 5$

$-4 = a$ $y = -4x^2 - 8x - 4 + 5$

$y = -4x^2 - 8x + 1$

91. Horizontal shift 3 units right

93. Horizontal shift 2 units right

Vertical shift 3 units down

95. $y = -\frac{1}{12}x^2 + 2x + 4$

(a) $y = -\frac{1}{12}(0)^2 + 2(0) + 4$

$y = 4$ feet

(b) $y = -\frac{1}{12}x^2 + 2x + 4$

$y = -\frac{1}{12}(x^2 - 24x + 144) + 4 + 12$

$y = -\frac{1}{12}(x - 12)^2 + 16$

Maximum height $= 16$ feet

(c) $0 = -\frac{1}{12}x^2 + 2x + 4$

$0 = x^2 - 24x - 48$

$x = \dfrac{24 \pm \sqrt{576 + 192}}{2}$

≈ 25.86 feet

97. $y = -\frac{4}{9}x^2 + \frac{24}{9}x + 10$

$y = -\frac{4}{9}(x^2 - 6x) + 10$

$y = -\frac{4}{9}(x^2 - 6x + 9 - 9) + 10$

$y = -\frac{4}{9}(x^2 - 6x + 9) + 4 + 10$

$y = -\frac{4}{9}(x - 3)^2 + 14$

The maximum height of the diver is 14 ft.

99. (a)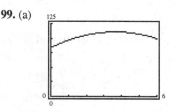

(b) vertex = (3.65, 110, 810)1993, 110,800 reserves

101. (a) $P = (100 + x)[90 - x(0.15)] - (100 + x)60$

$P = (100 + x)[90 - x(0.15) - 60]$

$P = (100 + x)(30 - 0.15x)$

$P = 3000 - 15x + 30x = 0.15x^2$

$P = 3000 + 15x - 0.15x^2$

$P = 3000 + 15x - \frac{3}{20}x^2$

(b) $P = -\frac{3}{20}x^2 + 15x + 3000$

$P = -\frac{3}{20}(x^2 - 100x + 2500) + 3000 + 375$

$P = -\frac{3}{20}(x - 50)^2 + 3375$

vertex = (50, 3375)

order size for maximum profit

$P = 100 + 50 = 150$ radios

(c) Recommend pricing scheme if price reductions are restricted to orders between 100 and 150 orders.

103. $A = \frac{2}{\pi}(100x - x^2)$

Keystrokes:

[Y=] [(] 2 [÷] [π] [)] [(] 100 [X,T,θ] [−] [X,T,θ] [x²] [)] [GRAPH]

$x \approx 50$ when A is maximum

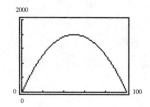

105. $100 = a(500 - 0)^2 + 0$

$100 = a(250{,}000)$

$\dfrac{100}{250{,}000} = a$

$\dfrac{1}{2500} = a$

$y = \dfrac{1}{2500}(x - 0)^2 + 0$

$y = \dfrac{1}{2500}x^2$

107. The graph of the quadratic function $f(x) = ax^2 + bx + c$ is a parabola.

109. To find any x-intercepts, set $y = 0$ and solve the resulting equation for x.

To find the y-intercept, set $x = 0$ and solve the resulting equation for y.

111. The discriminant of a quadratic function tells how many x-intercepts the parabola has. If positive, there are 2 x-intercepts; if zero, 1 x-intercept; and if negative, no x-intercepts.

113. Find the y-coordinate of the vertex. This is the maximum (or minimum) value of a quadratic function.

Mid-Chapter Quiz for Chapter 7

1. $A = kr^2$

2. $z = \dfrac{kx}{y^2}$

3. Distance: $d = rt$

Distance varies jointly proportional to rate and time.

4. Volume: $V = s^3$

The volume of a cube varies directly as the cube of the length of the sides.

5. $z = \dfrac{kx^2}{y}$ if $z = 6, x = 6, y = 4$ $z = \dfrac{2x^2}{3y}$

           then $6 = \dfrac{k(6)^2}{4}$

               $24 = k(6)^2$

               $\dfrac{24}{36} = k$

               $\dfrac{2}{3} = k$

6. $2x - 3y \le 4$

(a) $2(5) - 3(2) \overset{?}{\le} 4$

       $10 - 6 \le 4$

           $4 \le 4$

    $(5, 2)$ is a solution.

(c) $2(2) - 3(-4) \overset{?}{\le} 4$

       $4 + 12 \le 4$

         $16 \le 4$

    $(2, -4)$ is not a solution.

(b) $2(-2) - 3(4) \overset{?}{\le} 4$

       $-4 - 12 \le 4$

        $-16 \le 4$

    $(-2, 4)$ is a solution.

(d) $2(3) - 3(0) \overset{?}{\le} 4$

       $6 - 0 \le 4$

          $6 \le 4$

    $(3, 0)$ is not a solution.

7. $m = \dfrac{3 - 5}{5 - 1} = -\dfrac{2}{4} = -\dfrac{1}{2}$

    $y - 3 = -\dfrac{1}{2}(x - 5)$

    $y - 3 = -\dfrac{1}{2}x + \dfrac{5}{2}$

    $2y - 6 = -x + 5$

    $x + 2y = 11$ line

    Shaded region: $x + 2y \le 11$

8. $m = \dfrac{3 - 1}{4 - (-2)} = \dfrac{2}{6} = \dfrac{1}{3}$

    $y - 3 = \dfrac{1}{3}(x - 4)$

    $y - 3 = \dfrac{1}{3}x - \dfrac{4}{3}$

    $3y - 9 = x - 4$

    $x - 3y = -5$ line

    Shaded region: $x - 3y > -5$

9. $x > -2$

10. $2x + 3y \le 9$

11. $2x - y \le 4$

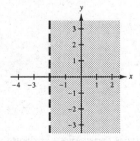

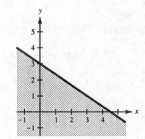

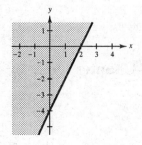

12. $3 = a(5 - 3)^2 - 1$ $y = 1(x - 3)^2 - 1$

$3 = a(4) - 1$

$4 = a(4)$

$1 = a$

13. $3 = a(3 - 5)^2 + 4$ $y = -\frac{1}{4}(x - 5)^2 + 4$

$3 = a(4) + 4$

$-1 = a(4)$

$-\frac{1}{4} = a$

14. vertex $= (-3, 2)$

$y = -\frac{1}{4}(x^2 + 6x\quad) - \frac{1}{4}$

$y = -\frac{1}{4}(x^2 + 6x + 9) - \frac{1}{4} + \frac{9}{4}$

$y = -\frac{1}{4}(x + 3)^2 + 2$

x-intercepts

$0 = -\frac{1}{4}(x^2 + 6x + 1)$

$0 = x^2 + 6x + 1$

$x = \dfrac{-6 \pm \sqrt{6^2 - 4(1)(1)}}{2(1)}$

$x = \dfrac{-6 \pm \sqrt{36 - 4}}{2}$

$x = \dfrac{-6 \pm \sqrt{32}}{2} = \dfrac{-6 \pm 4\sqrt{2}}{2} = \dfrac{-3 \pm 2\sqrt{2}}{2}$

$x \approx -0.17 \text{ and } -5.83$

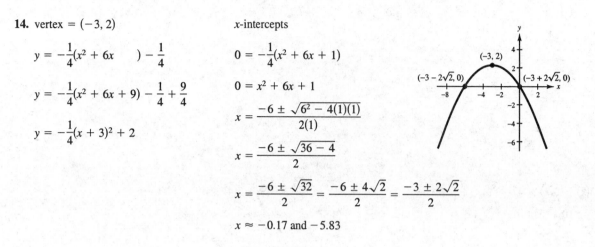

15. vertex $= (1, -9)$

$y = 2(x^2 - 2x\quad) - 7$

$y = 2(x^2 - 2x + 1) - 7 - 2$

$y = 2(x - 1)^2 - 9$

x-intercepts

$0 = 2x^2 - 4x - 7$

$x = \dfrac{-(-4) \pm \sqrt{(-4)^2 - 4(2)(-7)}}{2(2)}$

$x = \dfrac{4 \pm \sqrt{16 + 56}}{4}$

$x = \dfrac{4 \pm \sqrt{72}}{4}$

$x = \dfrac{4 \pm 6\sqrt{2}}{4}$

$x = \dfrac{2 \pm 3\sqrt{2}}{2} = 1 \pm \dfrac{3\sqrt{2}}{2}$

$x \approx -1.12 \text{ and } 3.12$

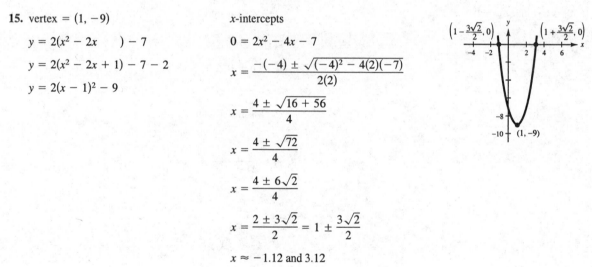

16. $g = kt$

$.02 = k(12)$

$\dfrac{.02}{12} = k$

$\dfrac{2}{1200} = k$

$\dfrac{1}{600} = k$

$.05 = \dfrac{1}{600}t$

$(.05)(600) = t$

$30 = t$ minutes

17. $900x + 1400y \leq 20{,}000$

$9x + 14y \leq 200$

18. $y = -0.005x^2 + x + 5$

$y = -0.005(x^2 - 200x \quad) + 5$

$y = -0.005(x^2 - 200x + 10,000) + 5 + 50$

$y = -0.005(x - 100)^2 + 55$

maximum height $= 55$ feet

Section 7.4   Conic Sections

1. $x^2 + y^2 = 9$ (c)

3. $\dfrac{x^2}{4} + \dfrac{y^2}{9} = 1$ (e)

5. $x^2 - y^2 = 4$ (a)

7. center: $(0, 0)$, radius: 5

$x^2 + y^2 = r^2$

$x^2 + y^2 = 5^2$

$x^2 + y^2 = 25$

9. center: $(0, 0)$, radius: $\frac{2}{3}$

$x^2 + y^2 = r^2$

$x^2 + y^2 = \left(\frac{2}{3}\right)^2$

$x^2 + y^2 = \frac{4}{9}$ or $9x^2 + 9y^2 = 4$

11. center: $(0, 0)$, point: $(0, 8)$

$r = \sqrt{(0 - 0)^2 + (8 - 0)^2}$

$r = \sqrt{64}$

$r = 8$

$x^2 + y^2 = r^2$

$x^2 + y^2 = 8^2$

$x^2 + y^2 = 64$

13. center: $(0, 0)$, point: $(5, 2)$

$r = \sqrt{(5 - 0)^2 + (2 - 0)^2}$

$r = \sqrt{25 + 4}$

$r = \sqrt{29}$

$x^2 + y^2 = r^2$

$x^2 + y^2 = \left(\sqrt{29}\right)^2$

$x^2 + y^2 = 29$

15. center: $(4, 3)$, radius: 10

$(x - h)^2 + (y - k)^2 = r^2$

$(x - 4)^2 + (y - 3)^2 = 10^2$

$(x - 4)^2 + (y - 3)^2 = 100$

17. center: $(5, -3)$, radius: 9

$(x - h)^2 + (y - k)^2 = r^2$

$(x - 5)^2 + [y - (-3)]^2 = 9^2$

$(x - 5)^2 + (y + 3)^2 = 81$

19. center: $(-2, 1)$, point: $(0, 1)$

$r = \sqrt{[0 - (-2)]^2 + (1 - 1)^2}$

$r = \sqrt{4 + 0}$

$r = 2$

$(x - h)^2 + (y - k)^2 = r^2$

$[x - (-2)]^2 + (y - 1)^2 = 2^2$

$(x + 2)^2 + (y - 1)^2 = 4$

21. center: $(3, 2)$, point: $(4, 6)$

$r = \sqrt{(4 - 3)^2 + (6 - 2)^2}$

$r = \sqrt{1 + 16}$

$ = \sqrt{17}$

$(x - h)^2 + (y - k)^2 = r^2$

$(x - 3)^2 + (y - 2)^2 = \left(\sqrt{17}\right)^2$

$(x - 3)^2 + (y - 2)^2 = 17$

23. $x^2 + y^2 = 16$

radius = 4   center = $(0, 0)$

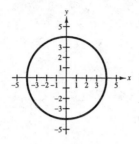

25. $x^2 + y^2 = 36$

center = $(0, 0)$

radius = 6

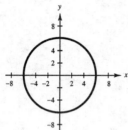

27. $4x^2 + 4y^2 = 1$ center = $(0, 0)$

$x^2 + y^2 = \frac{1}{4}$ radius = $\frac{1}{2}$

$r = \frac{1}{2}$

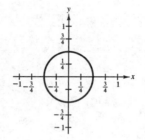

29. $(x - 2)^2 + (y - 3)^2 = 4$

center = $(2, 3)$

radius = 2

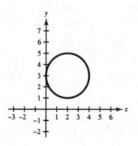

31. $\left(x + \frac{5}{2}\right)^2 + (y + 3)^2 = 9$

center = $\left(-\frac{5}{2}, -3\right)$

radius = 3

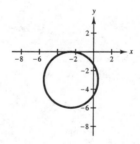

33. $x^2 + y^2 - 4x - 2y + 1 = 0$

$x^2 - 4x + y^2 - 2y = -1$

$(x^2 - 4x + 4) + (y^2 - 2y + 1) = -1 + 4 + 1$

$(x - 2)^2 + (y - 1)^2 = 4$

center = $(2, 1)$

radius = 2

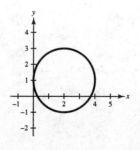

35. $x^2 + y^2 + 2x + 6y + 6 = 0$

$x^2 + 2x + y^2 + 6y = -6$

$(x^2 + 2x + 1) + (y^2 + 6y + 9) = -6 + 1 + 9$

$(x + 1)^2 + (y + 3)^2 = 4$

center = $(-1, -3)$

radius = 2

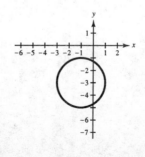

37. $x^2 + y^2 = 30$

$$y^2 = 30 - x^2$$

$$y = \pm\sqrt{30 - x^2}$$

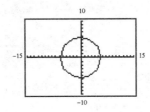

Keystrokes:

y_1 $\boxed{Y=}$ $\boxed{\sqrt{}}$ $\boxed{(}$ 30 $\boxed{-}$ $\boxed{X,T,\theta}$ $\boxed{x^2}$ $\boxed{)}$ $\boxed{ENTER}$

y_2 $\boxed{(-)}$ $\boxed{\sqrt{}}$ $\boxed{(}$ 30 $\boxed{-}$ $\boxed{X,T,\theta}$ $\boxed{x^2}$ $\boxed{)}$ $\boxed{GRAPH}$

39. $(x - 2)^2 + y^2 = 10$

$$y^2 = 10 - (x - 2)^2$$

$$y = \pm\sqrt{10 - (x - 2)^2}$$

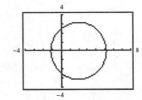

Keystrokes:

y_1 $\boxed{Y=}$ $\boxed{\sqrt{}}$ $\boxed{(}$ 10 $\boxed{-}$ $\boxed{(}$ $\boxed{X,T,\theta}$ $\boxed{-}$ 2 $\boxed{)}$ $\boxed{x^2}$ $\boxed{)}$ $\boxed{ENTER}$

y_2 $\boxed{(-)}$ $\boxed{\sqrt{}}$ $\boxed{(}$ 10 $\boxed{-}$ $\boxed{(}$ $\boxed{X,T,\theta}$ $\boxed{-}$ 2 $\boxed{)}$ $\boxed{x^2}$ $\boxed{)}$ $\boxed{GRAPH}$

41. center: $(0, 0)$

vertices: $(-4, 0), (4, 0)$

co-vertices: $(0, -3), (0, 3)$

$$\frac{x^2}{a^2} + \frac{y^2}{b^2} = 1$$

major axis is x-axis so $a = 4$

minor axis is y-axis so $b = 3$

$$\frac{x^2}{4^2} + \frac{y^2}{3^2} = 1$$

$$\frac{x^2}{16} + \frac{y^2}{9} = 1$$

43. center: $(0, 0)$

vertices: $(-2, 0), (2, 0)$

co-vertices: $(0, -1), (0, 1)$

$$\frac{x^2}{a^2} + \frac{y^2}{b^2} = 1$$

major axis is x-axis so $a = 2$

minor axis is y-axis so $b = 1$

$$\frac{x^2}{2^2} + \frac{y^2}{1^2} = 1$$

$$\frac{x^2}{4} + \frac{y^2}{1} = 1$$

45. center: $(0, 0)$

vertices: $(0, -4), (0, 4)$

co-vertices: $(-3, 0), (3, 0)$

$$\frac{x^2}{b^2} + \frac{y^2}{a^2} = 1$$

major axis is y-axis so $a = 4$

minor axis is x-axis so $b = 3$

$$\frac{x^2}{3^2} + \frac{y^2}{4^2} = 1$$

$$\frac{x^2}{9} + \frac{y^2}{16} = 1$$

47. center: $(0, 0)$

vertices: $(0, -2), (0, 2)$

co-vertices: $(-1, 0), (1, 0)$

$$\frac{x^2}{b^2} + \frac{y^2}{a^2} = 1$$

major axis is y-axis so $a = 2$

minor axis is x-axis so $b = 1$

$$\frac{x^2}{1^2} + \frac{y^2}{2^2} = 1$$

$$\frac{x^2}{1} + \frac{y^2}{4} = 1$$

49. center: $(0, 0)$

major axis (vertical) 10 units

minor axis 6 units

$$\frac{x^2}{b^2} + \frac{y^2}{a^2} = 1$$

$b = 3 \quad a = 5$

$$\frac{x^2}{3^2} + \frac{y^2}{5^2} = 1$$

$$\frac{x^2}{9} + \frac{y^2}{25} = 1$$

51. center: $(0, 0)$

major axis (horizontal) 20 units

minor axis 12 units

$$\frac{x^2}{a^2} + \frac{y^2}{b^2} = 1$$

$a = 10 \quad b = 6$

$$\frac{x^2}{10^2} + \frac{y^2}{6^2} = 1$$

$$\frac{x^2}{100} + \frac{y^2}{36} = 1$$

53. Vertices: $(-4, 0), (4, 0)$

Co-Vertices: $(0, 2), (0, -2)$

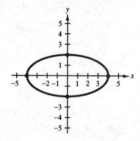

55. Vertices: $(0, 4), (0, -4)$

Co-Vertices: $(2, 0), (-2, 0)$

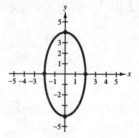

57. Vertices: $\left(-\frac{5}{3}, 0\right), \left(\frac{5}{3}, 0\right)$

Co-Vertices: $\left(0, \frac{4}{3}\right), \left(0, -\frac{4}{3}\right)$

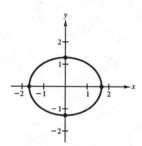

59. $4x^2 + y^2 - 4 = 0$

$$\frac{x^2}{1} + \frac{y^2}{4} = 1$$

Vertices: $(0, 2), (0, -2)$

Co-Vertices: $(1, 0), (-1, 0)$

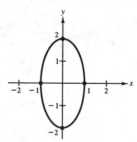

61. $10x^2 + 16y^2 - 160 = 0$

$$\frac{10x^2}{160} + \frac{16y^2}{160} = \frac{160}{160}$$

$$\frac{x^2}{16} + \frac{y^2}{10} = 1$$

Vertices: $(\pm 4, 0)$

Co-Vertices: $\left(0, \pm\sqrt{10}\right)$

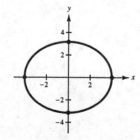

63. $x^2 + 2y^2 = 4$

$$2y^2 = 4 - x^2$$

$$y^2 = \frac{4 - x^2}{2}$$

$$y = \pm \sqrt{\frac{4 - x^2}{2}}$$

Keystrokes:

y_1 [Y=] [√] [(] [(] [(] 4 [−] [X,T,θ] [x²] [)] [÷] 2 [)] [ENTER]

y_2 [(−)] [√] [(] [(] [(] 4 [−] [X,T,θ] [x²] [)] [÷] 2 [)] [GRAPH]

Vertices: $(\pm 2, 0)$

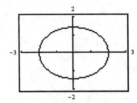

65. $3x^2 + y^2 - 12 = 0$

$$y^2 = 12 - 3x^2$$

$$y = \pm \sqrt{12 - 3x^2}$$

Keystrokes:

y_1 [Y=] [√] [(] 12 [−] 3 [X,T,θ] [x²] [)] [ENTER]

y_2 [(−)] [√] [(] 12 [−] 3 [X,T,θ] [x²] [)] [GRAPH]

Vertices: $\left(0, \pm 2\sqrt{3}\right)$

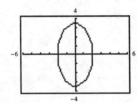

67. Vertices: $(3, 0)$, $(-3, 0)$

Asymptotes: $y = \dfrac{3}{3}x$ $y = -\dfrac{3}{3}x$

$\qquad\qquad y = x$ $y = -x$

Equation: $x^2 - y^2 = 9$

$$\frac{x^2}{9} - \frac{y^2}{9} = 1$$

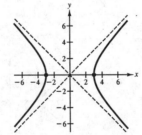

69. Vertices: $(0, \pm 1)$

Asymptotes: $y = \pm x$

Equation: $y^2 - x^2 = 1$

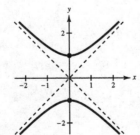

71. Vertices: $(3, 0), (-3, 0)$

Asymptotes: $y = \dfrac{5}{3}x$

$$y = -\dfrac{5}{3}x$$

Equation: $\dfrac{x^2}{9} - \dfrac{y^2}{25} = 1$

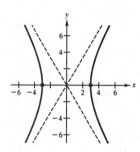

73. Vertices: $(0, \pm 2)$

Asymptotes: $y = \dfrac{2}{3}x$

$$y = -\dfrac{2}{3}x$$

Equation: $\dfrac{y^2}{4} - \dfrac{x^2}{9} = 1$

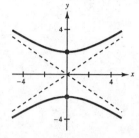

75. Vertices: $(\pm 1, 0)$

Asymptotes: $y = \pm\dfrac{\frac{3}{2}}{1}x$

$$y = \pm\dfrac{3}{2}x$$

Equation: $\dfrac{x^2}{1} - \dfrac{y^2}{\frac{9}{4}} = 1$

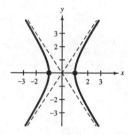

77. Vertices: $(4, 0), (-4, 0)$

Asymptotes: $y = \dfrac{2}{4}x = \dfrac{1}{2}x$

$$y = -\dfrac{2}{4}x = -\dfrac{1}{2}x$$

Equation: $4y^2 - x^2 + 16 = 0$

$$\dfrac{4y^2}{-16} - \dfrac{x^2}{-16} = \dfrac{-16}{-16}$$

$$\dfrac{-y^2}{4} + \dfrac{x^2}{16} = 1$$

$$\dfrac{x^2}{16} - \dfrac{y^2}{4} = 1$$

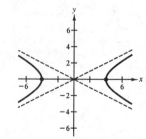

79. $\dfrac{x^2}{16} - \dfrac{y^2}{64} = 1$

81. $\dfrac{y^2}{16} - \dfrac{x^2}{64} = 1$

83. $\dfrac{x^2}{81} - \dfrac{y^2}{36} = 1$

85. $\dfrac{y^2}{1} - \dfrac{x^2}{\frac{1}{4}} = 1$

87. $\dfrac{x^2}{16} - \dfrac{y^2}{4} = 1$

$x^2 - 4y^2 = 16$

$x^2 - 16 = 4y^2$

$\dfrac{x^2 - 16}{4} = y^2$

$\pm\sqrt{\dfrac{x^2 - 16}{4}} = y$

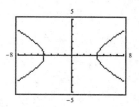

Keystrokes:

y_1: [Y=] [√] [(] [(] [X,T,θ] [x²] [−] 16 [)] [÷] 4 [)] [ENTER]

y_2: [(−)] [√] [(] [(] [X,T,θ] [x²] [−] 16 [)] [÷] 4 [)] [GRAPH]

89. $5x^2 - 2y^2 + 10 = 0$

$5x^2 + 10 = 2y^2$

$\dfrac{5x^2 + 10}{2} = y^2$

$\pm\sqrt{\dfrac{5x^2 + 10}{2}} = y$

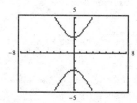

Keystrokes:

y_1: [Y=] [√] [(] [(] 5 [X,T,θ] [x²] [+] 10 [)] [÷] 2 [)] [ENTER]

y_2: [(−)] [√] [(] [(] 5 [X,T,θ] [x²] [+] 10 [)] [÷] 2 [)] [GRAPH]

91. Parabola

93. Ellipse

95. Hyperbola

97. Circle

99. Line

101. $x^2 + y^2 = 4500^2$

$x^2 + y^2 = 20{,}250{,}000$

103. (a) $x^2 + y^2 = 625$ (equation of circle)

(x, y) of the rectangle is also the point on the circle, so y-coordinate equals:

$x^2 + y^2 = 625$

$y^2 = 625 - x^2$

$y = \sqrt{625 - x^2}$

width $= 2\left(\sqrt{625 - x^2}\right)$

area $= 2x \cdot 2\left(\sqrt{625 - x^2}\right)$

area $= 4x\sqrt{625 - x^2}$

(b)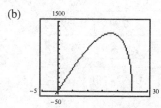

$x \approx 17.68$

105. Equation of ellipse $= \dfrac{x^2}{50^2} + \dfrac{y^2}{40^2} = 1$

or

$$\dfrac{x^2}{2500} + \dfrac{y^2}{1600} = 1$$

$$\dfrac{45^2}{2500} + \dfrac{y^2}{1600} = 1$$

$$\dfrac{y^2}{1600} = 0.19$$

$$y^2 = 304$$

$$y = 17.435596 \approx 17 \text{ feet}$$

107.

$A = \pi ab$	$a + b = 20$
$301.59 = \pi ab$	$b = 20 - a$

$$\dfrac{301.59}{\pi} = ab$$

$$96 \approx ab$$

$$96 = a(20 - a)$$

$$0 = -a^2 + 20a - 96$$

$$0 = a^2 - 20a + 96$$

$$0 = (a - 12)(a - 8)$$

$a = 12$	$a = 8$
$b = 8$	$b = 12$

$$\dfrac{x^2}{144} + \dfrac{y^2}{64} = 1$$

109. The four types of conics are circles, parabolas, ellipses, and hyperbolas.

111. An ellipse is the set of all points (x, y) such that the sum of the distances between (x, y) and two distinct fixed points is a constant.

$$\dfrac{x^2}{a^2} + \dfrac{y^2}{b^2} = 1 \quad \text{or} \quad \dfrac{x^2}{b^2} + \dfrac{y^2}{a^2} = 1$$

113. An ellipse is a circle if the coefficients of the second degree terms are equal.

115. The central rectangle of a hyperbola can be used to sketch its asymptotes because the asymptotes are the extended diagonals of the central rectangle.

117. $y = \dfrac{3}{2}\sqrt{x^2 - 4}$ is the top half of the hyperbola $\dfrac{x^2}{4} - \dfrac{y^2}{9} = 1$.

Section 7.5   Graphs of Rational Functions

1. (a)

x	0	0.5	0.9	0.99	0.999
y	-4	-8	-40	-400	-4000

x	2	1.5	1.1	1.01	1.001
y	4	8	40	400	4000

x	2	5	10	100	1000
y	4	1	0.44444	0.0404	0.004

(b)

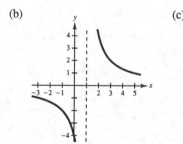

(c) Domain:

$$x - 1 \neq 0$$

$$x \neq 1$$

$$(-\infty, 1) \cup (1, \infty)$$

3. (a)

x	2	2.5	2.9	2.99	2.999
y	1	0	-8	-98	-998

x	4	3.5	3.1	3.01	3.001
y	3	4	12	102	1002

x	4	5	10	100	1000
y	3	2.5	2.143	2.010	2.001

(b)

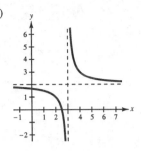

(c) Domain:

$$x - 3 \neq 0$$
$$x \neq 3$$
$$(-\infty, 3) \cup (3, \infty)$$

5. (a)

x	2	2.5	2.9	2.99	2.999
y	-1.2	-2.727	-14.75	-149.7	-1500

x	4	3.5	3.1	3.01	3.001
y	1.714	3.231	15.246	150.25	1500.2

x	4	5	10	100	1000
y	1.714	0.938	0.330	0.030	0.003

(b)

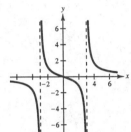

(c) Domain: $\qquad x^2 - 9 \neq 0$

$$(x - 3)(x + 3) \neq 0$$
$$x \neq 3 \quad x \neq -3$$
$$(-\infty, -3) \cup (-3, 3) \cup (3, \infty)$$

7. $f(x) = \dfrac{5}{x^2}$

Domain: $x^2 \neq 0$

$$x \neq 0$$
$$(-\infty, 0) \cup (0, \infty)$$

Vertical asymptote: $x = 0$

Horizontal asymptote: $y = 0$ since the degree of the numerator is less than the degree of the denominator.

9. $f(x) = \dfrac{x}{x + 8}$

Domain: $x + 8 \neq 0$

$$x \neq -8$$
$$(-\infty, -8) \cup (-8, \infty)$$

Vertical asymptote: $x = -8$

Horizontal asymptote: $y = 1$ since the degree of the numerator is equal to the degree of the denominator and the leading coefficients are 1.

11. $g(t) = \dfrac{2t - 5}{3t - 9}$

Domain: $3t - 9 \neq 0$

$$t \neq 3$$
$$(-\infty, 3) \cup (3, \infty)$$

Vertical asymptote: $t = 3$

Horizontal asymptote: $y = \frac{2}{3}$ since the degree of the numerator is equal to the degree of the denominator and the leading coefficient of the numerator is 2 and the leading coefficient of the denominator is 3.

13. $y = \dfrac{3 - 5x}{1 - 3x}$

Domain: $1 - 3x \neq 0$

$$1 \neq 3x$$
$$\tfrac{1}{3} \neq x$$
$$\left(-\infty, \tfrac{1}{3}\right) \cup \left(\tfrac{1}{3}, \infty\right)$$

Vertical asymptote: $x = \frac{1}{3}$

Horizontal asymptote: $y = \frac{5}{3}$ since the degree of the numerator is equal to the degree of the denominator and the leading coefficient of the numerator is -5 and the leading coefficient of the denominator is -3.

15. $g(t) = \dfrac{3}{t(t-1)}$

$t(t-1) \neq 0$

$t \neq 0 \quad t - 1 \neq 0$

$\qquad\qquad t \neq 1$

$(-\infty, 0) \cup (0, 1) \cup (1, \infty)$

Vertical asymptotes: $t = 0, t = 1$

Horizontal asymptote: $y = 0$ since the degree of the numerator is less than the degree of the denominator.

17. $y = \dfrac{2x^2}{x^2 + 1}$

Domain: $x^2 + 1 \neq 0$

$\qquad\quad (-\infty, \infty)$

$\qquad\quad$ no real solution

Vertical asymptote: none

Horizontal asymptote: $y = 2$ since the degree of the numerator is equal to the degree of the denominator and the leading coefficient of the numerator is 2 and the leading coefficient of the denominator is 1.

19. $y = \dfrac{x^2 - 4}{x^2 - 1}$

Domain: $\qquad\qquad x^2 - 1 \neq 0$

$\qquad\qquad (x - 1)(x + 1) \neq 0$

$\qquad\qquad\quad x \neq 1 \quad x \neq -1$

$\qquad\quad (-\infty, -1) \cup (-1, 1) \cup (1, \infty)$

Vertical asymptotes: $x = 1, x = -1$

Horizontal asymptote: $y = 1$ since the degree of the numerator is equal to the degree of the denominator and the leading coefficient of the numerator is 1 and the leading coefficient of the denominator is 1.

21. $g(z) = 1 - \dfrac{2}{z}$

$g(z) = \dfrac{z}{z} \cdot \dfrac{1}{1} - \dfrac{2}{z} = \dfrac{z - 2}{z}$

Domain: $z \neq 0$

$\qquad\quad (-\infty, 0) \cup (0, \infty)$

Vertical asymptote: $z = 0$

Horizontal asymptote: $y = 1$ since the degree of the numerator is equal to the degree of the denominator and the leading coefficients are 1.

23. $g(x) = 2x + \dfrac{4}{x} = \dfrac{x}{x} \cdot \dfrac{2x}{1} + \dfrac{4}{x} = \dfrac{2x^2 + 4}{x}$

Domain: $x \neq 0$

$\qquad\quad (-\infty, 0) \cup (0, \infty)$

Vertical asymptote: $x = 0$

Horizontal asymptote: none since the degree of the numerator is greater than the degree of the denominator.

25. $f(x) = \dfrac{2}{x + 1}$ matches with graph (d).

Vertical asymptote: $x + 1 = 0$

$\qquad\qquad\qquad\qquad x = -1$

Horizontal asymptote: $y = 0$

27. $f(x) = \dfrac{x - 2}{x - 1}$ matches with graph (b).

Vertical asymptote: $x - 1 = 0$

$\qquad\qquad\qquad\quad x = 1$

Horizontal asymptote: $y = 1$

29. (d)

31. (a)

33. $g(x) = \dfrac{5}{x}$

y-intercept: $g(0) = \dfrac{5}{0} =$ undefined, none

x-intercept: none, numerator is never zero.

Vertical asymptote: $x = 0$

Horizontal asymptote: $y = 0$ since the degree of the numerator is less than the degree of the denominator.

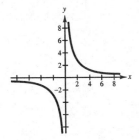

35. $g(x) = \dfrac{5}{x - 4}$

y-intercept: $g(0) = \dfrac{5}{0 - 4} = -\dfrac{5}{4}$

x-intercept: none, numerator is never zero.

Vertical asymptote: $x - 4 = 0$

$$x = 4$$

Horizontal asymptote: $y = 0$ since the degree of the numerator is less than the degree of the denominator.

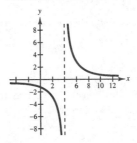

37. $f(x) = \dfrac{1}{x - 2}$

y-intercept: $f(0) = \dfrac{1}{0 - 2} = -\dfrac{1}{2}$

x-intercept: none, numerator is never zero.

Vertical asymptote: $x - 2 = 0$

$$x = 2$$

Horizontal asymptote: $y = 0$ since the degree of the numerator is less than the degree of the denominator.

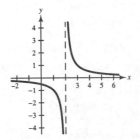

39. $g(x) = \dfrac{1}{2 - x}$

y-intercept: $g(0) = \dfrac{1}{2 - 0} = \dfrac{1}{2}$

x-intercept: none, numerator is never zero

Vertical asymptote: $2 - x = 0$

$$x = 2$$

Horizontal asymptote: $y = 0$ since the degree of the numerator is less than the degree of the denominator.

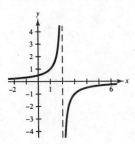

41. $y = \dfrac{3x}{x^2 + 4x}$

y-intercept: $y = \dfrac{3(0)}{0^2 + 4(0)} =$ undefined, none

x-intercept: $0 = \dfrac{3x}{x^2 + 4x} = \dfrac{3x}{x(x + 4)}$

$0 = \dfrac{3}{x + 4}$; none

Vertical asymptote: $x^2 + 4x = 0$

$$x(x + 4) = 0$$

$$x = -4$$

Horizontal asymptote: $y = 0$ since the degree of the numerator is less than the degree of the denominator.

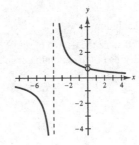

43. $h(u) = \dfrac{3u^2}{u^2 - 3u}$

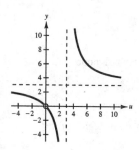

y-intercept: $h(0) = \dfrac{3(0)^2}{0^2 - 3(0)} =$ undefined, none

x-intercept: $0 = \dfrac{3u^2}{u^2 - 3u} = \dfrac{3u^2}{u(u - 3)}$

$\qquad\qquad 0 = \dfrac{3u}{u - 3}$

$\qquad\qquad 0 = 3u$

$\qquad\qquad 0 = u$, none, since $h(0)$ is undefined.

Vertical asymptote: $u^2 - 3u = 0$

$\qquad\qquad\qquad u(u - 3) = 0$

$\qquad\qquad\qquad\qquad u = 3$

Horizontal asymptote: $y = 3$ since the degrees are equal and the leading coefficient of the numerator is 3 and the leading coefficient of the denominator is 1.

45. $y = \dfrac{2x + 4}{x}$

y-intercept: $y = \dfrac{2(0) + 4}{0} =$ undefined, none.

x-intercept: $2x + 4 = 0$

$\qquad\qquad\qquad x = -2$

Vertical asymptote: $x = 0$

Horizontal asymptote: $y = 2$ since the degree of the numerator is equal to the degree of the denominator and the leading coefficient of the numerator is 2 and the leading coefficient of the denominator is 1.

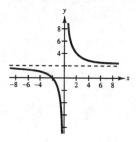

47. $y = \dfrac{2x^2}{x^2 + 1}$

y-intercept: $y = \dfrac{2(0)^2}{0^2 + 1} = 0$

x-intercept: $x = 0$

Vertical asymptote: none, $x^2 + 1 = 0$ has no real solutions.

Horizontal asymptote: $y = 2$ since the degree of the numerator is equal to the degree of the denominator and the leading coefficient of the numerator is 2 and the leading coefficient of the denominator is 1.

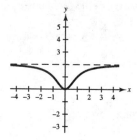

49. $y = \dfrac{4}{x^2 + 1}$

y-intercept: $y = \dfrac{4}{0^2 + 1} = 4$

x-intercept: none, numerator is never zero.

Vertical asymptote: none, $x^2 + 1 \neq 0$

$\qquad\qquad\qquad$ no real solution

Horizontal asymptote: $y = 0$ since the degree of the numerator is less than the degree of the denominator.

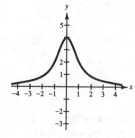

51. $g(t) = 3 - \dfrac{2}{t}$

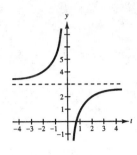

y-intercept: $g(0) = 3 - \dfrac{2}{0} =$ undefined, none

x-intercept: $0 = 3 - \dfrac{2}{t}$

$$0 = 3t - 2$$

$$2 = 3t$$

$$\frac{2}{3} = t$$

Vertical asymptote: $t = 0$

Horizontal asymptote: $y = 3$

53. $y = -\dfrac{x}{x^2 - 4}$

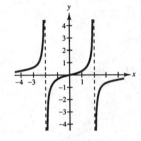

y-intercept: $y = \dfrac{-0}{0^2 - 4} = 0$

x-intercept: $0 = -\dfrac{x}{x^2 - 4}$

$$0 = -x$$

$$0 = x$$

Vertical asymptote: $x = 2, x = -2$

$$x^2 - 4 = 0$$

$$(x - 2)(x + 2) = 0$$

$$x = 2 \quad x = -2$$

Horizontal asymptote: $y = 0$ since the degree of the numerator is less than the degree of the denominator.

55. $f(x) = \dfrac{3x^2}{x^2 - x - 2}$

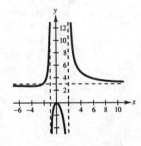

y-intercept: $y = \dfrac{3(0)^2}{0^2 - 0 - 2} = \dfrac{0}{-2} = 0$

x-intercept: $3x^2 = 0$

$$x^2 = 0$$

$$x = 0$$

Vertical asymptotes: $x^2 - x - 2 = 0$

$$(x - 2)(x + 1) = 0$$

$$x - 2 = 0 \quad x - 2 = 0$$

$$x = 2 \quad\quad x = 2$$

Vertical asymptote: none

Horizontal asymptote: $y = 3$ since the degree of the numerator is equal to the degree of the denominator and the leading coefficient of the numerator is 3 and the leading coefficient of the denominator is 1.

57. $f(x) = \dfrac{x^2 - 4}{x^2 - 3x - 10}$

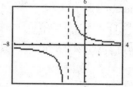

y-intercept: $f(0) = \dfrac{0^2 - 4}{0^2 - 3(0) - 10} = \dfrac{4}{10} = \dfrac{2}{5}$

x-intercept: $0 = \dfrac{x^2 - 4}{x^2 - 3x - 10}$

$0 = x^2 - 4$

$0 = (x - 2)(x + 2)$

$x = 2$ undefined at $x = -2$

Vertical asymptotes: $x^2 - 3x - 10 = 0$

$(x - 5)(x + 2) = 0$

$x = 5 \quad x = -2 \to$ hole in graph

Horizontal asymptote: $y = 1$ since the degrees are equal and the leading coefficients are 1.

$f(x) = \dfrac{(x - 2)(x + 2)}{(x - 5)(x + 2)} \Big\}$ gives a hole in graph at $x = -2$

59. $f(x) = \dfrac{3}{x + 2}$

Domain: $x + 2 \neq 0$

$x \neq -2$

$(-\infty, -2) \cup (-2, \infty)$

Vertical asymptote: $x = -2$

Horizontal asymptote: $y = 0$

Keystrokes:

y_1 [Y=] 3 [÷] [(] [X,T,θ] [+] 2 [)] [GRAPH]

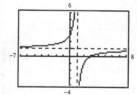

61. $h(x) = \dfrac{x - 3}{x - 1}$

Domain: $x - 1 \neq 0$

$x \neq 1$

$(-\infty, 1) \cup (1, \infty)$

Vertical asymptote: $x = 1$

Horizontal asymptote: $y = 1$

Keystrokes:

[Y=] [(] [X,T,θ] [−] 3 [)] [÷] [(] [X,T,θ] [−] 1 [GRAPH]

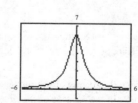

63. $f(t) = \dfrac{6}{t^2 + 1}$

Domain: $t^2 + 1 \neq 0$

$(-\infty, \infty)$

Vertical asymptote: none

Horizontal asymptote: $y = 0$

Keystrokes:

[Y=] 6 [÷] [(] [X,T,θ] [x²] [+] 1 [)] [GRAPH]

65. $y = \dfrac{2(x^2 + 1)}{x^2}$

Domain: $x^2 \neq 0$

$\qquad x \neq 0$

$\qquad (-\infty, 0) \cup (0, \infty)$

Vertical asymptote: $x = 0$

Horizontal asymptote: $y = 2$

Keystrokes:

 $\boxed{(\,(}$ 2 $\boxed{(\,(}$ $\boxed{\text{X,T,}\theta}$ $\boxed{x^2}$ $\boxed{+}$ 1 $\boxed{)\,)}$ $\boxed{)}$ $\boxed{\div}$ $\boxed{\text{X,T,}\theta}$ $\boxed{x^2}$ $\boxed{\text{GRAPH}}$

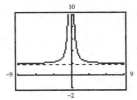

67. $y = \dfrac{3}{x} + \dfrac{1}{x - 2}$

$y = \dfrac{3}{x} + \dfrac{1}{x - 2} = \dfrac{4x - 6}{x^2 - 2x}$

Domain: $x \neq 0 \quad x - 2 \neq 0$

$\qquad\qquad\qquad x \neq 2$

$(-\infty, 0) \cup (0, 2) \cup (2, \infty)$

Vertical asymptotes: $x^2 - 2x = 0, x(x - 2) = 0, x = 0, x = 2$

Horizontal asymptote: $y = 0$ since the degree of the numerator is less than the degree of the denominator.

Keystrokes: $\boxed{\text{Y=}}$ 3 $\boxed{\div}$ $\boxed{\text{X,T,}\theta}$ $\boxed{+}$ 1 $\boxed{\div}$ $\boxed{(\,(}$ $\boxed{\text{X,T,}\theta}$ $\boxed{-}$ 2 $\boxed{)}$ $\boxed{\text{GRAPH}}$ or

$\qquad\qquad\quad$ $\boxed{\text{Y=}}$ $\boxed{(}$ 4 $\boxed{\text{X,T,}\theta}$ $\boxed{-}$ 6 $\boxed{)}$ $\div$ $\boxed{(\,(}$ $\boxed{\text{X,T,}\theta}$ $\boxed{x^2}$ $\boxed{-}$ 2 $\boxed{\text{X,T,}\theta}$ $\boxed{)}$ $\boxed{\text{GRAPH}}$

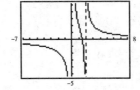

69. Reduce $g(x)$ to lowest terms.

$$g(x) = \frac{4 - 2x}{x - 2} = \frac{2(2 - x)}{x - 2} = -2$$

Keystrokes: $\boxed{\text{Y=}}$ $\boxed{(\,(}$ 4 $\boxed{-}$ 2 $\boxed{\text{X,T,}\theta}$ $\boxed{)}$ $\boxed{\div}$ $\boxed{(\,(}$ $\boxed{\text{X,T,}\theta}$ $\boxed{-}$ 2 $\boxed{)}$ $\boxed{\text{GRAPH}}$

There is no vertical asymptote because the fraction is not reduced to lowest terms.

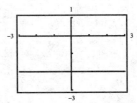

71. (a) Average cost $= \dfrac{\text{Cost}}{\text{Number of units}}$

$\qquad\qquad \overline{C} = \dfrac{2500 + 0.50x}{x}, \quad 0 < x$

$\quad$ (b) $\overline{C} = \dfrac{2500 + 0.50(1000)}{1000} = \$3$

$\qquad\quad \overline{C} = \dfrac{2500 + 0.50(10,000)}{10,000} = \$0.75$

(c) *Keystrokes:*

$\boxed{\text{Y=}}$ $\boxed{(\,(}$ 2500 $\boxed{+}$ .5 $\boxed{\text{X,T,}\theta}$ $\boxed{)}$ $\boxed{\div}$ $\boxed{\text{X,T,}\theta}$ $\boxed{\text{GRAPH}}$

Horizontal asymptote

$\overline{C} = \$0.50$ since the degree of the numerator is equal to the degree of the denominator and the leading coefficient of the numerator is 0.50 and the leading coefficient of the denominator is 1. As the number of units produced increases, the average cost is approximately \$0.50.

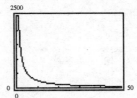

73. (a) $C = 0$ is the horizontal asymptote, since the degree of the numerator is less than the degree of the denominator. The meaning in the context of the problem is that the chemical is eliminated from the body.

$\quad$ (b) *Keystrokes:* $\boxed{\text{Y=}}$ 2 $\boxed{\text{X,T,}\theta}$ $\boxed{\div}$ $\boxed{(\,(}$ 4 $\boxed{\text{X,T,}\theta}$ $\boxed{x^2}$ $\boxed{+}$ 25 $\boxed{)}$ $\boxed{\text{GRAPH}}$

$\qquad\quad$ Maximum occurs when $t \approx 2.5$.

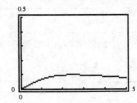

75. (a) answers will vary.

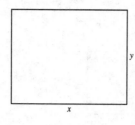

(b) $A = x \cdot y$ $P = 2l + 2w$

$400 = x \cdot y$ $P = 2(l + w)$

$\dfrac{400}{x} = y$ $P = 2\left(x + \dfrac{400}{x}\right)$

(c) Domain: $x > 0$ or $(0, \infty)$

(d) Minimum perimeter: 20 units × 20 units

Keystrokes:

[Y=] 2 [(] [X,T,θ] [+] 400 [÷] [X,T,θ] [)] [GRAPH]

77. $y = \dfrac{2(x + 1)}{x - 3}$

79. $y = \dfrac{x - 6}{(x - 4)(x + 2)}$

81. (c) $y = \dfrac{48.4 - 4.79x}{1 - 0.13x}$

Domain: $1 - 0.13x \neq 0$

$-0.13x \neq -1$

$x \neq \dfrac{-1}{-0.13}$

$x \neq 7.69$

x-intercept: $0 = \dfrac{48.4 - 4.79x}{1 - 0.13x}$

$0 = 48.4 - 4.79x$

$4.79x = 48.4$

$x = \dfrac{48.4}{4.79} = 10.10$

Horizontal asymptote: $y = \dfrac{-4.79}{-0.13}$

$y \approx 36.85$

since the degrees are equal.

Vertical asymptote: $x \approx 7.69$

(the excluded value of the domain)

(d) *Keystrokes:*

[Y=] [(] 48.4 [−] 4.79 [X,T,θ] [)] [÷] [(] 1 [−] .13 [X,T,θ] [)] [GRAPH]

Plot (1, 50.1), (2, 51.9), (3, 54.8), (4, 59.3), (5, 73.6), (6, 78.7)

in

[STAT] 1 then enter 1, 2, 3, 4, 5, 6, in L_1 and enter 50.1, 51.9, 54.8, 59.3, 73.6, 78.7, in L_2.

[STAT PLOT] 1 [ON] [GRAPH]

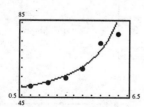

The model appears to be accurate for the restricted domain.

—CONTINUED—

81. **—CONTINUED—**

(e) The models are not accurate for the years before 1991 and after 1996. Use the quadratic model to estimate the value of the shipment in 1998, because the rational function evaluated at $x = 8$ is negative.

83. An asymptote of a graph is a line to which the graph becomes arbitrarily close as $|x|$ or $|y|$ increases without bound.

85. No, not when the domain is all reals. For example,

$$f(x) = \frac{1}{x^2 + 1} \text{ has no vertical asymptote.}$$

Review Exercises for Chapter 7

1. P varies directly as the cube of t. $P = kt^3$

3. z varies inversely as the square of s. $z = \dfrac{k}{s^2}$

5.
$$y = k\sqrt[3]{x}$$
$$12 = k\sqrt[3]{8}$$
$$6 = \frac{12}{\sqrt[3]{8}} = k$$
$$y = 6\sqrt[3]{x}$$

7. $T = krs^2$
$$5000 = k(0.09)(1000)^2$$
$$\frac{5000}{90,000} = k$$
$$\frac{1}{18} = k$$
$$T = \frac{1}{18}rs^2$$

9. $y > 4$

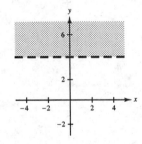

11. $x - 2 \geq 0$
$$x \geq 2$$

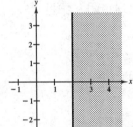

13. $2x + y < 1$ or $y < -2x + 1$

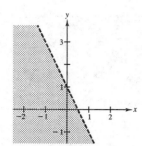

15. $-(x - 1) \leq 4y - 2$

$$-x + 1 \leq 4y - 2$$

$$-x + 3 \leq 4y$$

$$-\frac{x + 3}{4} \leq y$$

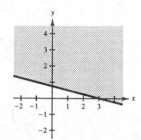

17. $y \leq 12 - \frac{3}{2}x$

Keystrokes:

[Y=] 12 [−] [(] 3 [÷] 2 [)] [X,T,θ]

[DRAW] 7 [(] [(−)] 10 [,] [Y-VARS] 1 1 [)] [ENTER]

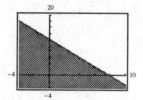

19. $x + y \geq 0$

$$y \geq -x$$

Keystrokes:

[Y=] [(−)] [X,T,θ]

[DRAW] 7 [(] [Y-VARS] 1 1 [,] 10 [)] [ENTER]

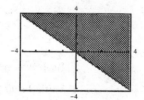

21. $f(x) = x^2 - 8x + 3$

$$= (x^2 - 8x + 16) + 3 - 16$$

$$= (x - 4)^2 - 13$$

vertex $= (4, -13)$

23. $h(u) = 2u^2 - u + 3$

$$= 2\left(u^2 - \frac{1}{2}u\right) + 3$$

$$= 2\left(u^2 - \frac{1}{2}u + \frac{1}{16}\right) + 3 - \frac{1}{8}$$

$$= 2\left(u - \frac{1}{4}\right)^2 + \frac{23}{8}$$

vertex $= \left(\frac{1}{4}, \frac{23}{8}\right)$

25. $y = x^2 + 8x$

x-intercepts	vertex
$0 = x^2 + 8x$	$y = x^2 + 8x + 16 - 16$
$0 = x(x + 8)$	$y = (x + 4)^2 - 16$
$x = 0$ $x = -8$	$(-4, -16)$

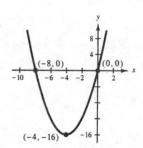

27. $y = x^2 - 6x + 5$

x-intercepts   vertex

$0 = x^2 - 6x + 5$ $y = (x^2 - 6x + 9) + 5 - 9$

$0 = (x - 5)(x - 1)$ $y = (x - 3)^2 - 4$

$x = 5 \quad x = 1$ $(3, -4)$

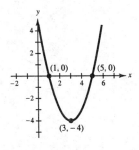

29. $h(x) = x^2 + 3$

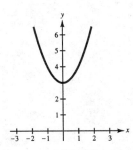

Vertical shift 3 units up

31. $h(x) = (x + 2)^2 - 3$

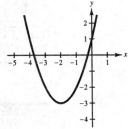

Horizontal shift 2 units left

Vertical shift 3 units down

33. vertex: $(3, 5)$

$a = -2$

$y = a(x - h)^2 + k$

$y = -2(x - 3)^2 + 5$

35. vertex: $(2, -5)$: y-intercept: $(0, 3)$

$y = a(x - h)^2 + k$ $y = 2(x - 2)^2 - 5$ or $y = 2x^2 - 8x + 3$

$y = a(x - 2)^2 - 5$

$3 = a(0 - 2)^2 - 5$

$3 = a(4) - 5$

$8 = a(4)$

$2 = a$

37. *Parabola:* vertex: $(5, 0)$; passes through the point $(1, 1)$

$y = a(x - h)^2 + k$

$1 = a(1 - 5)^2 + 0$

$1 = a(16)$

$\frac{1}{16} = a$

$y = \frac{1}{16}(x - 5)^2 + 0$ or $y = \frac{1}{16}x^2 - \frac{5}{8}x + \frac{25}{16}$

39. (c) matches $4x^2 + 4y^2 = 81$ **41.** (a) matches $\frac{y^2}{4} - x^2 = 1$

43. (b) matches $y = -x^2 + 6x - 5$

45. $x^2 - 2y = 0$

$$x^2 = 2y$$

$$\frac{x^2}{2} = y$$

parabola

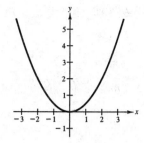

47. $x^2 + y^2 = 64$

circle

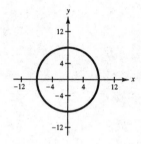

49. $y = (x - 6)^2 + 1$

parabola

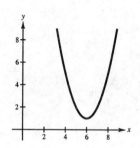

51. $\dfrac{x^2}{25} + \dfrac{y^2}{4} = 1$

ellipse

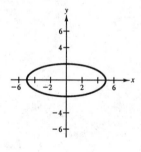

53. $4x^2 + 4y^2 - 9 = 0$

$$\frac{4x^2}{9} + \frac{4y^2}{9} = 1$$

$$\frac{x^2}{\frac{9}{4}} + \frac{y^2}{\frac{9}{4}} = 1$$

circle

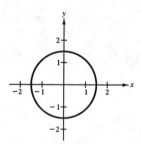

55. *Parabola:* vertex: $(5, 0)$; passes through the point $(1, 1)$

$$y = a(x - h)^2 + k$$

$$1 = a(1 - 5)^2 + 0$$

$$1 = a(16)$$

$$\tfrac{1}{16} = a$$

$$y = \tfrac{1}{16}(x - 5)^2 + 0 \text{ or } y = \tfrac{1}{16}x^2 - \tfrac{5}{8}x + \tfrac{25}{16}$$

57. *Ellipse:* vertices: $(0, -5), (0, 5)$; co-vertices: $(-2, 0), (2, 0)$

$$\frac{x^2}{4} + \frac{y^2}{25} = 1$$

59. *Circle:* center: $(0, 0)$; radius: 20

$$x^2 + y^2 = 400$$

61. *Hyperbola:* vertices: $(-3, 0), (3, 0)$; asymptotes: $y = -\frac{1}{2}x, y = \frac{1}{2}x$

$$\frac{x^2}{a^2} - \frac{y^2}{b^2} = 1 \qquad \frac{x^2}{3^2} - \frac{y^2}{\left(\frac{3}{2}\right)^2} = 1 \qquad \frac{x^2}{9} - \frac{y^2}{\frac{9}{4}} = 1$$

$$a = 3 \quad b = \frac{3}{2}$$

63. $f(x) = \dfrac{5}{x - 6}$

(b)

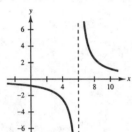

65. $f(x) = \dfrac{6x}{x - 5}$

(a)

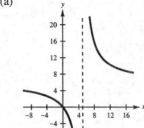

67. $f(x) = \dfrac{-5}{x^2}$

y-intercept: $f(0) = \dfrac{-5}{0^2} =$ undefined; none

x-intercept: $0 = \dfrac{-5}{x^2}$

$$0 = -5 \text{ none}$$

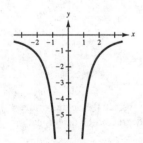

vertical asymptote: $x^2 = 0$

$$x = 0$$

horizontal asymptote: $y = 0$ since the degree of the numerator is less than the degree of the denominator.

69. $P(x) = \dfrac{3x + 6}{x - 2}$

y-intercept: $P(0) = \dfrac{3(0) + 6}{0 - 2} = -3$

x-intercept: $0 = \dfrac{3x + 6}{x - 2}$

$$0 = 3x + 6$$

$$-2 = x$$

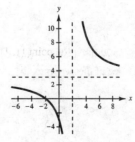

vertical asymptote: $x = 2$

horizontal asymptote: $y = 3$ since the degrees are equal and the leading coefficient of the numerator is 3 and the leading coefficient of the denominator is 1.

71. $g(x) = \dfrac{2+x}{1-x}$

y-intercept: $g(0) = \dfrac{2+0}{1-0} = 2$

x-intercept: $0 = \dfrac{2+x}{1-x}$

$\qquad\qquad\quad 0 = 2 + x$

$\qquad\qquad\quad -2 = x$

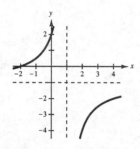

vertical asymptote: $x = 1$

horizontal asymptote: $y = -1$ since the degrees are equal and the leading coefficient of the number is 1 and the leading coefficient of the denominator is -1.

73. $f(x) = \dfrac{x}{x^2 + 1}$

y-intercept: $f(0) = \dfrac{0}{0^2 + 1} = 0$

x-intercept: $0 = \dfrac{x}{x^2 + 1}$

$\qquad\qquad\quad 0 = x$

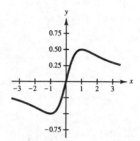

vertical asymptote: none $x^2 + 1 \neq 0$

horizontal asymptote: $y = 0$ since the degree of the numerator is less than the degree of the denominator.

75. $h(x) = \dfrac{4}{(x-1)^2}$

y-intercept: $h(0) = \dfrac{4}{(0-1)^2} = 4$

x-intercept: $0 = \dfrac{4}{(x-1)^2}$

$\qquad\qquad\quad 0 = 4 \text{ none}$

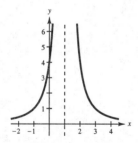

vertical asymptote: $x = 1$

horizontal asymptote: $y = 0$ since the degree of the numerator is less than the degree of the denominator.

77. $y = \dfrac{x}{x^2 - 1}$

y-intercept: $y = \dfrac{0}{0^2 - 1} = 0$

x-intercept: $0 = \dfrac{x}{x^2 - 1}$

$\qquad\qquad\quad 0 = x$

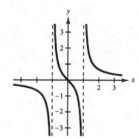

vertical asymptote: $x^2 - 1 = 0$

$\qquad\qquad\quad x = 1 \quad x = -1$

horizontal asymptote: $y = 0$ since the degree of the numerator is less than the degree of the denominator.

79. $y = \dfrac{2x^2}{x^2 - 4}$

y-intercept: $y = \dfrac{2(0)^2}{0^2 - 4} = 0$

x-intercept: $0 = \dfrac{2x^2}{x^2 - 4}$

$$0 = 2x^2$$

$$0 = x$$

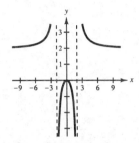

vertical asymptote: $x^2 - 4 = 0$

$$x = 2 \quad x = -2$$

horizontal asymptote: $y = 2$ since the degrees are equal and the leading coefficient of the numerator is 2 and the leading coefficient of the denominator is 1.

81. $y = \dfrac{x - 4}{x^2 - 3x - 4}$

$y = \dfrac{x - 4}{x^2 - 3x - 4} = \dfrac{x - 4}{(x - 4)(x + 1)} = \dfrac{1}{x + 1}$

y-intercept: $y = \dfrac{0 - 4}{0^2 - 3(0) - 4} = \dfrac{-4}{-4} = 1$

x-intercept: $0 = \dfrac{1}{x + 1}$

$$0 = 1 \text{ none}$$

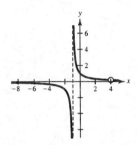

vertical asymptote: $x = -1$

horizontal asymptote: $y = 0$ since the degree of the number is less than the degree of the denominator.

83. Vertical asymptote: $x = 4$

Horizontal asymptote: $y = 3$

Zero of the function: $x = 0$

$y = \dfrac{3x}{x - 4}$

85. $d = kF$

$$4 = k(100)$$

$$\dfrac{4}{100} = k$$

$$\dfrac{1}{25} = k$$

$$6 = \dfrac{1}{25}F$$

$$150 \text{ pounds} = F$$

87. $x = \dfrac{k}{\sqrt{p}}$

$1000 = \dfrac{k}{\sqrt{25}}$

$5000 = k$

$x = \dfrac{5000}{\sqrt{28}}$

$x = 944.91118$

$x \approx 945 \text{ units}$

89. $8x + 10y \geq 200$

$8x + 10y \geq 200$

$10y \geq -8x + 200$

$y \geq -.8x + 20$

Ordered pair solutions:

$(0, 20), (25, 0), (10, 12),$

$(12, 11), (8, 15)$

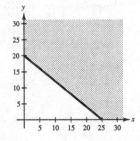

(*Note:* x and y cannot be negative.)

91. (a) *Keystrokes:*

$\boxed{Y=}$ $\boxed{(-)}$ $\boxed{X,T,\theta}$ $\boxed{x^2}$ $\boxed{\div}$ 10 $\boxed{+}$ 3 $\boxed{X,T,\theta}$ $\boxed{+}$ 6 $\boxed{GRAPH}$

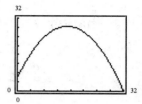

(b) $y = -\dfrac{1}{10}(0)^2 + 3(0) + 6$

$y = 0 + 0 + 6$

$y = 6 \text{ feet}$

(c) $x = -\dfrac{b}{2a}$

$\quad = -\dfrac{3}{2\left(-\dfrac{1}{10}\right)}$

$\quad = \dfrac{-3}{-\dfrac{1}{5}}$

$\quad = 15$

$y = \dfrac{1}{10}(15)^2 + 3(15) + 6$

$\quad = -\dfrac{1}{10}(225) + 45 + 6$

$\quad = -22.5 + 45 + 6$

$\quad = 28.5 \text{ feet}$

(d) $0 = \dfrac{-1}{10}x^2 + 3x + 6$

$x = \dfrac{-3 \pm \sqrt{3^2 - 4\left(-\dfrac{1}{10}\right)(6)}}{2\left(-\dfrac{1}{10}\right)}$

$x = \dfrac{-3 \pm \sqrt{9 + 2.4}}{-\dfrac{1}{5}}$

$x = \dfrac{-3 \pm \sqrt{11.4}}{-\dfrac{1}{5}}$

$x = -5\left(-3 \pm \sqrt{11.4}\right) = 15 \pm 5\sqrt{11.4} = 31.9$

The ball is 31.9 feet from the child when it hits the ground.

93. $x^2 + y^2 = r^2$

$x^2 + y^2 = 5000^2$

95. (a) $N(5) = \dfrac{20(4 + 3 \cdot 5)}{1 + 0.05(5)} = \dfrac{380}{1.25} = 304 \text{ thousand}$

$N(10) = \dfrac{20(4 + 3 \cdot 10)}{1 + 0.05(10)} = \dfrac{680}{1.5} \approx 453.3 \text{ thousand}$

$N(25) = \dfrac{20(4 + 3 \cdot 25)}{1 + 0.05(25)} = \dfrac{1580}{2.25} \approx 702.2 \text{ thousand}$

(b) The population is limited by the horizontal asymptote $N = 1200$ thousand fish.

Chapter Test for Chapter 7

1. $S = \dfrac{kx^2}{y}$

2. $v = k\sqrt{u}$

$\dfrac{3}{2} = k\sqrt{36}$

$\dfrac{1}{4} = k$

$v = \dfrac{1}{4}\sqrt{u}$

3. $y < 4$

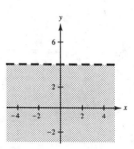

4. $3x - 2y > 6$

$-2y > -3x + 6$

$y < \dfrac{-3}{-2}x + \dfrac{6}{-2}$

$y < \dfrac{3}{2}x - 3$

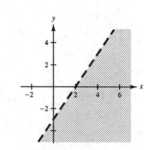

5. $m = \dfrac{5 - 0}{0 - \dfrac{7}{2}} \cdot \dfrac{2}{2} = \dfrac{10}{-7}$

$y - 5 = \dfrac{-10}{7}(x - 0)$

$y - 5 = \dfrac{-10}{7}x$

$y = \dfrac{-10}{7}x + 5$

$7y = -10x + 35$

$10x + 7y \le 35$

6. $y = -2(x - 2)^2 + 8$

vertex $= (2, 8)$

$y = -2(0 - 2)^2 + 8$

$y = -2(4) + 8$

$y = 0$ $(0, 0)$; x & y-intercept

$0 = -2(x - 2)^2 + 8$

$-8 = -2(x - 2)^2$

$4 = (x - 2)$

$\pm 2 = x - 2$

$2 \pm 2 = x$

$0, 4 = x$ $(0, 0), (4, 0)$; x-intercepts

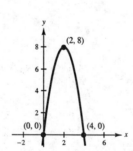

7. $x^2 + y^2 = 9$

Circle

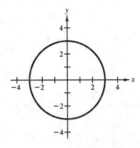

8. $\dfrac{x^2}{9} + \dfrac{y^2}{16} = 1$

Ellipse

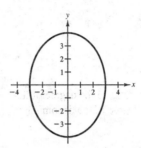

9. $\dfrac{x^2}{9} - \dfrac{y^2}{16} = 1$

Hyperbola

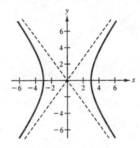

10. $y = (x - 3)^2$

Parabola

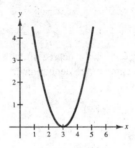

11. Circle with center at $(0, 0)$ and radius 5

$$x^2 + y^2 = r^2$$

$$x^2 + y^2 = 5^2$$

$$x^2 + y^2 = 25$$

12. Parabola with vertex $(-2, 1)$ and passing through $(6, 9)$

$$(y - k)^2 = a(x - h) \qquad (y - 1)^2 = 8(x + 2)$$

$$(9 - 1)^2 = a[6 - (-2)]$$

$$64 = a(8)$$

$$8 = a$$

13. $\dfrac{x^2}{9} + \dfrac{y^2}{100} = 1$

14. $\dfrac{x^2}{9} - \dfrac{y^2}{\frac{9}{4}} = 1$

$$\dfrac{x^2}{9} - \dfrac{4y^2}{9} = 1$$

or

$$x^2 - 4y^2 = 9$$

15. $f(x) = \dfrac{3}{x-3}$

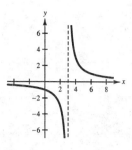

x-intercept: none, numerator is never zero

y-intercept: $f(0) = \dfrac{3}{0-3} = -1$

Vertical asymptote: $x - 3 = 0$

$$x = 3$$

Horizontal asymptote: $y = 0$ since the degree of the numerator is less than the degree of the denominator.

16. $f(x) = \dfrac{3x}{x^2 - 2x - 15} = \dfrac{3x}{(x-5)(x+3)}$

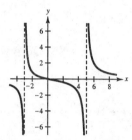

x-intercept: $x = 0$

y-intercept: $y = 0$

Vertical asymptotes: $x + 3 = 0 \qquad x - 5 = 0$

$$x = -3 \qquad x = 5$$

Horizontal asymptote: $y = 0$ since the degree of the numerator is less than the degree of the denominator.

17.
$$P = \frac{K}{V} \qquad\qquad P = \frac{180}{V} \qquad\qquad .75V = 180$$

$$1 = \frac{K}{180} \qquad\qquad .75 = \frac{180}{V} \qquad\qquad V = \frac{180}{.75}$$

$$180 = K \qquad\qquad\qquad\qquad\qquad\qquad V = 240 \text{ cubic meters}$$

18. $20x + 30y \le 24{,}000$

$$2x + 3y \le 2400$$

(*Note:* x and y cannot be negative.)

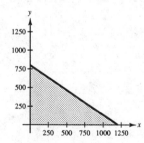

19. $R = -\dfrac{1}{20}(n^2 - 240n),\ 80 \le n \le 160$

$$R = -\frac{1}{20}(n^2 - 240n + 14{,}400) + 720$$

$$R = -\frac{1}{20}(n - 120)^2 + 720$$

$n = 120$ passengers will produce a maximum revenue

C H A P T E R 8
Systems of Equations

CHAPTER 8
Systems of Equations

Section 8.1 Systems of Equations

Solutions to Odd-Numbered Exercises

1. (a) $(1, 4)$

$1 + 2(4) \overset{?}{=} 9$

$9 = 9$

$-2(1) + 3(4) \overset{?}{=} 10$

$-2 + 12 \overset{?}{=} 10$

$10 = 10$

Solution

(b) $(3, -1)$

$3 + 2(-1) \overset{?}{=} 9$

$3 - 2 \overset{?}{=} 9$

$1 \neq 9$

Not a solution

3. (a) $(-3, 2)$

$-2(-3) + 7(2) \overset{?}{=} 46$

$6 + 14 \overset{?}{=} 46$

$20 \neq 46$

Not a solution

(b) $(-2, 6)$

$-2(-2) + 7(6) \overset{?}{=} 46$

$4 + 42 \overset{?}{=} 46$

$46 = 46$

$3(-2) + 6 \overset{?}{=} 0$

$-6 + 6 \overset{?}{=} 0$

$0 = 0$

Solution

5. (a) $(8, 4)$

$4(8) - 5(4) \overset{?}{=} 12$

$12 = 12$

$3(8) + 2(4) \overset{?}{=} -2.5$

$32 \neq -2.5$

Not a solution

(b) $\left(\frac{1}{2}, -2\right)$

$4\left(\frac{1}{2}\right) - 5(-2) \overset{?}{=} 12$

$12 = 12$

$3\left(\frac{1}{2}\right) + 2(-2) \overset{?}{=} -2.5$

$-2.5 = -2.5$

Solution

7. (a) $(5, -12)$

$5^2 + (-12)^2 \overset{?}{=} 169$

$169 = 169$

$17(5) - 7(-12) \overset{?}{=} 169$

$169 = 169$

Solution

(b) $(-7, 10)$

$(-7)^2 + (10)^2 \overset{?}{=} 169$

$149 \neq 169$

Not a solution

9. Solve each equation for y.

$x + 2y = 6$

$2y = -x + 6$

$y = -\frac{1}{2}x + 3$

$x + 2y = 3$

$2y = -x + 3$

$y = -\frac{1}{2}x + \frac{3}{2}$

Slopes are equal; therefore the system is inconsistent.

11. Solve each equation for y.

$2x - 3y = -12$

$-3y = -2x - 12$

$y = \frac{2}{3}x + 4$

$-8x + 12y = -12$

$12y = 8x - 12$

$y = \frac{2}{3}x - 1$

Slopes are equal; therefore the system is inconsistent.

13. Solve each equation for y.

$-x + 4y = 7$

$4y = x + 7$

$y = \frac{1}{4}x + \frac{7}{4}$

$3x - 12y = -21$

$-12y = -3x - 21$

$y = \frac{1}{4}x + \frac{7}{4}$

Lines are the same; therefore the system is consistent and dependent.

15. Solve each equation for y.

$5x - 3y = 1$

$-3y = -5x + 1$

$y = \frac{5}{3}x - \frac{1}{3}$

$6x - 4y = -3$

$-4y = -6x - 3$

$y = \frac{3}{2}x + \frac{3}{4}$

Slopes are not equal; therefore the system is consistent.

17. Solve each equation for y.

$$\tfrac{1}{3}x - \tfrac{1}{2}y = 1 \qquad\qquad -2x + 3y = 6$$
$$-\tfrac{1}{2}y = -\tfrac{1}{3}x + 1 \qquad\qquad 3y = 2x + 6$$
$$y = \tfrac{2}{3}x - 2 \qquad\qquad y = \tfrac{2}{3}x + 2$$

Keystrokes:

y_1 [Y=] [(] 2 [÷] 3 [)] [X,T,θ] [−] 2 [ENTER]

y_2 [(] 2 [÷] 3 [)] [X,T,θ] [+] 2 [GRAPH]

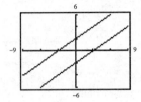

Inconsistent

21. No solution

Solve first equation for y.

$$x + y = 4 \qquad\qquad x + y = -1$$
$$y = -x + 4 \qquad\qquad y = -x - 1$$

Slopes are the same.

25. Infinite number of solutions

Solve each equation for y.

$$x - 2y = -4 \qquad\qquad -0.5x + y = 2$$
$$-2y = -x - 4 \qquad\qquad y = 0.5x + 2$$
$$y = \tfrac{1}{2}x + 2$$

Slopes are the same; lines are the same.

19. Solve each equation for y.

$$-2x + 3y = 6 \qquad\qquad x - y = -1$$
$$3y = 2x + 6 \qquad\qquad -y = -x - 1$$
$$y = \tfrac{2}{3}x + 2 \qquad\qquad y = x + 1$$

Keystrokes:

y_1 [Y=] [(] 2 [÷] 3 [)] [X,T,θ] [+] 2 [ENTER]

y_2 [X,T,θ] [+] 1 [GRAPH]

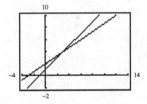

One solution

23. One solution

Solve first equation for y.

$$3y = 3 - 2x$$
$$y = \frac{3 - 2x}{3}$$

Substitute into second equation.

$$5x - 3\left(\frac{3 - 2x}{3}\right) = 4$$
$$5x - 3 + 2x = 4$$
$$7x - 3 = 4$$
$$7x = 7$$
$$x = 1$$
$$y = \frac{3 - 2(1)}{3}$$
$$y = \frac{1}{3}$$

$$\left(1, \frac{1}{3}\right)$$

27. No solution

Solve second equation for y.

$$x^2 - y = 0$$
$$x^2 = y$$

Substitute into first equation.

$$x - 2x^2 = 4$$
$$0 = 2x^2 - x + 4$$

no real solution

29.

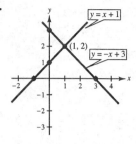

The two lines intersect in a point and the coordinates are $(1, 2)$.

31. Solve each equation for y.

$$x - y = 2 \qquad\qquad x + y = 2$$
$$-y = -x + 2 \qquad\qquad y = -x + 2$$
$$y = x - 2$$

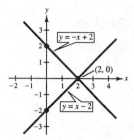

The two lines intersect in a point and the coordinates are $(2, 0)$.

33. Solve first equation for y.

$$3x - 4y = 5$$
$$-4y = -3x + 5$$
$$y = \tfrac{3}{4}x - \tfrac{5}{4}$$

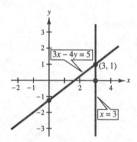

The two lines intersect in a point and the coordinates are $(3, 1)$.

35. Solve each equation for y.

$$4x + 5y = 20 \qquad\qquad \tfrac{4}{5}x + y = 4$$
$$5y = -4x + 20 \qquad\qquad y = -\tfrac{4}{5}x + 4$$
$$y = -\tfrac{4}{5}x + 4$$

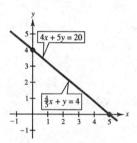

The lines representing the two equations are the same. System is dependent and has infinitely many solutions.

37. Solve each equation for y.

$$2x - 5y = 20 \qquad\qquad 4x - 5y = 40$$
$$-5y = -2x + 20 \qquad\qquad -5y = -4x + 40$$
$$y = \tfrac{2}{5}x - 4 \qquad\qquad y = \tfrac{4}{5}x - 8$$

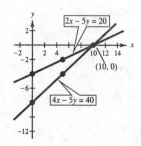

The two lines intersect in a point and the coordinates are $(10, 0)$.

39. Solve each equation for y.

$$x + y = 2 \qquad\qquad 3x + 3y = 6$$
$$y = -x + 2 \qquad\qquad 3y = -3x + 6$$
$$y = -x + 2$$

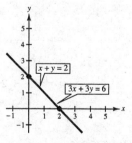

The lines representing the two equations are the same. System is dependent and has infinitely many solutions.

41. Solve each equation for y.

$$4x + 5y = 7 \qquad\qquad 2x - 3y = 9$$

$$5y = -4x + 7 \qquad\quad -3y = -2x + 9$$

$$y = -\tfrac{4}{5}x + \tfrac{7}{5} \qquad\qquad y = \tfrac{2}{3}x - 3$$

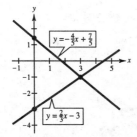

The two lines intersect in a point and the coordinates are $(3, -1)$.

43. *Keystrokes:*

y_1 [Y=] [X,T,θ] [x²] [ENTER]

y_2 4 [X,T,θ] [−] [X,T,θ] [x²] [GRAPH]

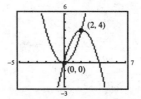

Points of intersection are $(0, 0)$ and $(2, 4)$.

45. *Keystrokes:*

y_1 [Y=] [X,T,θ] [∧] 3 [ENTER]

y_2 [X,T,θ] [∧] 3 [−] 3 [X,T,θ] [x²] [+] 3 [X,T,θ] [GRAPH]

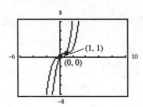

Points of intersection are $(0, 0)$ and $(1, 1)$.

47. Solve for x in first equation.

$$x = 2y$$

Substitute into second equation.

$$3(2y) + 2y = 8$$

$$6y + 2y = 8$$

$$8y = 8$$

$$y = 1$$

$$x = 2(1)$$

$$= 2$$

$$(2, 1)$$

49. $x = 4$

Substitute into second equation.

$$4 - 2y = -2$$

$$-2y = -6$$

$$y = 3$$

$$(4, 3)$$

51. Solve for y.

$$y = 3 - x$$

Substitute into second equation.

$$2x - (3 - x) = 0$$

$$2x - 3 + x = 0$$

$$3x = 3$$

$$x = 1$$

$$y = 3 - 1$$

$$y = 2$$

$$(1, 2)$$

53. Solve for x.

$x = 2 - y$

Substitute into second equation.

$2 - y - 4y = 12$

$-5y = 10$

$y = -2$

$x = 2 - (-2)$

$x = 4$

$(4, -2)$

55. Solve for x.

$x = -7 + 7y$

Substitute into first equation.

$-7 + 7y + 6y = 19$

$13y = 26$

$y = 2$

$x = -7 + 7(2) = 7$

$(7, 2)$

57. Solve for y.

$5y = -8x + 100$

$y = -\frac{8}{5}x + 20$

Substitute into second equation.

$9x - 10\left(-\frac{8}{5}x + 20\right) = 50$

$9x + 16x - 200 = 50$

$25x = 250$

$x = 10$

$y = -\frac{8}{5}(10) + 20$

$y = 4$

$(10, 4)$

59. Solve for y.

$16y = 13x + 10$

$y = \frac{13}{16}x + \frac{10}{16}$

Substitute into second equation.

$5x + 16\left(\frac{13}{16}x + \frac{10}{16}\right) = -26$

$5x + 13x + 10 = -26$

$18x = -36$

$x = -2$

$y = \frac{13}{16}(-2) + \frac{10}{16}$

$y = -\frac{13}{8} + \frac{5}{8}$

$y = -1$

$(-2, -1)$

61. Solve for x.

$4x = -15 + 14y$

$x = \frac{-15 + 14y}{4}$

Substitute into second equation.

$18\left(\frac{-15 + 14y}{4}\right) - 12y = 9$

$18(-15 + 14y) - 48y = 36$

$-270 + 252y - 48y = 36$

$204y = 306$

$y = \frac{3}{2}$

$x = \frac{-15 + 14\left(\frac{3}{2}\right)}{4}$

$= \frac{-15 + 21}{4} = \frac{3}{2}$

$\left(\frac{3}{2}, \frac{3}{2}\right)$

63. Solve for y.

$y = -x + 20$

Substitute into first equation.

$\frac{1}{5}x + \frac{1}{2}(-x + 20) = 8$

$\frac{1}{5}x - \frac{1}{2}x + 10 = 8$

$\frac{1}{5}x - \frac{1}{2}x = -2$

$2x - 5x = -20$

$-3x = -20$

$x = \frac{20}{3}$

$y = -\frac{20}{3} + 20$

$y = -\frac{20}{3} + \frac{60}{3}$

$y = \frac{40}{3}$

$\left(\frac{20}{3}, \frac{40}{3}\right)$

65. Substitute into second equation.

$$y = -2x + 12$$
$$2x^2 = -2x + 12$$
$$2x^2 + 2x - 12 = 0$$
$$x^2 + x - 6 = 0$$
$$(x + 3)(x - 2) = 0$$

$x = -3 \qquad\qquad x = 2$

$y = 2(-3)^2 \qquad y = 2(2)^2$

$\quad = 2(9) \qquad\qquad = 2(4)$

$\quad = 18 \qquad\qquad\quad = 8$

$(-3, 18)$ and $(2, 8)$

67. $y = 3x^2$

Substitute into first equation.

$$3x + 2(3x^2) = 30$$
$$3x + 6x^2 = 30$$
$$6x^2 + 3x - 30 = 0$$
$$2x^2 + x - 10 = 0$$
$$(2x + 5)(x - 2) = 0$$

$x = -\frac{5}{2} \qquad\qquad x = 2$

$y = 3\left(-\frac{5}{2}\right)^2 \qquad y = 3(2)^2$

$y = 3\left(\frac{25}{4}\right) \qquad\quad y = 3(4)$

$\quad = \frac{75}{4} \qquad\qquad\quad y = 12$

$\left(-\frac{5}{2}, \frac{75}{4}\right)$ and $(2, 12)$

69. Solve for x.

$x = -3 + y$

Substitute into first equation.

$$4(-3 + y)^2 + y = 9$$
$$9 - 6y + y^2 + y - 9 = 0$$
$$y^2 - 5y = 0$$
$$y(y - 5) = 0$$

$y = 0 \qquad\qquad y = 5$

$x = -3 + 0 \qquad x = -3 + 5$

$x = -3 \qquad\qquad x = 2$

$(-3, 0)$ and $(2, 5)$

71. Solve for y.

$y = -x + 2$

Substitute into first equation.

$$x^2 + (-x + 2)^2 = 100$$
$$x^2 + x^2 - 4x + 4 = 100$$
$$2x^2 - 4x - 96 = 0$$
$$x^2 - 2x - 48 = 0$$
$$(x - 8)(x + 6) = 0$$

$x = 8 \qquad\qquad x = -6$

$y = -8 + 2 \qquad y = -(-6) + 2$

$y = -6 \qquad\qquad y = 8$

$(8, -6)$ and $(-6, 8)$

73. Solve for y.

$y = -3x + 2$

Substitute into first equation.

$$x^2 - (-3x + 2) = 2$$
$$x^2 + 3x - 2 = 2$$
$$x^2 + 3x - 4 = 0$$
$$(x + 4)(x - 1) = 0$$

$x = -4 \qquad\qquad x = 1$

$y = -3(-4) + 2 \qquad y = -3(1) + 2$

$y = 14 \qquad\qquad\quad y = -1$

$(-4, 14)$ and $(1, -1)$

75. Solve for y.

$-y = -5 - 2x$

$y = 5 + 2x$

Substitute into first equation.

$$x^2 + (5 + 2x)^2 = 25$$
$$x^2 + 25 + 20x + 4x^2 - 25 = 0$$
$$5x^2 + 20x = 0$$
$$5x(x + 4) = 0$$

$x = 0 \qquad\qquad x = -4$

$y = 5 + 2(0) \qquad y = 5 + 2(-4)$

$y = 5 \qquad\qquad\quad y = -3$

$(0, 5) \qquad\qquad\quad (-4, -3)$

77. $x = -200 + 100y$

$\left.\begin{array}{r} 3(-200 + 100y) - 275y = 198 \\ -600 + 300y - 275y = 198 \\ 25y = 798 \\ y = \dfrac{798}{25} \\ y = 31.92 \end{array}\right\}$ by substitution

$x = -200 + 100(31.92) = -200 + 3192 = 2992$

$(2.992, 31.92)$ or $\left(2992, \frac{798}{25}\right)$

Solve each equation for y.

$x - 100y = -200 \qquad\qquad 3x - 275y = 198$

$\quad y = \dfrac{1}{100}x + 2 \qquad\qquad -275y = -3x + 198$

$\quad y = 0.01x + 2 \qquad\qquad y = \dfrac{-3}{-275}x + \dfrac{198}{-275}$

$\qquad\qquad\qquad\qquad\qquad\quad y = \dfrac{3}{275}x - 0.72$

Keystrokes:

y_1 [Y=] .01 [X,T,θ] [+] 2 [ENTER]

y_2 [(] 3 [÷] 275 [)] [X,T,θ] [−] .72 [GRAPH]

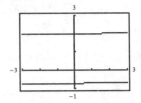

79. Answers will vary. Write equations so that $(4, 5)$ satisfies each equation.

$\begin{array}{l} 2x - 3y = -7 \\ x + y = 9 \end{array}$ or $\begin{array}{l} x - y = -1 \\ 2x + 3y = 23 \end{array}$

81. Answers will vary. Write equations so that $(-1, -2)$ satisfies each equation.

$\begin{array}{l} 7x + y = -9 \\ -x + 3y = -5 \end{array}$ or $\begin{array}{l} x + y = -3 \\ x - y = 1 \end{array}$

83. *Verbal Model:*

Total cost	=	Cost per unit	·	Number of units	+	Initial cost

Total Revenue	=	Price per unit	·	Number of units

Labels:

Total cost = C

Cost per unit = 1.20

Number of units = x

Initial cost = 8000

Total revenue = R

Price per unit = 2.00

System: $C = 1.20x + 8000$

$R = 2.00x$

Break-even point occurs when $R = C$ so

$1.20x + 8000 = 2.00x$

$8000 = 0.80x$

$10{,}000 = x$

10,000 items

85. *Verbal Model:*

| Total cost | = | Cost per unit | · | Number of units | + | Initial cost |

| Total Revenue | = | Price per unit | · | Number of units |

Labels: Total cost $= C$

Cost per unit $= 1.65$

Number of units $= x$

Initial cost $= 10,000$

Total revenue $= R$

Price per unit $= 3.25$

System: $C = 1.65x + 10,000$

$R = 3.25x$

Break-even point occurs when $R = C$ so

$1.65x + 10,000 = 3.25x$

$10,000 = 1.60x$

$6250 = x$

6250 units

87. *Verbal Model:*

| Amount at 8% | + | Amount at 9.5% | = | 20,000 |

| 8% | · | Amount at 8% | + | 9.5% | · | Amount at 9.5% | = | 1675 |

Labels: Amount at 8% $= x$

Amount at 9.5% $= y$

System: $x + y = 20,000$

$0.08x + 0.095y = 1675$

Solve for x.

$x = 20,000 - y$

Substitute into second equation.

$0.08(20,000 - y) + 0.095y = 1675$

$1600 - 0.08y + 0.095y = 1675$

$0.015y = 75$

$y = \$5000$ at 9.5%

$x = 20,000 - 5000 = \$15,000$ at 8%

89. *Verbal Model:* $\boxed{\text{Amount in 8\% fund}}$ $+$ $\boxed{\text{Amount in 8.5\% fund}}$ $=$ $\boxed{25,000}$

$\boxed{8\%}$ $\cdot$ $\boxed{\text{Amount in 8\% fund}}$ $+$ $\boxed{8.5\%}$ $\cdot$ $\boxed{\text{Amount in 8.5\% fund}}$ $=$ $\boxed{2060}$

Labels: Amount in 8% fund $= x$

Amount in 9.5% fund $= y$

System: $x + y = 25,000$

$0.08x + 0.085y = 2060$

Solve for x.

$x = 25,000 - y$

Substitute into second equation.

$0.08(25,000 - y) + 0.085y = 2060$

$2000 - 0.08y + 0.085y = 2060$

$0.005y = 60$

$y = \$12,000$ at 8.5%

$x = 25,000 - 12,000 = \$13,000$ at 8%

91. *Verbal Model:* $\boxed{\text{Larger number}}$ $+$ $\boxed{2}$ $\cdot$ $\boxed{\text{Smaller number}}$ $=$ $\boxed{61}$

$\boxed{\text{Larger number}}$ $-$ $\boxed{\text{Smaller number}}$ $=$ $\boxed{7}$

Labels: Larger number $= x$

Smaller number $= y$

System: $x + 2y = 61$

$x - 7 = 7$

Solve for x.

$x = y + 7$

Substitute into second equation.

$y + 7 + 2y = 61$

$3y + 7 = 61$

$3y = 54$

$y = 18$

$x = 18 + 7$

$x = 25$

$(25, 18)$

93. *Verbal Model:* $\boxed{\text{Larger number}}$ $+$ $\boxed{\text{Smaller number}}$ $=$ $\boxed{160}$

$\boxed{\text{Larger number}}$ $=$ $\boxed{3}$ $\cdot$ $\boxed{\text{Smaller number}}$

Labels: Larger number $= x$

Smaller number $= y$

System: $x + y = 160$

$x = 3y$

Substitute into first equation.

$3y + y = 160$

$4y = 160$

$y = 40$

$x = 3(40)$

$x = 120$

$(120, 40)$

Section 8.2   Linear Systems in Two Variables

1. $2x + y = 4$

$\underline{x - y = 2}$

$3x \qquad = 6$

$x \qquad = 2$

$2 - y = 0$

$-y = 0$

$y = 0$

$(2, 0)$

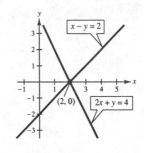

3. $-x + 2y = 1$

$\underline{x - \ y = 2}$

$y = 3$

$x - 3 = 2$

$x = 5$

$(5, 3)$

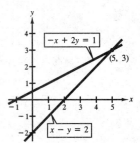

5. $3x + y = \ 3$

$\underline{2x - y = \ 7}$

$5x \qquad = 10$

$x \qquad = 2$

$3(2) + y = 3$

$6 + y = 3$

$y = -3$

$(2, -3)$

7. $\quad x - \ y = 1 \implies \quad 3x - 3y = \ 3$

$-3x + 3y = 8 \implies \underline{-3x + 3y = \ 8}$

$0 \neq 11$

No solution

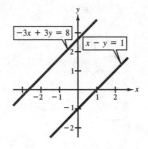

9. $\quad x - 3y = \quad \ 5 \implies \quad 2x - 6y = \quad 10$

$-2x + 6y = -10 \implies \underline{-2x + 6y = -10}$

$0 = \quad 0$

All solutions to $x - 3y = 5$

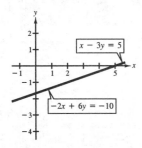

11. $2x - 8y = -11 \Rightarrow \quad 6x - 24y = -33$
$\quad\ 5x + 3y = \quad 7 \Rightarrow \quad \underline{40x + 24y = \quad 56}$
$$46x \quad\quad = 23$$
$$x \quad\quad = \frac{23}{46}$$
$$x \quad\quad = \frac{1}{2}$$

$$2\left(\frac{1}{2}\right) - 8y = -11$$
$$-8y = -12$$
$$y = \frac{-12}{-8}$$
$$y = \frac{3}{2}$$
$$\left(\frac{1}{2}, \frac{3}{2}\right)$$

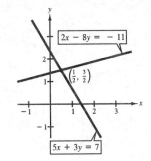

13. $3x - 2y = \ 5$
$\quad\ \underline{x + 2y = \ 5}$
$4x \quad\quad = 12$
$\ x \quad\quad = \ 3$

$3 + 2y = \ 7$
$2y = \ 4$
$y = \ 2$
$(3, 2)$

15. $\quad 4x + \ y = -3$
$\quad \underline{-4x + 3y = \ 23}$
$\quad\quad 4y = \ 20$
$\quad\quad\ y = \ \ 5$

$4x + 5 = -3$
$4x = -8$
$x = -2$
$(-2, 5)$

17. $3x - 5y = \ 1$
$\quad \underline{2x + 5y = \ 9}$
$5x \quad\quad = 10$
$\ x \quad\quad = \ 2$

$3(2) - 5y = \ 1$
$-5y = -5$
$y = \ 1$
$(2, 1)$

19. $5x + 2y = \ 7 \Rightarrow 5x + 2y = \ 7$
$\quad\ 3x - \ y = 13 \Rightarrow \underline{6x - 2y = 26}$
$\quad\quad\quad\quad\quad\quad 11x \quad\quad = 33$
$\quad\quad\quad\quad\quad\quad\ x \quad\quad = \ 3$

$3(3) - \ y = \ 13$
$-y = \ \ 4$
$y = -4$
$(3, -4)$

21. $\ x - 3y = 2 \Rightarrow \ -3x + 9y = -6$
$\quad 3x - 7y = 4 \Rightarrow \quad \underline{3x - 7y = \quad 4}$
$\quad\quad\quad\quad\quad\quad\quad\quad\quad 2y = -2$
$\quad\quad\quad\quad\quad\quad\quad\quad\quad\ y = -1$

$x - 3(-1) = 2$
$x = -1$
$(-1, -1)$

23. $2x + \ y = \ 9$
$\quad \underline{3x - y = 16}$
$5x \quad\quad = 25$
$\ x \quad\quad = \ 5$

$2(5) + y = 9$
$10 + y = 9$
$y = -1$
$(5, -1)$

25. $2u + 3v = \ 8 \Rightarrow \ -6u - 9v = 24$
$\quad\ 3u + 4v = 13 \Rightarrow \quad \underline{6u + 8v = 26}$
$\quad\quad\quad\quad\quad\quad\quad\quad\quad -v = \ 2$
$\quad\quad\quad\quad\quad\quad\quad\quad\quad\ v = -2$

$2u + 3(-2) = \ 8$
$2u \quad\quad\ = 14$
$u \quad\quad\ = \ 7$
$(7, -2)$

27. $12x - 5y = 2 \implies 24x - 10y = 4$
$-24x + 10y = 6 \implies \underline{-24x + 10y = 6}$
$ 0 \neq 10$

Inconsistent

29. $\frac{2}{3}r - s = 0 \implies 2r - 3s = 0 \implies 8r - 12s = 0$
$10r + 4s = 19 \implies 10r + 4s = 19 \implies \underline{30r + 12s = 57}$
$ 38r = 57$
$ r = \frac{57}{38}$
$ r = \frac{3}{2}$

$\frac{2}{3}\left(\frac{3}{2}\right) - s = 0$
$\phantom{\frac{2}{3}\left(\frac{3}{2}\right)} -s = -1$
$\phantom{\frac{2}{3}\left(\frac{3}{2}\right)} s = 1$

$\left(\frac{3}{2}, 1\right)$

31. $0.05x - 0.03y = 0.21 \implies 5x - 3y = 21$
$ x + y = 9 \implies \underline{3x + 3y = 27}$
$ 8x = 48$
$ x = 6$

$x + y = 9$
$6 + y = 9$
$ y = 3$

$(6, 3)$

33. $0.7u - v = -0.4 \implies 7u - 10v = -4 \implies 21u - 30v = -12$
$0.3u - 0.8v = 0.2 \implies 3u - 8v = 2 \implies \underline{-21u + 56v = -14}$
$ 26v = -26$
$ v = -1$

$7u - 10(1) = -4$
$7u = -14$
$u = -2$

$(-2, -1)$

35. $5x + 7y = 25 \implies 5x + 7y = 25$
$x + 1.4y = 5 \implies \underline{-5x - 7y = -25}$
$ 0 = 0$

All solutions of the form $x + 1.4y = 5$

37. $\frac{3}{2}x - y = 4 \implies 3x - 2y = 8$
$-x + \frac{2}{3}y = -1 \implies \underline{-3x + 2y = -3}$
$\phantom{-x + \frac{2}{3}y = -1 \implies} 0 \neq 5$

Inconsistent

39. $2x = 25 \implies -4x = -50$
$4x - 10y = 0.52 \implies \underline{4x - 10y = 0.52}$
$ -10y = -49.48$
$ y = 4.948$

$4x - 10(4.948) = 0.52$
$4x - 49.48 = 0.52$
$4x = 50$
$x = 12.5$

$(12.5, 4.948)$

41. $3x + 2y = 5$

$ y = 2x + 13$

$3x + 2(2x + 13) = 5$

$3x + 4x + 26 = 5$

$ 7x = -21$

$ x = -3$

$y = 2(-3) + 13$

$ = -6 + 13$

$ = 7$

$(-3, 7)$

43.
$$y = 5x - 3 \implies y = 5x - 3$$
$$y = -2x + 11 \implies \underline{-y = 2x - 11}$$
$$0 = 7x - 14$$
$$14 = 7x$$
$$2 = x$$

$$y = 5(2) - 3$$
$$y = 10 - 3$$
$$y = 7$$

$(2, 7)$

45.
$$2x - y = 20$$
$$\underline{-x + y = -5}$$
$$x = 15$$
$$-15 + y = -5$$
$$y = 10$$

$(15, 10)$

47. $\frac{3}{2}x + 2y = 12$

$$\frac{1}{4}x + y = 4$$
$$y = 4 - \frac{1}{4}x$$
$$\frac{3}{2}x + 2\left(4 - \frac{1}{4}x\right) = 12$$
$$\frac{3}{2}x + 8 - \frac{1}{2}x = 12$$
$$x = 4$$
$$y = 4 - \frac{1}{4}(4)$$
$$= 4 - 1 = 3$$

$(4, 3)$

49. $\quad 4x - 5y = 3 \implies -5y = -4x + 3 \implies y = \frac{4}{5}x - \frac{3}{5}$

$\quad -8x + 10y = -6 \implies 10y = 8x - 6 \implies y = \frac{4}{5}x - \frac{3}{5}$

Many solutions $\implies$ consistent

51. $-2x + 5y = 3 \implies 5y = 2x + 3 \implies y = \frac{2}{5}x + \frac{3}{5}$

$5x + 2y = 8 \implies 2y = -5x + 8 \implies y = -\frac{5}{2}x + 4$

One solution $\implies$ consistent

53. $-10x + 5y = 25 \implies 15y = 10x + 25 \implies y = \frac{2}{3}x + \frac{5}{3}$

$2x - 3y = -24 \implies -3y = -2x - 24 \implies y = \frac{2}{3}x + 8$

No solution $\implies$ inconsistent

55. $\quad 5x - 10y = 40 \implies y = \frac{1}{2}x - 4$

$\quad -2x + ky = 30 \implies y = \frac{2}{k}x + \frac{30}{16}$

$\quad$ so $\quad \frac{2}{k} = \frac{1}{2} \implies k = 4$

$\quad 5x - 10y = 40 \implies 10x - 20y = 80$

$\quad -2x + 4y = 30 \implies -10x + 20y = 150$

$ 0 \neq 230$

Inconsistent; no solution

57. Answers will vary. Write equations so that $\left(3, -\frac{3}{2}\right)$ satisfies each equation.

$x + 2y = 0$

$x - 4y = 9$

$$3 + 2\left(-\frac{3}{2}\right) \overset{?}{=} 0 \qquad\qquad 3 - 4\left(-\frac{3}{2}\right) \overset{?}{=} 9$$

$$0 = 0 \qquad\qquad\qquad\qquad 9 = 9$$

59. *Verbal Model:*

| Total cost | = | Cost per unit | · | Number of units | + | Initial cost |

| Total revenue | = | Price per unit | · | Number of units |

Labels: Total cost = C

           Cost per unit = 7400

           Number of weeks = x

           Initial cost = 85,000

           Total revenue = R

           Price per unit = 8100

System: $C = 7400x + 85{,}000$

           $R = 8100x$

Break-even point occurs when $R = C$

$7400x + 85{,}000 = 8100x$

$85{,}000 = 700x$

$121.4285 \approx x$

122 weeks

61. *Verbal Model:*

| Amount in 8% bond | + | Amount in 9.5% bond | = | Total investment |

| Interest in 8% bond | + | Interest in 9.5% bond | = | Total interest |

Labels: Amount in 8% bond = x

           Amount in 9.5% bond = y

System:

$$x + y = 20{,}000 \implies -0.08x - 0.08y = -1600$$
$$0.08x + 0.095y = 1675 \implies \underline{0.08x + 0.095y = 1675}$$
$$0.015y = 75$$
$$y = 5000$$

$x + 5000 = 20{,}000$ \$15,000 at 8%

$x = 15{,}000$ \$5,000 at 9.5%

63. *Verbal Model*: $\boxed{\text{Distance}} = \boxed{\text{Rate}} \cdot \boxed{\text{Time}}$

   Labels: Time at 55 mph $= x$

   $D_1 =$ distance at 40 mph for 2 hours $+$ at 55 mph for x hours

   $D_2 =$ distance at 50 mph for $2 + x$ hours

   $D_1 = 40(2) + 55(x)$

   $D_2 = 50(2 + x)$

   System: Since $D_1 = D_2$

   $40(2) + 55(x) = 50(2 + x)$

   $80 + 55x = 100 + 50x$

   $5x = 20$

   $x = 4$ hours

65. *Verbal Model*: $\boxed{\begin{array}{c}\text{Plane speed}\\ \text{(still air)}\end{array}} - \boxed{\begin{array}{c}\text{Speed}\\ \text{of air}\end{array}} = \boxed{\begin{array}{c}\text{Speed into}\\ \text{head wind}\end{array}}$

   $\boxed{\begin{array}{c}\text{Plane speed}\\ \text{(still air)}\end{array}} + \boxed{\begin{array}{c}\text{Speed}\\ \text{of air}\end{array}} = \boxed{\begin{array}{c}\text{Speed into}\\ \text{head wind}\end{array}}$

   Labels: Plane speed $= x$

   Speed of air $= y$

   System: $x - y = \frac{1800}{3.6} \implies x - y = 500$

   $x + y = \frac{1800}{3} \implies \underline{x + y = 600}$

   $2x \quad\;\; = 1100$

   $x \quad\;\; = \;\; 550$ mph

   $550 - y = 500$

   $-y = -50$

   $y = 50$ mph

67. *Verbal Model*: $\boxed{\begin{array}{c}\text{Number of}\\ \text{adult tickets}\end{array}} + \boxed{\begin{array}{c}\text{Number of}\\ \text{children tickets}\end{array}} = \boxed{500}$

   $\boxed{\begin{array}{c}\text{Value of}\\ \text{adult tickets}\end{array}} + \boxed{\begin{array}{c}\text{Value of}\\ \text{children tickets}\end{array}} = \boxed{3312.50}$

   Labels: Number of adult tickets $= x$

   Number of children tickets $= y$

   System: $x + y = 500$

   $7.50x + 4.00y = 3312.50$

   $y = 500 - x$

   $7.50x + 4.00(500 - x) = 3312.50$

   $7.50x + 2000 - 4.00x = 3312.50$

   $3.5x = 1312.50$

   $x = 375$ adult tickets

   $y = 500 - 375 = 125$ children tickets

69. *Verbal Model*: $12\left(\boxed{\begin{array}{l}\text{Cost of regular}\\ \text{gasoline}\end{array}}\right) + 8\left(\boxed{\begin{array}{l}\text{Cost of premium}\\ \text{gasoline}\end{array}}\right) = \boxed{\$23.08}$

$\boxed{\begin{array}{l}\text{Cost of premium}\\ \text{gasoline}\end{array}} = \boxed{\$0.11} + \boxed{\begin{array}{l}\text{Cost of regular}\\ \text{gasoline}\end{array}}$

Labels: Cost of regular gasoline $= x$

Cost of premium gasoline $= y$

System: $12x + 8y = 23.08$

$y = 0.11 + x$

$12x + 8(0.11 + x) = 23.08$

$12x + 0.88 + 8x = 23.08$

$20x = 22.20$

$x = \$1.11 \text{ regular}$

$y = 0.11 + 1.11 = \$1.22 \text{ premium}$

71. *Verbal Model*: $\boxed{\begin{array}{l}\text{Number of liters}\\ \text{Solution 1}\end{array}} + \boxed{\begin{array}{l}\text{Number of liters}\\ \text{Solution 2}\end{array}} = \boxed{20}$

$\boxed{\begin{array}{l}\text{Value of}\\ \text{Solution 1}\end{array}} + \boxed{\begin{array}{l}\text{Value of}\\ \text{Solution 2}\end{array}} = \boxed{20(0.50)}$

Labels: Number liters Solution 1 $= x$

Number liters Solution 2 $= y$

System: $x + \quad y = 20$

$0.40x + 0.65y = 20(0.50)$

$x = 20 - y$

$40(20 - y) + 65y = 20(50)$

$800 - 40y + 65y = 100$

$25y = 200$

$y = 8 \text{ liters at 65\% alcohol solution}$

$x = 20 - 8 = 12 \text{ liters at 40\% alcohol solution}$

73. *Verbal Model*:
$$\boxed{\begin{array}{c}\text{Amount of}\\\text{\$5.65 variety}\end{array}} + \boxed{\begin{array}{c}\text{Amount of}\\\text{\$8.95 variety}\end{array}} = \boxed{10}$$

$$\boxed{\begin{array}{c}\text{Cost for}\\\text{\$5.65 variety}\end{array}} + \boxed{\begin{array}{c}\text{Cost for}\\\text{\$8.95 variety}\end{array}} = \boxed{\text{Total cost}}$$

Labels: Amount of \$5.65 variety $= x$

Amount of \$8.95 variety $= y$

System: $x + y = 10$

$5.65x + 8.95y = 6.95(10)$

$y = 10 - x$

$5.65x + 8.95(10 - x) = 69.5$

$5.65x + 89.5 - 8.95x = 69.5$

$-3.3x = -20$

$x \approx 6.1$ lbs of \$5.65 variety

$y = 10 - x = 10 - 6.1 = 3.9$ lbs of \$8.95 variety

75. (a) $3b + 3m = 7$

$\underline{3b + 5m = 4}$

$-2m = 3$

$m = -\frac{3}{2}$

$3b + 3\left(-\frac{3}{2}\right) = 7$

$6b - 9 = 14$

$6b = 23$

$b = \frac{23}{6}$

$y = -\frac{3}{2}x + \frac{23}{6} = -1.5x + 3\frac{5}{6}$

(b)

77. (a) $y = \frac{2}{25}x - 10$ Solve by substitution.

$y = -\frac{5}{61}x - 10$

$\frac{2}{25}x - 10 = -\frac{5}{61}x - 10$ $y = \frac{2}{25}(0) - 10$

$\frac{2}{25}x = -\frac{5}{61}x$ $y = -10$

$x = 0$ $(0, -10)$

The memorial is 10 feet deep.

(b) $0 = \frac{2}{25}x - 10$ $0 = \frac{5}{61}x - 10$

$10 = \frac{2}{25}x$ $10 = \frac{5}{61}x$

$125 = x$ $122 = x$

122 feet and 125 feet

79. When solving a system by elimination, you can recognize that it has infinitely many solutions when adding a nonzero multiple of one equation to another equation to eliminate a variable, you get $0 = 0$ for the second equation.

81. (a) Obtain coefficients for x or y that differ only in sign by multiplying all terms of one or both equations by suitable chosen constants.

(b) Add the equations to eliminate one variable, and solve the resulting equation.

(c) Back-substitute the value obtained in Step (b) into either of the original equations and solve for the other variable.

(d) Check your solution in both of the original equations.

83. Substitution may be better than elimination when it is easy to solve for one of the variables in one of the equations of the system.

81. (a) Obtain coefficients for x or y that differ only in sign by multiplying all terms of one or both equations by suitable chosen constants.

   (b) Add the equations to eliminate one variable, and solve the resulting equation.

   (c) Back-substitute the value obtained in Step (b) into either of the original equations and solve for the other variable.

   (d) Check your solution in both of the original equations.

83. Substitution may be better than elimination when it is easy to solve for one of the variables in one of the equations of the system.

Section 8.3   Linear Systems in Three Variables

1. (a) $(0, 3, -2)$

$$0 + 3(3) + 2(-2) \overset{?}{=} 1$$

$$9 - 4 \neq 1$$

not a solution

   (c) $(1, -2, 3)$

$$1 + 3(-2) + 2(3) \overset{?}{=} 1$$

$$1 - 6 + 6 = 1$$

$$1 = 1$$

solution

   (b) $(12, 5, -13)$

$$12 + 3(5) + 2(-13) \overset{?}{=} 1$$

$$12 + 15 - 26 = 1$$

$$1 = 1$$

solution

   (d) $(-2, 5, -3)$

$$-2 + 3(5) + 2(-3) \overset{?}{=} 1$$

$$-2 + 15 - 6 = 1$$

$$7 \neq 1$$

not a solution

3. $3y - (-5) = 2$

$$3y = -3$$

$$y = -1$$

$$x - 2(-1) + 4(-5) = 4$$

$$x + 2 - 20 = 4$$

$$x - 18 = 4$$

$$x = 22$$

$(22, -1, -5)$

5. $3 + z = 2$

$$z = -1$$

$$x - 2(3) + 4(-1) = 4$$

$$x - 6 - 4 = 4$$

$$x - 10 = 4$$

$$x = 14$$

$(14, 3, -1)$

7. The two systems are not equivalent because when the first equation was multiplied by -2 and added to the second equation the constant term should have been -11.

9. $x - 2y = 8$

$\underline{-x + 3y = 6}$

$\qquad\quad y = 14$

This operation eliminated the x-term from the second equation.

11. $x - 2y + 3z = 5$

$\underline{-x + y + 5z = 4}$

$\qquad\quad -y + 8z = 9$

This operation eliminated the x-term in Equation 2.

13. $x + z = 4$

$y = 2$

$4x + z = 7$

$x + z = 4$

$y = 2$

$-3z = -9$

$x + z = 4$

$y = 2$

$z = 3$

$x = 1$

$y = 1$

$z = 3$

$(1, 2, 3)$

15. $x + y + z = 6$

$2x - y + z = 3$

$3x - z = 0$

$x + y + z = 6$

$-3y - z = -9$

$-3y - 4z = -18$

$x + y + z = 6$

$y + \frac{1}{3}z = 3$

$-3y - 4z = -18$

$x + y + z = 6$

$y + \frac{1}{3}z = 3$

$-3x = -9$

$x + y + z = 6$

$y + \frac{1}{3}z = 3$

$z = 3$

$y + \frac{1}{3}(3) = 3$

$y = 2$

$x + 2 + 3 = 6$

$x = 1$

$(1, 2, 3)$

17. $x + y + z = -3$

$-3y - 7z = 23$

$-5y = 15$

$x + y + z = -3$

$y + \frac{7}{3}z = -\frac{23}{3}$

$y = -3$

$x + y + z = -3$

$y + \frac{7}{3}z = -\frac{23}{3}$

$-\frac{7}{3}z = \frac{14}{3}$

$x + y + z = -3$

$y + \frac{7}{3}z = -\frac{23}{3}$

$z = -2$

$y + \frac{7}{3}(-2) = \frac{-23}{3}$

$y - \frac{14}{3} = \frac{-23}{3}$

$y = -\frac{9}{3}$

$y = -3$

$x + (-3) + (-2) = -3$

$x - 5 = -3$

$x = 2$

$(2, -3, -2)$

19. $x + 2y + 6z = 5$

   $-x + y - 2z = 3$

   $x - 4y - 2z = 1$

   $x + 2y + 6z = 5$

   $3y + 4z = 8$

   $x - 4y - 2z = 1$

   $x + 2y + 6z = 5$

   $3y + 4z = 8$

   $-6y - 8z = -4$

   $x + 2y + 6z = 5$

   $3y + 4z = 8$

   $0 = 12$

No solution

Inconsistent

21. $2x + 2z = 2$

   $5x + 3y = 4$

   $3y - 4z = 4$

   $x + z = 1$

   $5x + 3y = 4$

   $3y - 4z = 4$

   $x + z = 1$

   $3y - 5z = -1$

   $3y - 4z = 4$

   $x + z = 1$

   $y - \frac{5}{3}z = -\frac{1}{3}$

   $3y - 4z = 4$

   $x + z = 1$

   $y - \frac{5}{3}z = -\frac{1}{3}$

   $z = 5$

   $y - \frac{5}{3}(5) = -\frac{1}{3}$

   $y = 8$

   $x + 5 = 1$

   $x = -4$

$(-4, 8, 5)$

23. $x + y + 8z = 3$

   $2x + y + 11z = 4$

   $x + 3z = 0$

   $x + y + 8z = 3$

   $-y - 5z = -2$

   $-y - 5z = -3$

   $x + y + 8z = 3$

   $y + 5z = 2$

   $y + 5z = \frac{3}{5}$

No solution

Inconsistent

25. $2x + y + 3z = 1$

   $2x + 6y + 8z = 3$

   $6x + 8y + 18z = 5$

   $2x + y + 3z = 1$

   $5y + 5z = 2$

   $5y + 9z = 2$

   $2x + y + 3z = 1$

   $5y + 5z = 2$

   $4z = 0$

   $x + \frac{1}{2}y + \frac{3}{2}z = \frac{1}{2}$

   $y + z = \frac{2}{5}$

   $z = 0$

   $y + 0 = \frac{2}{5}$

   $y = \frac{2}{5}$

   $x + \frac{1}{2}\left(\frac{2}{5}\right) + \frac{3}{2}(0) = \frac{1}{2}$

   $x + \frac{1}{5} = \frac{1}{2}$

   $x = \frac{5}{10} - \frac{2}{10} = \frac{3}{10}$

$\left(\frac{3}{10}, \frac{2}{5}, 0\right)$

27.

$$y + z = 5$$
$$2x + 4z = 4$$
$$2x - 3y = -14$$

$$y + z = 5$$
$$2x + 4z = 4$$
$$-3y - 4z = -18$$

$$y + z = 5$$
$$2x + 4z = 4$$
$$-z = -3$$

$$y + z = 5$$
$$2x + 4z = 4$$
$$z = 3$$

$$y + 3 = 5$$
$$y = 2$$

$$2x + 4(3) = 4$$
$$2x + 12 = 4$$
$$2x = -8$$
$$x = -4$$

$$(-4, 2, 3)$$

29.

$$2x + 6y - 4z = 8$$
$$3x + 10y - 7z = 12$$
$$-2x - 6y + 5z = -3$$

$$x + 3y - 2z = 4$$
$$3x + 10y - 7z = 12$$
$$-2x - 6y + 5z = -3$$

$$x + 3y - 2z = 4$$
$$y - z = 0$$
$$z = 5$$

$$y - 5 = 0$$
$$y = 5$$

$$x + 3(5) - 2(5) = 4$$
$$x + 15 - 10 = 4$$
$$x + 5 = 4$$
$$x = -1$$

$$(-1, 5, 5)$$

31.

$$2x + z = 3$$
$$5y - 3z = 2$$
$$6x + 20y - 9z = 11$$

$$x + \tfrac{1}{2}z = \tfrac{1}{2}$$
$$5y - 3z = 2$$
$$6x + 20y - 9z = 11$$

$$x + \tfrac{1}{2}z = \tfrac{1}{2}$$
$$5y - 3z = 2$$
$$20y - 12z = 8$$

$$x + \tfrac{1}{2}z = \tfrac{1}{2}$$
$$y - \tfrac{3}{5}z = \tfrac{2}{5}$$
$$20y - 12z = 8$$

$$x + \tfrac{1}{2}z = \tfrac{1}{2}$$
$$y - \tfrac{3}{5}z = \tfrac{2}{5}$$
$$0 = 0$$

$$y = \tfrac{3}{5}z + \tfrac{2}{5}$$
$$x + \tfrac{1}{2}z = \tfrac{1}{2}$$
$$x = \tfrac{1}{2} - \tfrac{1}{2}z$$

let $a = z$ $\left(\tfrac{1}{2} - \tfrac{1}{2}a, \tfrac{3}{5}a + \tfrac{2}{5}, a\right)$

33.

$$3x + y + z = 2$$
$$4x + 2z = 1$$
$$5x - y + 3z = 0$$

$$x + \tfrac{1}{3}y + \tfrac{1}{3}z = \tfrac{2}{3}$$
$$4x + 2z = 1$$
$$5x - y + 3z = 0$$

$$x + \tfrac{1}{3}y + \tfrac{1}{3}z = \tfrac{2}{3}$$
$$-\tfrac{4}{3}y + \tfrac{2}{3}z = -\tfrac{5}{3}$$
$$-\tfrac{8}{3}y + \tfrac{4}{3}z = -\tfrac{10}{3}$$

$$x + \tfrac{1}{3}y + \tfrac{1}{3}z = \tfrac{2}{3}$$
$$y - \tfrac{1}{2}z = \tfrac{5}{4}$$
$$-8y + 4z = -10$$

$$x + \tfrac{1}{3}y + \tfrac{1}{3}z = \tfrac{2}{3}$$
$$y - \tfrac{1}{2}z = \tfrac{5}{4}$$
$$0 = 0$$

$$y = \tfrac{1}{2}z + \tfrac{5}{4}$$
$$x + \tfrac{1}{3}\left(\tfrac{1}{2}z + \tfrac{5}{4}\right) + \tfrac{1}{3}z = \tfrac{2}{3}$$
$$x + \tfrac{1}{6}z + \tfrac{5}{12} + \tfrac{1}{3}z = \tfrac{2}{3}$$
$$x + \tfrac{1}{2}z = \tfrac{1}{4}$$
$$= \tfrac{1}{4} - \tfrac{1}{2}z$$

let $a = z$ $\left(\tfrac{1}{4} - \tfrac{1}{2}a, \tfrac{1}{2}a + \tfrac{5}{4}, a\right)$

35. $0.2x + 1.3y + 0.6y = 0.1$

$\quad 0.1x \qquad + 0.3z = 0.7$

$\quad 2x + 10y + 8z = 8$

$\quad 2x + 13y + 6z = 1$

$\quad 1x \qquad + 3z = 7$

$\quad 2x + 10y + 8z = 8$

$\quad 1x \qquad + 3z = 7$

$\qquad 13y \qquad = -13$

$\qquad 10y + 2z = -6$

$\quad 1x \qquad + 3z = 7$

$\qquad y \qquad = -1$

$\qquad 10y + 2z = -6$

$\quad x \qquad + 3z = 7$

$\qquad y \qquad = -1$

$\qquad 2z = 4$

$\quad x + \qquad 3z = 7 \qquad x + 3(2) = 7$

$\qquad y \qquad = -1 \qquad\qquad x = 1$

$\qquad z = 2 \qquad (1, -1, 2)$

37. $\quad x + 4y - 2z = 2$

$\quad -3x + y + z = -2$

$\quad 5x + 7y - 5z = 6$

$\quad x + 4y - 2z = 2$

$\qquad 13y - 5z = 4$

$\qquad -13y + 5z = -4$

$\quad x + 4y - 2z = 2$

$\qquad y - \frac{5}{13}z = \frac{4}{13}$

$\qquad -13y + 5z = -4$

$\quad x + 4y - 2z = 2$

$\qquad y - \frac{5}{13}z = \frac{4}{13}$

$\qquad 0 = 0$

$y = \frac{5}{13}z + \frac{4}{13}$

$x + 4\left(\frac{5}{13}x + \frac{4}{13}\right) - 2z = 2$

$x + \frac{20}{13}x + \frac{16}{13} - \frac{26}{13}z = \frac{26}{13}$

$\qquad x - \frac{6}{13}z = \frac{10}{13} \qquad$ Let $z = a$

$\qquad x = \frac{6}{13}z + \frac{10}{13} \quad \left(\frac{6}{13}a + \frac{10}{13}, \frac{5}{13}a + \frac{4}{13}, a\right)$

39. $\quad -4x + y + 0.2z = 6$

$\quad 6x - 3y + 0.5z = -4$

$\quad -8x + 2y + 0.6z = 14$

$\quad -4x + y + 0.2z = 6$

$\quad -6x \qquad + 1.1z = 14$

$\qquad 0.2z = 2$

$\qquad z = 10$

$-6x \qquad + 1.1(10) = 14$

$\qquad -6x = 3$

$\qquad x = -\frac{1}{2}$

$-4\left(-\frac{1}{2}\right) + y + 0.2(10) = 6$

$2 + y + 2 = 6$

$\qquad y = 2$

$\left(-\frac{1}{2}, 2, 10\right)$

41. $\quad x + y + z = 3 \qquad x + 2y - z = -4$

$\quad 2x + y + 2z = 9 \quad$ or $\qquad y + 2z = 1$

$\quad x \qquad - 2z = 0 \qquad 3x + y + 3z = 15$

Many correct answers. Write equations so that $(4, -3, 2)$ satisfies each equation.

43.

$$128 = \tfrac{1}{2}a(1)^2 + v_0(1) + s_0$$
$$80 = \tfrac{1}{2}a(2)^2 + v_0(2) + s_0$$
$$0 = \tfrac{1}{2}a(3)^2 + v_0(3) + s_0$$

$$128 = \tfrac{1}{2}a + v_0 + s_0$$
$$80 = 2a + 2v_0 + s_0$$
$$0 = \tfrac{9}{2}a + 3v_0 + s_0$$

$$256 = a + 2v_0 + 2s_0$$
$$80 = 2a + 2v_0 + s_0$$
$$0 = \tfrac{9}{2}a + 3v_0 + s_0$$

$$256 = a + 2v_0 + 2s_0$$
$$-432 = - 2v_0 - 3s_0$$
$$-1152 = - 6v_0 - 8s_0$$

$$256 = a + 2v_0 + 2s_0$$
$$216 = v_0 + \tfrac{3}{2}s_0$$
$$1152 = - 6v_0 - 8s_0$$

$$256 = a + 2v_0 + 2s_0$$
$$216 = v_0 + \tfrac{3}{2}s_0$$
$$144 = + s_0$$

$$216 = v_0 + \tfrac{3}{2}(144)$$
$$0 = v_0$$

$$256 = a + 0 + 288$$
$$-32 = a$$

$$s = -16t^2 + 144$$

45.

$$32 = \tfrac{1}{2}a(1)^2 + v_0(1) + s_0$$
$$32 = \tfrac{1}{2}a(2)^2 + v_0(2) + s_0$$
$$0 = \tfrac{1}{2}a(3)^2 + v_0(3) + s_0$$

$$64 = a + 2v_0 + 2s_0$$
$$32 = 2a + 2v_0 + s_0$$
$$0 = 9a + 6v_0 + s_0$$

$$64 = a + 2v_0 + 2s_0$$
$$-96 = - 2v_0 - 3s_0$$
$$-576 = - 12v_0 - 16s_0$$

$$64 = a + 2v_0 + 2s_0$$
$$48 = v_0 + \tfrac{3}{2}s_0$$
$$-576 = - 12v_0 - 16s_0$$

$$64 = a + 2v_0 + 2s_0$$
$$48 = v_0 + \tfrac{3}{2}s_0$$
$$0 = + 2s_0$$

$$0 = s_0$$
$$48 = v_0 + 0$$
$$64 = a + 2(48) + 0$$

$$-32 = a$$
$$s = -16t^2 + 48t$$

47.

$$-4 = a(0)^2 + b(0) + c$$
$$1 = a(1)^2 + b(1) + c$$
$$10 = a(2)^2 + b(2) + c$$

$$-4 = c$$
$$1 = a + b + c$$
$$10 = 4a + 2b + c$$

$$-4 = c$$
$$1 = a + b + c$$
$$6 = -2b - 3c$$

$$c = -4$$
$$6 = -2b - 3(-4)$$
$$6 = -2b + 12$$

$$-6 = -2b$$
$$3 = b$$
$$1 = a + 3 + (-4)$$

$$1 = a - 1$$
$$2 = a$$
$$y = 2x^2 + 3x - 4$$

49. $\quad 0 = a(1)^2 + b(1) + c \implies \quad 0 = a + b + c$

$\qquad -1 = a(2)^2 + b(2) + c \implies -1 = 4a + 2b + c$

$\qquad 0 = a(3)^2 + b(3) + c \implies \quad 0 = 9a + 3b + c$

$\quad a + \quad b + \quad c = 0$

$\qquad\qquad -2b - \quad 3c = -1$

$\qquad\qquad -6b - \quad 8c = 0$

$\quad a + \quad b + \quad c = 0$

$\qquad\qquad b + \tfrac{3}{2}c = \tfrac{1}{2}$

$\qquad\qquad 3b + 4c = 0$

$\quad a + \qquad -\tfrac{1}{2}c = -\tfrac{1}{2}$

$\qquad\qquad b + \tfrac{3}{2}c = \tfrac{1}{2}$

$\qquad\qquad\qquad -\tfrac{1}{2}c = -\tfrac{3}{2}$

$\quad a \qquad\qquad -\tfrac{1}{2}c = -\tfrac{1}{2}$

$\qquad\qquad b + \tfrac{3}{2}c = \tfrac{1}{2}$

$\qquad\qquad\qquad c = 3$

$\quad a \qquad\qquad\qquad = 1$

$\qquad\qquad b \qquad\qquad = -4$

$\qquad\qquad\qquad c = 3$

$\quad y = x^2 - 4x + 3$

51. $\quad -3 = a(-1)^2 + b(-1) + \quad c$

$\qquad 1 = \quad a(1)^2 + \quad b(1) + \quad c$

$\qquad 0 = \quad a(2)^2 + \quad b(2) + \quad c$

$\quad -3 = \qquad a - \quad b + \quad c$

$\qquad 1 = \qquad a + \quad b + \quad c$

$\qquad 0 = \qquad 4 + \quad 2b + \quad c$

$\quad -3 = \qquad a - \quad b + \quad c$

$\qquad 4 = \qquad\qquad +2b$

$\qquad 12 = \qquad\qquad +6b - \quad 3c$

$\qquad 2 = \qquad\qquad b$

$\qquad 12 = \qquad\qquad 6(2) - \quad 3c$

$\qquad 0 = \qquad\qquad\qquad -3c$

$\qquad 0 = \qquad\qquad\qquad\qquad c$

$\quad -3 = \qquad a - \quad 2 + \quad 0$

$\quad -1 = \qquad a$

$\quad y = -1x^2 + 2x + 0$

53. $\quad 3 = a(3)^2 + b(3) + c$

$\qquad 6 = a(4)^2 + b(4) + c$

$\qquad 10 = a(5)^2 + b(5) + c$

$\qquad 3 = 9a + 3b + c \qquad\qquad 3 = 9a + 3b + c \qquad\qquad 3 = 9a + 3b + c$

$\qquad 6 = 16a + 4b + c \implies \tfrac{2}{3} = -\tfrac{4}{3}b - \tfrac{7}{9}c \implies \tfrac{2}{3} = -\tfrac{4}{3}b - \tfrac{7}{9}c$

$\qquad 10 = 25a + 5b + c \qquad \tfrac{5}{3} = -\tfrac{10}{3}b - \tfrac{16}{9}c \qquad 0 = \tfrac{3}{18}c$

$\qquad\qquad\qquad\qquad\qquad\qquad \tfrac{2}{3} = -\tfrac{4}{3}b - \tfrac{7}{9}(0) \qquad 3 = 9a + 3\left(-\tfrac{1}{2}\right) + 0$

$\qquad 0 = \tfrac{3}{18}c \qquad\qquad\qquad \tfrac{2}{3} = -\tfrac{4}{3}b \qquad\qquad\qquad 3 = 9a - \tfrac{3}{2}$

$\qquad 0 = c \qquad\qquad\qquad\qquad -\tfrac{1}{2} = b \qquad\qquad\qquad \tfrac{9}{2} = 9a$

$\qquad\qquad\qquad\qquad\qquad\qquad\qquad\qquad\qquad\qquad\qquad \tfrac{1}{2} = a$

$\quad y = \tfrac{1}{2}x^2 - \tfrac{1}{2}x = \tfrac{1}{2}x(x - 1)$

$\quad y = \tfrac{1}{2}(6)^2 - \tfrac{1}{2}(6) = \tfrac{1}{2}(36) - \tfrac{1}{2}(6) = 18 - 3 = 15 \text{ yes}$

55. $0^2 + 0^2 + D(0) + E(0) + F = 0$

$2^2 + (-2)^2 + D(2) + E(-2) + F = 0$

$4^2 + 0^2 + D(4) + E(0) + F = 0$

$$F = 0$$

$$2D - 2E + F = -8$$

$$4D + F = -16$$

$$4D + 0 = -16$$

$$4D = -16$$

$$D = -4$$

$$2(-4) - 2E + 0 = -8$$

$$-2E = 0$$

$$E = 0$$

$$x^2 + y^2 - 4x = 0$$

57. $3^2 + (-1)^2 + D(3) + E(-1) + F = 0$

$(-2)^2 + 4^2 + D(-2) + E(4) + F = 0$

$6^2 + 8^2 + D(6) + E(8) + F = 0$

$$3D - E + F = -10$$

$$-2D + 4E + F = -20$$

$$6D + 8E + F = -100$$

$$F + 3D - E = -10$$

$$F - 2D + 4E = -20$$

$$F + 6D + 8E = -100$$

$$F + 3D - E = -10$$

$$-5D + 5E = -10$$

$$3D + 9E = -90$$

$$F + 3D - E = -10$$

$$D + 3E = -30$$

$$-5D + 5E = -10$$

$$F + 3D - E = -10$$

$$D + 3E = -30$$

$$+20E = -160$$

$$F + 3D - E = -10$$

$$D + 3 = -30$$

$$E = -8$$

$$D + 3(-8) = -30$$

$$D = -6$$

$$F + 3(-6) - (-8) = -10$$

$$F = 0$$

$$x^2 + y^2 - 6x - 8y = 0$$

59. $(-3)^2 + 5^2 + D(-3) + E(5) + F = 0$

$4^2 + 6^2 + D(4) + E(6) + F = 0$

$5^2 + 5^2 + D(5) + E(5) + F = 0$

$$-3D + 5E + F = -34$$

$$4D + 6E + F = -52$$

$$5D + 5E + F = -50$$

$$D + E + \tfrac{1}{5}F = -10$$

$$4D + 6E + F = -52$$

$$-3D + 5E + F = -34$$

$$D + E + \tfrac{1}{5}F = -10$$

$$2E + \tfrac{1}{5}F = -12$$

$$8E + \tfrac{8}{5}F = -64$$

—CONTINUED—

59. —CONTINUED—

$$D + \quad E + \tfrac{1}{5}F = -10$$

$$E + \tfrac{1}{10}F = \quad -6$$

$$8E + \tfrac{8}{5}F = -64$$

$$D \quad + \tfrac{1}{10}F = \quad -4$$

$$E + \tfrac{1}{10}F = \quad -6$$

$$\tfrac{4}{5}F = -16$$

$$D \quad + \tfrac{1}{10}F = \quad -4$$

$$E + \tfrac{1}{10}F = \quad -6$$

$$F = -20$$

$$D \quad\quad = \quad -2$$

$$E \quad\quad = \quad -4$$

$$F = -20$$

$$x^2 + y^2 - 2x - 4y - 20 = 0$$

61. $.20x \quad\quad + .50z = 12$

$.40x \quad\quad + .50z = 16$

$.40x + 1y \quad\quad = 26$

$x \quad + 2.5z = 60$	$x \ + 2.5z = 60$	$x \ + 2.5z = 60$	$x = 20$
$.4x \quad + .5z = 16 \implies$	$-.5z = -8 \implies$	$y - z = 2 \implies$	$y = 18$
$.4x + 1y \quad = 26$	$1y - 1z = 2$	$z = 16$	$z = 16$

Spray X: 20 gal

Spray Y: 18 gal

Spray Z: 16 gal

63. $.40x + .30y + .50z = 30$

$.20x + .25y + .25z = 17$

$.10x + .15y + .25z = 10$

$x + .75y + 1.25z = 75$	$x + \ .75y + 1.25z = 75$	$x + \ .75y + 1.25z = 75$	
$.20x + .25y + \ .25z = 17 \implies$	$.1y \quad = 2 \implies$	$y \quad = 20 \implies$	
$.10x + .15y + \ .25z = 10$	$0.75y + .125z = 2.5$	$.075y + .125z = 2.5$	

$x \ + 1.25z = 60$	$x \ + 1.25z = 60$	$x = 50$
$y \quad = 20 \implies$	$y \quad = 20 \implies$	$y = 20$
$+ .125z = 1$	$z = 8$	$z = 8$

String: 50

Wind: 20

Percussion: 8

65. (d)
$$\begin{aligned} x + y + z &= 200 \\ 8x + 15y + 100z &= 4995 \\ x \phantom{{}+ y} - 4z &= 0 \end{aligned}$$

$$\begin{aligned} x + y + z &= 200 \\ 7y + 92z &= 3395 \\ -y - 5z &= -200 \end{aligned}$$

$$\begin{aligned} x + y + z &= 200 \\ y + 5z &= 200 \\ 57z &= 1995 \end{aligned}$$

$$\begin{aligned} z &= 35 \\ y + 5(35) &= 200 \\ y &= 25 \end{aligned}$$

$$\begin{aligned} x + 25 + 35 &= 200 \\ x &= 140 \end{aligned}$$

(e) Students: 140; Nonstudents: 25; Major contributors: 35

(f)
$$\begin{aligned} x + y + z &= 200 \\ 8x + 15y + 100z &= 4995 \\ z &= 18 \end{aligned}$$

$$x + y = 182$$
$$8x + 15y = 3195$$
$$y = 182 - x$$
$$8x + 15(182 - x) = 3195$$
$$8x + 2730 - 15x = 3195$$
$$-7x = 465$$
$$x = -\frac{465}{7} \quad \text{(not possible)}$$

67. Substitute $y = 3$ into the first equation to obtain $x + 2(3) = 2$ or $x = 2 - 6 = -4$.

69. Answers will vary.

Mid-Chapter Quiz for Chapter 8

1. $(1, -2)$ $\quad 5(1) - 12(-2) \overset{?}{=} 2$

$\qquad\qquad\qquad 5 + 24 \neq 2$

This is not the solution.

$(10, 4)$ $\quad 5(10) - 12(4) \overset{?}{=} 2$

$\qquad\qquad\qquad 50 - 48 = 2$

$\qquad\qquad\qquad\qquad 2 = 2$

$\qquad\qquad 2(10) + 1.5(4) \overset{?}{=} 26$

$\qquad\qquad\qquad 20 + 6 = 26$

$\qquad\qquad\qquad\quad 26 = 26$

This is a solution.

2.

No solution

3.

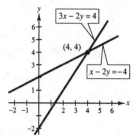

One solution

4.

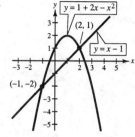

Two solutions

5.

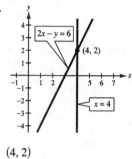

$(4, 2)$

6.

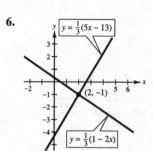

$(2, -1)$

7.

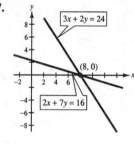

$(8, 0)$

8.

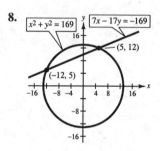

$(5, 12), (-12, 5)$

9. $2x - 3y = 4$

$y = 2$

$2x - 3(2) = 4$

$2x - 6 = 4$

$2x = 10$

$x = 5$

$(5, 2)$

10. $y = 5 - x^2$

$y = 2(x + 1)$

$5 - x^2 = 2(x + 1)$

$5 - x^2 = 2x + 2$

$0 = x^2 + 2x - 3$

$0 = (x + 3)(x - 1)$

$x = -3 \qquad x = 1$

$y = -4 \qquad y = 4$

$(-3, -4), (1, 4)$

11. $5x - y = 32 \quad \Rightarrow \quad -y = -5x + 32$

$6x - 9y = 18 \qquad\qquad y = 5x - 32$

$6x - 9(5x - 32) = 18$

$6x - 45x + 288 = 18$

$\qquad\qquad -39x = -270$

$\qquad\qquad x = \dfrac{-270}{-39} = \dfrac{90}{13}$

$y = 5\left(\dfrac{90}{13}\right) - 32$

$\quad = \dfrac{450}{13} - \dfrac{416}{13}$

$\quad = \dfrac{34}{13}$

$\left(\dfrac{90}{13}, \dfrac{34}{13}\right)$

12. $0.2x + 0.7y = 8$

$-x + 2y = 15 \quad \Rightarrow \quad -x = -2y + 15$

$0.2(2y - 15) + 0.7y = 8 \qquad x = 2y - 15$

$0.4y - 3 + 0.7y = 8$

$\qquad\qquad 1.1y = 11$

$\qquad\qquad y = 10$

$x = 2(10) - 15$

$\quad = 20 - 15$

$\quad = 5$

$(5, 10)$

13. $x + 10y = 18$

$5x + 2y = 42$

$x + 10y = 18$

$\quad -48y = -48$

$x + 10y = 18$

$\qquad\quad y = 1$

$x \qquad\quad = 8$

$\qquad\quad y = 1$

$(8, 1)$

14. $3x + 11y = 38$

$7x - 5y = -34$

$x + \tfrac{11}{3}y = \tfrac{38}{3}$

$7x - 5y = -34$

$x + \tfrac{11}{3}y = \tfrac{38}{3}$

$\quad -\tfrac{92}{3}y = -\tfrac{368}{3}$

$x + \tfrac{11}{3}y = \tfrac{38}{3}$

$\qquad\quad y = 4$

$x \qquad\quad = -2$

$\qquad\quad y = 4$

$(-2, 4)$

15.
$$a + b + c = 1$$
$$4a + 2b + c = 2$$
$$9a + 3b + c = 4$$

$$a + b + c = 1$$
$$-2b - 3c = -2$$
$$-6b - 8c = -5$$

$$a + b + c = 1$$
$$b + \tfrac{3}{2}c = 1$$
$$-6b - 8c = -5$$

$$a \quad -\tfrac{1}{2}c = 0$$
$$b + \tfrac{3}{2}c = 1$$
$$c = 1$$

$$a \quad = \tfrac{1}{2}$$
$$b \quad = -\tfrac{1}{2}$$
$$c = 1$$

$$\left(\tfrac{1}{2}, -\tfrac{1}{2}, 1\right)$$

16.
$$x \quad + 4z = 17$$
$$-3x + 2y - z = -20$$
$$x - 5y + 3z = 19$$

$$x \quad + 4z = 17$$
$$2y + 11z = 31$$
$$-5y - z = 2$$

$$x \quad + 4z = 17$$
$$y + \tfrac{11}{2}z = \tfrac{31}{2}$$
$$\tfrac{53}{2}z = \tfrac{159}{2}$$

$$x \quad + 4z = 17$$
$$y + \tfrac{11}{2}z = \tfrac{31}{2}$$
$$z = 3$$

$$x \quad = 5$$
$$y \quad = -1$$
$$z = 3$$

$$(5, -1, 3)$$

17.
$$x + y = -2$$
$$2x - y = 32$$

18.
$$x + y - z = 11$$
$$x + 2y - z = 14$$
$$-2x + y + z = -6$$

19. *Verbal model:*

$$\boxed{\begin{array}{c}\text{Amount}\\\text{Solution 1}\end{array}} + \boxed{\begin{array}{c}\text{Amount}\\\text{Solution 2}\end{array}} = \boxed{\begin{array}{c}\text{Amount}\\\text{Mixture}\end{array}}$$

$$0.20\,\boxed{\begin{array}{c}\text{Amount}\\\text{Solution 1}\end{array}} + 0.50\,\boxed{\begin{array}{c}\text{Amount}\\\text{Solution 2}\end{array}} = 0.30 \cdot 20$$

Labels: Amount Solution 1 = x By substitution $y = 20 - x$

Amount Solution 2 = y $20x + 50(20 - x) = 600$

System of equations: $x + y = 20$ $20x + 1000 - 50x = 600$

$0.20x + 0.50y = 0.30(20)$ $-30x = -400$

$x + y = 20$ $x = 13\tfrac{1}{3}$ gallons at 20% solution

$20x + 50y = 600$ $20 - x = 6\tfrac{2}{3}$ galllons at 50% solution

20.
$$2 = a(1)^2 + b(1) + c \implies a + b + c = 2$$
$$-4 = a(-1)^2 + b(-1) + c \implies a - b + c = -4$$
$$8 = a(2)^2 + b(2) + c \implies 4a + 2b + c = 8$$

$$
\begin{aligned}
a + b + c &= 2 \\
-2b &= -6 \\
-2b - 3c &= 0
\end{aligned}
$$

$$
\begin{aligned}
a + b + c &= 2 \\
b &= 3 \\
-2b - 3c &= 0
\end{aligned}
$$

$$
\begin{aligned}
a + c &= -1 \\
b &= 3 \\
-3c &= 6
\end{aligned}
$$

$$
\begin{aligned}
a + c &= -1 \\
b &= 3 \\
c &= -2
\end{aligned}
$$

$$
\begin{aligned}
a &= 1 \\
b &= 3 \\
c &= -2
\end{aligned}
$$

$$y = x^2 + 3x - 2$$

Section 8.4   Matrices and Linear Systems

1. 4×2

3. 2×3

5. 4×1

7. $\begin{bmatrix} 4 & -5 & \vdots & -2 \\ -1 & 8 & \vdots & 10 \end{bmatrix}$

9. $\begin{bmatrix} 1 & 10 & -3 & \vdots & 2 \\ 5 & -3 & 4 & \vdots & 0 \\ 2 & 4 & 0 & \vdots & 6 \end{bmatrix}$

11. $\begin{bmatrix} 5 & 1 & -3 & \vdots & 7 \\ 0 & 2 & 4 & \vdots & 12 \end{bmatrix}$

13.
$$\begin{aligned} 4x + 3y &= 8 \\ x - 2y &= 3 \end{aligned}$$

15.
$$\begin{aligned} x + 2z &= -10 \\ 3y - z &= 5 \\ 4x + 2y &= 3 \end{aligned}$$

17.
$$\begin{aligned} 5x + 8y + 2z &= -1 \\ -2x + 15y + 5z + w &= 9 \\ x + 6y - 7z &= -3 \end{aligned}$$

19.
$$\begin{bmatrix} 1 & 4 & 3 \\ 2 & 10 & 5 \end{bmatrix}$$
$$-2R_1 + R_2 \begin{bmatrix} 1 & 4 & 3 \\ 0 & 2 & -1 \end{bmatrix}$$

21.
$$\begin{bmatrix} 9 & -18 & 6 \\ 2 & 8 & 15 \end{bmatrix}$$
$$\tfrac{1}{9}R_1 \begin{bmatrix} 1 & -2 & \tfrac{2}{3} \\ 2 & 8 & 15 \end{bmatrix}$$

23.
$$\begin{bmatrix} 1 & 1 & 4 & -1 \\ 3 & 8 & 10 & 3 \\ -2 & 1 & 12 & 6 \end{bmatrix}$$
$$\begin{matrix} -3R_1 + R_2 \\ \\ 2R_1 + R_3 \end{matrix} \begin{bmatrix} 1 & 1 & 4 & -1 \\ 0 & 5 & -2 & 6 \\ 0 & 3 & 20 & 4 \end{bmatrix}$$
$$\tfrac{1}{5}R_2 \begin{bmatrix} 1 & 1 & 4 & -1 \\ 0 & 1 & -\tfrac{2}{5} & \tfrac{6}{5} \\ 0 & 3 & 20 & 4 \end{bmatrix}$$

25. $\begin{bmatrix} 1 & 2 & 3 \\ 2 & -1 & -4 \end{bmatrix}$

$-2R_1 + R_2 \begin{bmatrix} 1 & 2 & 3 \\ 0 & -5 & -10 \end{bmatrix}$

$-\frac{1}{5}R_2 \begin{bmatrix} 1 & 2 & 3 \\ 0 & 1 & 2 \end{bmatrix}$

27. $\begin{bmatrix} 4 & 6 & 1 \\ -2 & 2 & 5 \end{bmatrix}$

$\frac{1}{4}R_1 \begin{bmatrix} 1 & \frac{3}{2} & \frac{1}{4} \\ -2 & 2 & 5 \end{bmatrix}$

$2R_1 + R_2 \begin{bmatrix} 1 & \frac{3}{2} & \frac{1}{4} \\ 0 & 5 & \frac{11}{2} \end{bmatrix}$

$\frac{1}{5}R_2 \begin{bmatrix} 1 & \frac{3}{2} & \frac{1}{4} \\ 0 & 1 & \frac{11}{10} \end{bmatrix}$

$-\frac{3}{2}R_3 + R_2 \begin{bmatrix} 1 & 0 & -\frac{7}{5} \\ 0 & 1 & \frac{11}{10} \end{bmatrix}$

29. $\begin{bmatrix} 1 & 1 & 0 & 5 \\ -2 & -1 & 2 & -10 \\ 3 & 6 & 7 & 14 \end{bmatrix}$

$\begin{matrix} 2R_1 + R_2 \\ -3R_1 + R_3 \end{matrix} \begin{bmatrix} 1 & 1 & 0 & 5 \\ 0 & 1 & 2 & 0 \\ 0 & 3 & 7 & -1 \end{bmatrix}$

$-3R_2 + R_3 \begin{bmatrix} 1 & 1 & 0 & 5 \\ 0 & 1 & 2 & 0 \\ 0 & 0 & 1 & -1 \end{bmatrix}$

31. $\begin{bmatrix} 1 & -1 & -1 & 1 \\ 4 & -4 & 1 & 8 \\ -6 & 8 & 18 & 0 \end{bmatrix}$

$\begin{matrix} -4R_1 + R_2 \\ 6R_1 + R_3 \end{matrix} \begin{bmatrix} 1 & -1 & -1 & 1 \\ 0 & 0 & 5 & 4 \\ 0 & 2 & 12 & 6 \end{bmatrix}$

$\begin{matrix} R_3 \\ R_2 \end{matrix} \begin{bmatrix} 1 & -1 & -1 & 1 \\ 0 & 2 & 12 & 6 \\ 0 & 0 & 5 & 4 \end{bmatrix}$

$\begin{matrix} \frac{1}{2}R_2 \\ \frac{1}{5}R_3 \end{matrix} \begin{bmatrix} 1 & -1 & -1 & 1 \\ 0 & 1 & 6 & 3 \\ 0 & 0 & 1 & \frac{4}{5} \end{bmatrix}$

33. $\begin{bmatrix} 1 & 1 & -1 & 3 \\ 2 & 1 & 2 & 5 \\ 3 & 2 & 1 & 8 \end{bmatrix}$

$\begin{matrix} -2R_1 + R_2 \\ -3R_1 + R_3 \end{matrix} \begin{bmatrix} 1 & 1 & -1 & 3 \\ 0 & -1 & 4 & -1 \\ 0 & 1 & 4 & -1 \end{bmatrix}$

$R_2 + R_3 \begin{bmatrix} 1 & 1 & -1 & 3 \\ 0 & -1 & 4 & -1 \\ 0 & 0 & 8 & -2 \end{bmatrix}$

$-R_2 \begin{bmatrix} 1 & 1 & -1 & 3 \\ 0 & 1 & -4 & 1 \\ 0 & 0 & 8 & -2 \end{bmatrix}$

35. $\begin{aligned} x - 2y &= 4 \\ y &= -3 \end{aligned}$ $\begin{aligned} x - 2(-3) &= 4 \\ x + 6 &= 4 \\ x &= -2 \end{aligned}$

$(-2, -3)$

37. $x + 5y = 3$

$y = -2$

$x + 5(-2) = 3$

$x - 10 = 3$

$x = 13$

$(13, -2)$

39. $\begin{aligned} x - y + 2z &= 4 \\ y - z &= 2 \\ z &= -2 \end{aligned}$ $\begin{aligned} y - (-2) &= 2 \\ y + 2 &= 2 \\ y &= 0 \end{aligned}$

$x - 0 + 2(-2) = 4$

$x - 4 = 4$

$x = 8$

$(8, 0, -2)$

41. $\begin{bmatrix} 1 & 2 & \vdots & 7 \\ 3 & 1 & \vdots & 8 \end{bmatrix}$

$-3R_1 + R_2 \begin{bmatrix} 1 & 2 & \vdots & 7 \\ 0 & -5 & \vdots & -13 \end{bmatrix}$

$-\frac{1}{5}R_2 \begin{bmatrix} 1 & 2 & \vdots & 7 \\ 0 & 1 & \vdots & \frac{13}{5} \end{bmatrix}$

$-2R_2 + R_1 \begin{bmatrix} 1 & 0 & \vdots & \frac{9}{5} \\ 0 & 1 & \vdots & \frac{13}{5} \end{bmatrix}$

$\left(\frac{9}{5}, \frac{13}{5} \right)$

43. $\begin{bmatrix} 6 & -4 & \vdots & 2 \\ 5 & 2 & \vdots & 7 \end{bmatrix}$

$\frac{1}{6}R_1 \begin{bmatrix} 1 & -\frac{2}{3} & \vdots & \frac{1}{3} \\ 5 & 2 & \vdots & 7 \end{bmatrix}$

$-5R_1 + R_2 \begin{bmatrix} 1 & -\frac{2}{3} & \vdots & \frac{1}{3} \\ 0 & \frac{16}{3} & \vdots & \frac{16}{3} \end{bmatrix}$

$\frac{3}{16}R_2 \begin{bmatrix} 1 & -\frac{2}{3} & \vdots & \frac{1}{3} \\ 0 & 1 & \vdots & 1 \end{bmatrix}$

$\frac{2}{3}R_2 + R_1 \begin{bmatrix} 1 & 0 & \vdots & 1 \\ 0 & 1 & \vdots & 1 \end{bmatrix}$

$(1, 1)$

45. $\begin{bmatrix} -1 & 2 & \vdots & 1.5 \\ 2 & -4 & \vdots & 3 \end{bmatrix}$

$-R_1 \begin{bmatrix} 1 & -2 & \vdots & -1.5 \\ 2 & -4 & \vdots & 3 \end{bmatrix}$

$-2R_1 + R_2 \begin{bmatrix} 1 & -2 & \vdots & -1.5 \\ 0 & 0 & \vdots & 6 \end{bmatrix}$

Inconsistent; no solution

47.
$$\begin{bmatrix} 1 & -2 & -1 & \vdots & 6 \\ 0 & 1 & 4 & \vdots & 5 \\ 4 & 2 & 3 & \vdots & 8 \end{bmatrix}$$

$$-4R_1 + R_3 \begin{bmatrix} 1 & -2 & -1 & \vdots & 6 \\ 0 & 1 & 4 & \vdots & 5 \\ 0 & 10 & 7 & \vdots & -16 \end{bmatrix}$$

$$-10R_2 + R_3 \begin{bmatrix} 1 & -2 & -1 & \vdots & 6 \\ 0 & 1 & 4 & \vdots & 5 \\ 0 & 0 & -33 & \vdots & -66 \end{bmatrix}$$

$$\tfrac{1}{-33}R_3 \begin{bmatrix} 1 & -2 & -1 & \vdots & 6 \\ 0 & 1 & 4 & \vdots & 5 \\ 0 & 0 & 1 & \vdots & 2 \end{bmatrix}$$

$z = 2$ $y + 4(2) = 5$ $x - 2(-3) - (2) = 6$

$y = -3$ $x + 6 - 2 = 6$

$x = 2$

$(2, -3, 2)$

49.
$$\begin{bmatrix} 1 & 1 & -5 & \vdots & 3 \\ 1 & 0 & -2 & \vdots & 1 \\ 2 & -1 & -1 & \vdots & 0 \end{bmatrix}$$

$$\begin{matrix} -R_1 + R_2 \\ -2R_1 + R_3 \end{matrix} \begin{bmatrix} 1 & 1 & -5 & \vdots & 3 \\ 0 & -1 & 3 & \vdots & -2 \\ 0 & -3 & 9 & \vdots & -6 \end{bmatrix}$$

$$-R_2 \begin{bmatrix} 1 & 1 & -5 & \vdots & 3 \\ 0 & 1 & -3 & \vdots & 2 \\ 0 & -3 & 9 & \vdots & -6 \end{bmatrix}$$

$$3R_2 + R_3 \begin{bmatrix} 1 & 1 & -5 & \vdots & 3 \\ 0 & 1 & -3 & \vdots & 2 \\ 0 & 0 & 0 & \vdots & 0 \end{bmatrix}$$

$y - 3z = 2$ $x + (2 + 3z) - 5z = 3$

$y = 2 + 3z$ $x = 1 + 2z$

let $a = z$ (a is any real number)

$(1 + 2a, 2 + 3a, a)$

51.
$$\begin{bmatrix} 2 & 4 & 0 & \vdots & 10 \\ 2 & 2 & 3 & \vdots & 3 \\ -3 & 1 & 2 & \vdots & -3 \end{bmatrix}$$

$$-R_1 + R_2 \begin{bmatrix} 2 & 4 & 0 & \vdots & 10 \\ 0 & -2 & 3 & \vdots & -7 \\ -3 & 1 & 2 & \vdots & -3 \end{bmatrix}$$

$$\tfrac{1}{2}R_1 \begin{bmatrix} 1 & 2 & 0 & \vdots & 5 \\ 0 & -2 & 3 & \vdots & -7 \\ -3 & 1 & 2 & \vdots & -3 \end{bmatrix}$$

$$3R_1 + R_3 \begin{bmatrix} 1 & 2 & 0 & \vdots & 5 \\ 0 & -2 & 3 & \vdots & -7 \\ 0 & 7 & 2 & \vdots & 12 \end{bmatrix}$$

$$-\tfrac{1}{2}R_2 \begin{bmatrix} 1 & 2 & 0 & \vdots & 5 \\ 0 & 1 & -\tfrac{3}{2} & \vdots & \tfrac{7}{2} \\ 0 & 7 & 2 & \vdots & 12 \end{bmatrix}$$

$$-7R_2 + R_3 \begin{bmatrix} 1 & 2 & 0 & \vdots & 5 \\ 0 & 1 & -\tfrac{3}{2} & \vdots & \tfrac{7}{2} \\ 0 & 0 & \tfrac{25}{2} & \vdots & -\tfrac{25}{2} \end{bmatrix}$$

$$\tfrac{2}{25}R_3 \begin{bmatrix} 1 & 2 & 0 & \vdots & 5 \\ 0 & 1 & -\tfrac{3}{2} & \vdots & \tfrac{7}{2} \\ 0 & 0 & 1 & \vdots & -1 \end{bmatrix}$$

$z = -1$ $y - \tfrac{3}{2}(-1) = \tfrac{7}{2}$ $x + 2(2) = 5$

$y = \tfrac{4}{2}$ $x + 4 = 5$

$y = 2$ $x = 1$

$(1, 2, -1)$

53.
$$\begin{bmatrix} 1 & -3 & 2 & \vdots & 8 \\ 0 & 2 & -1 & \vdots & -4 \\ 1 & 0 & 1 & \vdots & 3 \end{bmatrix}$$

$$\begin{matrix} \tfrac{1}{2}R_2 \\ -R_1 + R_3 \end{matrix} \begin{bmatrix} 1 & -3 & 2 & \vdots & 8 \\ 0 & 1 & -\tfrac{1}{2} & \vdots & -2 \\ 0 & 3 & -1 & \vdots & -5 \end{bmatrix}$$

$$\begin{matrix} 3R_2 + R_1 \\ \\ -3R_2 + R_3 \end{matrix} \begin{bmatrix} 1 & 0 & \tfrac{1}{2} & \vdots & 2 \\ 0 & 1 & -\tfrac{1}{2} & \vdots & -2 \\ 0 & 0 & \tfrac{1}{2} & \vdots & 1 \end{bmatrix}$$

$$2R_3 \begin{bmatrix} 1 & 0 & \tfrac{1}{2} & \vdots & 2 \\ 0 & 1 & -\tfrac{1}{2} & \vdots & -2 \\ 0 & 0 & 1 & \vdots & 2 \end{bmatrix}$$

$$\begin{matrix} -\tfrac{1}{2}R_3 + R_1 \\ \tfrac{1}{2}R_3 + R_2 \end{matrix} \begin{bmatrix} 1 & 0 & 0 & \vdots & 1 \\ 0 & 1 & 0 & \vdots & -1 \\ 0 & 0 & 1 & \vdots & 2 \end{bmatrix}$$

$(1, -1, 2)$

55.
$$\begin{bmatrix} -2 & -2 & -15 & \vdots & 0 \\ 1 & 2 & 2 & \vdots & 18 \\ 3 & 3 & 22 & \vdots & 2 \end{bmatrix}$$

$$\begin{matrix} R_2 \\ R_1 \end{matrix} \begin{bmatrix} 1 & 2 & 2 & \vdots & 18 \\ -2 & -2 & -15 & \vdots & 0 \\ 3 & 3 & 22 & \vdots & 2 \end{bmatrix}$$

$$\begin{matrix} \\ 2R_1 + R_2 \\ -3R_1 + R_3 \end{matrix} \begin{bmatrix} 1 & 2 & 2 & \vdots & 18 \\ 0 & 2 & -11 & \vdots & 36 \\ 0 & -3 & 16 & \vdots & -52 \end{bmatrix}$$

$$\begin{matrix} \\ \\ \tfrac{3}{2}R_2 + R_3 \end{matrix} \begin{bmatrix} 1 & 2 & 2 & \vdots & 18 \\ 0 & 2 & -11 & \vdots & 36 \\ 0 & 0 & -\tfrac{1}{2} & \vdots & 2 \end{bmatrix}$$

$$\begin{matrix} \\ \tfrac{1}{2}R_2 \\ -2R_3 \end{matrix} \begin{bmatrix} 1 & 2 & 2 & \vdots & 18 \\ 0 & 1 & -\tfrac{11}{2} & \vdots & 18 \\ 0 & 0 & 1 & \vdots & -4 \end{bmatrix}$$

$z = -4 \quad y - \tfrac{11}{2}(-4) = 18 \quad x + 2(-4) + 2(-4) = 18$

$\qquad\qquad\quad y + 22 = 18 \qquad\qquad x - 8 - 8 = 18$

$\qquad\qquad\qquad y = -4 \qquad\qquad\qquad x - 16 = 18$

$\qquad\qquad\qquad\qquad\qquad\qquad\qquad\qquad x = 34$

$(34, -4, -4)$

57.
$$\begin{bmatrix} 2 & 0 & 4 & \vdots & 1 \\ 1 & 1 & 3 & \vdots & 0 \\ 1 & 3 & 5 & \vdots & 0 \end{bmatrix}$$

$$\begin{matrix} R_2 \\ R_1 \end{matrix} \begin{bmatrix} 1 & 1 & 3 & \vdots & 0 \\ 2 & 0 & 4 & \vdots & 1 \\ 1 & 3 & 5 & \vdots & 0 \end{bmatrix}$$

$$\begin{matrix} \\ -2R_1 + R_2 \\ -R_1 + R_3 \end{matrix} \begin{bmatrix} 1 & 1 & 3 & \vdots & 0 \\ 0 & -2 & -2 & \vdots & 1 \\ 0 & 2 & 2 & \vdots & 0 \end{bmatrix}$$

$$\begin{matrix} \\ -\tfrac{1}{2}R_2 \\ \\ \end{matrix} \begin{bmatrix} 1 & 1 & 3 & \vdots & 0 \\ 0 & 1 & 1 & \vdots & -\tfrac{1}{2} \\ 0 & 2 & 2 & \vdots & 0 \end{bmatrix}$$

$$\begin{matrix} \\ \\ -2R_2 + R_3 \end{matrix} \begin{bmatrix} 1 & 1 & 3 & \vdots & 0 \\ 0 & 1 & 1 & \vdots & -\tfrac{1}{2} \\ 0 & 0 & 0 & \vdots & 1 \end{bmatrix}$$

Inconsistent; no solution

59.
$$\begin{bmatrix} 1 & 3 & 0 & \vdots & 2 \\ 2 & 6 & 0 & \vdots & 4 \\ 2 & 5 & 4 & \vdots & 3 \end{bmatrix}$$

$$\begin{matrix} \\ -2R_1 + R_2 \\ -2R_1 + R_3 \end{matrix} \begin{bmatrix} 1 & 3 & 0 & \vdots & 2 \\ 0 & 0 & 0 & \vdots & 0 \\ 0 & -1 & 4 & \vdots & -1 \end{bmatrix}$$

$$\begin{matrix} -R_3 \\ R_2 \end{matrix} \begin{bmatrix} 1 & 3 & 0 & \vdots & 2 \\ 0 & 1 & -4 & \vdots & 1 \\ 0 & 0 & 0 & \vdots & 0 \end{bmatrix}$$

let $z = a$

then $y = 1 + 4a$

$\quad x = 2 - 3(1 + 4a)$

$\qquad = 2 - 3 - 12a$

$\qquad = -1 - 12a$

$(-12a - 1, 1 + 4a, a)$

61.
$$\begin{bmatrix} 2 & 1 & -2 & \vdots & 4 \\ 3 & -2 & 4 & \vdots & 6 \\ -4 & 1 & 6 & \vdots & 12 \end{bmatrix}$$

$$\begin{matrix} \\ -\tfrac{3}{2}R_1 + R_2 \\ 2R_1 + R_3 \end{matrix} \begin{bmatrix} 2 & 1 & -2 & \vdots & 4 \\ 0 & -\tfrac{7}{2} & 7 & \vdots & 0 \\ 0 & 3 & 2 & \vdots & 20 \end{bmatrix}$$

$$\begin{matrix} \tfrac{1}{2}R_1 \\ -\tfrac{2}{7}R_2 \\ \end{matrix} \begin{bmatrix} 1 & \tfrac{1}{2} & -1 & \vdots & 2 \\ 0 & 1 & -2 & \vdots & 0 \\ 0 & 3 & 2 & \vdots & 20 \end{bmatrix}$$

$$\begin{matrix} \\ \\ -3R_2 + R_3 \end{matrix} \begin{bmatrix} 1 & \tfrac{1}{2} & -1 & \vdots & 2 \\ 0 & 1 & -2 & \vdots & 0 \\ 0 & 0 & 8 & \vdots & 20 \end{bmatrix}$$

$$\begin{matrix} \\ \\ \tfrac{1}{8}R_3 \end{matrix} \begin{bmatrix} 1 & \tfrac{1}{2} & -1 & \vdots & 2 \\ 0 & 1 & -2 & \vdots & 0 \\ 0 & 0 & 1 & \vdots & \tfrac{5}{2} \end{bmatrix}$$

$z = \tfrac{5}{2} \qquad y - 2\left(\tfrac{5}{2}\right) = 0 \qquad x + \tfrac{1}{2}(5) - \left(\tfrac{5}{2}\right) = 2$

$\qquad\qquad\qquad y - 5 = 0 \qquad\qquad x + \tfrac{5}{2} - \tfrac{5}{2} = 2$

$\qquad\qquad\qquad\qquad y = 5 \qquad\qquad\qquad\qquad x = 2$

$\left(2, 5, \tfrac{5}{2}\right)$

63. *Verbal model:*

$$\boxed{\text{Money 1}} + \boxed{\text{Money 2}} + \boxed{\text{Money 3}} = \boxed{1{,}500{,}000}$$

$$\boxed{0.08 \cdot \text{Money 1}} + \boxed{0.09 \cdot \text{Money 2}} + \boxed{0.12 \cdot \text{Money 3}} = \boxed{113{,}000}$$

$$\boxed{\text{Money 1}} = 4 \cdot \boxed{\text{Money 3}}$$

Labels: $x =$ Money 1
$y =$ Money 2
$z =$ Money 3

System of equations:
$$x + y + z = 1{,}500{,}000$$
$$0.08x + 0.09y + 0.12y = 133{,}000$$
$$x = 4z$$

$$\begin{bmatrix} 1 & 1 & 1 & \vdots & 1{,}500{,}000 \\ 8 & 9 & 12 & \vdots & 13{,}300{,}000 \\ 1 & 0 & -4 & \vdots & 0 \end{bmatrix}$$

$$\begin{matrix} \\ -8R_1 + R_2 \\ -R_1 + R_3 \end{matrix} \begin{bmatrix} 1 & 1 & 1 & \vdots & 1{,}500{,}000 \\ 0 & 1 & 4 & \vdots & 1{,}300{,}000 \\ 0 & -1 & -5 & \vdots & -1{,}500{,}000 \end{bmatrix}$$

$$\begin{matrix} \\ \\ R_2 + R_3 \end{matrix} \begin{bmatrix} 1 & 1 & 1 & \vdots & 1{,}500{,}000 \\ 0 & 1 & 4 & \vdots & 1{,}300{,}000 \\ 0 & 0 & -1 & \vdots & -200{,}000 \end{bmatrix}$$

$$\begin{matrix} \\ \\ -R_3 \end{matrix} \begin{bmatrix} 1 & 1 & 1 & \vdots & 1{,}500{,}000 \\ 0 & 1 & 4 & \vdots & 1{,}300{,}000 \\ 0 & 0 & 1 & \vdots & 200{,}000 \end{bmatrix}$$

$$z = 200{,}000 \qquad y + 4(200{,}000) = 1{,}300{,}000 \qquad x + 500{,}000 + 200{,}000 = 1{,}500{,}000$$
$$y = 500{,}000 \qquad\qquad x = 800{,}000$$

$800{,}000 at 8%, $500{,}000 at 90%, $200{,}000 at 12%

65. *Verbal model:*

$$0.10 \cdot \boxed{\text{CDs}} + 0.08 \boxed{\text{Bonds}} + 0.12 \boxed{\text{BC stocks}} + 0.13 \boxed{\text{G stocks}} = 50{,}000$$

$$\boxed{\text{BC stocks}} + \boxed{\text{G stocks}} = 125{,}000$$

$$\boxed{\text{CDs}} + \boxed{\text{Bonds}} = 375{,}00$$

Labels:
$x =$ certificates of deposit
$y =$ municipal bonds
$z =$ blue-chip stocks
$w =$ growth stocks

System of equations:
$$0.10x + 0.08y + 0.12z + 0.13w = 50{,}000$$
$$z + w = 125{,}000$$
$$x + y = 375{,}000$$

$$\begin{bmatrix} 10 & 8 & 12 & 13 & \vdots & 5{,}000{,}000 \\ 0 & 0 & 1 & 1 & \vdots & 125{,}000 \\ 1 & 1 & 0 & 0 & \vdots & 375{,}000 \end{bmatrix}$$

$$\begin{matrix} R_1 \\ R_2 \\ \\ \end{matrix} \begin{bmatrix} 1 & 1 & 0 & 0 & \vdots & 375{,}000 \\ 0 & 0 & 1 & 1 & \vdots & 125{,}000 \\ 10 & 8 & 12 & 13 & \vdots & 5{,}000{,}000 \end{bmatrix}$$

$$\begin{matrix} \\ \\ -10R_1 + R_3 \end{matrix} \begin{bmatrix} 1 & 1 & 0 & 0 & \vdots & 375{,}000 \\ 0 & 0 & 1 & 1 & \vdots & 125{,}000 \\ 0 & -2 & 12 & 13 & \vdots & 1{,}250{,}000 \end{bmatrix}$$

$$\begin{matrix} \\ \\ -\frac{1}{2}R_3 \end{matrix} \begin{bmatrix} 1 & 1 & 0 & 0 & \vdots & 375{,}000 \\ 0 & 0 & 1 & 1 & \vdots & 125{,}000 \\ 0 & 1 & -6 & -\frac{13}{2} & \vdots & -625{,}000 \end{bmatrix}$$

—CONTINUED—

65. —CONTINUED—

$$-R_3 + R_1 \begin{bmatrix} 1 & 0 & 6 & \frac{13}{2} & \vdots & 1{,}000{,}000 \\ 0 & 0 & 1 & 1 & \vdots & 125{,}000 \\ 0 & 1 & -6 & -\frac{13}{2} & \vdots & -625{,}000 \end{bmatrix}$$

$$\begin{matrix} -6R_2 + R_1 \\ 6R_2 + R_3 \end{matrix} \begin{bmatrix} 1 & 0 & 0 & .5 & \vdots & 250{,}000 \\ 0 & 0 & 1 & 1 & \vdots & 125{,}000 \\ 0 & 1 & 0 & -.5 & \vdots & 125{,}000 \end{bmatrix}$$

so let $w = s$

then $x + .5w = 250{,}000$

$x = -.5s + 250{,}000$

$z + w = 125{,}000$

$z = -s + 125{,}000$

$y - .5w = 125{,}000$

$y = .5s + 125{,}000$

Certificates of deposit: $250{,}000 - .5s$

Municipal bonds: $125{,}000 + .5s$

Blue-chip stocks: $125{,}000 - s$

Growth stocks: s

If $s = \$100{,}000$

CD $= \$200{,}000$

M Bonds $= \$175{,}000$

BC Stocks $= \$25{,}000$

G Stocks $= \$100{,}000$

67. *Verbal model:*

$$\boxed{\begin{array}{c}\text{Pounds}\\\text{Nut 1}\end{array}} + \boxed{\begin{array}{c}\text{Pounds}\\\text{Nut 2}\end{array}} + \boxed{\begin{array}{c}\text{Pounds}\\\text{Nut 3}\end{array}} = \boxed{\text{50 pounds}}$$

$$\boxed{3.50\ (\text{Nut 1})} + \boxed{4.50\ (\text{Nut 2})} + \boxed{6.00\ (\text{Nut 3})} = \boxed{50(4.95)}$$

$$\boxed{\begin{array}{c}\text{Pounds}\\\text{Nut 1}\end{array}} + \boxed{\begin{array}{c}\text{Pounds}\\\text{Nut 2}\end{array}} = \boxed{\text{25 pounds}}$$

Labels:

Pounds Nut 1 $= x$

Pounds Nut 2 $= y$

Pounds Nut 3 $= z$

System of equations:

$x + y + z = 50$

$3.50x + 4.50y + 6.00z = 50(4.95)$

$x + y = 25$

$$\begin{bmatrix} 1 & 1 & 1 & \vdots & 50 \\ 350 & 450 & 600 & \vdots & 24{,}750 \\ 1 & 1 & 0 & \vdots & 25 \end{bmatrix}$$

$$\begin{matrix} -350R_1 + R_2 \\ -R_1 + R_3 \end{matrix} \begin{bmatrix} 1 & 1 & 1 & \vdots & 50 \\ 0 & 100 & 250 & \vdots & 7250 \\ 0 & 0 & -1 & \vdots & -25 \end{bmatrix}$$

$$\begin{matrix} \frac{1}{100}R_2 \\ -R_3 \end{matrix} \begin{bmatrix} 1 & 1 & 1 & \vdots & 50 \\ 0 & 1 & 2.5 & \vdots & 72.5 \\ 0 & 0 & 1 & \vdots & 25 \end{bmatrix}$$

$z = 25 \qquad y + 2.5(25) = 72.5 \qquad x + 10 + 25 = 50$

$y = 10 \qquad\qquad x = 15$

15 pounds at \$3.50, 10 pounds at \$4.50, 25 pounds at \$6.00

69. *Verbal model:* $\boxed{\text{Number 1}} + \boxed{\text{Number 2}} + \boxed{\text{Number 3}} = \boxed{33}$

$\boxed{\text{Number 2}} = 3 + \boxed{\text{Number 1}}$

$\boxed{\text{Number 3}} = 4 \cdot \boxed{\text{Number 1}}$

Labels: Number 1 = x

Number 2 = y

Number 3 = z

System of
equations: $x + y + z = 33$

$y = 3 + x$

$z = 4x$

$$\begin{bmatrix} 1 & 1 & 1 & \vdots & 33 \\ -1 & 1 & 0 & \vdots & 3 \\ -4 & 0 & 1 & \vdots & 0 \end{bmatrix}$$

$\begin{matrix} \\ R_1 + R_2 \\ 4R_1 + R_3 \end{matrix} \begin{bmatrix} 1 & 1 & 1 & \vdots & 33 \\ 0 & 2 & 1 & \vdots & 36 \\ 0 & 4 & 5 & \vdots & 132 \end{bmatrix}$

$\begin{matrix} \\ \frac{1}{2}R_2 \\ \\ \end{matrix} \begin{bmatrix} 1 & 1 & 1 & \vdots & 33 \\ 0 & 1 & \frac{1}{2} & \vdots & 18 \\ 0 & 4 & 5 & \vdots & 132 \end{bmatrix}$

$\begin{matrix} \\ \\ -4R_2 + R_3 \end{matrix} \begin{bmatrix} 1 & 1 & 1 & \vdots & 33 \\ 0 & 1 & \frac{1}{2} & \vdots & 18 \\ 0 & 0 & 3 & \vdots & 60 \end{bmatrix}$

$\begin{matrix} \\ \\ \frac{1}{3}R_3 \end{matrix} \begin{bmatrix} 1 & 1 & 1 & \vdots & 33 \\ 0 & 1 & \frac{1}{2} & \vdots & 18 \\ 0 & 0 & 1 & \vdots & 20 \end{bmatrix}$

$z = 20$ $y + \frac{1}{2}(20) = 18$ $x + 8 + 20 = 33$

$y = 8$ $x = 5$

$(5, 8, 20)$

71. $7 = a(1)^2 + b(1) + c \implies 7 = a + b + c$

$12 = a(2)^2 + b(2) + c \implies 12 = 4a + 2b + c$

$19 = a(3)^2 + b(3) + c \implies 19 = 9a + 3b + c$

$$\begin{bmatrix} 1 & 1 & 1 & \vdots & 7 \\ 4 & 2 & 1 & \vdots & 12 \\ 9 & 3 & 1 & \vdots & 19 \end{bmatrix}$$

$\begin{matrix} \\ -4R_1 + R_2 \\ -9R_1 + R_3 \end{matrix} \begin{bmatrix} 1 & 1 & 1 & \vdots & 7 \\ 0 & -2 & -3 & \vdots & -16 \\ 0 & -6 & -8 & \vdots & -44 \end{bmatrix}$

$\begin{matrix} \\ -\frac{1}{2}R_2 \\ -\frac{1}{2}R_3 \end{matrix} \begin{bmatrix} 1 & 1 & 1 & \vdots & 7 \\ 0 & 1 & \frac{3}{2} & \vdots & 8 \\ 0 & 3 & 4 & \vdots & 22 \end{bmatrix}$

$\begin{matrix} -R_2 + R_1 \\ \\ -3R_2 + R_3 \end{matrix} \begin{bmatrix} 1 & 0 & -\frac{1}{2} & \vdots & -1 \\ 0 & 1 & \frac{3}{2} & \vdots & 8 \\ 0 & 0 & -\frac{1}{2} & \vdots & -2 \end{bmatrix}$

—CONTINUED—

71. —CONTINUED —

$$-2R_3 \begin{bmatrix} 1 & 0 & -\frac{1}{2} & : & -1 \\ 0 & 1 & \frac{3}{2} & : & 8 \\ 0 & 0 & 1 & : & 4 \end{bmatrix}$$

$$\begin{matrix} \frac{1}{2}R_3 + R_1 \\ -\frac{3}{2}R_3 + R_2 \\ \\ \end{matrix} \begin{bmatrix} 1 & 0 & 0 & : & 1 \\ 0 & 1 & 0 & : & 2 \\ 0 & 0 & 1 & : & 4 \end{bmatrix}$$

$a = 1, b = 2, c = 4$

$y = x^2 + 2x + 4$

73.
$$8 = a(1)^2 + b(1) + c \implies 8 = a + b + c$$
$$2 = a(2)^2 + b(2) + c \implies 2 = 4a + 2b + c$$
$$-25 = a(3)^2 + b(3) + c \implies -25 = 9a + 3b + c$$

$$\begin{bmatrix} 1 & 1 & 1 & : & 8 \\ 4 & 2 & 1 & : & 2 \\ 9 & 3 & 1 & : & -25 \end{bmatrix}$$

$$\begin{matrix} \\ -4R_1 + R_2 \\ -9R_1 + R_3 \end{matrix} \begin{bmatrix} 1 & 1 & 1 & : & 8 \\ 0 & -2 & -3 & : & -30 \\ 0 & -6 & -81 & : & -97 \end{bmatrix}$$

$$\begin{matrix} \\ -\frac{1}{2}R_2 \\ -\frac{1}{2}R_3 \end{matrix} \begin{bmatrix} 1 & 1 & 1 & : & 8 \\ 0 & 1 & 1.5 & : & 15 \\ 0 & 3 & 4 & : & 48.5 \end{bmatrix}$$

$$\begin{matrix} -R_2 + R_1 \\ \\ -3R_2 + R_3 \end{matrix} \begin{bmatrix} 1 & 0 & -0.5 & : & -7 \\ 0 & 1 & 1.5 & : & 15 \\ 0 & 0 & -0.5 & : & 3.5 \end{bmatrix}$$

$$\begin{matrix} \\ \\ -2R_3 \end{matrix} \begin{bmatrix} 1 & 0 & -0.5 & : & -7 \\ 0 & 1 & 1.5 & : & 15 \\ 0 & 0 & 1 & : & -7 \end{bmatrix}$$

$z = -7$ $y + 1.5(-7) = 15$ $x + -0.5(-7) = -7$

                  $y = 25.5$ $x = -10.5$

$y = -10.5x^2 + 25.5x - 7$

75. $1^2 + 1^2 + D(1) + E(1) + F = 0 \implies D + E + F = -2$

$3^2 + 3^2 + D(3) + E(3) + F = 0 \implies 3D + 3E + F = -18$

$4^2 + 2^2 + D(4) + E(2) + F = 0 \implies 4D + 2E + F = -20$

$$\begin{bmatrix} 1 & 1 & 1 & : & -2 \\ 3 & 3 & 1 & : & -18 \\ 4 & 2 & 1 & : & -20 \end{bmatrix}$$

$$\begin{matrix} \\ -3R_1 + R_2 \\ -4R_1 + R_3 \end{matrix} \begin{bmatrix} 1 & 1 & 1 & : & -2 \\ 0 & 0 & -2 & : & -12 \\ 0 & -2 & -3 & : & -12 \end{bmatrix}$$

—CONTINUED —

75. —CONTINUED —

$$\begin{matrix} R_2 \\ R_3 \end{matrix} \begin{bmatrix} 1 & 1 & 1 & : & -2 \\ 0 & -2 & -3 & : & -12 \\ 0 & 0 & -2 & : & -12 \end{bmatrix}$$

$$\begin{matrix} \\ -\frac{1}{2}R_2 \\ -\frac{1}{2}R_3 \end{matrix} \begin{bmatrix} 1 & 1 & 1 & : & -2 \\ 0 & 1 & \frac{3}{2} & : & 6 \\ 0 & 0 & 1 & : & 6 \end{bmatrix}$$

$F = 6 \qquad E + \frac{3}{2}(6) = 6 \qquad D + (-3) + 6 = -2$

$\qquad\qquad\qquad E + 9 = 6 \qquad\qquad D + 3 = -2$

$\qquad\qquad\qquad\qquad E = -3 \qquad\qquad\qquad D = -5$

$x^2 + y^2 - 5x - 3y + 6 = 0$

77. (a) $\quad 6 = a(0)^2 + b(0) + c \implies \quad 6 = \qquad\qquad c$

$\qquad 18.5 = a(25)^2 + b(25) + c \implies 18.5 = 625a + 25b + c$

$\qquad 26 = a(50)^2 + b(50) + c \implies 26 = 2500a + 50b + c$

$$\begin{bmatrix} 0 & 0 & 1 & : & 6 \\ 625 & 25 & 1 & : & 18.5 \\ 2500 & 50 & 1 & : & 26 \end{bmatrix}$$

$$\begin{matrix} R_1 \\ R_2 \\ R_3 \end{matrix} \begin{bmatrix} 625 & 25 & 1 & : & 18.5 \\ 2500 & 50 & 1 & : & 26 \\ 0 & 0 & 1 & : & 6 \end{bmatrix}$$

$$\frac{1}{625}R_1 \begin{bmatrix} 1 & 0.04 & 0.0016 & : & 0.0296 \\ 2500 & 50 & 1 & : & 26 \\ 0 & 0 & 1 & : & 6 \end{bmatrix}$$

$$-2500R_1 + R_2 \begin{bmatrix} 1 & 0.04 & 0.0016 & : & 0.0296 \\ 0 & -50 & -3 & : & -48 \\ 0 & 0 & 1 & : & 6 \end{bmatrix}$$

$$-\frac{1}{50}R_2 \begin{bmatrix} 1 & 0.04 & 0.0016 & : & 0.0296 \\ 0 & 1 & 0.06 & : & 0.96 \\ 0 & 0 & 1 & : & 6 \end{bmatrix}$$

$$-.04R_2 + R_1 \begin{bmatrix} 1 & 0 & -0.0008 & : & -0.0088 \\ 0 & 1 & 0.06 & : & 0.96 \\ 0 & 0 & 1 & : & 6 \end{bmatrix}$$

$$\begin{matrix} .0008R_3 + R_1 \\ -.06R_3 + R_2 \end{matrix} \begin{bmatrix} 1 & 0 & 0 & : & -0.004 \\ 0 & 1 & 0 & : & 0.6 \\ 0 & 0 & 1 & : & 6 \end{bmatrix}$$

so $a = -0.004$

$\quad b = 0.6$

$\quad c = 6$

$\quad y = -0.004x^2 + 0.6x + 6$

(b) *Keystrokes:*

[Y=] [(−)] .004 [X,T,θ] [x^2] [+] .6 [X,T,θ] [+] 6 [GRAPH]

(c) Maximum height = 28.5 feet

Point at which the ball struck the ground = 159.4 feet

79.
$$\begin{bmatrix} 4 & -2 & 1 & \vdots & 0 \\ -4 & 1 & 0 & \vdots & -9 \\ 1 & 0 & 0 & \vdots & 2 \end{bmatrix}$$

$$\begin{matrix} R_1 \\ \\ R_3 \end{matrix} \begin{bmatrix} 1 & 0 & 0 & 2 \\ -4 & 1 & 0 & -9 \\ 4 & -2 & 1 & 0 \end{bmatrix}$$

$$\begin{matrix} \\ 4R_1 + R_2 \\ -4R_1 + R_2 \end{matrix} \begin{bmatrix} 1 & 0 & 0 & \vdots & 2 \\ 0 & 1 & 0 & \vdots & -1 \\ 0 & -2 & 1 & \vdots & -8 \end{bmatrix}$$

$$\begin{matrix} \\ \\ 2R_2 + R_3 \end{matrix} \begin{bmatrix} 1 & 0 & 0 & \vdots & 2 \\ 0 & 1 & 0 & \vdots & -1 \\ 0 & 0 & 1 & \vdots & -10 \end{bmatrix}$$

$$\frac{2x^2 - 9x}{(x - 2)^3} = \frac{2}{x - 2} - \frac{1}{(x - 2)^2} - \frac{10}{(x - 2)^3}$$

81. (a) Interchange two rows.

(b) Multiply a row by a nonzero constant.

(c) Add a multiple of a row to another row.

83. The one matrix can be obtained from the other by using the elementary row operations.

85. There will be a row in the matrix with all zero entries except in the last column.

Section 8.5   Determinants and Linear Systems

1. $\det(A) = \begin{vmatrix} 2 & 1 \\ 3 & 4 \end{vmatrix} = 2(4) - 3(1) = 8 - 3 = 5$

3. $\det(A) = \begin{vmatrix} 5 & 2 \\ -5 & 3 \end{vmatrix} = 5(3) - (-6)(2) = 15 + 12 = 27$

5. $\det(A) = \begin{vmatrix} 5 & -4 \\ -10 & 8 \end{vmatrix} = 5(8) - (-10)(-4)$
$$= 40 - 40 = 0$$

7. $\det(A) = \begin{vmatrix} 2 & 6 \\ 0 & 3 \end{vmatrix} = 2(3) - 0(6) = 6 - 0 = 6$

9. $\det(A) = \begin{vmatrix} -7 & 3 \\ \frac{1}{2} & 6 \end{vmatrix} = (-7)(3) - (\frac{1}{2})(6)$
$$= -21 - 3 = -24$$

11. $\det(A) = \begin{vmatrix} 0.3 & 0.5 \\ 0.5 & 0.3 \end{vmatrix} = (0.3)(0.3) - (0.5)(0.5)$
$$= .09 - .25 = -0.16$$

13. $\det(A) = \begin{vmatrix} 2 & 3 & -1 \\ 6 & 0 & 0 \\ 4 & 1 & 1 \end{vmatrix}$

$$= -(6)\begin{vmatrix} 3 & -1 \\ 1 & 1 \end{vmatrix} + 0 + 0 \text{ (second row)}$$

$$= (-6)(4)$$

$$= -24$$

15. $\det(A) = \begin{vmatrix} 1 & 1 & 2 \\ 3 & 1 & 0 \\ -2 & 0 & 3 \end{vmatrix}$

$= (2)\begin{vmatrix} 3 & 1 \\ -2 & 0 \end{vmatrix} - (0)\begin{vmatrix} 1 & 1 \\ -2 & 0 \end{vmatrix} + (3)\begin{vmatrix} 1 & 1 \\ 3 & 1 \end{vmatrix}$ (third column)

$= (2)(2) - 0 + (3)(-2)$

$= 4 - 6 = -2$

17. $\det(A) = \begin{vmatrix} 2 & 4 & 6 \\ 0 & 3 & 1 \\ 0 & 0 & -5 \end{vmatrix}$

$= (2)\begin{vmatrix} 3 & 1 \\ 0 & -5 \end{vmatrix} - 0 + 0$ (first column)

$= (2)(-15) = -30$

19. $\det(A) = \begin{vmatrix} -2 & 2 & 3 \\ 1 & -1 & 0 \\ 0 & 1 & 4 \end{vmatrix}$

$= -(1)\begin{vmatrix} 2 & 3 \\ 1 & 4 \end{vmatrix} + (-1)\begin{vmatrix} -2 & 3 \\ 0 & 4 \end{vmatrix} - 0$ (second row)

$= (-1)(5) + (-1)(-8)$

$= -5 + 8 = 3$

21. $\det(A) = \begin{vmatrix} 1 & 4 & -2 \\ 3 & 6 & -6 \\ -2 & 1 & 4 \end{vmatrix}$

$= (1)\begin{vmatrix} 6 & -6 \\ 1 & 4 \end{vmatrix} - (4)\begin{vmatrix} 3 & -6 \\ -2 & 4 \end{vmatrix} + (-2)\begin{vmatrix} 3 & 6 \\ -2 & 1 \end{vmatrix}$ (first row)

$= (1)(30) - (4)(0) + (-2)(15)$

$= 30 - 0 - 30 = 0$

23. $\det(A) = \begin{vmatrix} -3 & 2 & 1 \\ 4 & 5 & 6 \\ 2 & 3 & 1 \end{vmatrix}$

$= (1)\begin{vmatrix} 4 & 5 \\ 2 & -3 \end{vmatrix} - (6)\begin{vmatrix} -3 & 2 \\ 2 & -3 \end{vmatrix} + (1)\begin{vmatrix} -3 & 2 \\ 4 & 5 \end{vmatrix}$ (third column)

$= (1)(-22) - (6)(5) + (1)(-3)$

$= -22 - 30 - 23 = -75$

25. $\det(A) = \begin{vmatrix} 1 & 4 & -2 \\ 3 & 2 & 0 \\ -1 & 4 & 3 \end{vmatrix}$

$= -(3)\begin{vmatrix} 4 & -2 \\ 4 & 3 \end{vmatrix} + (2)\begin{vmatrix} 1 & -2 \\ -1 & 3 \end{vmatrix} - 0$ (second row)

$= (-3)(20) + (2)(1)$

$= -60 + 2$

$= -58$

27. $\det(A) = \begin{vmatrix} 2 & -5 & 0 \\ 4 & 7 & 0 \\ -7 & 25 & 3 \end{vmatrix}$

$= 0 - 0 + 3\begin{vmatrix} 2 & -5 \\ 4 & 7 \end{vmatrix}$ (third column)

$= (3)(34)$

$= 102$

29. $\det(A) = \begin{vmatrix} 0.1 & 0.2 & 0.3 \\ -0.3 & 0.2 & 0.2 \\ 5 & 4 & 4 \end{vmatrix}$

$\qquad = (5)\begin{vmatrix} 0.2 & 0.3 \\ 0.2 & 0.2 \end{vmatrix} - (4)\begin{vmatrix} 0.1 & 0.3 \\ -0.3 & 0.2 \end{vmatrix} + (4)\begin{vmatrix} 0.1 & 0.2 \\ -0.3 & 0.2 \end{vmatrix}$ (third row)

$\qquad = (5)(-0.02) - (4)(0.11) + (4)(0.08)$

$\qquad = -0.1 - 0.44 + 0.32$

$\qquad = -0.22$

31. $\det(A) = \begin{vmatrix} x & y & 1 \\ 3 & 1 & 1 \\ -2 & 0 & 1 \end{vmatrix}$

$\qquad = (-2)\begin{vmatrix} y & 1 \\ 1 & 1 \end{vmatrix} - 0 + (1)\begin{vmatrix} x & y \\ 3 & 1 \end{vmatrix}$ (third row)

$\qquad = (-2)(y - 1) + (1)(x - 3y)$

$\qquad = -2y + 2 + x - 3y$

$\qquad = x - 5y + 2$

33. *Keystrokes:*

[MATRX] [EDIT 1] 3 [ENTER] 3 [ENTER] 5 [ENTER] [(−)] 3 [ENTER] 2 [ENTER] 7 [ENTER] 5 [ENTER] [(−)] 7 [ENTER]

0 [ENTER] 6 [ENTER] [(−)] 1 [ENTER] [QUIT]

[MATRX] [MATH 1] [MATRX 1] [ENTER]

Solution is 248.

35. *Keystrokes:*

[MATRX] [EDIT 1] 3 [ENTER] 3 [ENTER] 3 [ENTER] [(−)] 1 [ENTER]

2 [ENTER] 1 [ENTER] [(−)] 1 [ENTER] 2 [ENTER] [(−)] 2 [ENTER] 3 [ENTER] 10 [ENTER] [QUIT]

[MATRX] [MATH 1] [MATRX 1] [ENTER]

Solution is −32.

37. *Keystrokes:*

[MATRX] [EDIT 1] 3 [ENTER] 3 [ENTER] .2 [ENTER] .8 [ENTER] [(−)] [ENTER] .3

.1 [ENTER] .8 [ENTER] .6 [ENTER] [(−)] 10 [ENTER] [(−)] 5 [ENTER]

1 [ENTER] [QUIT]

[MATRX] [MATH 1] [MATRX 1] [ENTER]

Solution is −6.37

39. $\begin{bmatrix} 1 & 2 & \vdots & 5 \\ -1 & 1 & \vdots & 1 \end{bmatrix}$

$D = \begin{vmatrix} 1 & 2 \\ -1 & 1 \end{vmatrix} = 1 - (-2) = 3$

$x = \dfrac{D_x}{D} = \dfrac{\begin{vmatrix} 5 & 2 \\ 1 & 1 \end{vmatrix}}{3} = \dfrac{5-2}{3} = \dfrac{3}{3} = 1$

$y = \dfrac{D_y}{D} = \dfrac{\begin{vmatrix} 1 & 5 \\ -1 & 1 \end{vmatrix}}{3} = \dfrac{1-(-5)}{3} = \dfrac{6}{3} = 2$

$(1, 2)$

41. $\begin{bmatrix} 3 & 4 & \vdots & -2 \\ 5 & 3 & \vdots & 4 \end{bmatrix}$

$D = \begin{vmatrix} 3 & 4 \\ 5 & 3 \end{vmatrix} = 9 - 20 = -11$

$x = \dfrac{D_x}{D} = \dfrac{\begin{vmatrix} -2 & 4 \\ 4 & 3 \end{vmatrix}}{-11} = \dfrac{-6-16}{-11} = \dfrac{-22}{-11} = 2$

$y = \dfrac{D_y}{D} = \dfrac{\begin{vmatrix} 3 & -2 \\ 5 & 4 \end{vmatrix}}{-11} = \dfrac{12-(-10)}{-11} = \dfrac{22}{-11} = -2$

$(2, -2)$

43. $\begin{bmatrix} 20 & 8 & \vdots & 11 \\ 12 & -24 & \vdots & 21 \end{bmatrix}$

$D = \begin{vmatrix} 20 & 8 \\ 12 & -24 \end{vmatrix} = -480 - 96 = -576$

$x = \dfrac{D_x}{D} = \dfrac{\begin{vmatrix} 11 & 8 \\ 21 & -24 \end{vmatrix}}{-576} = \dfrac{-264-168}{-576} = \dfrac{-432}{-576} = \dfrac{3}{4}$

$y = \dfrac{D_y}{D} = \dfrac{\begin{vmatrix} 20 & 11 \\ 12 & 21 \end{vmatrix}}{-576} = \dfrac{420-132}{-576} = \dfrac{288}{-576} = -\dfrac{1}{2}$

$\left(\dfrac{3}{4}, -\dfrac{1}{2}\right)$

45. $\begin{bmatrix} -0.4 & 0.8 & \vdots & 1.6 \\ 2 & -4 & \vdots & 5 \end{bmatrix}$

$D = \begin{vmatrix} -0.4 & 0.8 \\ 2 & -4 \end{vmatrix} = 1.6 - 1.6 = 0$

Cannot be solved by Cramer's Rule because $D = 0$.

Solve by elimination.

$\begin{aligned} -4x + 8y &= 16 \implies -4x + 8y = 16 \\ 2x - 4y &= 5 \implies \underline{4x - 8y = 10} \\ & \qquad\qquad\qquad\qquad 0 \neq 26 \end{aligned}$

Inconsistent; no solution

47. $\begin{bmatrix} 3 & 6 & \vdots & 5 \\ 6 & 14 & \vdots & 11 \end{bmatrix}$

$D = \begin{vmatrix} 3 & 6 \\ 6 & 14 \end{vmatrix} = 42 - 36 = 6$

$x = \dfrac{D_x}{D} = \dfrac{\begin{vmatrix} 5 & 6 \\ 11 & 14 \end{vmatrix}}{6} = \dfrac{70-66}{6} = \dfrac{4}{6} = \dfrac{2}{3}$

$y = \dfrac{D_y}{D} = \dfrac{\begin{vmatrix} 3 & 5 \\ 6 & 11 \end{vmatrix}}{6} = \dfrac{33-30}{6} = \dfrac{3}{6} = \dfrac{1}{2}$

$\left(\dfrac{2}{3}, \dfrac{1}{2}\right)$

49. $\begin{bmatrix} 4 & -1 & 1 & \vdots & -5 \\ 2 & 2 & 3 & \vdots & 10 \\ 5 & -2 & 6 & \vdots & 1 \end{bmatrix}$

$D = \begin{vmatrix} 4 & -1 & 1 \\ 2 & 2 & 3 \\ 5 & -2 & 6 \end{vmatrix} = (1)\begin{vmatrix} 2 & 2 \\ 5 & -2 \end{vmatrix} - (3)\begin{vmatrix} 4 & -1 \\ 5 & -2 \end{vmatrix} + (6)\begin{vmatrix} 4 & -1 \\ 2 & 2 \end{vmatrix}$

$\qquad = (1)(-14) + (-3)(-3) + (6)(10)$

$\qquad = -14 + 9 + 60 = 55$

—CONTINUED—

49. —CONTINUED—

$$x = \dfrac{\begin{vmatrix} -5 & -1 & 1 \\ 10 & 2 & 3 \\ 1 & -2 & 6 \end{vmatrix}}{55} = \dfrac{(1)\begin{vmatrix} 10 & 2 \\ 1 & -2 \end{vmatrix} - (3)\begin{vmatrix} -5 & -1 \\ 1 & -2 \end{vmatrix} + (6)\begin{vmatrix} -5 & -1 \\ 10 & 2 \end{vmatrix}}{55}$$

$$= \dfrac{(1)(-22) + (-3)(11) + (6)(0)}{55}$$

$$= \dfrac{-22 - 33}{55} = \dfrac{-55}{55} = -1$$

$$y = \dfrac{\begin{vmatrix} 4 & -5 & 1 \\ 2 & 10 & 3 \\ 5 & 1 & 6 \end{vmatrix}}{55} = \dfrac{(1)\begin{vmatrix} 2 & 10 \\ 5 & 1 \end{vmatrix} - (3)\begin{vmatrix} 4 & -5 \\ 5 & 1 \end{vmatrix} + (6)\begin{vmatrix} 4 & -5 \\ 2 & 10 \end{vmatrix}}{55}$$

$$= \dfrac{(1)(-48) + (-3)(29) + (6)(50)}{55}$$

$$= \dfrac{-48 - 87 + 300}{55} = \dfrac{165}{55} = 3$$

$$z = \dfrac{\begin{vmatrix} 4 & -1 & -5 \\ 2 & 2 & 10 \\ 5 & -2 & 1 \end{vmatrix}}{55} = \dfrac{(5)\begin{vmatrix} -1 & -5 \\ 2 & 10 \end{vmatrix} - (-2)\begin{vmatrix} 4 & -5 \\ 2 & 10 \end{vmatrix} + (1)\begin{vmatrix} 4 & -1 \\ 2 & 2 \end{vmatrix}}{55}$$

$$= \dfrac{(5)(0) + (2)(50) + (1)(10)}{55}$$

$$= \dfrac{0 + 100 + 10}{55} = \dfrac{110}{55} = 2$$

$(-1, 3, 2)$

51. $\begin{bmatrix} 3 & 4 & 4 & \vdots & 11 \\ 4 & -4 & 6 & \vdots & 11 \\ 6 & -6 & 0 & \vdots & 3 \end{bmatrix}$

$$D = \begin{vmatrix} 3 & 4 & 4 \\ 4 & -4 & 3 \\ 6 & -6 & 0 \end{vmatrix} = (4)\begin{vmatrix} 4 & -4 \\ 6 & -6 \end{vmatrix} - (6)\begin{vmatrix} 3 & 4 \\ 6 & -6 \end{vmatrix} + 0$$

$$= (4)(0) - (6)(-42) + 0$$

$$= 252$$

$$x = \dfrac{\begin{vmatrix} 11 & 4 & 4 \\ 11 & -4 & 6 \\ 3 & -6 & 0 \end{vmatrix}}{252} = \dfrac{(4)\begin{vmatrix} 11 & -4 \\ 3 & -6 \end{vmatrix} - (6)\begin{vmatrix} 11 & 4 \\ 3 & -6 \end{vmatrix} + 0}{252}$$

$$= \dfrac{(4)(-54) - (6)(-78)}{252}$$

$$= \dfrac{-216 - 468}{252} = \dfrac{252}{252} = 1$$

—CONTINUED—

51. —CONTINUED—

$$y = \frac{\begin{vmatrix} 3 & 11 & 4 \\ 4 & 11 & 6 \\ 6 & 3 & 0 \end{vmatrix}}{252} = \frac{(4)\begin{vmatrix} 4 & 11 \\ 6 & 3 \end{vmatrix} - (6)\begin{vmatrix} 3 & 11 \\ 6 & 3 \end{vmatrix} + 0}{252}$$

$$= \frac{(4)(-54) - (6)(-57)}{252}$$

$$= \frac{-216 + 342}{252} = \frac{126}{252} = \frac{1}{2}$$

$$z = \frac{\begin{vmatrix} 3 & 4 & 11 \\ 4 & -4 & 11 \\ 6 & -6 & 3 \end{vmatrix}}{252} = \frac{(3)\begin{vmatrix} -4 & 11 \\ -6 & 3 \end{vmatrix} - (4)\begin{vmatrix} 4 & 11 \\ -6 & 3 \end{vmatrix} + (6)\begin{vmatrix} 4 & 11 \\ -4 & 11 \end{vmatrix}}{252}$$

$$= \frac{(3)(54) - (4)(78) + (6)(88)}{252}$$

$$= \frac{162 - 312 + 528}{252} = \frac{378}{252} = \frac{3}{2}$$

$$\left(1, \frac{1}{2}, \frac{3}{2}\right)$$

53. $\begin{bmatrix} 3 & 3 & 4 & \vdots & 1 \\ 3 & 5 & 9 & \vdots & 2 \\ 5 & 9 & 14 & \vdots & 4 \end{bmatrix}$

$$D = \begin{vmatrix} 3 & 3 & 4 \\ 3 & 5 & 9 \\ 5 & 9 & 17 \end{vmatrix} = (3)\begin{vmatrix} 5 & 9 \\ 9 & 17 \end{vmatrix} - (3)\begin{vmatrix} 3 & 4 \\ 9 & 17 \end{vmatrix} + (5)\begin{vmatrix} 3 & 4 \\ 5 & 9 \end{vmatrix}$$

$$= (3)(4) - (3)(15) + (5)(7)$$

$$= 12 - 45 + 35$$

$$= 2$$

$$a = \frac{\begin{vmatrix} 1 & 3 & 4 \\ 2 & 5 & 9 \\ 4 & 9 & 17 \end{vmatrix}}{2} = \frac{(1)\begin{vmatrix} 5 & 9 \\ 9 & 17 \end{vmatrix} - (2)\begin{vmatrix} 3 & 4 \\ 9 & 17 \end{vmatrix} + (4)\begin{vmatrix} 3 & 4 \\ 5 & 9 \end{vmatrix}}{2}$$

$$= \frac{(1)(4) - (2)(15) + (4)(7)}{2}$$

$$= \frac{4 - 30 + 28}{2} = \frac{2}{2} = 1$$

$$b = \frac{\begin{vmatrix} 3 & 1 & 4 \\ 3 & 2 & 9 \\ 5 & 4 & 17 \end{vmatrix}}{2} = \frac{(3)\begin{vmatrix} 2 & 9 \\ 4 & 17 \end{vmatrix} - (2)\begin{vmatrix} 3 & 9 \\ 5 & 17 \end{vmatrix} + (4)\begin{vmatrix} 3 & 2 \\ 5 & 4 \end{vmatrix}}{2}$$

$$= \frac{(3)(-2) - (1)(6) + (4)(2)}{2}$$

$$= \frac{-6 - 6 + 8}{2} = \frac{-4}{2} = -2$$

—CONTINUED—

53. —CONTINUED—

$$c = \dfrac{\begin{vmatrix} 3 & 3 & 1 \\ 3 & 5 & 2 \\ 5 & 9 & 4 \end{vmatrix}}{2} = \dfrac{(1)\begin{vmatrix} 3 & 5 \\ 5 & 9 \end{vmatrix} - (2)\begin{vmatrix} 3 & 3 \\ 5 & 9 \end{vmatrix} + (4)\begin{vmatrix} 3 & 3 \\ 3 & 5 \end{vmatrix}}{2}$$

$$= \dfrac{(1)(2) - (2)(12) + (4)(6)}{2}$$

$$= \dfrac{2 - 24 + 24}{2} = \dfrac{2}{2} = 1$$

$(1, -2, 1)$

55. $\begin{bmatrix} 5 & -3 & 2 & \vdots & 2 \\ 2 & 2 & -3 & \vdots & 3 \\ 1 & -7 & 8 & \vdots & -4 \end{bmatrix}$

$$D = \begin{vmatrix} 5 & -3 & 2 \\ 2 & 2 & -3 \\ 1 & 7 & 8 \end{vmatrix} = (5)\begin{vmatrix} 2 & -3 \\ -7 & 8 \end{vmatrix} - (2)\begin{vmatrix} -3 & 2 \\ -7 & 8 \end{vmatrix} + (1)\begin{vmatrix} -3 & 2 \\ 2 & -3 \end{vmatrix}$$

$$= (5)(-5) - (2)(-10) + (1)(5)$$

$$= -25 + 20 + 5$$

$$= 0$$

Cannot be solved by Cramer's Rule because $D = 0$.

57. $\begin{bmatrix} -3 & 10 & \vdots & 22 \\ 9 & -3 & \vdots & 0 \end{bmatrix}$

$$D = \begin{vmatrix} -3 & 10 \\ 9 & -3 \end{vmatrix} = -81$$

$$x = \dfrac{D_x}{D} = \dfrac{\begin{vmatrix} 22 & 10 \\ 0 & -3 \end{vmatrix}}{-81} = \dfrac{-66}{-81} = \dfrac{22}{27}$$

$$y = \dfrac{D_y}{D} = \dfrac{\begin{vmatrix} -3 & 22 \\ 9 & 0 \end{vmatrix}}{-81} = \dfrac{-198}{-81} = \dfrac{22}{9}$$

Keystrokes:

det D

[MATRX] [EDIT 1] 2 [ENTER] 2 [ENTER]

Enter each number in matrix followed by [ENTER]

[QUIT]

[MATRX] [MATH 1] [MATRX 1] [ENTER]

det D_x

[MATRX] [EDIT 2] 2 [ENTER] 2 [ENTER]

Enter each number in matrix followed by [ENTER]

[QUIT]

[MATRX] [MATH 1] [MATRX 2] [ENTER]

det D_y

[MATRX] [EDIT 3] 2 [ENTER] 2 [ENTER]

Enter each number in matrix followed by [ENTER]

[QUIT]

[MATRX] [MATH 1] [MATRX 3] [ENTER]

59. $D = \begin{vmatrix} 3 & -2 & 3 \\ 1 & 3 & 6 \\ 1 & 2 & 9 \end{vmatrix} = 48$

$$x = \frac{D_x}{D} = \frac{\begin{vmatrix} 8 & -2 & 3 \\ -3 & 3 & 6 \\ -5 & 2 & 9 \end{vmatrix}}{48} = \frac{153}{48} = \frac{51}{16}$$

$$y = \frac{D_y}{D} = \frac{\begin{vmatrix} 3 & 8 & 3 \\ 1 & -3 & 6 \\ 1 & -5 & 9 \end{vmatrix}}{48} = \frac{-21}{48} = \frac{-7}{16}$$

$$z = \frac{D_z}{D} = \frac{\begin{vmatrix} 3 & -2 & 8 \\ 1 & 3 & -3 \\ 1 & 2 & -5 \end{vmatrix}}{48} = \frac{-39}{48} = -\frac{13}{16}$$

$\left(\dfrac{51}{16}, -\dfrac{7}{16}, -\dfrac{13}{16} \right)$

Keystrokes:

det D [MATRX] [EDIT 1] 3 [ENTER] 3 [ENTER]

Enter each number in matrix followed by [ENTER] .

[QUIT]

[MATRX] [MATH 1] [MATRX 1] [ENTER]

det D_x [MATRX] [EDIT 2] 3 [ENTER] 3 [ENTER]

Enter each number in matrix followed by [ENTER] .

[QUIT]

[MATRX] [MATH 1] [MATRX 2] [ENTER]

det D_y [MATRX] [EDIT 3] 3 [ENTER] 3 [ENTER]

Enter each number in matrix followed by [ENTER] .

[QUIT]

[MATRX] [MATH 1] [MATRX 3] [ENTER]

det D_z [MATRX] [EDIT 4] 3 [ENTER] 3 [ENTER]

Enter each number in matrix followed by [ENTER] .

[QUIT]

[MATRX] [MATH 1] [MATRX 4] [ENTER]

61. $(5 - x)(2 - x) - 4 = 0$

$10 - 7x + x^2 - 4 = 0$

$x^2 - 7x + 6 = 0$

$(x - 6)(x - 1) = 0$

$x = 6 \quad x = 1$

63. $(x_1, y_1) = (0, 3), (x_2, y_2) = (4, 0), (x_3, y_3) = (8, 5)$

$$\begin{vmatrix} x_1 & y_1 & 1 \\ x_2 & y_2 & 1 \\ x_3 & y_3 & 1 \end{vmatrix} = \begin{vmatrix} 0 & 3 & 1 \\ 4 & 0 & 1 \\ 8 & 5 & 1 \end{vmatrix} = 32$$

Area $= +\dfrac{1}{2}(32) = 16$

65. $(x_1, y_1) = (0, 0), (x_2, y_2) = (3, 1), (x_3, y_3) = (1, 5)$

$$\begin{vmatrix} x_1 & y_1 & 1 \\ x_2 & y_2 & 1 \\ x_3 & y_3 & 1 \end{vmatrix} = \begin{vmatrix} 0 & 0 & 1 \\ 3 & 1 & 1 \\ 1 & 5 & 1 \end{vmatrix} = (1)\begin{vmatrix} 3 & 1 \\ 1 & 5 \end{vmatrix}$$

$$= (1)(14) = 14$$

Area $= +\dfrac{1}{2}(14) = 7$

67. $(x_1, y_1) = (-2, 1), (x_2, y_2) = (3, -1), (x_3, y_3) = (1, 6)$

$$\begin{vmatrix} x_1 & y_1 & 1 \\ x_2 & y_2 & 1 \\ x_3 & y_3 & 1 \end{vmatrix} = \begin{vmatrix} -2 & 1 & 1 \\ 3 & -1 & 1 \\ 1 & 6 & 1 \end{vmatrix} = (1)\begin{vmatrix} 3 & -1 \\ 1 & 6 \end{vmatrix} - (1)\begin{vmatrix} -2 & 1 \\ 1 & 6 \end{vmatrix} + (1)\begin{vmatrix} -2 & 1 \\ 3 & -1 \end{vmatrix}$$

$$= (1)(19) - (1)(-13) + (1)(-1)$$

$$= 19 + 13 - 1$$

$$= 31$$

Area $= +\dfrac{1}{2}(31) = \dfrac{31}{2}$ or $15\dfrac{1}{2}$

69. $(x_1, y_1) = \left(0, \frac{1}{2}\right)$ $(x_2, y_2) = \left(\frac{5}{2}, 0\right)$ $(x_3, y_3) = (4, 3)$

$$\begin{vmatrix} x_1 & y_1 & 1 \\ x_2 & y_2 & 1 \\ x_3 & y_3 & 1 \end{vmatrix} = \begin{vmatrix} 0 & \frac{1}{2} & 1 \\ \frac{5}{2} & 0 & 1 \\ 4 & 3 & 1 \end{vmatrix} = 0\begin{vmatrix} 0 & 1 \\ 3 & 1 \end{vmatrix} - \frac{1}{2}\begin{vmatrix} \frac{5}{2} & 1 \\ 4 & 1 \end{vmatrix} + 1\begin{vmatrix} \frac{5}{2} & 0 \\ 4 & 3 \end{vmatrix}$$

$$= 0 - \frac{1}{2}\left(\frac{5}{2} - 4\right) + 1\left(\frac{15}{2} - 0\right)$$

$$= -\frac{1}{2}\left(-\frac{3}{2}\right) + 1\left(\frac{15}{2}\right)$$

$$= \frac{3}{4} + \frac{15}{2}$$

$$= \frac{3}{4} + \frac{30}{4}$$

$$= \frac{33}{4}$$

Area $= \frac{1}{2}\left(\frac{33}{4}\right) = \frac{33}{8}$

71. Verbal model: $\boxed{\begin{array}{c}\text{Area of}\\\text{Shaded Region}\end{array}} = \boxed{\begin{array}{c}\text{Area of}\\\text{Triangle 1}\end{array}} + \boxed{\begin{array}{c}\text{Area of}\\\text{Triangle 2}\end{array}}$

Equation: $A = 11.5 + 4.5$

$\qquad = 16$

Let $(x_1, y_1) = (-1, 2)$ $(x_2, y_2) = (4, 0)$ $(x_3, y_3) = (3, 5)$

$$\begin{vmatrix} x_1 & y_1 & 1 \\ x_2 & y_2 & 1 \\ x_3 & y_3 & 1 \end{vmatrix} = \begin{vmatrix} -1 & 2 & 1 \\ 4 & 0 & 1 \\ 3 & 5 & 1 \end{vmatrix} = -4\begin{vmatrix} 2 & 1 \\ 5 & 1 \end{vmatrix} + 0 - 1\begin{vmatrix} -1 & 2 \\ 3 & 5 \end{vmatrix}$$

$$= -4(-3) - 1(-11) = 12 + 11 = 23$$

Area $= \frac{1}{2}(23) = 11.5$

Let $(x_1, y_1) = (3, 5)$ $(x_2, y_2) = (4, 0)$ $(x_3, y_3) = (5, 4)$

$$\begin{vmatrix} x_1 & y_1 & 1 \\ x_2 & y_2 & 1 \\ x_3 & y_3 & 1 \end{vmatrix} = \begin{vmatrix} 3 & 5 & 1 \\ 4 & 0 & 1 \\ 5 & 4 & 1 \end{vmatrix} = -4\begin{vmatrix} 5 & 1 \\ 4 & 1 \end{vmatrix} + 0 - 1\begin{vmatrix} 3 & 5 \\ 5 & 4 \end{vmatrix}$$

$$= -4(1) - 1(-13) = -4 + 13 = 9$$

Area $= \frac{1}{2}(9) = 4.5$

73. *Verbal Model:* $\boxed{\begin{array}{c}\text{Area of}\\\text{Shaded Region}\end{array}} = \boxed{\begin{array}{c}\text{Area of}\\\text{Rectangle}\end{array}} - \boxed{\begin{array}{c}\text{Area of}\\\text{Triangle}\end{array}}$

Equation: $A = (9)(4) - 9.5$

$\qquad = 36 - 9.5$

$\qquad = 26.5$

Let $(x_1, y_1) = (-3, -1), (x_2, y_2) = (2, -2), (x_3, y_3) = (1, 2)$

$$\begin{vmatrix} x_1 & y_1 & 1 \\ x_2 & y_2 & 1 \\ x_3 & y_3 & 1 \end{vmatrix} = \begin{vmatrix} -3 & -1 & 1 \\ 2 & -2 & 1 \\ 1 & 2 & 1 \end{vmatrix} = 19$$

Area $= \frac{1}{2}(19) = 9.5$

75.

From diagram the coordinates of A, B, C are determined to be $A(0, 20)$, $B(10, -5)$ and $C(28, 0)$.

$$\begin{vmatrix} x_1 & y_1 & 1 \\ x_2 & y_2 & 1 \\ x_3 & y_3 & 1 \end{vmatrix} = \begin{vmatrix} 0 & 20 & 1 \\ 10 & -5 & 1 \\ 28 & 0 & 1 \end{vmatrix} = -500$$

Area $= -\frac{1}{2}(-500) = 250 \text{ mi}^2$

77. Let $(x_1, y_1) = (-1, 11)$, $(x_2, y_2) = (0, 8)$, $(x_3, y_3) = (2, 2)$

$$\begin{vmatrix} x_1 & y_1 & 1 \\ x_2 & y_2 & 1 \\ x_3 & y_3 & 1 \end{vmatrix} = \begin{vmatrix} -1 & 11 & 1 \\ 0 & 8 & 1 \\ 2 & 2 & 1 \end{vmatrix} = (-1)\begin{vmatrix} 8 & 1 \\ 2 & 1 \end{vmatrix} + 0 + (2)\begin{vmatrix} 11 & 1 \\ 8 & 1 \end{vmatrix}$$

$$= (-1)(6) + (2)(3)$$

$$= -6 + 6$$

$$= 0$$

The three points are collinear.

79. $(x_1, y_1) = (-1, -5)$, $(x_2, y_2) = (1, -1)$, $(x_3, y_3) = (4, 5)$

$$\begin{vmatrix} x_1 & y_1 & 1 \\ x_2 & y_2 & 1 \\ x_3 & y_3 & 1 \end{vmatrix} = \begin{vmatrix} -1 & -5 & 1 \\ 1 & -1 & 1 \\ 4 & 5 & 1 \end{vmatrix} = (1)\begin{vmatrix} 1 & -1 \\ 4 & 5 \end{vmatrix} - (1)\begin{vmatrix} -1 & -5 \\ 4 & 5 \end{vmatrix} + (1)\begin{vmatrix} -1 & -5 \\ 1 & -1 \end{vmatrix}$$

$$= (1)(9) - (1)(15) + (1)(6)$$

$$= 9 - 15 + 6$$

$$= 0$$

The three points are collinear.

81. Let $(x_1, y_1) = \left(-2, \frac{1}{3}\right)$, $(x_2, y_2) = (2, 1)$, $(x_3, y_3) = \left(3, \frac{1}{5}\right)$

$$\begin{vmatrix} x_1 & y_1 & 1 \\ x_2 & y_2 & 1 \\ x_3 & y_3 & 1 \end{vmatrix} = \begin{vmatrix} -2 & \frac{1}{3} & 1 \\ 2 & 1 & 1 \\ 3 & \frac{1}{5} & 1 \end{vmatrix} = (1)\begin{vmatrix} 2 & 1 \\ 3 & \frac{1}{5} \end{vmatrix} - (1)\begin{vmatrix} -2 & \frac{1}{3} \\ 3 & \frac{1}{5} \end{vmatrix} + (1)\begin{vmatrix} -2 & \frac{1}{3} \\ 2 & 1 \end{vmatrix}$$

$$= (1)\left(-\frac{13}{5}\right) - (1)\left(-\frac{7}{5}\right) + (1)\left(-\frac{8}{3}\right)$$

$$= -\frac{13}{5} + \frac{7}{5} - \frac{8}{3}$$

$$= -\frac{18}{15} - \frac{40}{15}$$

$$= -\frac{58}{15}$$

The three points are not collinear.

83. $(x_1, y_1) = (0, 0)$, $(x_2, y_2) = (5, 3)$

$$\begin{vmatrix} x & y & 1 \\ 0 & 0 & 1 \\ 5 & 3 & 1 \end{vmatrix} = 0$$

$$(1)\begin{vmatrix} x & y \\ 5 & 3 \end{vmatrix} = 0$$

$$(1)(3x - 5y) = 0$$

$$3x - 5y = 0$$

85. $(x_1, y_1) = (10, 7)$, $(x_2, y_2) = (-2, -7)$

$$\begin{vmatrix} x & y & 1 \\ 10 & 7 & 1 \\ -2 & -7 & 1 \end{vmatrix} = 0$$

$$(1)\begin{vmatrix} 10 & 7 \\ -2 & -7 \end{vmatrix} - (1)\begin{vmatrix} x & y \\ -2 & -7 \end{vmatrix} + (1)\begin{vmatrix} x & y \\ 10 & 7 \end{vmatrix} = 0$$

$$(1)(-56) - (-7x + 2y) + (1)(7x - 10y) = 0$$

$$-56 + 7x - 2y + 7x - 10y = 0$$

$$14x - 12y - 56 = 0$$

$$7x - 6y - 28 = 0$$

87. $(x_1, y_1) = \left(-2, \frac{3}{2}\right)$, $(x_2, y_2) = (3, -3)$

$$\begin{vmatrix} x & y & 1 \\ -2 & \frac{3}{2} & 1 \\ 3 & -3 & 1 \end{vmatrix} = 0$$

$$x\begin{vmatrix} \frac{3}{2} & 1 \\ -3 & 1 \end{vmatrix} - y\begin{vmatrix} -2 & 1 \\ 3 & 1 \end{vmatrix} + 1\begin{vmatrix} -2 & \frac{3}{2} \\ 3 & -3 \end{vmatrix} = 0$$

$$\frac{9}{2}x + 5y + \frac{3}{2} = 0$$

$$9x + 10y + 3 = 0$$

89. $(x_1, y_1) = (2, 3.6)$ $(x_2, y_2) = (8, 10)$

$$\begin{vmatrix} x & y & 1 \\ 2 & 3.6 & 1 \\ 8 & 10 & 1 \end{vmatrix} = 0$$

$$x\begin{vmatrix} 3.6 & 1 \\ 10 & 1 \end{vmatrix} - y\begin{vmatrix} 2 & 1 \\ 8 & 1 \end{vmatrix} + 1\begin{vmatrix} 2 & 3.6 \\ 8 & 10 \end{vmatrix} = 0$$

$$x(3.6 - 10) - y(2 - 8) + 1(20 - 28.8) = 0$$

$$-6.4x + 6y - 8.8 = 0$$

$$-3.2x + 3y - 4.4 = 0$$

$$32x - 30y + 44 = 0$$

91.
$$1 = a(0)^2 + b(0) + c \implies 1 = \quad + c$$
$$-3 = a(1)^2 + b(1) + c \implies -3 = a + b + c$$
$$21 = a(-2)^2 + b(-2) + c \implies 21 = 4a + 2b + c$$

$$\begin{bmatrix} 0 & 0 & 1 & \vdots & 1 \\ 1 & 1 & 1 & \vdots & -3 \\ 4 & -2 & 1 & \vdots & 21 \end{bmatrix}$$

$$D = \begin{vmatrix} 0 & 0 & 1 \\ 1 & 1 & 1 \\ 4 & -2 & 1 \end{vmatrix} = (1)\begin{vmatrix} 1 & 1 \\ 4 & -2 \end{vmatrix} = (1)(-6) = -6$$

$$a = \frac{\begin{vmatrix} 1 & 0 & 1 \\ -3 & 1 & 1 \\ 21 & -2 & 1 \end{vmatrix}}{-6} = \frac{(1)\begin{vmatrix} 1 & 1 \\ -2 & 1 \end{vmatrix} - 0 + (1)\begin{vmatrix} -3 & 1 \\ 21 & -2 \end{vmatrix}}{-6}$$

$$= \frac{(1)(3) + (1)(-15)}{-6} = \frac{-12}{-6} = 2$$

$$b = \frac{\begin{vmatrix} 0 & 1 & 1 \\ 1 & -3 & 1 \\ 4 & 21 & 1 \end{vmatrix}}{-6} = \frac{-(1)\begin{vmatrix} 1 & 1 \\ 4 & 1 \end{vmatrix} + (1)\begin{vmatrix} 1 & -3 \\ 4 & 21 \end{vmatrix}}{-6}$$

$$= \frac{(-1)(3) + (1)(33)}{-6} = \frac{36}{-6} = -6$$

$$c = \frac{\begin{vmatrix} 0 & 0 & 1 \\ 1 & 1 & -3 \\ 4 & -2 & 21 \end{vmatrix}}{-6} = \frac{(1)\begin{vmatrix} 1 & 1 \\ 4 & -2 \end{vmatrix}}{-6} = \frac{(1)(-6)}{-6} = 1$$

$$y = 2x^2 - 6x + 1$$

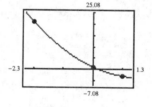

93. $6 = a(-2)^2 + b(-2) + c \implies 6 = 4a - 2b + c$

  $-2 = a \;(2)^2 + b \;(2) + c \implies -2 = 4a + 2b + c$

  $0 = a \;(4)^2 + b \;(4) + c \implies 6 = 16a + 4b + c$

$$\begin{bmatrix} 4 & -2 & 1 & \vdots & 6 \\ 4 & 2 & 1 & \vdots & -2 \\ 16 & 4 & 1 & \vdots & 0 \end{bmatrix} \qquad D = \begin{vmatrix} 4 & -2 & 1 \\ 4 & 2 & 1 \\ 16 & 4 & 1 \end{vmatrix} = -48$$

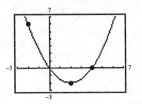

$$a = \frac{D_a}{D} = \frac{\begin{vmatrix} 6 & -2 & 1 \\ -2 & 2 & 1 \\ 0 & 4 & 1 \end{vmatrix}}{-48} = \frac{-24}{-48} = \frac{1}{2}$$

$$b = \frac{D_b}{D} = \frac{\begin{vmatrix} 4 & 6 & 1 \\ 4 & -2 & 1 \\ 16 & 0 & 1 \end{vmatrix}}{-48} = \frac{96}{-48} = -2$$

$$c = \frac{D_c}{D} = \frac{\begin{vmatrix} 4 & -2 & 6 \\ 4 & 2 & -2 \\ 16 & 4 & 0 \end{vmatrix}}{-48} = \frac{0}{-48} = 0$$

$$y = \frac{1}{2}x^2 - 2x$$

95. $-1 = a(1)^2 + b(1) + c \implies -1 = a + b + c$

  $-5 = a(-1)^2 + b(-1) + c \implies -5 = a - b + c$

  $\frac{1}{4} = a\left(\frac{1}{2}\right)^2 + b\left(\frac{1}{2}\right) + c \implies \frac{1}{4} = \frac{1}{4}a + \frac{1}{2}b + c$ or $1 = a + 2b + 4c$

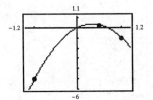

$$\begin{bmatrix} 1 & 1 & 1 & \vdots & -1 \\ 1 & -1 & 1 & \vdots & -5 \\ 1 & 2 & 4 & \vdots & 1 \end{bmatrix}$$

$$D = \begin{vmatrix} 1 & 1 & 1 \\ 1 & -1 & 1 \\ 1 & 2 & 4 \end{vmatrix} = (1)\begin{vmatrix} -1 & 1 \\ 2 & 4 \end{vmatrix} - (1)\begin{vmatrix} 1 & 1 \\ 2 & 4 \end{vmatrix} + (1)\begin{vmatrix} 1 & 1 \\ -1 & 1 \end{vmatrix}$$

$$= (1)(-6) - (1)(2) + (1)(2)$$

$$= -6 - 2 + 2$$

$$= -6$$

$$a = \frac{\begin{vmatrix} -1 & 1 & 1 \\ -5 & -1 & 1 \\ 1 & 2 & 4 \end{vmatrix}}{-6} = \frac{(-1)\begin{vmatrix} -1 & 1 \\ 2 & 4 \end{vmatrix} - (1)\begin{vmatrix} -5 & 1 \\ 1 & 4 \end{vmatrix} + (1)\begin{vmatrix} -5 & -1 \\ 1 & 2 \end{vmatrix}}{-6}$$

$$= \frac{(-1)(-6) - (1)(-21) + (1)(-9)}{-6}$$

$$= \frac{6 + 21 - 9}{-6} = \frac{18}{-6} = -3$$

—CONTINUED—

95. —CONTINUED—

$$b = \frac{\begin{vmatrix} 1 & -1 & 1 \\ 1 & -5 & 1 \\ 1 & 1 & 4 \end{vmatrix}}{-6} = \frac{(1)\begin{vmatrix} -5 & 1 \\ 1 & 4 \end{vmatrix} - (1)\begin{vmatrix} -1 & 1 \\ 1 & 4 \end{vmatrix} + (1)\begin{vmatrix} -1 & 1 \\ -5 & 1 \end{vmatrix}}{-6}$$

$$= \frac{(1)(-21) - (1)(-5) + (1)(4)}{-6}$$

$$= \frac{-21 + 5 + 4}{-6} = \frac{-12}{-6} = 2$$

$$c = \frac{\begin{vmatrix} 1 & 1 & -5 \\ 1 & -1 & -5 \\ 1 & 2 & 1 \end{vmatrix}}{-6} = \frac{(1)\begin{vmatrix} -1 & -5 \\ 2 & 1 \end{vmatrix} - (1)\begin{vmatrix} 1 & -1 \\ 2 & 1 \end{vmatrix} + (1)\begin{vmatrix} 1 & -1 \\ -1 & -5 \end{vmatrix}}{-6}$$

$$= \frac{(1)(9) - (1)(3) + (1)(-5)}{-6} = \frac{9 - 3 - 6}{-6} = 0$$

$$y = -3x^2 + 2x$$

97. (a) $(5, 584.7)$ $(6, 624.8)$ $(7, 689.2)$

$a(5)^2 + b(5) + c = 584.7 \Longrightarrow 25a + 5b + c = 584.7$

$a(6)^2 + b(6) + c = 624.8 \Longrightarrow 36a + 6b + c = 624.8$

$a(7)^2 + b(7) + c = 689.2 \Longrightarrow 49a + 7b + c = 689.2$

$$\det(A) = \begin{vmatrix} 25 & 5 & 1 \\ 36 & 6 & 1 \\ 49 & 7 & 1 \end{vmatrix} = -2$$

$$a_1 = \frac{\begin{vmatrix} 584.7 & 5 & 1 \\ 624.8 & 6 & 1 \\ 689.2 & 7 & 1 \end{vmatrix}}{-2} = \frac{-24.3}{-2} \qquad\qquad b_1 = \frac{\begin{vmatrix} 25 & 584.7 & 1 \\ 36 & 624.8 & 1 \\ 49 & 689.2 & 1 \end{vmatrix}}{-2} = \frac{187.1}{-2}$$

$$= 12.15 \qquad\qquad\qquad\qquad = -93.55$$

$$c_1 = \frac{\begin{vmatrix} 25 & 5 & 584.7 \\ 36 & 6 & 624.8 \\ 49 & 7 & 689.2 \end{vmatrix}}{-2} = \frac{-1497.4}{-2} = 748.7$$

$$y_1 = 12.15t^2 - 93.55t + 748.7$$

(b) $(5, 743.4)$ $(6, 791.4)$ $(7, 870.7)$

$a(5)^2 + b(5) + c = 743.4 \Longrightarrow 25a^2 + 5b + c = 743.4$

$a(6)^2 + b(6) + c = 791.4 \Longrightarrow 36a^2 + 6b + c = 791.4$

$a(7)^2 + b(7) + c = 870.7 \Longrightarrow 49a^2 + 7b + c = 870.7$

$$\det(A) = \begin{vmatrix} 25 & 5 & 1 \\ 36 & 6 & 1 \\ 49 & 7 & 1 \end{vmatrix} = -2 \qquad\qquad a_2 = \frac{\begin{vmatrix} 743.4 & 5 & 1 \\ 791.4 & 6 & 1 \\ 870.7 & 7 & 1 \end{vmatrix}}{-2} = \frac{-31.3}{-2} = 15.65$$

—CONTINUED—

97. —CONTINUED—

$$b_2 = \frac{\begin{vmatrix} 25 & 743.4 & 1 \\ 36 & 791.4 & 1 \\ 49 & 870.7 & 1 \end{vmatrix}}{-2} = \frac{248.3}{-2}$$

$$= -124.15$$

$$c_2 = \frac{\begin{vmatrix} 25 & 5 & 743.4 \\ 36 & 6 & 791.4 \\ 49 & 7 & 870.7 \end{vmatrix}}{-2} = \frac{-1945.8}{-2}$$

$$= 972.9$$

$$y_2 = 15.65t^2 - 124.15t + 972.9$$

(c)

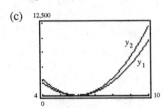

(d) $y_1 - y_2 = (12.15t^2 - 93.55t + 748.7) - (15.65t^2 - 124.15t + 972.9)$

$$= -3.5t^2 + 30.6t - 224.2$$

(e)

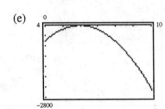

The trade deficit is increasing.

99. (a) $\begin{bmatrix} k & 1-k & \vdots & 1 \\ 1-k & k & \vdots & 3 \end{bmatrix}$

$$D = \begin{vmatrix} k & 1-k \\ 1-k & k \end{vmatrix} = k^2 - (1-k)^2 = k^2 - (1 - 2k + k^2) = k^2 - 1 + 2k - k^2 = 2k - 1$$

$$x = \frac{D_x}{D} = \frac{\begin{vmatrix} 1 & 1-k \\ 3 & k \end{vmatrix}}{2k - 1} = \frac{k - 3(1-k)}{2k - 1} = \frac{k - 3 + 3k}{2k - 1} = \frac{4k - 3}{2k - 1}$$

$$y = \frac{D_y}{D} = \frac{\begin{vmatrix} k & 1 \\ 1-k & 3 \end{vmatrix}}{2k - 1} = \frac{3k - 1(1-k)}{2k - 1} = \frac{3k - 1 + k}{2k - 1} = \frac{4k - 1}{2k - 1}$$

$$\left(\frac{4k - 3}{2k - 1}, \frac{4k - 1}{2k - 1} \right)$$

(b) $2k - 1 = 0$

$$2k = 1$$

$$k = \frac{1}{2}$$

101. A determinant is a real number associated with a square matrix.

103. The minor of an entry of a square matrix is the determinant of the matrix that remains after deleting the row and column in which the entry occurs.

Review Exercises for Chapter 8

1. (a) $(3, 4)$

$$3(3) + 7(4) \stackrel{?}{=} 2$$

$$37 \neq 2$$

Not a solution

(b) $(3, -1)$

$$3(3) + 7(-1) \stackrel{?}{=} 2 \qquad 5(3) + 6(-1) \stackrel{?}{=} 9$$

$$2 = 2 \qquad\qquad\qquad 9 = 9$$

Solution

3. (a) $(4, -5)$

$$4^2 + (-5)^2 \overset{?}{=} 41$$

$$41 = 41$$

$$20(4) + 10(-5) \overset{?}{=} 30$$

$$80 - 50 \overset{?}{=} 30$$

$$30 = 30$$

Solution

(b) $(7, 12)$

$$7^2 + 12^2 \overset{?}{=} 41$$

$$193 \neq 41$$

Not a solution

5. Solve each equation for y.

$$x + y = 2 \qquad\qquad x - y = 0$$

$$y = -x + 2 \qquad\qquad -y = -x$$

$$\qquad\qquad\qquad\qquad y = x$$

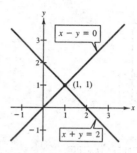

Point of intersection is $(1, 1)$.

7. Solve each equation for y.

$$x - y = 3 \qquad\qquad -x + y = 1$$

$$-y = -x + 3 \qquad\qquad y = x + 1$$

$$y = x - 3$$

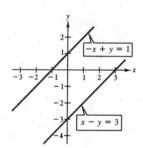

No solution

9. Solve each equation for y.

$$2x - y = 0 \qquad\qquad -x + y = 4$$

$$-y = -2x \qquad\qquad y = x + 4$$

$$y = 2x$$

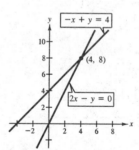

Point of intersection is $(4, 8)$.

11. Solve each equation for y.

$$2x + y = 4 \qquad\qquad -4x - 2y = -8$$

$$y = -2x + 4 \qquad\qquad -2y = 4x - 8$$

$$\qquad\qquad\qquad\qquad y = -2x + 4$$

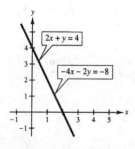

Infinite number of solutions.

13. Solve each equation for y.

$$3x - 2y = -2 \qquad\qquad -5x + 2y = 2$$

$$-2y = -3x - 2 \qquad\qquad 2y = 5x + 2$$

$$y = \tfrac{3}{2}x + 1 \qquad\qquad y = \tfrac{5}{2}x + 1$$

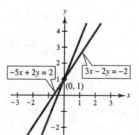

Point of intersection is $(0, 1)$.

15. Solve each equation for y.

$$5x - 3y = 3 \qquad\qquad 2x + 2y = 14$$

$$-3y = -5x + 3 \qquad\quad 2y = -2x + 14$$

$$y = \tfrac{5}{3}x - 1 \qquad\qquad y = -1x + 7$$

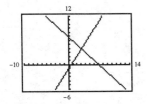

Keystrokes:

y_1 [Y=] [(] 5 [÷] 3 [)] [X,T,θ] [−] 1 [ENTER]

y_2 [(−)] [X,T,θ] [+] 7 [GRAPH]

Solution is $(3, 4)$

17. Solve each equation for y.

$$y = x^2 - 4 \qquad 2x - 3y = 11$$

$$-3y = -2x + 11$$

$$y = \tfrac{2}{3}x - \tfrac{11}{3}$$

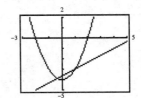

Keystrokes:

y_1 [Y=] [X,T,θ] [x^2] [−] 4 [ENTER]

y_2 [(] 2 [÷] 3 [)] [X,T,θ] [−] 11 [÷] 3 [GRAPH]

Solutions are $(1, -3)$ and $\left(-\tfrac{1}{3}, -\tfrac{35}{9}\right)$

19. $x = -2 - 4y$

$$2(-2 - 4y) + 3y = 1$$

$$-4 - 8y + 3y = 1$$

$$-5y = 5$$

$$y = -1$$

$$x = -2 - 4(-1)$$

$$x = 2$$

$(2, -1)$

21. $2y = 5x + 4$

$$y = \frac{5x + 4}{2}$$

$$10x - 4\left(\frac{5x + 4}{2}\right) = 7$$

$$10x - 2(5x + 4) = 7$$

$$10x - 10x - 8 = 7$$

$$-8 \neq 7$$

No solution

23. $3x = 7y + 5$

$$x = \frac{7y + 5}{3}$$

$$5\left(\frac{7y + 5}{3}\right) - 9y = -5$$

$$5(7y + 5) - 27y = -15$$

$$35y + 25 - 27y = -15$$

$$8y = -40$$

$$y = -5$$

$$x = \frac{7(-5) + 5}{3}$$

$$x = -10$$

$$(-10, -5)$$

25. $y = 5x^2$

$$y = -15x - 10$$

$$5x^2 = -15x - 10$$

$$5x^2 + 15x + 10 = 0$$

$$x^2 + 3x + 2 = 0$$

$$(x + 2)(x + 1) = 0$$

$$x = -2 \qquad x = -1$$

$$y = 5(-2)^2 \qquad y = 5(-1)^2$$

$$= 20 \qquad\qquad = 5$$

$$(-2, 20), (-1, 5)$$

27. $x^2 + y^2 = 1$

$$x + y = -1$$

$$y = -1 - x$$

$$x^2 + (-1 - x)^2 = 1$$

$$x^2 + 1 + 2x + x^2 = 1$$

$$2x^2 + 2x = 0$$

$$2x(x + 1) = 0$$

$$x = 0 \qquad x = -1$$

$$y = -1 \qquad y = 0$$

$$(0, -1), (-1, 0)$$

29. $x + y = 0 \implies \quad x + y = 0$

$2x + y = 0 \implies \underline{-2x - y = 0}$

$$-x \quad\;\; = 0$$

$$x \quad\;\; = 0$$

$$0 + y = 0$$

$$y = 0$$

$$(0, 0)$$

31. $2x - y = 2 \implies 16x - 8y = 16$

$6x + 8y = 39 \implies \underline{6x + 8y = 39}$

$$22x \qquad = 55$$

$$x \qquad = \frac{55}{22} = \frac{5}{2}$$

$$2\left(\frac{5}{2}\right) - y = 2$$

$$5 - y = 2$$

$$-y = -3$$

$$y = 3$$

$$\left(\frac{5}{2}, 3\right)$$

33. $0.2x + 0.3y = 0.14 \implies 2x + 3y = 1.4 \implies -4x - 6y = -2.8$
$0.4x + 0.5y = 0.20 \implies 4x + 5y = 2 \implies \underline{4x + 5y = 2}$

$$-y = -0.8$$
$$y = 0.8$$

$$2x + 3(0.8) = 1.4$$
$$2x + 2.4 = 1.4$$
$$2x = -1$$
$$x = -\tfrac{1}{2} = -0.5$$

$(-0.5, 0.8)$

35.
$$x - y - 2z = -1$$
$$2x + 3y + z = -2$$
$$5x + 4y + 2z = 4$$

$$x - y - 2z = -1$$
$$5y + 5z = 0$$
$$9y + 12z = 9$$

$$x - y - 2z = -1$$
$$y + z = 0$$
$$9y + 12z = 9$$

$$x - y - 2z = -1$$
$$y + z = 0$$
$$3z = 9$$

$$x - y - 2z = -1$$
$$y + z = 0$$
$$z = 3$$

$$y + 3 = 0$$
$$y = -3$$

$$x - (-3) - 2(3) = -1$$
$$x + 3 - 6 = -1$$
$$x = 2$$

$(2, -3, 3)$

37.
$$x - y - z = 1$$
$$-2x + y + 3z = -5$$
$$3x + 4y - z = 6$$

$$x - y - z = 1$$
$$-y + z = -3$$
$$7y + 2z = 3$$

$$x - y - z = 1$$
$$-y + z = -3$$
$$9z = -18$$
$$z = -2$$

$$-y + (-2) = -3$$
$$-y = -1$$
$$y = 1$$

$$x - 1 - (-2) = 1$$
$$x = 0$$

$(0, 1, -2)$

39.
$$x - 4z = 17$$
$$-2x + 4y + 3z = -14$$
$$5x - y + 2z = -3$$

$$x - 4z = 17$$
$$18x + 11z = -26$$
$$5x - y + 2z = -3$$

$$x - 4z = 17$$
$$83z = -332$$
$$5x - y + 2z = -3$$

$$z = -4$$

$$x - 4(-4) = 17$$
$$x = 1$$

$$5(1) - y + 2(-4) = -3$$
$$-y = 0$$
$$y = 0$$

$(1, 0, -4)$

41.
$$\begin{bmatrix} 5 & 4 & \vdots & 2 \\ -1 & 1 & \vdots & -22 \end{bmatrix}$$

$$\begin{matrix} R_1 \\ R_2 \end{matrix} \begin{bmatrix} -1 & 1 & \vdots & -22 \\ 5 & 4 & \vdots & 2 \end{bmatrix}$$

$$-R_1 \begin{bmatrix} 1 & -1 & \vdots & 22 \\ 5 & 4 & \vdots & 2 \end{bmatrix}$$

$$-5R_1 + R_2 \begin{bmatrix} 1 & -1 & \vdots & 22 \\ 0 & 9 & \vdots & -108 \end{bmatrix}$$

$$\tfrac{1}{9}R_2 \begin{bmatrix} 1 & -1 & \vdots & 22 \\ 0 & 1 & \vdots & -12 \end{bmatrix}$$

$$y = -12 \qquad x - (-12) = 22 \qquad (10, -12)$$
$$x = 10$$

43.
$$\begin{bmatrix} .2 & -.1 & \vdots & .07 \\ .4 & -.5 & \vdots & -.01 \end{bmatrix}$$

$$\begin{matrix} 10R_1 \\ 10R_2 \end{matrix} \begin{bmatrix} 2 & -1 & \vdots & .7 \\ 4 & -5 & \vdots & -.1 \end{bmatrix}$$

$$\tfrac{1}{2}R_1 \begin{bmatrix} 1 & -\tfrac{1}{2} & \vdots & .35 \\ 4 & -5 & \vdots & -.1 \end{bmatrix}$$

$$-4R_1 + R_2 \begin{bmatrix} 1 & -\tfrac{1}{2} & \vdots & .35 \\ 0 & -3 & \vdots & -1.5 \end{bmatrix}$$

$$-\tfrac{1}{3}R_2 \begin{bmatrix} 1 & -\tfrac{1}{2} & \vdots & .35 \\ 0 & 1 & \vdots & 5 \end{bmatrix}$$

$$y = .5 \qquad x - \tfrac{1}{2}(.5) = .35 \qquad (0.6, 0.5)$$
$$x = .6$$

45.
$$\begin{bmatrix} 1 & 2 & 6 & \vdots & 4 \\ -3 & 2 & -1 & \vdots & -4 \\ 4 & 0 & 2 & \vdots & 16 \end{bmatrix}$$

$$\begin{matrix} 3R_1 + R_2 \\ -4R_1 + R_3 \end{matrix} \begin{bmatrix} 1 & 2 & 6 & \vdots & 4 \\ 0 & 8 & 17 & \vdots & 8 \\ 0 & -8 & -22 & \vdots & 0 \end{bmatrix}$$

$$\tfrac{1}{8}R_2 \begin{bmatrix} 1 & 2 & 6 & \vdots & 4 \\ 0 & 1 & \tfrac{17}{8} & \vdots & 1 \\ 0 & -8 & -22 & \vdots & 0 \end{bmatrix}$$

$$8R_2 + R_3 \begin{bmatrix} 1 & 2 & 6 & \vdots & 4 \\ 0 & 1 & \tfrac{17}{8} & \vdots & 1 \\ 0 & 0 & -5 & \vdots & 8 \end{bmatrix}$$

$$-\tfrac{1}{5}R_3 \begin{bmatrix} 1 & 2 & 6 & \vdots & 4 \\ 0 & 1 & \tfrac{17}{8} & \vdots & 1 \\ 0 & 0 & 1 & \vdots & -\tfrac{8}{5} \end{bmatrix}$$

$$z = -\tfrac{8}{5} \qquad y + \tfrac{17}{8}\left(-\tfrac{8}{5}\right) = 1 \qquad x + 2\left(\tfrac{22}{5}\right) + 6\left(-\tfrac{8}{5}\right) = 4$$
$$y = \tfrac{22}{5} \qquad\qquad x = \tfrac{24}{5}$$

$$\left(\tfrac{24}{5}, \tfrac{22}{5}, -\tfrac{8}{5}\right)$$

47.
$$\begin{bmatrix} 2 & 3 & 3 & \vdots & 3 \\ 6 & 6 & 12 & \vdots & 13 \\ 12 & 9 & -1 & \vdots & 2 \end{bmatrix}$$

$$\tfrac{1}{2}R_1 \begin{bmatrix} 1 & \tfrac{3}{2} & \tfrac{3}{2} & \vdots & \tfrac{3}{2} \\ 6 & 6 & 12 & \vdots & 13 \\ 12 & 9 & -1 & \vdots & 2 \end{bmatrix}$$

$$\begin{matrix} -6R_1 + R_2 \\ -12R_1 + R_3 \end{matrix} \begin{bmatrix} 1 & \tfrac{3}{2} & \tfrac{3}{2} & \vdots & \tfrac{3}{2} \\ 0 & -3 & 3 & \vdots & 4 \\ 0 & -9 & -19 & \vdots & -16 \end{bmatrix}$$

$$-\tfrac{1}{3}R_2 \begin{bmatrix} 1 & \tfrac{3}{2} & \tfrac{3}{2} & \vdots & \tfrac{3}{2} \\ 0 & 1 & -1 & \vdots & -\tfrac{4}{3} \\ 0 & -9 & -19 & \vdots & -16 \end{bmatrix}$$

$$9R_2 + R_3 \begin{bmatrix} 1 & \tfrac{3}{2} & \tfrac{3}{2} & \vdots & \tfrac{3}{2} \\ 0 & 1 & -1 & \vdots & -\tfrac{4}{3} \\ 0 & 0 & -28 & \vdots & -28 \end{bmatrix}$$

$$-\tfrac{1}{28}R_3 \begin{bmatrix} 1 & \tfrac{3}{2} & \tfrac{3}{2} & \vdots & \tfrac{3}{4} \\ 0 & 1 & -1 & \vdots & -\tfrac{4}{5} \\ 0 & 0 & 0 & \vdots & 1 \end{bmatrix}$$

$$x_3 = 1$$
$$x_2 - 1 = -\tfrac{4}{3}$$
$$x_2 = -\tfrac{1}{3}$$
$$x_1 + \tfrac{3}{2}\left(\tfrac{-1}{3}\right) + \tfrac{3}{2}(1) = \tfrac{3}{2}$$
$$x_1 - \tfrac{1}{2} + \tfrac{3}{2} = \tfrac{3}{2}$$
$$x_1 + 1 = \tfrac{3}{2}$$
$$x_1 = \tfrac{1}{2}$$

$$\left(\tfrac{1}{2}, \tfrac{-1}{3}, 1\right)$$

49. $\det(A) = \begin{vmatrix} 7 & 10 \\ 10 & 15 \end{vmatrix} = (7)(15) - (10)(10) = 105 - 100 = 5$

51. $\det(A) = \begin{vmatrix} 8 & 6 & 3 \\ 6 & 3 & 0 \\ 3 & 0 & 2 \end{vmatrix}$

$= (3)\begin{vmatrix} 6 & 3 \\ 3 & 0 \end{vmatrix} - 0\begin{vmatrix} 8 & 3 \\ 6 & 0 \end{vmatrix} + 2\begin{vmatrix} 8 & 6 \\ 6 & 3 \end{vmatrix}$ (third row)

$= (3)(-9) - 0 + (2)(-12)$

$= -27 - 24$

$= -51$

53. $\det(A) = \begin{vmatrix} 8 & 3 & 2 \\ 1 & -2 & 4 \\ 6 & 0 & 5 \end{vmatrix}$

$= 6\begin{vmatrix} 3 & 2 \\ -2 & 4 \end{vmatrix} - 0 + 5\begin{vmatrix} 8 & 3 \\ 1 & -2 \end{vmatrix}$ (third row)

$= (6)(16) + (5)(-19)$

$= 1$

55. $\begin{bmatrix} 7 & 12 & \vdots & 63 \\ 2 & 3 & \vdots & 15 \end{bmatrix}$

$D = \begin{vmatrix} 7 & 12 \\ 2 & 3 \end{vmatrix} = 21 - 24 = -3$

$x = \dfrac{D_x}{D} = \dfrac{\begin{vmatrix} 63 & 12 \\ 15 & 3 \end{vmatrix}}{-3} = \dfrac{189 - 180}{-3} = \dfrac{9}{-3} = -3$

$y = \dfrac{D_y}{D} = \dfrac{\begin{vmatrix} 7 & 63 \\ 2 & 15 \end{vmatrix}}{-3} = \dfrac{105 - 126}{-3} = \dfrac{-21}{-3} = 7$

$(-3, 7)$

57. $\begin{bmatrix} 3 & -2 & \vdots & 16 \\ 12 & -8 & \vdots & -5 \end{bmatrix}$

$D = \begin{vmatrix} 3 & -2 \\ 12 & -8 \end{vmatrix} = -24 + 24 = 0$

Cannot be solved by Cramer's Rule because $D = 0$. Solve by elimination.

$-12x + 8y = -64$

$\underline{12x - 8y = -5}$

$0 \neq -69$

Inconsistent; no solution

59. $\begin{bmatrix} -1 & 1 & 2 & \vdots & 1 \\ 2 & 3 & 1 & \vdots & -2 \\ 5 & 4 & 2 & \vdots & 4 \end{bmatrix}$

$D = \begin{vmatrix} -1 & 1 & 2 \\ 2 & 3 & 1 \\ 5 & 4 & 2 \end{vmatrix} = (-1)\begin{vmatrix} 3 & 1 \\ 4 & 2 \end{vmatrix} - (1)\begin{vmatrix} 2 & 1 \\ 5 & 2 \end{vmatrix} + (2)\begin{vmatrix} 2 & 3 \\ 5 & 4 \end{vmatrix}$

$= (-1)(2) - (1)(-1) + (2)(-7)$

$= -2 + 1 - 14 = -15$

$x = \dfrac{\begin{vmatrix} 1 & 1 & 2 \\ -2 & 3 & 1 \\ 4 & 4 & 2 \end{vmatrix}}{-15} = \dfrac{(1)\begin{vmatrix} 3 & 1 \\ 4 & 2 \end{vmatrix} - (1)\begin{vmatrix} -2 & 1 \\ 4 & 2 \end{vmatrix} + (2)\begin{vmatrix} -2 & 3 \\ 4 & 4 \end{vmatrix}}{-15}$

$= \dfrac{(1)(2) - (1)(-8) + (2)(-20)}{-15}$

$= \dfrac{2 + 8 - 40}{-15} = \dfrac{-30}{-15} = 2$

$y = \dfrac{\begin{vmatrix} -1 & 1 & 2 \\ 2 & -2 & 1 \\ 5 & 4 & 2 \end{vmatrix}}{-15} = \dfrac{(-1)\begin{vmatrix} -2 & 1 \\ 4 & 2 \end{vmatrix} - (1)\begin{vmatrix} 2 & 1 \\ 5 & 2 \end{vmatrix} + (2)\begin{vmatrix} 2 & -2 \\ 5 & 4 \end{vmatrix}}{-15}$

$= \dfrac{(-1)(-8) - (1)(-1) + (2)(18)}{-15}$

$= \dfrac{8 + 1 + 36}{-15} = \dfrac{45}{-15} = -3$

—CONTINUED—

59. —CONTINUED—

$$z = \frac{\begin{vmatrix} -1 & 1 & 1 \\ 2 & 2 & -2 \\ 5 & 4 & 4 \end{vmatrix}}{-15} = \frac{(-1)\begin{vmatrix} 3 & -2 \\ 4 & 4 \end{vmatrix} - (1)\begin{vmatrix} 2 & -2 \\ 5 & 4 \end{vmatrix} + (1)\begin{vmatrix} 2 & 3 \\ 5 & 4 \end{vmatrix}}{-15}$$

$$= \frac{(-1)(20) - (1)(18) + (1)(-7)}{-15}$$

$$= \frac{-20 - 18 - 7}{-15} = \frac{-45}{-15} = 3 \qquad (2, -3, 3)$$

61. $3x - y = 6$

$-3x + 2y = -10$

There are many other correct solutions. Write equations so that $\left(\frac{2}{3}, -4\right)$ satisfies each equation.

63. *Verbal Model:*

| Total Cost | = | Cost per unit | · | Number of units | + | Initial cost |

| Total Revenue | = | Price per unit | · | Number of units |

Labels: Total cost $= C$

Cost per unit $= 3.75$

Number of units $= x$

Initial cost $= 25,000$

Total revenue $= R$

Price per unit $= 5.25$

System of equations:

$C = 3.75x + 25,000$

$R = 5.25x$

$R = C$

$5.25x = 3.75x + 25,000$

$1.50x = 25,000$

$x = 16,666.\overline{6} \approx 16,667$ items

65. *Verbal Model:*

| Gallons Solution 1 | + | Gallons Solution 2 | = | 100 |

| Value Solution 1 | + | Value Solution 2 | = | 0.60(100) |

Labels: Gallons Solution 1 $= x$

Gallons Solution 2 $= y$

System of equations:

$x + y = 100$

$0.75x + 0.50y = 0.60(100)$

$x = 100 - y$

$75(100 - y) + 50y = 60(100)$

$7500 - 75y + 50y = 6000$

$-25y = -1500$

$y = 60$ gallons at 50% solution

$x = 100 - 60 = 40$ gallons at 75% solution

67. *Verbal model:*

$2 \cdot$ | Length | $+ 2 \cdot$ | Width | $=$ | Perimeter |

| Length | $= 1.50 \cdot$ | Width |

Labels: Length $= x$

Width $= y$

System of equations:

$2x + 2y = 480$

$x = 1.50y$

$2(1.50y) + 2y = 480$

$3y + 2y = 480$

$5y = 480$

$y = 96$ meters in width

$x = 1.50(96) = 144$ meters in length

69. *Verbal Model:* $\boxed{\begin{array}{c}\text{Number}\\\text{Tapes 1}\end{array}} + \boxed{\begin{array}{c}\text{Number}\\\text{Tapes 2}\end{array}} = 650$

$\boxed{\begin{array}{c}\text{Receipts}\\\text{Tapes 1}\end{array}} + \boxed{\begin{array}{c}\text{Receipts}\\\text{Tapes 2}\end{array}} = 7717.50$

Labels: Number Tapes 1 $= x$

Number Tapes 2 $= y$

System of equations:
$$x + \quad y = 650$$
$$9.95x + 14.95y = 7717.50$$

$$y = 650 - x$$

$$9.95x + 14.95(650 - x) = 7717.50$$

$$9.95x + 9717.50 - 14.95x = 7717.50$$

$$-5x = -2000$$

$$x = 400 \text{ tapes at } \$9.95$$

$$y = 650 - 400 = 250 \text{ tapes at } \$14.95$$

71. *Verbal Model:* $\boxed{\begin{array}{c}\text{Speed}\\\text{Plane 1}\end{array}} \cdot \boxed{\text{Time}} + \boxed{\begin{array}{c}\text{Speed}\\\text{Plane 2}\end{array}} \cdot \boxed{\text{Time}} = \boxed{\text{Distance}}$

$\boxed{\begin{array}{c}\text{Speed}\\\text{Plane 2}\end{array}} = \boxed{\begin{array}{c}\text{Speed}\\\text{Plane 1}\end{array}} + 40$

Labels: Speed Plane 1 $= x$

Speed Plane 2 $= y$

Time $= \frac{50}{60} = \frac{5}{6}$ hr

Distance $= 450$ miles

System of equations:
$$x \cdot \tfrac{5}{6} + y \cdot \tfrac{5}{6} = 450$$
$$y = x + 40$$

$$\tfrac{5}{6}x + \tfrac{5}{6}(x + 40) = 450$$

$$\tfrac{5}{6}(2x + 40) = 450$$

$$2x + 40 = 540$$

$$2x = 500$$

$$x = 250 \text{ mph}$$

$$y = 250 + 40 = 290 \text{ mph}$$

73. *Verbal model:*

$$\boxed{\begin{array}{c}\text{Number}\\1\end{array}} + \boxed{\begin{array}{c}\text{Number}\\2\end{array}} + \boxed{\begin{array}{c}\text{Number}\\3\end{array}} = 68$$

$$\boxed{\begin{array}{c}\text{Number}\\2\end{array}} = 4 + \boxed{\begin{array}{c}\text{Number}\\1\end{array}}$$

$$\boxed{\begin{array}{c}\text{Number}\\3\end{array}} = 2 \cdot \boxed{\begin{array}{c}\text{Number}\\1\end{array}}$$

Labels: Number 1 $= x$ Number 2 $= y$ Number 3 $= z$

System of equations:

$$\begin{aligned} x + y + z &= 68 \\ y &= 4 + x \\ z &= 2x \end{aligned}$$

$$\begin{array}{ll} x + y + z = 68 & x + y + z = 68 \\ -x + y \phantom{{}+z} = 4 & y + \tfrac{1}{2}z = 36 \\ -2x \phantom{{}+y} + z = 0 & 2z = 64 \end{array}$$

$$\begin{array}{ll} x + y + z = 68 & z = 32 \\ 2y + z = 72 & y + \tfrac{1}{2}(32) = 36 \\ 2y + 3z = 136 & y = 20 \end{array}$$

$$\begin{array}{ll} x + y + z = 68 & \\ y + \tfrac{1}{2}z = 36 & x + 20 + 32 = 68 \\ 2y + 3z = 136 & x = 16 \end{array}$$

$(16, 20, 32)$

75.

$$\begin{aligned} 0 = a(-5)^2 + b(-5) + c &\implies 0 = 25a - 5b + c \\ -6 = a(1)^2 + b(1) + c &\implies -6 = a + b + c \\ 14 = a(2)^2 + b(2) + c &\implies 14 = 4a + 2b + c \end{aligned}$$

$$\begin{bmatrix} 25 & -5 & 1 & \vdots & 0 \\ 1 & 1 & 1 & \vdots & -6 \\ 4 & 2 & 1 & \vdots & 14 \end{bmatrix}$$

$$D = \begin{vmatrix} 25 & -5 & 1 \\ 1 & 1 & 1 \\ 4 & 2 & 1 \end{vmatrix} = -42$$

$$a = \frac{D_a}{D} = \frac{\begin{vmatrix} 0 & -5 & 1 \\ -6 & 1 & 1 \\ 14 & 2 & 1 \end{vmatrix}}{-42} = \frac{-126}{-42} = 3$$

$$b = \frac{D_b}{D} = \frac{\begin{vmatrix} 25 & 0 & 1 \\ 1 & -6 & 1 \\ 4 & 14 & 1 \end{vmatrix}}{-42} = \frac{-462}{-42} = 11$$

$$c = \frac{\begin{vmatrix} 25 & -5 & 0 \\ 1 & 1 & -6 \\ 4 & 2 & 14 \end{vmatrix}}{-42} = \frac{840}{-42} = -20 \qquad y = 3x^2 + 11x - 20$$

77. $(x_1, y_1) = (1, 0), (x_2, y_2) = (5, 0), (x_3, y_3) = (5, 8)$

$$\begin{vmatrix} x_1 & y_1 & 1 \\ x_2 & y_2 & 1 \\ x_3 & y_3 & 1 \end{vmatrix} = \begin{vmatrix} 1 & 0 & 1 \\ 5 & 0 & 1 \\ 5 & 8 & 1 \end{vmatrix} = -0 + 0 - (8)\begin{vmatrix} 1 & 1 \\ 5 & 1 \end{vmatrix} = (-8)(-4) = 32$$

Area $= +\dfrac{1}{2}(32) = 16$

79. $(x_1, y_1) = (1, 2), (x_2, y_2) = (4, -5), (x_3, y_3) = (3, 2)$

$$\begin{vmatrix} x_1 & y_1 & 1 \\ x_2 & y_2 & 1 \\ x_3 & y_3 & 1 \end{vmatrix} = \begin{vmatrix} 1 & 2 & 1 \\ 4 & -5 & 1 \\ 3 & 2 & 1 \end{vmatrix} = (1)\begin{vmatrix} 4 & -5 \\ 3 & 2 \end{vmatrix} - (1)\begin{vmatrix} 1 & 2 \\ 3 & 2 \end{vmatrix} + (1)\begin{vmatrix} 1 & 2 \\ 4 & -5 \end{vmatrix}$$

$$= (1)(23) - (1)(-4) + (1)(-13)$$

$$= 23 + 4 - 13$$

$$= 14$$

Area $= +\dfrac{1}{2}(14) = 7$

81. $\begin{vmatrix} x & y & 1 \\ -4 & 0 & 1 \\ 4 & 4 & 1 \end{vmatrix} = 0$

$-(-4)\begin{vmatrix} y & 1 \\ 4 & 1 \end{vmatrix} + 0 - (1)\begin{vmatrix} x & y \\ 4 & 4 \end{vmatrix} = 0$

$(4)(y - 4) - (1)(4x - 4y) = 0$

$4y - 16 - 4x + 4y = 0$

$-4x + 8y - 16 = 0$

$x - 2y + 4 = 0$

83. $\begin{vmatrix} x & y & 1 \\ -\frac{5}{2} & 3 & 1 \\ \frac{7}{2} & 1 & 1 \end{vmatrix} = 0$

$(1)\begin{vmatrix} -\frac{5}{2} & 3 \\ \frac{7}{2} & 1 \end{vmatrix} - (1)\begin{vmatrix} x & y \\ \frac{7}{2} & 1 \end{vmatrix} + (1)\begin{vmatrix} x & y \\ -\frac{5}{2} & 3 \end{vmatrix} = 0$

$(1)(-13) - (1)\left(x - \frac{7}{2}y\right) + (1)\left(3x + \frac{5}{2}y\right) = 0$

$-13 - x + \frac{7}{2}y + 3x + \frac{5}{2}y = 0$

$2x + 6y - 13 = 0$

Chapter Test for Chapter 8

1. (a) $(3, -4)$

$2(3) - 2(-4) \stackrel{?}{=} 1$

$6 + 8 \neq 1$

Not a solution

(b) $\left(1, \frac{1}{2}\right)$

$2(1) - 2\left(\frac{1}{2}\right) \stackrel{?}{=} 1$ $-1 + 2\left(\frac{1}{2}\right) \stackrel{?}{=} 0$

$2 - 1 = 1$ $-1 + 1 = 0$

$1 = 1$ $0 = 0$

Solution

2. $5x - y = 6$ $4x - 3(5x - 6) = -4$

$4x - 3y = -4$ $4x - 15x + 18 = -4$

$-y = -5x + 6$ $-11x = -22$

$y = 5x - 6$ $x = 2$

$y = 5(2) - 6$

$y = 4$

$(2, 4)$

3. $x + y = 8$ $x + (10 - x^2) = 8$ $y = 10 - 2^2$ $y = 10 - (-1)^2$

$x^2 + y = 10$ $0 = x^2 - x - 2$ $y = 6$ $y = 9$

$\quad\quad y = 10 - x^2$ $0 = (x - 2)(x + 1)$

$(2, 6), (-1, 9)$ $x = 2$ $x = -1$

4.

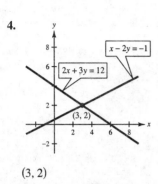

$(3, 2)$

5. $3x - 4y = -14$

$\underline{-3x + \ y = \quad 8}$

$\quad\quad -3y = \ -6$ $3x - 4(2) = -14$

$\quad\quad\quad y = \quad 2$ $3x \quad\quad = \ -6$

$\quad\quad\quad\quad\quad\quad\quad\quad\quad\quad\quad x \quad\quad = \ -2$

$(-2, 2)$

6. $8x + 3y = \quad 3 \implies 16x + 6y = \quad 6$ $8\left(\frac{1}{4}\right) + 3y = 3$

$4x - 6y = -1 \implies \underline{\ 4x - 6y = -1\ }$ $3y = 1$

$\quad\quad\quad\quad\quad\quad\quad\quad 20x \quad\quad = \quad 5$ $y = \frac{1}{3}$

$\quad\quad\quad\quad\quad\quad\quad\quad\quad x \quad\quad = \quad \frac{1}{4}$

$\left(\frac{1}{4}, \frac{1}{3}\right)$

7. $x + 2y - 4z = \quad 0$

$3x + \ y - 2z = \quad 5$

$3x - \ y + 2z = \quad 7$

$x + 2y - 4z = \quad 0$

$\quad\quad -5y + 10z = \quad 5$

$\quad\quad -7y + 14z = \quad 7$

$x + 2y - 4z = \quad 0$

$\quad\quad\quad y - 2z = -1$

$\quad\quad -7y + 14z = \quad 7$

$x + 2y - 4z = \quad 0$

$\quad\quad\quad y - 2z = -1$

$\quad\quad\quad\quad\quad 0 = \quad 0$

let $a = z$ (a is any real number)

$y = \quad 2z - 1$

$x = -2y + 4z$

$\quad = -2(2z - 1) + 4z$

$\quad = -4z + 2 + 4z$

$x = \quad 2$

$(2, 2a - 1, a)$

8.
$$\begin{bmatrix} 1 & 0 & -3 & : & -10 \\ 0 & -2 & 2 & : & 0 \\ 1 & -2 & 0 & : & -7 \end{bmatrix}$$

$-\frac{1}{2}R_2$
$-R_1 + R_3$
$$\begin{bmatrix} 1 & 0 & -3 & : & -10 \\ 0 & 1 & -1 & : & 0 \\ 0 & -2 & 3 & : & 3 \end{bmatrix}$$

$2R_2 + R_3$
$$\begin{bmatrix} 1 & 0 & -3 & : & -10 \\ 0 & 1 & -1 & : & 0 \\ 0 & 0 & 1 & : & 3 \end{bmatrix}$$

$z = 3$ $y - 3 = 0$ $x - 3(3) = -10$

$\quad\quad\quad\quad\quad y = 3$ $x = -1$

$(-1, 3, 3)$

9.
$$\begin{bmatrix} 1 & -3 & 1 & \vdots & -3 \\ 3 & 2 & -5 & \vdots & 18 \\ 0 & 1 & 1 & \vdots & -1 \end{bmatrix}$$

$$-3R_1 + R_2 \begin{bmatrix} 1 & -3 & 1 & \vdots & -3 \\ 0 & 11 & -8 & \vdots & 27 \\ 0 & 1 & 1 & \vdots & -1 \end{bmatrix}$$

$$\begin{matrix} R_2 \\ R_3 \end{matrix} \begin{bmatrix} 1 & -3 & 1 & \vdots & -3 \\ 0 & 1 & 1 & \vdots & -1 \\ 0 & 11 & -8 & \vdots & 27 \end{bmatrix}$$

$$\begin{matrix} 3R_2 + R_1 \\ \\ -11R_2 + R_3 \end{matrix} \begin{bmatrix} 1 & 0 & 4 & \vdots & -6 \\ 0 & 1 & 1 & \vdots & -1 \\ 0 & 0 & -19 & \vdots & 38 \end{bmatrix}$$

$$-\tfrac{1}{19}R_3 \begin{bmatrix} 1 & 0 & 4 & \vdots & -6 \\ 0 & 1 & 1 & \vdots & -1 \\ 0 & 0 & 1 & \vdots & -2 \end{bmatrix}$$

$z = -2 \qquad y + (-2) = -1 \qquad x + 4(-2) = -6$
$$y = 1 \qquad\qquad x = 2$$

$(2, 1, -2)$

10. $\begin{bmatrix} 2 & -7 & \vdots & 7 \\ 3 & 7 & \vdots & 13 \end{bmatrix}$ •

$D = \begin{vmatrix} 2 & -7 \\ 3 & 7 \end{vmatrix} = 14 + 21 = 35$

$x = \dfrac{D_x}{D} = \dfrac{\begin{vmatrix} 7 & -7 \\ 13 & 7 \end{vmatrix}}{35} = \dfrac{49 + 91}{35} = \dfrac{140}{35} = 4$

$y = \dfrac{D_y}{D} = \dfrac{\begin{vmatrix} 2 & 7 \\ 3 & 13 \end{vmatrix}}{35} = \dfrac{26 - 21}{35} = \dfrac{5}{35} = \dfrac{1}{7}$

$\left(4, \tfrac{1}{7}\right)$

11.

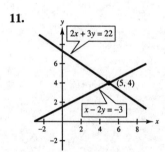

Solution: $(5, 4)$

12.
$$\begin{bmatrix} 3 & -2 & 1 & \vdots & 12 \\ 1 & -3 & 0 & \vdots & 2 \\ -3 & 0 & -9 & \vdots & -6 \end{bmatrix}$$

$$\begin{matrix} R_1 \\ \\ -\tfrac{1}{3}R_3 \end{matrix} \begin{bmatrix} 1 & 0 & 3 & \vdots & 2 \\ 1 & -3 & 0 & \vdots & 2 \\ 3 & -2 & 1 & \vdots & 12 \end{bmatrix}$$

$$\begin{matrix} -1R_1 + R_2 \\ -3R_1 + R_3 \end{matrix} \begin{bmatrix} 1 & 0 & 3 & \vdots & 2 \\ 0 & -3 & -3 & \vdots & 0 \\ 0 & -2 & -8 & \vdots & 6 \end{bmatrix}$$

$$\begin{matrix} -\tfrac{1}{3}R_2 \\ -\tfrac{1}{2}R_3 \end{matrix} \begin{bmatrix} 1 & 0 & 3 & \vdots & 2 \\ 0 & 1 & 1 & \vdots & 0 \\ 0 & 1 & 4 & \vdots & -3 \end{bmatrix}$$

$$-R_2 + R_3 \begin{bmatrix} 1 & 0 & 3 & \vdots & 2 \\ 0 & 1 & 1 & \vdots & 0 \\ 0 & 0 & 3 & \vdots & -3 \end{bmatrix}$$

$$\tfrac{1}{3}R_3 \begin{bmatrix} 1 & 0 & 3 & \vdots & 2 \\ 0 & 1 & 1 & \vdots & 0 \\ 0 & 0 & 1 & \vdots & -1 \end{bmatrix}$$

$$\begin{matrix} -3R_3 + R_1 \\ -R_3 + R_2 \end{matrix} \begin{bmatrix} 1 & 0 & 0 & \vdots & 5 \\ 0 & 1 & 0 & \vdots & 1 \\ 0 & 0 & 1 & \vdots & -1 \end{bmatrix}$$

$(5, 1, -1)$

13.

$$\begin{bmatrix} 4 & 1 & 2 & \vdots & -4 \\ 0 & 3 & 1 & \vdots & 8 \\ -3 & 1 & -3 & \vdots & 5 \end{bmatrix}$$

$$\frac{1}{4}R_1 \begin{bmatrix} 1 & \frac{1}{4} & \frac{1}{2} & \vdots & -1 \\ 0 & 3 & 1 & \vdots & 8 \\ -3 & 1 & -3 & \vdots & 5 \end{bmatrix}$$

$$\begin{matrix} \\ \frac{1}{3}R_2 \\ 3R_1 + R_3 \end{matrix} \begin{bmatrix} 1 & \frac{1}{4} & \frac{1}{2} & \vdots & -1 \\ 0 & 1 & \frac{1}{3} & \vdots & \frac{8}{3} \\ 0 & \frac{7}{4} & -\frac{3}{2} & \vdots & 2 \end{bmatrix}$$

$$\begin{matrix} -\frac{1}{4}R_2 + R_1 \\ \\ -\frac{7}{4}R_2 + R_3 \end{matrix} \begin{bmatrix} 1 & 0 & \frac{5}{12} & \vdots & -\frac{5}{3} \\ 0 & 1 & \frac{1}{3} & \vdots & \frac{8}{3} \\ 0 & 0 & -\frac{25}{12} & \vdots & -\frac{8}{3} \end{bmatrix}$$

$$\begin{matrix} \\ \\ -\frac{12}{25}R_3 \end{matrix} \begin{bmatrix} 1 & 0 & \frac{5}{12} & \vdots & -\frac{5}{3} \\ 0 & 1 & \frac{1}{3} & \vdots & \frac{8}{3} \\ 0 & 0 & 1 & \vdots & \frac{32}{25} \end{bmatrix}$$

$$\begin{matrix} -\frac{5}{12}R_3 + R_1 \\ -\frac{1}{3}R_3 + R_2 \\ \\ \end{matrix} \begin{bmatrix} 1 & 0 & 0 & \vdots & -\frac{11}{5} \\ 0 & 1 & 0 & \vdots & \frac{56}{25} \\ 0 & 0 & 1 & \vdots & \frac{32}{25} \end{bmatrix}$$

$$\left(-\frac{11}{5}, \frac{56}{25}, \frac{32}{25}\right)$$

14. Inconsistent: no solutions

Consistent: one solution or infinitely many solutions

15. $\begin{vmatrix} 3 & -2 & 0 \\ -1 & 5 & 3 \\ 2 & 7 & 1 \end{vmatrix} = 0 - (3)\begin{vmatrix} 3 & -2 \\ 2 & 7 \end{vmatrix} + (1)\begin{vmatrix} 3 & -2 \\ -1 & 5 \end{vmatrix}$

$$= (-3)(25) + (1)(13)$$

$$= -75 + 13$$

$$= -62$$

16. $\begin{vmatrix} 5 & -8 \\ 3 & a \end{vmatrix} = 0$

$$5a + 24 = 0$$

$$5a = -24$$

$$a = -\frac{24}{5}$$

17. $x + y = 2$

$2x - y = 13$

There are many correct answers.

Write equations so that $(5, -3)$ satisfies each equation.

18. *Verbal model:*

| Distance Person 1 Drives | + | Distance Person 2 Drives | = | Total Distance |

| Distance Person 1 Drives | = | 4 · | Distance Person 2 Drives |

Labels: Distance Person 1 Drives $= x$

Distance Person 2 Drives $= y$

System of equations: $x + y = 200$

$x = 4y$

By substitution

$$4y + y = 200$$

$$5y = 200$$

$$y = 40 \text{ miles}$$

$$x = 4(40) = 160 \text{ miles}$$

19. $4 = a(0)^2 + b(0) + c \implies 4 = \qquad + c$

$3 = a(1)^2 + b(1) + c \implies 3 = a + b + c$

$6 = a(2)^2 + b(2) + c \implies 6 = 4a + 2b + c$

$$\begin{bmatrix} 0 & 0 & 1 & \vdots & 4 \\ 1 & 1 & 1 & \vdots & 3 \\ 4 & 2 & 1 & \vdots & 6 \end{bmatrix}$$

$$\begin{bmatrix} 1 & 1 & 1 & \vdots & 3 \\ 4 & 2 & 1 & \vdots & 6 \\ 0 & 0 & 1 & \vdots & 4 \end{bmatrix} = \begin{bmatrix} 1 & 1 & 1 & \vdots & 3 \\ 0 & -2 & -3 & \vdots & -6 \\ 0 & 0 & 1 & \vdots & 4 \end{bmatrix} = \begin{bmatrix} 1 & 1 & 1 & \vdots & 3 \\ 0 & 1 & \frac{3}{2} & \vdots & 3 \\ 0 & 0 & 1 & \vdots & 4 \end{bmatrix}$$

$c = 4 \qquad b + \frac{3}{2}(4) = 3 \qquad a + (-3) + 4 = 3$

$\qquad\qquad\qquad b = -3 \qquad\qquad\qquad a = 2$

$y = 2x^2 - 3x + 4$

20. Verbal model:
$$\boxed{\begin{array}{c}\text{Investment} \\ 1\end{array}} + \boxed{\begin{array}{c}\text{Investment} \\ 2\end{array}} + \boxed{\begin{array}{c}\text{Investment} \\ 3\end{array}} = \$25{,}000$$

$$4.5\% \cdot \boxed{\begin{array}{c}\text{Investment} \\ 1\end{array}} + 5\% \cdot \boxed{\begin{array}{c}\text{Investment} \\ 2\end{array}} + 8\% \cdot \boxed{\begin{array}{c}\text{Investment} \\ 3\end{array}} = \$1275$$

$$\boxed{\begin{array}{c}\text{Investment} \\ 1\end{array}} + 4000 = \boxed{\begin{array}{c}\text{Investment} \\ 3\end{array}} + 10{,}000$$

Labels: Investment 1 $= x$

Investment 2 $= y$

Investment 3 $= z$

System of $x + y + z = 25{,}000$
equations: $0.045x + 0.05y + 0.08z = 1275$

$y + 4000 = z + 10{,}000 \implies y - z = 6000$

Using determinants and Cramer's Rule:

$$\begin{bmatrix} 1 & 1 & 1 & 25{,}000 \\ .045 & .05 & .08 & 1275 \\ 0 & 1 & -1 & 6000 \end{bmatrix} \qquad D = \begin{vmatrix} 1 & 1 & 1 \\ .045 & .05 & .08 \\ 0 & 1 & -1 \end{vmatrix} = -.04$$

$$x = \frac{D_x}{D} = \frac{\begin{vmatrix} 25{,}000 & 1 & 1 \\ 1275 & .05 & .08 \\ 6000 & 1 & -1 \end{vmatrix}}{-.04} = \frac{-520}{-0.4} = \$13{,}000$$

$$y = \frac{D_y}{D} = \frac{\begin{vmatrix} 1 & 25{,}000 & 1 \\ .045 & 1275 & .08 \\ 0 & 6000 & -1 \end{vmatrix}}{-.04} = \frac{-360}{-.04} = \$9{,}000$$

$$z = \frac{D_z}{D} = \frac{\begin{vmatrix} 1 & 1 & 25{,}000 \\ .045 & .05 & 1275 \\ 0 & 1 & 6000 \end{vmatrix}}{-.04} = \frac{-120}{-.04} = \$3{,}000$$

Use your graphing calculator to find each determinant.

$\$13{,}000$ at 4.5% $\$9{,}000$ at 5% $\$3{,}000$ at 8%

21. $(x_1, y_1) = (0, 0)$, $(x_2, y_2) = (5, 4)$, $(x_3, y_3) = (6, 0)$

$$\begin{vmatrix} x_1 & y_1 & 1 \\ x_2 & y_2 & 1 \\ x_3 & y_3 & 1 \end{vmatrix} = \begin{vmatrix} 0 & 0 & 1 \\ 5 & 4 & 1 \\ 6 & 0 & 1 \end{vmatrix} = (1)\begin{vmatrix} 5 & 4 \\ 6 & 0 \end{vmatrix} = (1)(-24) = -24$$

Area $= -\frac{1}{2}(-24) = 12$

CHAPTER 9
Exponential and Logarithmic Functions

CHAPTER 9
Exponential and Logarithmic Functions

Section 9.1   Exponential Functions

Solutions to Odd-Numbered Exercises

1. $2^x \cdot 2^{x-1} = 2^{x+(x-1)} = 2^{2x-1}$

3. $\dfrac{e^{x+2}}{e^x} = e^{x+2-x} = e^2$

5. $\left(2e^x\right)^3 = 8e^{3x}$

7. $\sqrt[3]{-8e^{3x}} = -2e^x$ because
$-2 \cdot -2 \cdot -2 \cdot e^x \cdot e^x \cdot e^x = -8e^{3x}.$

9. $4^{\sqrt{3}} \approx 11.036$

Keystrokes:

Scientific: 4 [y^x] 3 [$\sqrt{\ }$] [=]

Graphing: 4 [^] [$\sqrt{\ }$] 3 [ENTER]

11. $e^{1/3} \approx 1.396$

Keystrokes:

Scientific: [(] 1 [÷] 3 [)] [Inv] [ln x] [=]

Graphing: [e^x] [(] 1 [÷] 3 [)] [ENTER]

13. $4(3e^4)^{1/2} = 4 \cdot 3^{1/2} \cdot e^2 \approx 51.193$

Keystrokes:

Scientific: 4 [×] 3 [y^x] 0.5 [×] 2 [Inv] [ln x] [=]

Graphing: 4 [×] 3 [^] 0.5 [×] [e^x] 2 [ENTER]

15. $\dfrac{4e^3}{12e^2} = \dfrac{e}{3} \approx 0.906$

Keystrokes:

Scientific: 1 [Inv] [ln x] [÷] 3 [=]

Graphing: [e] [÷] 3 [ENTER]

17. (a) $f(-2) = 3^{-2} = \dfrac{1}{9}$

(b) $f(0) = 3^0 = 1$

(c) $f(1) = 3^1 = 3$

19. (a) $g(-1) = 1.07^{-1} \approx 0.935$

(b) $g(3) = 1.07^3 \approx 1.225$

(c) $g\left(\sqrt{5}\right) = 1.07^{\sqrt{5}} \approx 1.163$

21. (a) $f(0) = 500\left(\tfrac{1}{2}\right)^0 = 500$

(b) $f(1) = 500\left(\tfrac{1}{2}\right)^1 = 250$

(c) $f(\pi) = 500\left(\tfrac{1}{2}\right)^\pi = 56.657$

23. (a) $f(0) = 1000(1.05)^{(2)(0)} = 1000$

(b) $f(5) = 1000(1.05)^{2(5)} = 1628.895$

(c) $f(10) = 1000(1.05)^{2(10)} = 2653.298$

25. (a) $h(5) = \dfrac{5000}{(1.06)^{8(5)}} \approx 486.11$

(b) $h(10) = \dfrac{5000}{(1.06)^{8(10)}} \approx 47.261$

(c) $h(20) = \dfrac{5000}{(1.06)^{8(20)}} \approx 0.447$

27. (a) $g(-4) = 10e^{-0.5(-4)} = 10e^2 \approx 73.891$

(b) $g(4) = 10e^{-0.5(4)} = 10e^{-2} \approx 1.353$

(c) $g(8) = 10e^{-0.5(8)} = 10e^{-4} \approx 0.183$

29. (a) $g(0) = \dfrac{1000}{2 + e^{-0.12(0)}} \approx 333.333$

(b) $g(10) = \dfrac{1000}{2 + e^{-0.12(10)}} \approx 434.557$

(c) $g(50) = \dfrac{1000}{2 + e^{-0.12(50)}} \approx 499.381$

31.

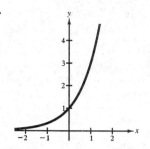

Table of values:

x	-2	-1	0	1	2
$f(x)$	0.1	0.3	1	3	9

33.

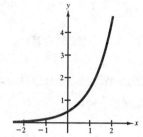

Table of values:

x	-2	-1	0	1	2
$h(x)$	0.1	0.2	0.5	1.5	4.5

35.

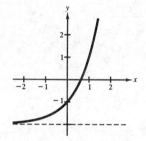

Table of values:

x	-2	-1	0	1	2
$g(x)$	-1.9	-1.7	-1	1	7

37.

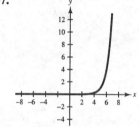

Table of values:

x	-1	0	1	5	6
$f(x)$	2.4×10^{-4}	9.8×10^{-4}	0.004	1	4

39.

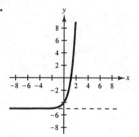

Table of values:

x	-2	-1	0	1	2
$f(x)$	-4.9	-4.8	-4	-1	11

41.

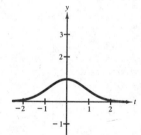

Table of values:

t	-2	-1	0	1	2
$f(t)$	0.1	0.5	1	0.5	0.1

43.

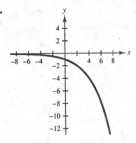

Table of values:

x	-2	-1	0	1	2
$f(x)$	-5	-0.7	-1	-1.4	-2

45.

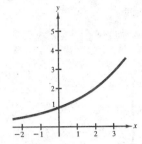

Table of values:

x	-2	-1	0	1	2
$h(x)$	0.5	0.7	1	1.4	2

47.

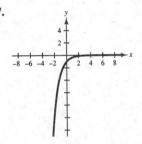

Table of values:

x	-2	-1	0	1	2
$f(x)$	-9	-3	-1	-0.3	-0.1

49.

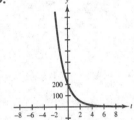

Table of values:

t	-2	-1	0	1	2
$g(t)$	800	400	200	100	50

51. $f(x) = 2^x$

(b) Basic graph

53. $f(x) = 2^{-x}$

(e) Basic graph reflected in the y-axis

55. $f(x) = 2^{x-1}$

(f) Basic graph shifted 1 unit right

57. $f(x) = \left(\frac{1}{2}\right)^x - 2$

(h) Basic graph reflected in y-axis and shifted 2 units down

59. $y = 5^{x/3}$

Keystrokes:

Y= 5 ^ (X,T,θ ÷ 3) GRAPH

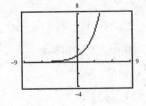

61. $y = 5^{(x-2)/3}$

Keystrokes:

Y= 5 ^ ((X,T,θ − 2) ÷ 3) GRAPH

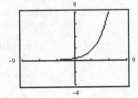

63. $y = 500(1.06)^t$

Keystrokes:

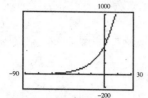

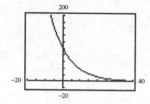

65. $y = 3e^{0.2x}$

Keystrokes:

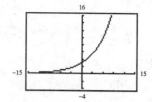

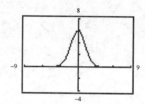

67. $P(t) = 100e^{-0.1t}$

Keystrokes:

$\boxed{Y=}$ 100 $\boxed{e^x}$ $\boxed{(-)}$ 0.1 $\boxed{X,T,\theta}$ $\boxed{GRAPH}$

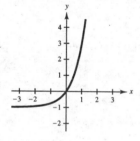

69. $y = 6e^{-x^2/3}$

Keystrokes:

$\boxed{Y=}$ 6 $\boxed{e^x}$ $\boxed{(-)}$ $\boxed{(}$ $\boxed{X,T,\theta}$ $\boxed{x^2}$ $\boxed{\div}$ 3 $\boxed{)}$ $\boxed{GRAPH}$

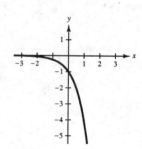

71. Vertical shift 1 unit down

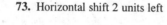

73. Horizontal shift 2 units left

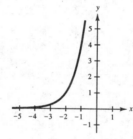

75. Reflection in the *x*-axis

77. (a) $f(x) = 2x$ Algebraic (Linear)

   (b) $f(x) = \sqrt{2x}$ Algebraic (Radical)

   (c) $f(x) = 2^x$ Exponential

   (d) $f(x) = 2x^2$ Algebraic (Quadratic)

79. $y = 16\left(\frac{1}{2}\right)^{80/30} = 2.520$ grams

Keystrokes:

16 $\boxed{\times}$ 0.5 $\boxed{y^x}$ $\boxed{(}$ 8 $\boxed{\div}$ 3 $\boxed{)}$ $\boxed{=}$ Scientific

16 $\boxed{\times}$ 0.5 $\boxed{\wedge}$ $\boxed{(}$ 8 $\boxed{\div}$ 3 $\boxed{)}$ $\boxed{ENTER}$ Graphing

81.

n	1	4	12	365	Continuous
A	\$466.10	\$487.54	\$492.68	\$495.22	\$495.30

Compounded 1 time:

$A = 100\left(1 + \dfrac{0.08}{1}\right)^{1(20)}$

$\quad = \$466.10$

Compounded 4 times:

$A = 100\left(1 + \dfrac{0.08}{4}\right)^{4(20)}$

$\quad = \$487.54$

Compounded 12 times:

$A = 100\left(1 + \dfrac{0.08}{12}\right)^{12(20)}$

$\quad = \$492.68$

Compounded 365 times:

$A = 100\left(1 + \dfrac{0.08}{365}\right)^{365(20)}$

$\quad = \$495.22$

Compounded continuously:

$A = Pe^{rt}$

$\quad = 100e^{0.08(20)}$

$\quad = 495.30$

83.

n	1	4	12	365	Continuous
A	\$4734.73	\$4870.38	\$4902.71	\$4918.66	\$4919.21

Compounded 1 time: $A = 2000\left(1 + \dfrac{0.09}{1}\right)^{1(10)}$

$\qquad\qquad\qquad = \$4734.73$

Compounded 4 times: $A = 2000\left(1 + \dfrac{0.09}{4}\right)^{4(10)}$

$\qquad\qquad\qquad = \$4870.38$

Compounded 12 times: $A = 2000\left(1 + \dfrac{0.09}{12}\right)^{12(10)}$

$\qquad\qquad\qquad = \$4902.71$

Compounded 365 times: $A = 2000\left(1 + \dfrac{0.09}{365}\right)^{365(10)}$

$\qquad\qquad\qquad = \$4918.66$

Compounded continuously: $A = 2000e^{0.09(10)}$

$\qquad\qquad\qquad = \$4919.21$

85.

n	1	4	12	365	Continuous
A	\$226,296.28	\$259,889.34	\$268,503.32	\$272,841.23	\$272,990.75

Compounded 1 time: $A = 5000\left(1 + \dfrac{0.10}{1}\right)^{1(40)}$

$\qquad\qquad\qquad = \$226,296.28$

Compounded 4 times: $A = 5000\left(1 + \dfrac{0.10}{4}\right)^{4(40)}$

$\qquad\qquad\qquad = \$259,889.34$

Compounded 12 times: $A = 5000\left(1 + \dfrac{0.10}{12}\right)^{12(40)}$

$\qquad\qquad\qquad = \$268,503.32$

Compounded 365 times: $A = 5000\left(1 + \dfrac{0.10}{365}\right)^{365(40)}$

$\qquad\qquad\qquad = \$272,841.23$

Compounded continuously: $A = 5000^{0.10(40)}$

$\qquad\qquad\qquad = \$272,990.75$

87.

n	1	4	12	365	Continuous
P	\$2541.75	\$2498.00	\$2487.98	\$2483.09	\$2482.93

Compounded 1 time: $\quad 5000 = P\left(1 + \dfrac{0.07}{1}\right)^{1(10)}$

$\qquad\qquad\qquad \dfrac{5000}{(1.07)^{10}} = P$

$\qquad\qquad\qquad \$2541.75 = P$

Compounded 4 times: $\quad 5000 = \left(1 + \dfrac{0.07}{4}\right)^{4(10)}$

$\qquad\qquad\qquad \dfrac{5000}{(1.0175)^{40}} = P$

$\qquad\qquad\qquad \$2498.00 = P$

Compounded 12 times: $\quad 5000 = P\left(1 + \dfrac{0.07}{12}\right)^{12(10)}$

$\qquad\qquad\qquad \dfrac{5000}{(1.00583)^{120}} = P$

$\qquad\qquad\qquad \$2487.98 = P$

Compounded Continuously: $\quad 5000 = Pe^{0.07(10)}$

$\qquad\qquad\qquad \dfrac{5000}{e^{0.7}} = P$

$\qquad\qquad\qquad \$2482.93 = P$

Compounded 365 times:

$\qquad\qquad\qquad 5000 = P\left(1 + \dfrac{0.07}{365}\right)^{365(10)}$

$\qquad\qquad\qquad \dfrac{5000}{(1.0001918)^{3.650}} = P$

$\qquad\qquad\qquad \$2483.09 = P$

89.

n	1	4	12	365	Continuous
P	$18,429.30	$15,830.43	$15,272.04	$15,004.64	$14,995.58

Compounded 1 time: $\quad 1,000,000 = P\left(1 + \dfrac{0.105}{1}\right)^{1(40)}$

$$\frac{1,000,000}{(1.105)^{40}} = P$$

$$\$18,429.30 = P$$

Compounded 4 times: $\quad 1,000,000 = P\left(1 + \dfrac{0.105}{4}\right)^{4(40)}$

$$\frac{1,000,000}{(1.02625)^{160}} = P$$

$$\$15,830.43 = P$$

Compounded 12 times: $\quad 1,000,000 = P\left(1 + \dfrac{0.105}{12}\right)^{12(40)}$

$$\frac{1,000,000}{(1.00875)^{480}} = P$$

$$\$15,272.04 = P$$

Compounded 365 times: $\quad 1,000,000 = P\left(1 + \dfrac{0.105}{365}\right)^{365(40)}$

$$\frac{1,000,000}{(1.002877)^{14,600}} = P$$

$$\$15,004.64 = P$$

Compounded continuously: $\quad 1,000,000 = Pe^{0.105(40)}$

$$\frac{1,000,000}{e^{4.2}} = P$$

$$\$14,995.58 = P$$

91. (a) $p = 25 - 0.4e^{0.02(100)}$

$\qquad = 25 - 0.4e^2$

$\qquad \approx \$22.04$

(b) $p = 25 - 0.4e^{0.02(125)}$

$\qquad = 25 - 0.4e^{2.5}$

$\qquad \approx \$20.13$

93. (a) $v(5) = 64,000(2)^{5/15}$

$\qquad = 64,000(2)^{1/3}$

$\qquad \approx \$80,634.95$

(b) $v(20) = 64,000(2)^{20/15}$

$\qquad = 64,000(2)^{4/3}$

$\qquad \approx \$161,269.89$

95. (a) $V(t) = 16,000\left(\frac{3}{4}\right)^t$

(b)

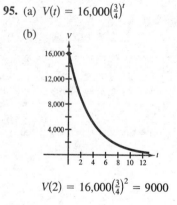

$$V(2) = 16,000\left(\tfrac{3}{4}\right)^2 = 9000$$

97. (a) The balances in the accounts after t years are modeled by $A_1 = 500e^{0.06t}$ and $A_2 = 500e^{0.08t}$.

(b) *Keystrokes:*

y_1 [Y=] 500 [e^x] 0.06 [X,T,θ] [ENTER]

y_2 500 [e^x] 0.08 [X,T,θ] [GRAPH]

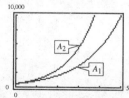

(d) The difference between the functions increases at an increasing rate.

(c) $A_2 - A_1 = 500e^{0.08t} - 500e^{0.06t}$

$\qquad = 500(e^{0.08t} - e^{0.06t})$

Keystrokes:

y_1 [Y=] 500 [(] [e^x] 0.08 [X,T,θ] [−] [e^x]

0.06 [X,T,θ] [)] [GRAPH]

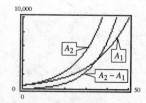

99. (a) *Keystrokes:*

Y= 1950 + 50 e^x (-) 1.6 X,T,θ −

20 X,T,θ GRAPH

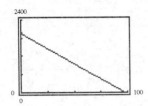

(b) $h = 1950 + 50e^{-1.6(0)} - 20(0) = 2000$ feet

$h = 1950 + 50e^{-1.6(25)} - 20(25) = 1450$ feet

$h = 1950 + 50e^{-1.6(50)} - 20(50) = 950$ feet

$h = 1950 + 50e^{-1.6(75)} - 20(75) = 450$ feet

(c) The parachutist will reach the ground at 97.5 seconds.

101. (a) *Graph model:*

Plot data:

Keystrokes: STAT EDIT 1

Enter each *x* entry in L 1 followed by ENTER.

Enter each *y* entry in L 2 followed by ENTER.

STAT PLOT ENTER ENTER ZOOM 9 or set window.

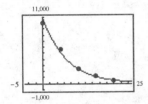

(b) *Keystrokes:* Y= 10,958 e^x (-) .15 X,T,θ
The model fits the data.

(c)

h	0	5	10	15	20
P	10,332	5583	2376	1240	517
Approx.	10,958	5176	2445	1155	546

(d) At an altitude of 8 kilometers, *P* is 3300 kilograms per square meter. Use table.

Keystrokes: TABLE 8 ENTER

(e) If *P* is 2000 kilograms per square meter, altitude is 11.3 kilometers. Graph $y_2 = 2000$ and find the intersection point.

103. (a)

x	1	10	100	1000	10,000
$\left(1 + \dfrac{1}{x}\right)^x$	2	2.5937	2.7048	2.7169	2.7181

(c) As *x* gets larger and larger, $\left(1 + \dfrac{1}{x}\right)^x$ approaches *e*.

(b) *Keystrokes:*

Y= (1 + 1 ÷ X,T,θ) ^ X,T,θ GRAPH

Yes, the graph is approaching a horizontal asymptote.

105. Polynomial functions have terms with variable bases and constant exponents. Exponential functions have terms with constant bases and variable exponents.

107. $f(x) = 3^x$ is an increasing function and $g(x) = \left(\frac{1}{3}\right)^x$ is a decreasing function.

109. False. *e* is an irrational number.

$\dfrac{271,801}{99,990}$ is rational because its equivalent decimal form is a repeating decimal.

Section 9.2   Inverse Functions

1. (a) $(f \circ g)(x) = (2x - 4) - 3 = 2x - 7$

(b) $(g \circ f)(x) = 2(x - 3) - 4 = 2x - 6 - 4 = 2x - 10$

(c) $(f \circ g)(4) = 2(4) - 7 = 1$

(d) $(g \circ f)(7) = 2(7) - 10 = 4$

3. (a) $(f \circ g)(x) = (2x^2 - 6) + 5 = 2x^2 - 1$

(b) $(g \circ f)(x) = 2(x + 5)^2 - 6 = 2(x^2 + 10x + 25) - 6$
$$= 2x^2 + 20x + 50 - 6$$
$$= 2x^2 + 20x + 44$$

(c) $(f \circ g)(2) = 2(2)^2 - 1 = 2(4) - 1 = 7$

(d) $(g \circ f)(-3) = 2(-3)^2 + 20(-3) + 44$
$$= 2(9) - 60 + 44$$
$$= 2$$

5. (a) $(f \circ g)(x) = |3x - 3|$

(b) $(g \circ f)(x) = 3|x - 3|$

(c) $(f \circ g)(1) = |3 - 3| = 0$

(d) $(g \circ f)(2) = 3|2 - 3| = 3$

7. (a) $(f \circ g)(x) = \sqrt{x + 5 - 4} = \sqrt{x + 1}$

(b) $(g \circ f)(x) = \sqrt{x - 4} + 5$

(c) $(f \circ g)(3) = \sqrt{3 + 1} = 2$

(d) $(g \circ f)(8) = \sqrt{8 - 4} + 5 = 2 + 5 = 7$

9. (a) $(f \circ g)(x) = \dfrac{1}{\dfrac{2}{x^2} - 3} \cdot \dfrac{x^2}{x^2} = \dfrac{x^2}{2 - 3x^2}$

(b) $(g \circ f)(x) = \dfrac{2}{\left(\dfrac{1}{x - 3}\right)^2} = 2(x - 3)^2$

(c) $(f \circ g)(-1) = \dfrac{(-1)^2}{2 - 3(-1)^2} = \dfrac{1}{2 - 3} = \dfrac{1}{-1} = -1$

(d) $(g \circ f)(2) = 2(2 - 3)^2 = 2(-1)^2 = 2$

11. (a) $f(1) = -1$

(b) $g(-1) = -2$

(c) $(g \circ f)(1) = g[f(1)]$
$$= g[-1]$$
$$= -2$$

13. (a) $(f \circ g)(-3) = f[g(-3)] = f[1] = -1$

(b) $(g \circ f)(-2) = g[f(-2)] = g[3] = 1$

15. (a) $f(3) = 10$

(b) $g(10) = 1$

(c) $(g \circ f)(3) = g[f(3)] = g[10] = 1$

17. (a) $(g \circ f)(4) = g[f(4)] = g[17] = 0$

(b) $(f \circ g)(2) = f[g(2)] = f[3] = 10$

19. $f(x) = x + 1, \quad g(x) = 2x - 5$

(a) $f \circ g = (2x - 5) + 1 = 2x - 4$
Domain: $(-\infty, \infty)$

(b) $g \circ f = 2(x + 1) - 5 = 2x + 2 - 5 = 2x - 3$
Domain: $(-\infty, \infty)$

21. $f(x) = \sqrt{x}, \quad g(x) = x - 2$

(a) $f \circ g = \sqrt{x - 2}$ Domain: $[2, \infty)$

(b) $g \circ f = \sqrt{x} - 2$ Domain: $[0, \infty)$

23. $f(x) = x^2 - 1, \quad g(x) = \sqrt{x + 3}$

(a) $f \circ g = \left(\sqrt{x + 3}\right)^2 - 1 = x + 3 - 1 = x + 2$
Domain: $[-3, \infty)$

(b) $g \circ f = \sqrt{(x^2 - 1) + 3} = \sqrt{x^2 + 2}$
Domain: $(-\infty, \infty)$

25. $f(x) = \dfrac{x}{x+5}$, $g(x) = \sqrt{x-1}$

(a) $f \circ g = \dfrac{\sqrt{x-1}}{\sqrt{x-1}+5}$ Domain: $[1, \infty)$

(b) $g \circ f = \sqrt{\dfrac{x}{x+5} - 1}$ Domain: $(-\infty, -5)$

27. $f(x) = x^2 - 2$

No, it does not have an inverse because it is possible to find a horizontal line that intersects the graph of f at more than one point.

29. $f(x) = x^2$, $x \geq 0$

Yes, it does have an inverse because no horizontal line intersects the graph of f at more than one point.

31. $g(x) = \sqrt{25 - x^2}$

No, it does not have an inverse because it is possible to find a horizontal line that intersects the graph of g at more than one point.

33. *Keystrokes:*

$\boxed{\text{Y=}}$ $\boxed{\text{X,T,}\theta}$ $\boxed{\land}$ 3 $\boxed{-}$ 1 $\boxed{\text{GRAPH}}$

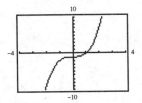

One-to-one

35. *Keystrokes:*

$\boxed{\text{Y=}}$ $\boxed{\text{MATH}}$ 4 $\boxed{(}$ 5 $\boxed{-}$ $\boxed{\text{X,T,}\theta}$ $\boxed{)}$ $\boxed{\text{GRAPH}}$

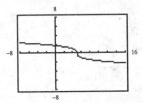

One-to-one

37. *Keystrokes:*

$\boxed{\text{Y=}}$ $\boxed{\text{X,T,}\theta}$ $\boxed{\land}$ 4 $\boxed{-}$ 6 $\boxed{\text{GRAPH}}$

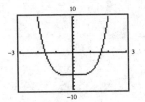

Not one-to-one

39. *Keystrokes:*

$\boxed{\text{Y=}}$ 5 $\boxed{\div}$ $\boxed{\text{X,T,}\theta}$ $\boxed{\text{GRAPH}}$

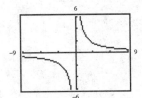

One-to-one

41. *Keystrokes:*

$\boxed{\text{Y=}}$ 4 $\boxed{\div}$ $\boxed{(}$ $\boxed{\text{X,T,}\theta}$ $\boxed{x^2}$ $\boxed{+}$ 1 $\boxed{)}$ $\boxed{\text{GRAPH}}$

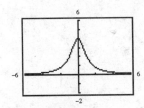

Not one-to-one

43. $f(g(x)) = 10\left(\dfrac{1}{10}x\right) = x$

$g(f(x)) = \dfrac{10x}{10} = x$

45. $f(g(x)) = (x - 15) + 15 = x$

$g(f(x)) = (x + 15) - 15 = x$

47. $f(g(x)) = 1 - 2\left[\tfrac{1}{2}(1 - x)\right]$

$\qquad = 1 - (1 - x) = 1 - 1 + x = x$

$g(f(x)) = \tfrac{1}{2}\left[1 - (1 - 2x)\right]$

$\qquad = \tfrac{1}{2}\left[1 - 1 + 2x\right] = \tfrac{1}{2}\left[2x\right] = x$

49. $f(g(x)) = 2 - 3\left[\frac{1}{3}(2-x)\right] = 2 - (2-x) = x$

$g(f(x)) = \frac{1}{3}[2 - (2-3x)] = \frac{1}{3}[3x] = x$

51. $f(g(x)) = \sqrt[3]{x^3 - 1 + 1} = \sqrt[3]{x^3} = x$

$g(f(x)) = \left(\sqrt[3]{x+1}\right)^3 - 1 = x + 1 - 1 = x$

53. $f(g(x)) = \dfrac{1}{\frac{1}{x}} = x$

$g(f(x)) = \dfrac{1}{\frac{1}{x}} = x$

55. $f^{-1}(x) = \dfrac{x}{5}$

$f(f^{-1}(x)) = f\left(\dfrac{x}{5}\right) = 5\left(\dfrac{x}{5}\right) = x$

$f^{-1}(f(x)) = f^{-1}(5x) = \dfrac{5x}{5} = x$

57. $f^{-1}(x) = 2x$

$f(f^{-1}(x)) = f(2x) = \frac{1}{2}(2x) = x$

$f^{-1}(f(x)) = f^{-1}\left(\frac{1}{2}x\right) = 2\left(\frac{1}{2}x\right) = x$

59. $f^{-1}(x) = x - 10$

$f(f^{-1}(x)) = f(x - 10) = x - 10 + 10 = x$

$f^{-1}(f(x)) = f^{-1}(x + 10) = x + 10 - 10 = x$

61. $f^{-1}(x) = 3 - x$

$f(f^{-1}(x)) = f(3 - x) = 3 - (3 - x) = 3 - 3 + x = x$

$f^{-1}(f(x)) = f^{-1}(3 - x) = 3 - (3 - x) = 3 - 3 + x = x$

63. $f^{-1}(x) = \sqrt[7]{x}$

$f(f^{-1}(x)) = f(\sqrt[7]{x}) = \left(\sqrt[7]{x}\right)^7 = x$

$f^{-1}(f(x)) = f^{-1}(x^7) = \sqrt[7]{x^7} = x$

65. $f^{-1}(x) = x^3$

$f(f^{-1}(x)) = f(x^3) = \sqrt[3]{x^3} = x$

$f^{-1}(f(x)) = f^{-1}(\sqrt[3]{x}) = \left(\sqrt[3]{x}\right)^3 = x$

67. $f(x) = 8x$

$y = 8x$

$x = 8y$

$\dfrac{x}{8} = y$

$f^{-1}(x) = \dfrac{x}{8}$

69. $g(x) = x + 25$

$y = x + 25$

$x = y + 25$

$x - 25 = y$

$g^{-1}(x) = x - 25$

71. $g(x) = 3 - 4x$

$y = 3 - 4x$

$x = 3 - 4y$

$x - 3 = -4y$

$\dfrac{x - 3}{-4} = y$

$\dfrac{3 - x}{4}$ or $\dfrac{x - 3}{-4} = g^{-1}(x)$

73. $g(t) = \frac{1}{4}t + 2$

$y = \frac{1}{4}t + 2$

$t = \frac{1}{4}y + 2$

$t - 2 = \frac{1}{4}y$

$4(t - 2) = y$

$4t - 8 = g^{-1}(t)$

75. $h(x) = \sqrt{x}$

$y = \sqrt{x}$

$x = \sqrt{y}$

$x^2 = y$

$x^2 = h^{-1}(x), \quad x \geq 0$

77. $f(t) = t^3 - 1$

$y = t^3 - 1$

$t = y^3 - 1$

$t + 1 = y^3$

$\sqrt[3]{t + 1} = y$

$\sqrt[3]{t + 1} = f^{-1}(t)$

79. $g(s) = \dfrac{5}{s + 4}$

$y = \dfrac{5}{s + 4}$

$s = \dfrac{5}{y + 4}$

$y + 4 = \dfrac{5}{s}$

$g^{-1}(s) = \dfrac{5}{s} - 4, \quad s \neq 0$

81. $f(x) = \sqrt{x + 3}$

$y = \sqrt{x + 3}$

$x = \sqrt{y + 3}$

$x^2 = y + 3$

$x^2 - 3 = y$

$x^2 - 3 = f^{-1}(x), \quad x \geq 0$

83. $f(x) = x + 4$, $f^{-1}(x) = x - 4$

$(0, 4)$ $(4, 0)$

$(-4, 0)$ $(0, -4)$

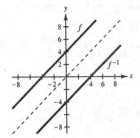

85. $f(x) = 3x - 1$, $f^{-1}(x) = \frac{1}{3}(x + 1)$

$(0, -1)$ $(-1, 0)$

$\left(\frac{1}{3}, 0\right)$ $\left(0, \frac{1}{3}\right)$

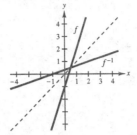

87. $f(x) = x^2 - 1$, $f^{-1}(x) = \sqrt{x + 1}$

$(0, -1)$ $(-1, 0)$

$(1, 0)$ $(0, 1)$

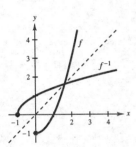

89. (b)   **91.** (d)

93. *Keystrokes:*

y_1 Y= (1 ÷ 3) X,T,θ ENTER

y_2 3 X,T,θ GRAPH

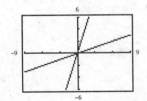

95. *Keystrokes:*

y_1 Y= √ (X,T,θ + 1) ENTER

y_2 X,T,θ x^2 − 1 ÷ (X,T,θ TEST 4 0) GRAPH

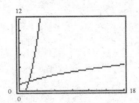

97. *Keystrokes:*

y_1 Y= (1 ÷ 8) X,T,θ MATH 3 ENTER

y_2 2 MATH 4 X,T,θ GRAPH

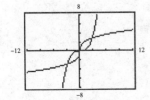

99. *Keystrokes:*

y_1 Y= 3 X,T,θ + 4 ENTER

y_2 (X,T,θ − 4) ÷ 3 GRAPH

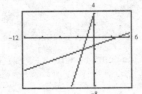

101. $f(x) = (x - 2)^2,\ \ x \geq 2$

$\qquad y = (x - 2)^2$

$\qquad x = (y - 2)^2$

$\qquad \sqrt{x} = y - 2$

$\qquad \sqrt{x} + 2 = y$

$\qquad \sqrt{x} + 2 = f^{-1}(x),\ \ x \geq 0$

103. $f(x) = |x| + 1,\ \ x \geq 0$

$\qquad y = |x| + 1$

$\qquad x = |y| + 1$

$\qquad x - 1 = |y|$

$\qquad x - 1 = y$

$\qquad x - 1 = f^{-1}(x),\ \ x \geq 1$

105.

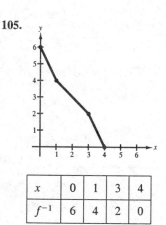

x	0	1	3	4
f^{-1}	6	4	2	0

107.

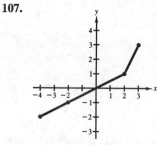

x	-4	-2	2	3
f^{-1}	-2	-1	1	3

109. (a) $y = 3 - 2x$

$\qquad x = 3 - 2y$

$\qquad 2y = 3 - x$

$\qquad y = \dfrac{3 - x}{2}$

$\qquad f^{-1}(x) = \dfrac{3 - x}{2}$

(b) $y = \dfrac{3 - x}{2}$

$\qquad x = \dfrac{3 - y}{2}$

$\qquad 2x = 3 - y$

$\qquad y = 3 - 2x$

$\qquad (f^{-1})^{-1}(x) = 3 - 2x$

111. (a) Total cost $=$ Cost of \$0.50 commodity $+$ Cost of \$0.75 commodity

$\qquad y = 0.50x + 0.75(100 - x)$

(b) $\qquad y = 0.50x + 0.75(100 - x)$

$\qquad y = 0.50x + 75 - 0.75x$

$\qquad y = -0.25x + 75$

$\qquad x = -0.25y + 75$

$\qquad x - 75 = -0.25y$

$\qquad \dfrac{x - 75}{-0.25} = y$

$\qquad -4(x - 75) = y$

$\qquad 4(75 - x) = y$

x: total cost

y: number of pounds at \$0.50 per pound

(c) $50 \leq x \leq 75$

If you buy only the cheaper commodity, your cost will be \$50. If you buy only the more expensive commodity, your cost will be \$75. Any combination will lie between \$50 and \$75.

(d) $y = 4(75 - 60)$

$\qquad y = 4(15)$

$\qquad y = 60$

Thus, 60 pounds of the \$0.50 per pound commodity is purchased.

113. (a) $f(g(x)) = 0.02x - 200{,}000$

(b) $g(f(x)) = 0.02(x - 200{,}000),\ \ x > 200{,}000$

This part represents the bonus because it gives 2% of sales over \$200,000.

115. (a) $R = p - 2000$

(c) $(R \circ S)(p) = R[S(p)] = R(0.95p) = 0.95p - 2000$

5% discount before the $2000 rebate is given.

$(S \circ R)(p) = S[R(p)]$

$= S(p - 2000) = 0.95(p - 2000)$

The 5% discount is given after the $2000 rebate is applied.

(b) $S = p - 0.05p$

$S = 0.95p$

(d) $(R \circ S)(26{,}000) = 0.95(26{,}000) - 2000 = \$22{,}700$

$(S \circ R)(26{,}000) = 0.95(26{,}000 - 2000) = \$22{,}800$

$R \circ S$ yields the smaller cost because the dealer discount is based on a larger amount.

117. True, the x-coordinate of a point on the graph of f becomes the y-coordinate of a point on the graph of f^{-1}.

119. False: $f(x) = \sqrt{x - 1}$ Domain $[1, \infty)$

$f^{-1}(x) = x^2 + 1$ Domain $[0, \infty)$

121. If $f(x) = 2x$ and $g(x) = x^2$, then $(f \circ g)(x) = 2x^2$ and $(g \circ f)(x) = 4x^2$.

123. (a) In the equation for $f(x)$, replace $f(x)$ by y.

(b) Interchange the roles of x and y.

(c) If the new equation represents y as a function of x, solve the new equation for y.

(d) Replace y by $f^{-1}(x)$.

125. Graphically, a function f has an inverse function if and only if no horizontal line intersects the graph of f at more than one point. This is equivalent to saying that the function f is one-to-one.

Section 9.3   Logarithmic Functions

1. $\log_5 25 = 2$

$5^2 = 25$

3. $\log_4 \frac{1}{16} = -2$

$4^{-2} = \frac{1}{16}$

5. $\log_3 \frac{1}{243} = -5$

$3^{-5} = \frac{1}{243}$

7. $\log_{36} 6 = \frac{1}{2}$

$36^{1/2} = 6$

9. $\log_8 4 = \frac{2}{3}$

$8^{2/3} = 4$

11. $\log_2 2.462 \approx 1.3$

$2^{1.3} \approx 2.462$

13. $7^2 = 49$

$\log_7 49 = 2$

15. $3^{-2} = \frac{1}{9}$

$\log_3 \frac{1}{9} = -2$

17. $8^{2/3} = 4$

$\log_8 4 = \frac{2}{3}$

19. $25^{-1/2} = \frac{1}{5}$

$\log_{25} \frac{1}{5} = -\frac{1}{2}$

21. $4^0 = 1$

$\log_4 1 = 0$

23. $5^{1.4} \approx 9.518$

$\log_5 9.518 \approx 1.4$

25. $\log_2 8 = 3$ because $2^3 = 8$.

27. $\log_{10} 10 = 1$ because $10^1 = 10$.

29. $\log_{10} 1000 = 3$ because $10^3 = 1000$.

31. $\log_2 \frac{1}{4} = -2$ because $2^{-2} = \frac{1}{4}$.

33. $\log_4 \frac{1}{64} = -3$ because $4^{-3} = \frac{1}{64}$.

35. $\log_{10} \frac{1}{10{,}000} = -4$ because $10^{-4} = \frac{1}{10{,}000}$.

37. $\log_2(-3)$ is not possible because there is no power to which 2 can be raised to obtain -3.

39. $\log_4 1 = 0$ because $4^0 = 1$.

41. $\log_5 (-6)$ is not possible because there is no power to which 5 can be raised to obtain -6.

43. $\log_9 3 = \frac{1}{2}$ because $9^{1/2} = 3$.

45. $\log_{16} 8 = \frac{3}{4}$ because $16^{3/4} = 8$.

47. $\log_7 7^4 = 4$ because $7^4 = 7^4$.

49. $\log_{10} 31 \approx 1.4914$

51. $\log_{10} 0.85 \approx -0.0706$

53. $\log_{10}\left(\sqrt{2} + 4\right) \approx 0.7335$

55.

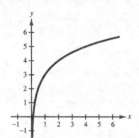

f and *g* are inverse functions.

57.

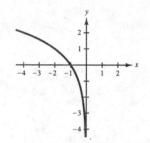

f and *g* are inverse functions.

59. *f* and *g* are inverse functions.

61. *f* and *g* are inverse functions.

63. $h(x) = 3 + \log_2 x$

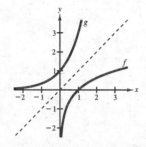

Vertical shift 3 units up

65. $h(x) = \log_2(x - 2)$

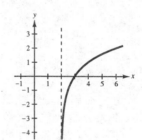

Horizontal shift 2 units right

67. $h(x) = \log_2(-x)$

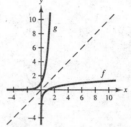

Reflection in the *x*-axis

69. $f(x) = 4 + \log_3 x$
matches graph (e)

71. $f(x) = -\log_3 x$
matches graph (d)

73. $f(x) = \log_3(x - 4)$
matches graph (a)

75. $f(x) = \log_5 x$

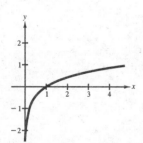

Table of values:

x	1	5
y	0	1

77. $f(x) = -\log_2 t$

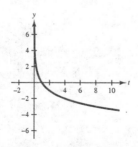

Table of values:

x	1	2
y	0	-1

79. $f(x) = 3 + \log_2 x$

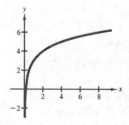

Table of values:

x	1	2
y	3	4

81. $g(x) = \log_2(x - 3)$

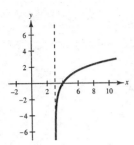

Table of values:

x	4	7
y	0	2

83. $f(x) = \log_{10}(10x)$

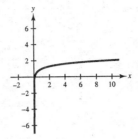

Table of values:

x	1	10
y	1	2

85. $f(x) = \log_4 x$

Domain: $(0, \infty)$

Vertical asymptote: $x = 0$

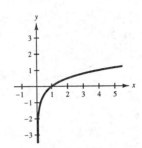

Table of values:

x	1	4
y	0	1

87. $h(x) = \log_4(x - 3)$

Domain: $(3, \infty)$

Vertical asymptote: $x = 3$

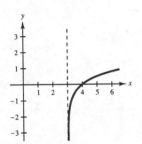

Table of values:

x	4	13
y	0	1

89. $y = -\log_3 x + 2$

Domain: $(0, \infty)$

Vertical asymptote: $x = 0$

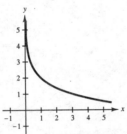

Table of values:

x	1	3
y	2	1

91. $y = 5 \log_{10} x$

Keystrokes:

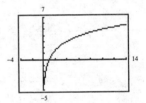

Domain: $(0, \infty)$

Vertical asymptote: $x = 0$

93. $y = -3 + 5 \log_{10} x$

Keystrokes: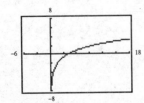

Domain: $(0, \infty)$

Vertical asymptote: $x = 0$

95. $y = \log_{10}\left(\dfrac{x}{5}\right)$

Keystrokes: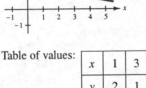

Domain: $(0, \infty)$

Vertical asymptote: $x = 0$

97. $\ln 25 \approx 3.2189$

99. $\ln 0.75 \approx -0.2877$

101. $\ln\left(\dfrac{1 + \sqrt{5}}{3}\right) \approx 0.0757$

103. (b) Basic graph shifted 1 unit left

105. (d) Basic graph shifted $\frac{3}{2}$ unit right

107. (f) Basic graph multiplied by 10

109. $f(x) = -\ln x$

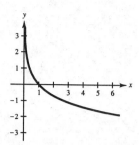

Table of values:

x	1	e
y	0	-1

111. $f(x) = 3 \ln x$

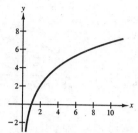

Table of values:

x	1	e
y	0	3

113. $f(x) = 1 + \ln x$

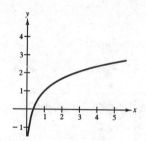

Table of values:

x	1	e
y	1	2

115. $g(t) = 2 \ln(t - 4)$

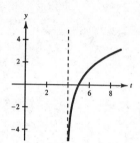

Table of values:

x	5	6
y	0	1.4

117. *Keystrokes:*

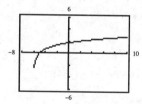

Domain: $(-6, \infty)$

Vertical asymptote: $x = -6$

119. *Keystrokes:*

$\boxed{Y=}$ 3 $\boxed{+}$ 2 $\boxed{LN}$ $\boxed{X,T,\theta}$ $\boxed{GRAPH}$

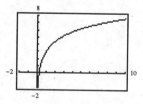

Domain: $(0, \infty)$

Vertical asymptote: $t = 0$

121. $\log_8 132 = \dfrac{\log 132}{\log 8} \approx 2.3481$

$= \dfrac{\ln 132}{\ln 8} \approx 2.3481$

123. $\log_3 7 = \dfrac{\log 7}{\log 3} \approx 1.7712$

$= \dfrac{\ln 7}{\ln 3} \approx 1.7712$

125. $\log_2 0.72 = \dfrac{\log 0.72}{\log 2} \approx -0.4739$

$= \dfrac{\ln 0.72}{\ln 2} \approx -0.4739$

127. $\log_{15} 1250 = \dfrac{\log 1250}{\log 15} \approx 2.6332$

$= \dfrac{\ln 1250}{\ln 15} \approx 2.6332$

129. $\log_{(1/2)} 4 = \dfrac{\log 4}{\log 0.5} = -2$

$= \dfrac{\ln 4}{\ln 0.5} = -2$

131. $\log_4 \sqrt{42} = \dfrac{\log \sqrt{42}}{\log 4} \approx 1.3481$

$= \dfrac{\ln \sqrt{42}}{\ln 4} \approx 1.3481$

133. $\log_2(1 + e) = \dfrac{\log(1 + e)}{\log 2} \approx 1.8946$

$= \dfrac{\ln(1 + e)}{\ln 2} \approx 1.8946$

135. $h = 116 \log_{10}(55 + 40) - 176$

$= 116 \log_{10}(95) - 176$

≈ 53.4 inches

137. r of 0.07: $t = \dfrac{\ln 2}{0.07} \approx 9.9021$ $\qquad$ r of 0.08: $t = \dfrac{\ln 2}{0.08} \approx 8.6643$

r of 0.09: $t = \dfrac{\ln 2}{0.09} \approx 7.7016$ $\qquad$ r of 0.10: $t = \dfrac{\ln 2}{0.10} \approx 6.9315$

r of 0.11: $t = \dfrac{\ln 2}{0.11} \approx 6.3013$ $\qquad$ r of 0.12: $t = \dfrac{\ln 2}{0.12} \approx 5.7762$

r	0.07	0.08	0.09	0.10	0.11	0.12
t	9.9	8.7	7.7	6.9	6.3	5.8

139. (a) *Keystrokes:*

$\boxed{Y=}$ 10 $\boxed{LN}$ $\boxed{(}$ $\boxed{(}$ 10 $\boxed{+}$ $\boxed{\sqrt{}}$ $\boxed{(}$ 100 $\boxed{-}$ $\boxed{X,T,\theta}$ $\boxed{x^2}$ $\boxed{)}$ $\boxed{)}$

$\boxed{\div}$ $\boxed{X,T,\theta}$ $\boxed{)}$ $\boxed{-}$ $\boxed{\sqrt{}}$ $\boxed{(}$ 100 $\boxed{-}$ $\boxed{X,T,\theta}$ $\boxed{x^2}$ $\boxed{)}$ $\boxed{GRAPH}$

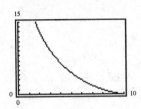

Domain: $(0, 10]$

(b) Vertical asymptote: $x = 0$

(c) $y = 13.126$ when $x = 2$. Trace to $x = 2$.

141. (a) *Graph model:*

Plot data:

Keystrokes: $\boxed{STAT}$ $\boxed{EDIT 1}$

Enter each x entry in L1 followed by $\boxed{ENTER}$.

Enter each y entry in L2 followed by $\boxed{ENTER}$.

$\boxed{STAT\ PLOT}$ $\boxed{ENTER}$ $\boxed{ENTER}$ $\boxed{ZOOM\ 9}$ or set window.

Keystrokes: $\boxed{Y=}$ 435.33 $\boxed{-}$ 527.72 $\boxed{X,T,\theta}$ $\boxed{+}$ 396.68 $\boxed{LN}$ $\boxed{X,T,\theta}$ $\boxed{+}$ 88.05 $\boxed{X,T,\theta}$ $\boxed{x^2}$ $\boxed{GRAPH}$

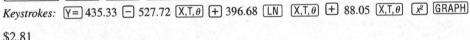

(b) $\$2.81$

Keystrokes: $\boxed{TABLE}$ 1.59 $\boxed{ENTER}$

143. $f(x) = 2^x$ and $g(x) = \log_2 x$ are inverse functions.

145. $\log_a a^x = x$ because $a^x = a^x$.

147. $\log_b x = \dfrac{\log x}{\log b} = \dfrac{\ln x}{\ln b}$

149. $f(x) = \log_{10} x$

$f^{-1}(x) = 10^x$

151. If $f(x)$ is negative, then $0 < x < 1$.

153. $f(a) = \log_{10} a \qquad f(b) = \log_{10} b$

$10^{f(a)} = a \qquad 10^{f(b)} = b$

$\dfrac{a}{b} = \dfrac{10^{f(a)}}{10^{f(b)}} = \dfrac{10^{3f(b)}}{10^{f(b)}} = 10^{2f(b)} = 10^{2\log_{10}b}$

$= 10^{\log_{10} b^2} = b^2$

Mid-Chapter Quiz for Chapter 9

1. (a) $f(2) = \left(\dfrac{4}{3}\right)^2 = \dfrac{16}{9}$

    (b) $f(0) = \left(\dfrac{4}{3}\right)^0 = 1$

    (c) $f(-1) = \left(\dfrac{4}{3}\right)^{-1} = \dfrac{3}{4}$

    (d) $f(1.5) = \left(\dfrac{4}{3}\right)^{1.5} \approx 1.54$

            $= \dfrac{8\sqrt{3}}{9}$

2. $g(x) = 2^{-0.5x}$

    Domain: $(-\infty, \infty)$

    Range: $(0, \infty)$

3.

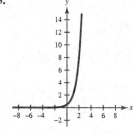

4.

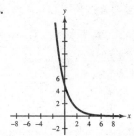

5.

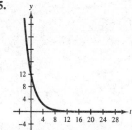

6.

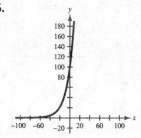

7. Compounded 1 time per year: $A = 750\left(1 + \dfrac{0.075}{1}\right)^{1(20)}$

                      $\approx \$3185.89$

Compounded 4 times per year: $A = 750\left(1 + \dfrac{0.075}{4}\right)^{4(20)}$

                      $\approx \$3314.90$

Compounded 12 times per year: $A = 750\left(1 + \dfrac{0.075}{12}\right)^{12(20)}$

                      $\approx \$3345.61$

Compounded 365 times per year: $A = 750\left(1 + \dfrac{0.075}{365}\right)^{365(20)}$

                      $\approx \$3360.75$

Compounded continuously: $A = Pe^{rt}$

                      $= 750e^{0.075(20)}$

                      $\approx \$3361.27$

8. $A = 2.23e^{(0.04)(5)} = \$2.72$

9. (a) $(f \circ g)(x) = f[g(x)] = 2x^3 - 3$

    (b) $(g \circ f)(x) = g[f(x)] = (2x - 3)^3$

    (c) $(fg)(-2) = f[g(-2)] = f[-8] = 2(-8) - 3 = -19$

    (d) $(g \circ f)(4) = g[f(4)] = g[5] = 5^3 = 125$

10. $f[g(x)] = 3 - 5\left[\dfrac{1}{5}(3 - x)\right] = 3 - 1(3 - x) = 3 - 3 + x = x$

     $g[f(x)] = \dfrac{1}{5}[3 - (3 - 5x)] = \dfrac{1}{5}[3 - 3 + 5x] = \dfrac{1}{5}[5x] = x$

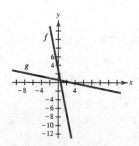

11. $h(x) = 10x + 3$

  $y = 10x + 3$

  $x = 10y + 3$

$x - 3 = 10y$

$\dfrac{x - 3}{10} = y$

$\dfrac{x - 3}{10} = h^{-1}(x)$

12. $g(t) = \dfrac{1}{2}t^3 + 2$

  $y = \dfrac{1}{2}t^3 + 2$

  $t = \dfrac{1}{2}y^3 + 2$

$t - 2 = \dfrac{1}{2}y^3$

$2t - 4 = y^3$

$\sqrt[3]{2t - 4} = y$

$\sqrt[3]{2t - 4} = g^{-1}(t)$

13. $\log_4\!\left(\dfrac{1}{16}\right) = -2$

  $4^{-2} = \dfrac{1}{16}$

14. $3^4 = 81$

  $\log_3 81 = 4$

15. $\log_5 125 = 3$ because $5^3 = 125$.

16. f and g are inverse functions because the graphs of f and g reflect about the line $y = x$.

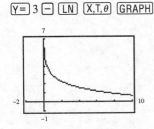

17. *Keystrokes:*

  $\boxed{Y=}$ .5 $\boxed{LN}$ $\boxed{X,T,\theta}$ $\boxed{GRAPH}$

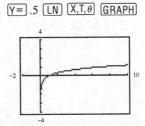

18. *Keystrokes:*

  $\boxed{Y=}$ 3 $\boxed{-}$ $\boxed{LN}$ $\boxed{X,T,\theta}$ $\boxed{GRAPH}$

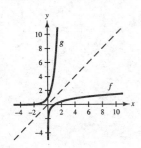

19. $f(x) = \log_5(x - 2) + 1$

The graph of $f(x) = \log_5 x$ has been shifted 3 units right and 1 unit up, so $h = 2$, $k = 1$.

20. $\log_6 450 = \dfrac{\log 450}{\log 6} \approx 3.4096$

Section 9.4   Properties of Logarithms

1. $\log_5 5^2 = 2 \cdot \log_5 5 = 2 \cdot 1 = 2$

3. $\log_2\!\left(\dfrac{1}{8}\right)^3 = \log_2\left(2^{-3}\right)^3 = \log_2 2^{-9}$

  $= -9 \cdot \log_2 2 = -9 \cdot 1 = -9$

5. $\log_6 \sqrt{6} = \log_6 6^{1/2} = \dfrac{1}{2}$ because $6^{1/2} = 6^{1/2}$.

7. $\ln 8^0 = 0 \cdot \ln 8 = 0$ *or* $\ln 8^0 = \ln 1 = 0$

9. $\ln e^4 = 4 \ln e = 4(1) = 4$

11. $\log_4 2 + \log_4 8 = \log_4 2 \cdot 8 = \log_4 16 = 2$ because $4^2 = 16$.

13. $\log_8 4 + \log_8 16 = \log_8 4 \cdot 16 = \log_8 64 = 2$ because $8^2 = 64$.

15. $\log_4 8 - \log_4 2 = \log_4 \frac{8}{2} = \log_4 4 = 1$ because $4^1 = 4$.

17. $\log_6 72 - \log_6 2 = \log_6 \frac{72}{2} = \log_6 36 = 2$ because $6^2 = 36$.

19. $\log_2 5 - \log_2 40 = \log_2 \frac{5}{40} = \log_2 \frac{1}{8} = \log_2 2^{-3} = -3$ because $2^{-3} = 2^{-3}$.

21. $\ln e^8 + \ln e^4 = \ln e^8 \cdot e^4 = \ln e^{12}$
$= 12 \ln e = 12 \cdot 1 = 12$

23. $\ln \frac{e^3}{e^2} = \ln e = 1$

25. $\log_4 4 = \log_4 2 + \log_4 2 = 0.5000 + 0.5000 = 1$

27. $\log_4 6 = \log_4 2 \cdot 3 = \log_4 2 + \log_4 3$
$= 0.5000 + 0.7925 \approx 1.2925$

29. $\log_4 \frac{3}{2} = \log_4 3 - \log_4 2 = 0.7925 - 0.5000 \approx 0.2925$

31. $\log_4 \sqrt{2} = \frac{1}{2} \log_4 2 = \frac{1}{2}(0.5000) = 0.25$

33. $\log_4(3 \cdot 2^4) = \log_4 3 + 4 \log_4 2$
$= 0.7925 + 4(0.5000) \approx 2.7925$

35. $\log_4 3^0 = \log_4 1 = 0$

37. $\log_{10} 9 = \log_{10} 3^2 = 2 \log_{10} 3 \approx 2(0.477) \approx 0.954$

39. $\log_{10} 36 = \log_{10}(3 \cdot 12) = \log_{10} 3 + \log_{10} 12$
$\approx 0.477 + 1.079$
≈ 1.556

41. $\log_{10} \sqrt{36} = \log_{10} 36^{1/2} = \frac{1}{2} \log_{10} 36$
$\approx \frac{1}{2}(1.556)$
≈ 0.778

43. $\log_3 11x = \log_3 11 + \log_3 x$

45. $\log_7 x^2 = 2 \log_7 x$

47. $\log_5 x^{-2} = -2 \log_5 x$

49. $\log_4 \sqrt{3x} = \log_4(3x)^{1/2} = \frac{1}{2} \log_4(3x)$
$= \frac{1}{2}(\log_4 3 + \log_4 x)$

51. $\ln 3y = \ln 3 + \ln y$

53. $\log_2 \frac{z}{17} = \log_2 z - \log_2 17$

55. $\ln \frac{5}{x-2} = \ln 5 - \ln(x-2)$

57. $\ln x^2(y-2) = \ln x^2 + \ln(y-2)$
$= 2 \ln x + \ln(y-2)$

59. $\log_4[x^6(x-7)^2] = \log_4 x^6 + \log_4(x-7)^2$
$= 6 \log_4 x + 2 \log_4(x-7)$

61. $\log_3 \sqrt[3]{x+1} = \frac{1}{3} \log_3(x+1)$

63. $\ln \sqrt{x(x+2)} = \frac{1}{2}[\ln x + \ln(x+2)]$

65. $\ln\left(\frac{x+1}{x-1}\right)^2 = 2 \ln\left(\frac{x+1}{x-1}\right)$
$= 2[\ln(x+1) - \ln(x-1)]$

67. $\ln \sqrt[3]{\frac{x^2}{x+1}} = \ln\left(\frac{x^2}{x+1}\right)^{1/3} = \frac{1}{3} \ln\left(\frac{x^2}{x+1}\right)$
$= \frac{1}{3}[\ln x^2 - \ln(x+1)]$
$= \frac{1}{3}[2 \ln x - \ln(x+1)]$

69. $\ln \dfrac{a^3(b-4)}{c^2} = \ln a^3 + \ln(b-4) - \ln c^2$

$\qquad\qquad = 3 \ln a + \ln(b-4) - 2 \ln c$

71. $\ln \dfrac{x\sqrt[3]{y}}{(wz)^4} = \ln x + \ln \sqrt[3]{y} - \ln(wz)^4$

$\qquad\qquad = \ln x + \ln y^{1/3} - 4 \ln(wz)$

$\qquad\qquad = \ln x + \dfrac{1}{3} \ln y - 4(\ln w + \ln z)$

73. $\log_6[a\sqrt{b}(c-d)^3] = \log_6 a + \log_6 \sqrt{b} + \log_6(c-d)^3$

$\qquad\qquad = \log_6 a + \log_6 b^{1/2} + 3 \log_6(c-d)$

$\qquad\qquad = \log_6 a + \dfrac{1}{2} \log_6 b + 3 \log_6(c-d)$

75. $\ln\left[(x+y)\dfrac{\sqrt[5]{w+2}}{3t}\right] = \ln(x+y) + \ln \sqrt[5]{w+2} - \ln(3t)$

$\qquad\qquad = \ln(x+y) + \ln(w+2)^{1/5} - (\ln 3 + \ln t)$

$\qquad\qquad = \ln(x+y) + \dfrac{1}{5} \ln(w+2) - (\ln 3 + \ln t)$

77. $\log_{12} x - \log_{12} 3 = \log_{12} \dfrac{x}{3}$

79. $\log_2 3 + \log_2 x = \log_2 3x$

81. $\log_{10} 4 - \log_{10} x = \log_{10} \dfrac{4}{x}$

83. $4 \ln b = \ln b^4, \quad b > 0$

85. $-2 \log_5 2x = \log_5(2x)^{-2}$

$\qquad\qquad = \log_5 \dfrac{1}{4x^2}, \quad x > 0$

87. $\dfrac{1}{3} \ln(2x+1) = \ln \sqrt[3]{2x+1}$

89. $\log_3 2 + \dfrac{1}{2} \log_3 y = \log_3 2 + \log_3 \sqrt{y}$

$\qquad\qquad = \log_3 2\sqrt{y}$

91. $2 \ln x + 3 \ln y - \ln z = \ln \dfrac{x^2 y^3}{z}, \quad x > 0, \ y > 0, \ z > 0$

93. $5 \ln 2 - \ln x + 3 \ln y = \ln 2^5 - \ln x + \ln y^3$

$\qquad\qquad = \ln 32 - \ln x + \ln y^3$

$\qquad\qquad = \ln \dfrac{32y^3}{x}, \quad x > 0, \ y > 0$

95. $4(\ln x + \ln y) = \ln(xy)^4 \quad \text{or} \quad \ln x^4 y^4, \quad x > 0, \ y > 0$

97. $2[\ln x - \ln(x+1)] = 2 \ln \dfrac{x}{x+1} = \ln\left(\dfrac{x}{x+1}\right)^2$

$\qquad\qquad = \ln \dfrac{x^2}{(x+1)^2}, \quad x > 0$

99. $\log_4(x+8) - 3 \log_4 x = \log_4(x+8) - \log_4 x^3$

$\qquad\qquad = \log_4 \dfrac{(x+8)}{x^3}, \quad x > 0$

101. $\dfrac{1}{2} \log_5(x+2) - \log_5(x-3) = \log_5(x+2)^{1/2} - \log(x-3)$

$\qquad\qquad = \log_5 \dfrac{\sqrt{x+2}}{x-3}$

103. $5 \log_6(c+d) - \dfrac{1}{2} \log_6(m-n) = \log_6(c+d)^5 - \log_6(m-n)^{1/2}$

$\qquad\qquad = \log_6 \dfrac{(c+d)^5}{\sqrt{m-n}}$

105. $\dfrac{1}{5}(3\log_2 x - 4\log_2 y) = \dfrac{1}{5}(\log_2 x^3 - \log_2 y^4)$

$$= \dfrac{1}{5}\left(\log_2 \dfrac{x^3}{y^4}\right)$$

$$= \log_2 \sqrt[5]{\dfrac{x^3}{y^4}},\ y > 0$$

107. $\dfrac{1}{5}\log_6(x - 3) - 2\log_6 x - 3\log(x + 1) = \log_6(x - 3)^{1/5} - \log_6 x^2 - \log_6(x + 1)^3$

$$= \log_6 \dfrac{\sqrt[5]{x - 3}}{x^2(x + 1)^3},\quad x > 3$$

109. $\ln 3e^2 = \ln 3 + \ln e^2$

$ = \ln 3 + 2\ln e$

$ = \ln 3 + 2$

111. $\log_5 \sqrt{50} = \dfrac{1}{2}[\log_5(5^2 \cdot 2)]$

$\phantom{\log_5 \sqrt{50}} = \dfrac{1}{2}[2\log_5 5 + \log_5 2]$

$\phantom{\log_5 \sqrt{50}} = \dfrac{1}{2}[2 + \log_5 2]$

$\phantom{\log_5 \sqrt{50}} = 1 + \dfrac{1}{2}\log_5 2$

113. $\log_4 \dfrac{4}{x^2} = \log_4 4 - \log_4 x^2$

$\phantom{\log_4 \dfrac{4}{x^2}} = 1 - \log_4 x^2$

$\phantom{\log_4 \dfrac{4}{x^2}} = 1 - 2\log_4 x$

115.

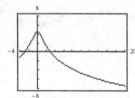

Keystrokes:

y_1 [Y=] [(] 10 [÷] [(] [X,T,θ] [x²] [+] 1 [)] [)] [x²] [ENTER]

y_2 [LN] [y_1] [ENTER]

y^3 2 [(] [LN] 10 [−] [LN] [(] [X,T,θ] [x²] [+] 1 [)] [)] [GRAPH]

Graph y_2 and y_3.

117.

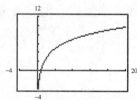

Keystrokes:

y_1 [Y=] [LN] [(] [X,T,θ] [x²] [(] [X,T,θ] [+] 2 [)] [)] [ENTER]

y_2 2 [LN] [X,T,θ] [+] [LN] [(] [X,T,θ] [+] 2 [)] [GRAPH]

119. Choose two values for x and y, such as $x = 3$ and $y = 5$, and show the two expressions are not equal.

$\dfrac{\ln 3}{\ln 5} \neq \ln \dfrac{3}{5} = \ln 3 - \ln 5$ $\qquad$ or $\qquad$ $\dfrac{\ln e}{\ln e} \neq \ln \dfrac{e}{e}$

$0.6826062 \neq -0.5108256 = -0.5108256$ $\qquad\qquad\qquad$ $1 \neq \ln 1$

$\qquad\qquad\qquad\qquad\qquad\qquad\qquad\qquad\qquad\qquad\qquad\ $ $1 \neq 0$

121. $B = 10\log_{10}\left(\dfrac{I}{10^{-16}}\right)$ $\qquad$ or $\qquad$ $B = 10[\log_{10} 10^{-10} + 16]$

$ = 10[\log_{10} I - \log_{10} 10^{-16}]$ $\qquad\qquad\qquad$ $ = 10[-10 + 16]$

$ = 10[\log_{10} I - (-16)]$ $\qquad\qquad\qquad\qquad$ $ = 60$ decibels

$ = 10[\log_{10} I + 16]$

123. $E = 1.4(\log_{10} C_2 - \log_{10} C_1) = 1.4\left(\log_{10} \dfrac{C_2}{C_1}\right)$ $\qquad$ **125.** True, $\ln e^{2-x} = (2 - x)\ln e$

$\qquad\qquad\qquad\qquad\qquad\qquad\qquad\qquad\qquad\qquad\qquad\qquad\qquad\ $ $= (2 - x)(1) = 2 - x$

127. True, $\log_8 4 + \log_8 16 = \log_8 4 \cdot 16$
$$= \log_8 64$$
$$= 2$$

129. False, $\log_3(u \cdot v) = \log_3 u + \log_3 v$

131. True, $f(ax) = \log_a ax = \log_a a + \log_a x$
$$= 1 + \log_a x$$
$$= 1 + f(x)$$

133. False; 0 is not in the domain of f.

135. False; $f(x - 3) = \ln(x - 3) \neq \ln x - \ln 3$.

137. False; if $v = u^2$, then $f(v) = \ln u^2 = 2 \ln u = 2f(u)$.

Section 9.5   Solving Exponential and Logarithmic Equations

1. (a) $3^{2(1)-5} \overset{?}{=} 27$
$$3^{-3} \neq 27$$
not a solution

   (b) $3^{2(4)-5} \overset{?}{=} 27$
$$3^3 = 27$$
solution

3. (a) $e^{-5+\ln 45 + 5} \overset{?}{=} 45$
$$e^{\ln 45} \overset{?}{=} 45$$
$$45 = 45$$
solution

   (b) $e^{-5 + e^{45} + 5} \overset{?}{=} 45$
$$e^{e^{45}} \neq 45$$
not a solution

5. (a) $\log_9(6 \cdot 27) \overset{?}{=} \frac{3}{2}$
$$\log_9 162 \neq \frac{3}{2}$$
not a solution

   (b) $\log_9\left(6 \cdot \frac{9}{2}\right) \overset{?}{=} \frac{3}{2}$
$$\log_9 27 = \frac{3}{2}$$
solution

7. $2^x = 2^5$
so $x = 5$

9. $3^{x+4} = 3^{12}$
so $x + 4 = 12$
$$x = 8$$

11. $3^{x-1} = 3^7$
so $x - 1 = 7$
$$x = 8$$

13. $4^{3x} = 16$
$$4^{3x} = 4^2$$
so $3x = 2$
$$x = \frac{2}{3}$$

15. $6^{2x-1} = 216$
$$6^{2x-1} = 6^3$$
so $2x - 1 = 3$
$$2x = 4$$
$$x = 2$$

17. $5^x = \frac{1}{125}$
$$5^x = 5^{-3}$$
so $x = -3$

19. $2^{x+2} = \frac{1}{16}$
$$2^{x+2} = 2^{-4}$$
so $x + 2 = -4$
$$x = -6$$

21. $4^{x+3} = 32^x$
$$(2^2)^{x+3} = (2^5)^x$$
so $2(x + 3) = 5x$
$$2x + 6 = 5x$$
$$6 = 3x$$
$$2 = x$$

23. $\ln 5x = \ln 22$
so $5x = 22$
$$x = \frac{22}{5}$$

25. $\log_6 3x = \log_6 18$
so $3x = 18$
$$x = 6$$

27. $\ln(2x - 3) = \ln 15$
so $2x - 3 = 15$
$$2x = 18$$
$$x = 9$$

29. $\log_2(x + 3) = \log_2 7$
so $x + 3 = 7$
$$x = 4$$

31. $\log_5(2x - 3) = \log_5(4x - 5)$
so $2x - 3 = 4x - 5$
$$2 = 2x$$
$$1 = x$$

No solution since expressions on either side are undefined for $x = 1$.

33. $\log_3(2 - x) = 2$
$2 - x = 3^2$
$-x = 7$
$x = -7$

35. $\ln e^{2x-1} = (2x - 1) \ln e$
$= (2x - 1)(1)$
$= 2x - 1$

37. $10^{\log_{10} 2x} = 2x, \quad x > 0$

39. $2^x = 45$
$\log_2 2^x = \log_2 45$
$x = \dfrac{\log 45}{\log 2}$
$x \approx 5.49$

41. $3^x = 3.6$
$\log_3 3^x = \log_3 3.6$
$x = \dfrac{\log 3.6}{\log 3} \approx 1.17$

43. $10^{2y} = 52$
$\log 10^{2y} = \log 52$
$2y = \log 52$
$y = \dfrac{\log 52}{2}$
$y \approx 0.86$

45. $7^{3y} = 126$
$\log_7 7^{3y} = \log_7 126$
$3y = \log_7 126$
$y = \dfrac{\log_7 126}{3}$
$y = \dfrac{\log 126}{3 \log 7}$
$y \approx 0.83$

47. $3^{x+4} = 6$
$\log_3 3^{x+4} = \log_3 6$
$x + 4 = \log_3 6$
$x = \dfrac{\log 6}{\log 3} - 4$
$x \approx -2.37$

49. $10^{x+6} = 250$
$\log 10^{x+6} = \log 250$
$x + 6 = \log 250$
$x = \log 250 - 6$
$x \approx -3.60$

51. $3e^x = 42$
$e^x = 14$
$\ln e^x = \ln 14$
$x = \ln 14$
$x \approx 2.64$

53. $\dfrac{1}{4} e^x = 5$
$e^x = 20$
$\ln e^x = \ln 20$
$x = \ln 20$
$x \approx 3.00$

55. $\dfrac{1}{2} e^{3x} = 20$
$e^{3x} = 40$
$\ln e^{3x} = \ln 40$
$3x = \ln 40$
$x = \dfrac{\ln 40}{3} \approx 1.23$

57. $250(1.04)^x = 1000$
$(1.04)^x = 4$
$\log_{1.04} 1.04^x = \log_{1.04} 4$
$x = \log_{1.04} 4$
$x = \dfrac{\log 4}{\log 1.04}$
$x \approx 35.35$

59. $300 e^{x/2} = 9000$
$e^{x/2} = 30$
$\ln e^{x/2} = \ln 30$
$\dfrac{x}{2} = \ln 30$
$x = 2 \ln 30$
$x \approx 6.80$

61. $1000^{0.12x} = 25{,}000$
$\log_{1000} 1000^{0.12x} = \log_{1000} 25{,}000$
$0.12x = \log_{1000} 25{,}000$
$x = \dfrac{\log_{1000} 25{,}000}{0.12}$
$x = \dfrac{\log 25{,}000}{0.12 \log 1000}$
$x \approx 12.22$

63. $\dfrac{1}{5} 4^{x+2} = 300$
$4^{x+2} = 1500$
$\log_4 4^{x+2} = \log_4 1500$
$x + 2 = \dfrac{\log 1500}{\log 4}$
$x = \dfrac{\log 1500}{\log 4} - 2$
$x \approx 3.28$

65. $6 + 2^{x-1} = 1$
$2^{x-1} = -5$
$\log_2 2^{x-1} = \log_2(-5)$
No solution
$\log_2(-5)$ is not possible.

67. $7 + e^{2-x} = 28$
$e^{2-x} = 21$
$\ln e^{2-x} = \ln 21$
$2 - x = \ln 21$
$-x = \ln 21 - 2$
$x = 2 - \ln 21$
$x \approx -1.04$

69. $8 - 12e^{-x} = 7$

$-12e^{-x} = -1$

$e^{-x} = \dfrac{1}{12}$

$\ln e^{-x} = \ln \dfrac{1}{12}$

$-x = \ln \dfrac{1}{12}$

$x = -\ln \dfrac{1}{12} \approx 2.48$

71. $4 + e^{2x} = 10$

$e^{2x} = 6$

$\ln e^{2x} = \ln 6$

$2x = \ln 6$

$x = \dfrac{\ln 6}{2}$

$x \approx 0.90$

73. $32 + e^{7x} = 46$

$e^{7x} = 14$

$\ln e^{7x} = \ln 14$

$7x = \ln 14$

$x = \dfrac{\ln 14}{7}$

$x \approx 0.38$

75. $23 - 5e^{x+1} = 3$

$-5e^{x+1} = -20$

$e^{x+1} = 4$

$\ln e^{x+1} = \ln 4$

$x + 1 = \ln 4$

$x = \ln 4 - 1$

$x \approx 0.39$

77. $4(1 + e^{x/3}) = 84$

$1 + e^{x/3} = 21$

$e^{x/3} = 20$

$\ln e^{x/3} = \ln 20$

$\dfrac{x}{3} = \ln 20$

$x = 3 \ln 20$

$x \approx 8.99$

79. $\dfrac{8000}{(1.03)^t} = 6000$

$\dfrac{8000}{6000} = (1.03)^t$

$\dfrac{4}{3} = (1.03)^t$

$\log_{1.03} \dfrac{4}{3} = \log_{1.03} 1.03^t$

$\log_{1.03} \dfrac{4}{3} = t$

$9.73 \approx t$

81. $\dfrac{300}{2 - e^{-0.15t}} = 200$

$\dfrac{300}{200} = 2 - e^{-0.15t}$

$\dfrac{3}{2} - 2 = -e^{-0.15t}$

$-\dfrac{1}{2} = -e^{-0.15t}$

$\ln\!\left(\dfrac{1}{2}\right) = \ln e^{-0.15t}$

$\ln\!\left(\dfrac{1}{2}\right) = -0.15t$

$\dfrac{\ln\!\left(\frac{1}{2}\right)}{-0.15} = t \approx 4.62$

83. $\log_{10} x = 3$

$10^{\log_{10} x} = 10^3$

$x = 1000.00$

85. $\log_2 x = 4.5$

$2^{\log_2 x} = 2^{4.5}$

$x = 2^{4.5}$

$x = 22.63$

87. $4 \log_3 x = 28$

$\log_3 x = 7$

$3^{\log_3 x} = 3^7$

$x = 3^7$

$x = 2187.00$

89. $16 \ln x = 30$

$\ln x = \dfrac{30}{16}$

$e^{\ln x} = e^{15/8}$

$x = e^{15/8}$

$x \approx 6.52$

91. $\log_{10} 4x = 2$

$10^{\log_{10} 4x} = 10^2$

$4x = 10^2$

$x = \dfrac{10^2}{4}$

$x = \dfrac{100}{4} = 25.00$

93. $\ln 2x = 3$

$e^{\ln 2x} = e^3$

$2x = e^3$

$x = \dfrac{e^3}{2}$

$x \approx 10.04$

95. $\ln x^2 = 6$

$e^{\ln x^2} = e^6$

$x^2 = e^6$

$x = \pm \sqrt{e^6}$

$x \approx \pm 20.09$

97. $2 \log_4(x + 5) = 3$

$\log_4(x + 5) = \dfrac{3}{2}$

$4^{\log_4(x+5)} = 4^{1.5}$

$x + 5 = 4^{1.5}$

$x = 4^{1.5} - 5$

$x = 3.00$

99. $2 \log_8(x + 3) = 3$

$\log_8(x + 3) = \dfrac{3}{2}$

$8^{\log_8(x+3)} = 8^{3/2}$

$x + 3 = 8^{1.5}$

$x = 8^{1.5} - 3$

$x \approx 19.63$

101. $1 - 2 \ln x = -4$

$-2 \ln x = -5$

$\ln x = \dfrac{5}{2}$

$e^{\ln x} = e^{2.5}$

$x = e^{2.5}$

$x \approx 12.18$

103. $-1 + 3 \log_{10} \dfrac{x}{2} = 8$

$3 \log_{10} \dfrac{x}{2} = 9$

$\log_{10} \dfrac{x}{2} = 3$

$10^{\log_{10}(x/2)} = 10^3$

$\dfrac{x}{2} = 10^3$

$x = 2(10)^3$

$x = 2000.00$

105. $\log_4 x + \log_4 5 = 2$

$\log_4 x(5) = 2$

$4^{\log_4 5x} = 4^2$

$5x = 16$

$x = \dfrac{16}{5}$

$x = 3.20$

107. $\log_6(x + 8) + \log_6 3 = 2$

$\log_6(x + 8)(3) = 2$

$6^{\log_6 3(x+8)} = 6^2$

$3x + 24 = 36$

$3x = 12$

$x = 4.00$

109. $\log_5(x + 3) - \log_5 x = 1$

$\log_5\left(\dfrac{x + 3}{x}\right) = 1$

$5^{\log_5[(x+3)/x]} = 5^1$

$\dfrac{x + 3}{x} = 5$

$x + 3 = 5x$

$3 = 4x$

$\dfrac{3}{4} = x$

$0.75 = x$

111. $\log_{10} x + \log_{10}(x - 3) = 1$

$\log_{10} x(x - 3) = 1$

$10^{\log_{10} x(x-3)} = 10^1$

$x(x - 3) = 10$

$x^2 - 3x - 10 = 0$

$(x - 5)(x + 2) = 0$

$x = 5, \; x = -2 \text{ (which is extraneous)}$

113. $\log_2(x - 1) + \log_2(x + 3) = 3$

$\log_2(x - 1)(x + 3) = 3$

$x^2 + 2x - 3 = 2^3$

$x^2 + 2x - 11 = 0$

$x = \dfrac{-2 \pm \sqrt{4 - 4(1)(-11)}}{2(1)} = \dfrac{-2 \pm \sqrt{4 + 44}}{2}$

$= \dfrac{-2 \pm \sqrt{48}}{2}$

$x \approx 2.46 \text{ and } -4.46 \text{ (which is extraneous)}$

115. $\log_4 3x + \log_4(x - 2) = \dfrac{1}{2}$

$$\log_4 3x(x - 2) = \dfrac{1}{2}$$

$$4^{\log_4 3x(x-2)} = 4^{1/2}$$

$$3x(x - 2) = 2$$

$$3x^2 - 6x = 2$$

$$3x^2 - 6x - 2 = 0$$

$$x = \dfrac{-(-6) \pm \sqrt{(-6)^2 - 4(3)(-2)}}{2(3)}$$

$$= \dfrac{6 \pm \sqrt{36 + 24}}{6} = \dfrac{6 \pm \sqrt{60}}{6}$$

$x \approx 2.29$ and -0.29 (which is extraneous)

117. $\log_2 x + \log_2(x + 2) - \log_2 3 = 4$

$$\log_2 \dfrac{x(x + 2)}{3} = 4$$

$$2^{\log_2(x^2 + 2x/3)} = 2^4$$

$$\dfrac{x^2 + 2x}{3} = 16$$

$$x^2 + 2x = 48$$

$$x^2 + 2x - 48 = 0$$

$$(x + 8)(x - 6) = 0$$

$x = -8$ (which is extraneous)

$x = 6.00$

119. *Keystrokes:*

Y= 10 ^ ((X,T,θ ÷ 2) − 5 GRAPH

x-intercept

$1.3974 \approx 1.40$

$(1.40, 0)$

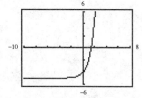

121. *Keystrokes:*

Y= 6 LN (.4 X,T,θ) − 13 GRAPH

x-intercept

$21.822846 \approx 21.82$

$(21.82, 0)$

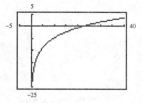

123. *Keystrokes:*

y_1 Y= 2 ENTER

y_2 e^x X,T,θ GRAPH

Point of intersection: $(0.69, 2)$

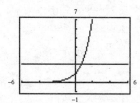

125. *Keystrokes:*

y_1 Y= 3 ENTER

y_2 2 LN (X,T,θ + 3) GRAPH

Point of intersection: $(1.48, 3)$

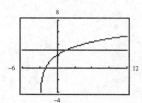

127. *Formula:* $A = Pe^{rt}$

Labels: Principal $= P = \$10{,}000$

Amount $= A = \$11{,}972.17$

Time $= t = 2$ years

Annual interest rate $= r$

Equation: $11{,}972.17 = 10{,}000e^{r(2)}$

$$\dfrac{11{,}972.17}{10{,}000} = e^{2r}$$

$$1.197217 = e^{2r}$$

$$\ln 1.197217 = \ln(e^{2r})$$

$$0.18 \approx 2r$$

$$0.09 \approx r \approx 9\%$$

129. $5000 = 2500e^{0.09t}$

$$\dfrac{5000}{2500} = e^{0.09t}$$

$$2 = e^{0.09t}$$

$$\ln 2 = \ln(e^{0.09t})$$

$$\ln 2 = 0.09t$$

$$\dfrac{\ln 2}{0.09} = t$$

7.70 years $\approx t$

131.
$$B = 10 \log_{10}\left(\frac{I}{10^{-16}}\right)$$

$$75 = 10 \log_{10}\left(\frac{I}{10^{-16}}\right)$$

$$7.5 = \log_{10}\left(\frac{I}{10^{-16}}\right)$$

$$10^{7.5} = 10^{\log_{10}(I/10^{-16})}$$

$$10^{7.5} = \frac{I}{10^{-16}}$$

$$(10^{7.5})(10^{-16}) = I$$

$$10^{-8.5} = I$$

$$3.1623 \times 10^{-9} = I \text{ watts per square centimeter}$$

133.
$$2.5 = 15.7 - 2.48 \ln m$$

$$-13.2 = -2.48 \ln m$$

$$5.322580645 = \ln m$$

$$e^{5.322580645} = m$$

$$205 \approx m$$

135. (a)
$$72 = 80 - \log_{10}(t + 1)^{12}$$

$$-8 = -\log_{10}(t + 1)^{12}$$

$$8 = \log_{10}(t + 1)^{12}$$

$$8 = 12 \log_{10}(t + 1)$$

$$\frac{8}{12} = \log_{10}(t + 1)$$

$$\frac{2}{3} = \log_{10}(t + 1)$$

$$t + 1 = 10^{2/3}$$

$$t = 10^{2/3} - 1$$

$$t \approx 3.64 \text{ months}$$

(b) *Keystrokes:*

y_1 [Y=] 80 [−] 12 [LOG] [(] [X,T,θ] [+] 1 [)] [ENTER]

y_2 72 [GRAPH]

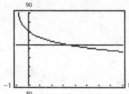

(c) Answers will vary.

137. (a)
$$Kt = \ln \frac{T - S}{T_0 - S}$$

$$K(4) = \ln \frac{32° - 0°}{60° - 0°}$$

$$K(4) = \ln \frac{32°}{60°}$$

$$K = \frac{1}{4} \ln \frac{8}{15}$$

$$K \approx -0.1572$$

(b)
$$t = \frac{1}{K} \ln \frac{T - S}{T_0 - S}$$

$$t = \frac{1}{-0.1572} \ln \frac{32° - (-10°)}{60° - (-10°)}$$

$$t = \frac{1}{-0.1572} \ln \frac{42°}{70°}$$

$$t \approx 3.25 \text{ hours}$$

(c)
$$t = \frac{1}{K} \ln \frac{T - S}{T_0 - S}$$

$$t = \frac{1}{-0.1572} \ln \frac{32° - 0°}{50° - 0°}$$

$$t = \frac{1}{-0.1572} \ln \frac{32°}{50°}$$

$$t \approx 2.84 \text{ hours}$$

139. (c) Formula: $A = P\left(1 + \frac{r}{n}\right)^{nt}$

$$6200 = 5000\left(1 + \frac{r}{12}\right)^{12(3)}$$

$$1.24 = \left(1 + \frac{r}{12}\right)^{36}$$

$$(1.24)^{1/36} = 1 + \frac{r}{12}$$

$$1.005993204 = 1 + \frac{r}{12}$$

$$0.005993204 = \frac{r}{12}$$

$$0.0719184469 = r$$

$$7.2\% \approx r$$

—CONTINUED—

139. —CONTINUED—

(d) Formula: $A = Pe^{rt}$

$$7500 = 5000e^{0.06t}$$

$$1.5 = e^{0.06t}$$

$$\ln 1.5 = \ln e^{0.06t}$$

$$\ln 1.5 = 0.06t$$

$$\frac{\ln 1.5}{0.06} = t$$

$$6\frac{3}{4} \text{ years} \approx t$$

(e) Formula: $A = P\left(1 + \dfrac{r}{n}\right)^{nt}$

$$A = 1000\left(1 + \frac{0.08}{4}\right)^{4(1)}$$

$$A = 1000(1.02)^4$$

$$A = \$1082.43$$

$$\text{Effective yield} = \frac{82.43}{1000} = 0.08243 \approx 8.24\%$$

(f) Formula: $A = Pe^{rt}$

$$10{,}000 = 5000e^{0.06t}$$

$$2 = e^{0.06t}$$

$$\ln 2 = \ln e^{0.06t}$$

$$\ln 2 = 0.06t$$

$$\frac{\ln 2}{0.06} = t$$

$$11.6 \text{ years} \approx t$$

$$20{,}000 = 5000e^{0.06t}$$

$$4 = e^{0.06t}$$

$$\ln 4 = \ln e^{0.06t}$$

$$\ln 4 = 0.06t$$

$$\frac{\ln 4}{0.06} = t$$

$$23.1 \text{ years} \approx t$$

141. $2^{x-1} = 30$ requires logarithms because $2^{x-1} = 32$ can be rewritten as $2^{x-1} = 2^5$ and the exponents set equal.

143. To solve an exponential equation, first isolate the exponential expression, then take the logarithms of both sides of the equation, and solve for the variable.

To solve a logarithmic equation, first isolate the logarithmic expression, then exponentiate both sides of the equation, and solve for the variable.

Section 9.6   Applications

1. $A = P\left(1 + \dfrac{r}{n}\right)^{nt}$

$$1004.83 = 500\left(1 + \frac{r}{12}\right)^{12(10)}$$

$$2.00966 = \left(1 + \frac{r}{12}\right)^{120}$$

$$(2.00966)^{1/120} = 1 + \frac{r}{12}$$

$$1.0058333 = 1 + \frac{r}{12}$$

$$0.0058333 = \frac{r}{12}$$

$$0.07 \approx r$$

$$7\% \approx r$$

3. $A = P\left(1 + \dfrac{r}{n}\right)^{nt}$

$$36{,}581.00 = 1000\left(1 + \frac{r}{365}\right)^{365(40)}$$

$$36.581 = \left(1 + \frac{r}{365}\right)^{14{,}600}$$

$$(36.581)^{1/14{,}600} = 1 + \frac{r}{365}$$

$$1.0002466 = 1 + \frac{r}{365}$$

$$0.0002466 = \frac{r}{365}$$

$$0.0899981 = r$$

$$9\% \approx r$$

5.
$$A = Pe^{rt}$$
$$8267.38 = 750e^{r(30)}$$
$$11.023173 = e^{r(30)}$$
$$\ln 11.023173 = \ln e$$
$$\ln 11.023173 = 30r$$
$$\frac{\ln 11.023173}{30} = r$$
$$0.08 \approx r$$
$$8\% \approx r$$

7.
$$A = P\left(1 + \frac{r}{n}\right)^{nt}$$
$$22{,}405.68 = 5000\left(1 + \frac{r}{365}\right)^{365(25)}$$
$$4.481136 = \left(1 + \frac{r}{365}\right)^{9125}$$
$$(4.481136)^{1/9125} = 1 + \frac{r}{365}$$
$$1.000164384 = 1 + \frac{r}{365}$$
$$0.00164384 = \frac{r}{365}$$
$$0.059 \approx r$$
$$6\% \approx r$$

9.
$$A = P\left(1 + \frac{r}{n}\right)^{nt}$$
$$12{,}000 = 6000\left(1 + \frac{0.08}{4}\right)^{4t}$$
$$2 = (1.02)^{4t}$$
$$\log_{1.02} 2 = \log_{1.02} 1.02^{4t}$$
$$\frac{\log 2}{\log 1.02} = 4t$$
$$\frac{\log 2}{\log 1.02} \div 4 = t$$
$$8.75 \text{ years} \approx t$$

11.
$$A = P\left(1 + \frac{r}{n}\right)^{nt}$$
$$4000 = 2000\left(1 + \frac{0.105}{365}\right)^{365t}$$
$$2 = (1.0002877)^{365t}$$
$$\log_{1.0002877} 2 = \log_{1.0002877} 1.0002877^{365t}$$
$$\frac{\log 2}{\log 1.0002877} = 365t$$
$$\frac{\log 2}{\log 1.0002877} \div 365 = t$$
$$6.60 \text{ years} \approx t$$

13.
$$A = Pe^{rt}$$
$$3000 = 1500e^{0.075t}$$
$$2 = e^{0.075t}$$
$$\ln 2 = \ln e^{0.075t}$$
$$\ln 2 = 0.075t$$
$$\frac{\ln 2}{0.075} = t$$
$$9.24 \text{ years} \approx t$$

15.
$$A = P\left(1 + \frac{r}{n}\right)^{nt}$$
$$600 = 300\left(1 + \frac{0.05}{1}\right)^{1(t)}$$
$$2 = 1.05^{t}$$
$$\log_{1.05} 2 = \log_{1.05} 1.05^{t}$$
$$\log_{1.05} 2 = t$$
$$14.21 \text{ years} \approx t$$

17. $1587.75 = 750\left(1 + \dfrac{0.075}{n}\right)^{n(10)}$

$1587.75 = 750e^{0.075(10)}$

$1587.75 = 1587.75$

Continuous compounding

19. $141.48 = 100\left(1 + \dfrac{0.07}{n}\right)^{n(5)}$

$141.48 = 100\left(1 + \dfrac{0.07}{4}\right)^{4(5)}$

$141.48 = 141.48$

Quarterly compounding

21. $A = Pe^{rt}$

$A = 1000e^{0.08(1)}$

$A = \$1083.29$

Effective yield $= \dfrac{83.29}{1000}$

$= 0.08329 \approx 8.33\%$

23. $A = P\left(1 + \dfrac{r}{n}\right)^{nt}$

$A = 1000\left(1 + \dfrac{0.07}{12}\right)^{12(1)}$

$A = \$1072.29$

Effective yield $= \dfrac{72.29}{1000}$

$= 0.07229 \approx 7.23\%$

25. $A = P\left(1 + \dfrac{r}{n}\right)^{nt}$

$A = 1000\left(1 + \dfrac{0.06}{4}\right)^{4(1)}$

$A = \$1061.36$

Effective yield $= \dfrac{61.36}{1000}$

$= 0.06136$

$\approx 6.136\%$

27. $A = P\left(1 + \dfrac{r}{n}\right)^{nt}$

$A = 1000\left(1 + \dfrac{0.08}{12}\right)^{12(1)}$

$A = \$1083.00$

Effective yield $= \dfrac{83.00}{1000}$

$= 0.083 = 8.300\%$

29. No. Each time the amount is divided by the principal, the result is always 2.

31. $\qquad A = Pe^{rt}$

$10,000 = Pe^{0.09(20)}$

$\dfrac{10,000}{e^{1.8}} = P$

$\$1652.99 \approx P$

33. $\qquad\qquad A = P\left(1 + \dfrac{r}{n}\right)^{nt}$

$750 = P\left(1 + \dfrac{0.06}{365}\right)^{365(3)}$

$\dfrac{750}{(1.0001644)^{1095}} = P$

$\$626.46 \approx P$

35. $\qquad\qquad A = P\left(1 + \dfrac{r}{n}\right)^{nt}$

$25,000 = P\left(1 + \dfrac{0.07}{12}\right)^{12(30)}$

$\dfrac{25,000}{(1.005833)^{360}} = P$

$\$3080.15 \approx P$

37. $\qquad\qquad A = P\left(1 + \dfrac{r}{n}\right)^{nt}$

$1000 = P\left(1 + \dfrac{0.05}{365}\right)^{365(1)}$

$\dfrac{1000}{(1.000136986)^{365}} = P$

$\$951.23 \approx P$

39. $A = \dfrac{P(e^{rt} - 1)}{e^{r/12} - 1}$

$A = \dfrac{30(e^{0.08(10)} - 1)}{e^{0.08/12} - 1}$

$A \approx \$5496.57$

41. $A = \dfrac{P(e^{rt} - 1)}{e^{r/12} - 1}$

$A = \dfrac{50(e^{0.10(40)} - 1)}{e^{0.10/12} - 1}$

$A \approx \$320,250.81$

43. $A = \dfrac{P(e^{rt} - 1)}{e^{r/12} - 1}$

$A = \dfrac{30(e^{0.08(20)} - 1)}{e^{0.08(20)} - 1}$

$A \approx \$17,729.42$

Total interest $= \$17,729.42 - 7200 \approx \$10,529.42$

45. $y = Ce^{kt}$ $\qquad 8 = 3e^{k(2)}$

$3 = Ce^{k(0)}$ $\qquad \dfrac{8}{3} = e^{2k}$

$3 = C$

$\ln\dfrac{8}{3} = \ln e^{2k}$

$\ln\dfrac{8}{3} = 2k$

$\dfrac{\ln\frac{8}{3}}{2} = k \approx 0.4904$

47. $y = Ce^{kt}$ $\qquad 200 = 400e^{k(3)}$

$400 = Ce^{k(0)}$ $\qquad \dfrac{1}{2} = e^{3k}$

$400 = C$

$\ln\dfrac{1}{2} = \ln e^{3k}$

$\ln\dfrac{1}{2} = 3k$

$\dfrac{\ln\frac{1}{2}}{3} = k \approx -0.2310$

49. $y = Ce^{kt}$ $14.3 = 12.2e^{k(21)}$ $y = 12.2e^{0.0076t}$

$12.2 = Ce^{k(0)}$ $\dfrac{14.3}{12.2} = e^{21k}$ $y = 12.2e^{0.0076(26)}$

$12.2 = C$ $y \approx 14.9$ million

$\ln\dfrac{143}{122} = \ln e^{21k}$

$\ln\dfrac{143}{122} = 21k$

$\dfrac{1}{21}\ln\dfrac{143}{122} = k$

$0.0076 \approx k$

51. $y = Ce^{kt}$ $23.4 = 14.7e^{k(21)}$ $y = 14.7e^{0.0221t}$

$14.7 = Ce^{k(0)}$ $\dfrac{23.4}{14.7} = e^{21k}$ $y = 14.7e^{0.0221(26)}$

$14.7 = C$ $y \approx 26.1$ million

$\ln\dfrac{234}{147} = \ln e^{21k}$

$\ln\dfrac{234}{147} = 21k$

$\dfrac{1}{21}\ln\dfrac{234}{147} = k$

$0.0221 \approx k$

53. $y = Ce^{kt}$ $10.6 = 10.5e^{k(21)}$ $y = 10.5e^{0.0005t}$

$10.5 = Ce^{k(0)}$ $\dfrac{10.6}{10.5} = e^{21k}$ $y = 10.5e^{0.0005(26)}$

$10.5 = C$ $y \approx 10.6$ million

$\ln\dfrac{106}{105} = \ln e^{21k}$

$\dfrac{\ln\left(\frac{106}{105}\right)}{21} = k$

$0.0005 \approx k$

55. $y = Ce^{kt}$ $18.8 = 15.5^{k(21)}$ $y = 15.5e^{0.0092t}$

$15.5 = Ce^{k(0)}$ $\dfrac{18.8}{15.5} = e^{21k}$ $y = 15.5e^{0.0092(26)}$

$15.5 = C$ $y \approx 19.7$ million

$\ln\left(\dfrac{188}{155}\right) = \ln e^{21k}$

$\dfrac{\ln\left(\frac{188}{155}\right)}{21} = k$

$0.0092 \approx k$

57. (a) k is larger in Exercise 51, because the population of Shanghai is increasing faster than the population of Osaka.

(b) k corresponds to r; k gives the annual percentage rate of growth.

59. $y = Ce^{kt}$ $3 = 6e^{k(1620)}$ $y = 6e^{-0.00043(1000)}$

$6 = Ce^{k(0)}$ $0.5 = e^{1620k}$ $y \approx 3.91$ grams

$6 = C$ $\ln 0.5 = \ln e^{1620k}$

$\dfrac{\ln 0.5}{1620} = k$

$-0.00043 \approx k$

61. $y = Ce^{kt}$ $4 = Ce^{-0.00012(1000)}$

$0.5C = Ce^{k(5730)}$ $4 = Ce^{-0.12}$

$0.5 = e^{5730k}$

$\ln 0.5 = \ln e^{5730k}$ $\dfrac{4}{e^{-0.12}} = C$

$\ln 0.5 = 5730k$ 4.51 grams $\approx C$

$\dfrac{\ln 0.5}{5730} = k$

$-0.00012 \approx k$

63. $y = Ce^{kt}$ $2.1 = 4.2e^{k(24,360)}$ $y = 4.2e^{-0.00003(1000)}$

$4.2 = Ce^{k(0)}$ $0.5 = e^{24,360k}$ $y \approx 4.08$ grams

$4.2 = C$ $\ln 0.5 = \ln e^{24,360k}$

$\dfrac{\ln 0.5}{24,360} = k$

$-0.00003 \approx k$

65. $y = Ce^{kt}$ $\qquad$ $2.5 = 5e^{k(1620)}$ $\qquad$ $y = 5e^{-0.00043(1000)}$ $\qquad$ **67.** $y = Ce^{kt}$ $\qquad$ $2.5 = 5e^{k(5730)}$ $\qquad$ $y = 5e^{-0.00012(1000)}$

$5 = Ce^{k(0)}$ $\qquad$ $0.5 = e^{1620k}$ $\qquad$ $y \approx 3.25$ grams $\qquad$ $5 = Ce^{k(0)}$ $\qquad$ $0.5 = e^{5730k}$ $\qquad$ $y \approx 4.43$ grams

$5 = C$ $\qquad$ $\ln 0.5 = \ln e^{1620k}$ $\qquad\qquad\qquad$ $5 = C$ $\qquad$ $\ln 0.5 = \ln e^{5730k}$

$\qquad\qquad\qquad$ $\ln 0.5 = 1620k$ $\qquad\qquad\qquad\qquad\qquad\qquad\qquad$ $\ln 0.5 = 5730k$

$\qquad\qquad\qquad$ $\dfrac{\ln 0.5}{1620} = k$ $\qquad\qquad\qquad\qquad\qquad\qquad\qquad$ $\dfrac{\ln 0.5}{5730} = k$

$\qquad\qquad\qquad\qquad$ $-0.00043 \approx k$ $\qquad\qquad\qquad\qquad\qquad\qquad\qquad$ $-0.00012 \approx k$

69. $\qquad$ $16{,}500 = 22{,}000e^{k(1)}$

$\qquad$ $\dfrac{16{,}500}{22{,}000} = e^{k}$

$\qquad$ $\ln \dfrac{16{,}500}{22{,}000} = \ln e^{k}$

$\qquad$ $\ln \dfrac{16{,}500}{22{,}000} = k$

$\qquad$ $-0.2876821 = k$

$\qquad\qquad$ $y = 22{,}000e^{-0.2876821(3)} \approx \$9281.25$

71. $R = \log_{10} I$

Alaska:	San Fernando Valley:	Ratio of two intensitiies:

$\qquad$ $8.4 = \log_{10} I$ $\qquad\qquad$ $6.6 = \log_{10} I$ $\qquad\qquad$ $\dfrac{I \text{ for Alaska}}{I \text{ for San Fernando Valley}} = \dfrac{10^{8.4}}{10^{6.6}}$

$\qquad$ $10^{8.4} = 10^{\log_{10} I}$ $\qquad$ $10^{6.6} = 10^{\log_{10} I}$ $\qquad\qquad\qquad\qquad\qquad\quad = 10^{8.4 - 6.6} = 10^{1.8} \approx 63$

$\qquad$ $10^{8.4} = I$ $\qquad\qquad\qquad$ $10^{6.6} = I$

The earthquake in Alaska was 63 times as great.

73. $R = \log_{10} I$

Mexico City:	Nepal:	Ratio of two intensities:

$\qquad$ $8.1 = \log_{10} I$ $\qquad\qquad$ $6.5 = \log_{10} I$ $\qquad\qquad$ $\dfrac{I \text{ for Mexico City}}{I \text{ for Nepal}} = \dfrac{10^{8.1}}{10^{6.5}}$

$\qquad$ $10^{8.1} = 10^{\log_{10} I}$ $\qquad$ $10^{6.5} = 10^{\log_{10} I}$ $\qquad\qquad\qquad\qquad\qquad = 10^{8.1 - 6.5} = 10^{1.6} \approx 40$

$\qquad$ $10^{8.1} = I$ $\qquad\qquad\qquad$ $10^{6.5} = I$ $\qquad\qquad\qquad\qquad\qquad\qquad = 10^{1.6} \approx 40$

The earthquake in Mexico City was 40 times as great.

75. $\text{pH} = -\log_{10}[\text{H}^{+}]$

$\qquad$ $\text{pH} = -\log_{10}(9.2 \times 10^{-8}) \approx 7.04$

77. $\text{pH} = -\log_{10}[\text{H}^{+}]$

fruit:	tablet:	

$\qquad\qquad\qquad\qquad\qquad\qquad\qquad\qquad\qquad\qquad\qquad$ $\dfrac{\text{H}^{+} \text{ of fruit}}{\text{H}^{+} \text{ of tablet}} = \dfrac{0.0031623}{3.1623 \times 10^{-10}}$

$\qquad$ $2.5 = -\log_{10}[\text{H}^{+}]$ $\qquad\qquad$ $9.5 = -\log_{10}[\text{H}^{+}]$ $\qquad\qquad\qquad\qquad\qquad = 10{,}000{,}071$

$\qquad$ $-2.5 = \log_{10}[\text{H}^{+}]$ $\qquad\qquad$ $-9.5 = \log_{10}[\text{H}^{+}]$

$\qquad$ $10^{-2.5} = 10^{\log_{10}[\text{H}^{+}]}$ $\qquad\quad$ $10^{-9.5} = 10^{\log_{10}[\text{H}^{+}]}$

$\qquad$ $0.0031623 = \text{H}^{+}$ $\qquad\qquad$ $3.1623 \times 10^{-10} = \text{H}^{+}$

The H^{+} of fruit is 10^{7} times as great.

79. (a) *Keystrokes:*

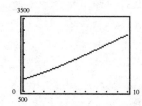

$$\boxed{Y=}\ 5000\ \boxed{\div}\ \boxed{(}\ 1\ \boxed{+}\ 4\ \boxed{e^x}\ \boxed{(}\ \boxed{(-)}\ \boxed{X,T,\theta}\ \boxed{\div}\ 6\ \boxed{)}\ \boxed{)}\ \boxed{GRAPH}$$

(b) $p(0) = \dfrac{5000}{1 + 4e^{-0/6}} = \dfrac{5000}{5} = 1000$

(c) $p(9) = \dfrac{5000}{1 + 4e^{-9/6}} \approx 2642$

(d)
$$2000 = \frac{5000}{1 + 4e^{-t/6}}$$
$$1 + 4e^{-t/6} = 2.5$$
$$4e^{-t/6} = 1.5$$
$$e^{-t/6} = 0.375$$
$$\ln e^{-t/6} = \ln 0.375$$
$$-\frac{t}{6} = \ln 0.375$$
$$t = (\ln 0.375)(-6)$$
$$t \approx 5.88 \text{ years}$$

81. (a)
$$S = 10(1 - e^{kx})$$
$$2.5 = 10(1 - e^{k(5)})$$
$$0.25 = 1 - e^{5k}$$
$$-0.75 = -e^{5k}$$
$$0.75 = e^{5k}$$
$$\ln 0.75 = \ln e^{5k}$$
$$\ln 0.75 = 5k$$
$$\frac{\ln 0.75}{5} = k$$
$$-0.0575 \approx k$$
$$S = 10(1 - e^{-0.0575x})$$

(b) $S = 10(1 - e^{-0.0575(7)})$
$$= 10(1 - e^{-0.4025})$$
$$= 10(0.3313536611)$$
$$\approx 3.314$$

Thus, 3314 units must be sold.

83. If the equation $y = Ce^{kt}$ models exponential decay, $k < 0$ because decay is decreasing so k must be negative.

85. The effective yield of an investment collecting compound interest is the simple interest rate that would yield the same balance at the end of 1 year. To compute the effective yield, divide the interest earned in 1 year by the amount invested.

87. If the reading on the Richter scale is increased by 1, the intensity of the earthquake is increased by a factor of 10.

Review Exercises for Chapter 9

1. (a) $f(-3) = 2^{-3} = \frac{1}{8}$

(b) $f(1) = 2^1 = 2$

(c) $f(2) = 2^2 = 4$

3. (a) $g(-3) = e^{-(-3)/3} = e^1 \approx 2.718$

(b) $g(\pi) = e^{-\pi/3} \approx 0.351$

(c) $g(6) = e^{-6/3} = e^{-2} \approx 0.135$

5. (c) Basic graph

7. (a) Basic graph reflected in the x-axis

9.

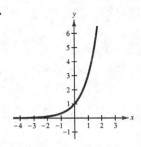

Table of values:

x	-1	0	1
y	$\frac{1}{3}$	1	3

11.

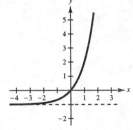

Table of values:

x	-1	0	1
y	$-\frac{2}{3}$	0	2

13.

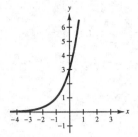

Table of values:

x	-1	0	1
y	1	3	9

15.

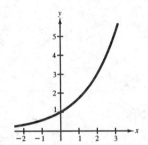

Table of values:

x	0	2	-2
y	1	3	$\frac{1}{3}$

17.

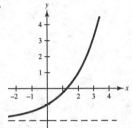

Table of values:

x	-2	0	2
y	$-\frac{7}{3}$	-1	1

19. *Keystrokes:*

$\boxed{Y=}$ 5 $\boxed{e^x}$ $\boxed{(}$ $\boxed{(-)}$ $\boxed{X,T,\theta}$ $\boxed{\div}$ 4 $\boxed{)}$ $\boxed{GRAPH}$

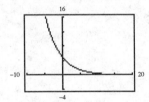

21. *Keystrokes:*

$\boxed{Y=}$ $\boxed{e^x}$ $\boxed{(}$ $\boxed{X,T,\theta}$ $\boxed{+}$ 2 $\boxed{)}$ $\boxed{GRAPH}$

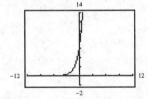

23. (a) $(f \circ g)(x) = x^2 + 2$

so $(f \circ g)(2) = 2^2 + 2 = 6$

(b) $(g \circ f)(x) = (x + 2)^2$

$= x^2 + 4x + 4$

so $(g \circ f)(-1) = (-1)^2 + 4(-1) + 4$

$= 1 - 4 + 4$

$= 1$

25. (a) $(f \circ g)(x) = \sqrt{x^2 - 1 + 1}$

$= \sqrt{x^2}$

$= |x|$

so $(f \circ g)(5) = |5| = 5$

(b) $(g \circ f)(x) = \left(\sqrt{x + 1}\right)^2 - 1$

$= x + 1 - 1$

$= x$

so $(g \circ f)(-1) = -1$

27. (a) $(f \circ g) = \sqrt{2x - 4}$

Domain: $[2, \infty)$

(b) $g \circ f = 2\sqrt{x - 4}$

Domain: $[4, \infty)$

29. No, $f(x)$ does not have an inverse. f is not one-to-one.   **31.** Yes, $h(x)$ does have an inverse. f is one-to-one.

33. $f(x) = 3x + 4$
$$y = 3x + 4$$
$$x = 3y + 4$$
$$x - 4 = 3y$$
$$\frac{x - 4}{3} = y$$
$$\frac{x - 4}{3} = f^{-1}(x) = \frac{1}{3}(x - 4)$$

35. $y = \sqrt{x}$
$$x = \sqrt{y}$$
$$x^2 = y$$
$$x^2 = f^{-1}(x)$$
$$(x \geq 0)$$

37. $f(t) = t^3 + 4$
$$y = t^3 + 4$$
$$t = y^3 + 4$$
$$t - 4 = y^3$$
$$\sqrt[3]{t - 4} = y$$
$$\sqrt[3]{t - 4} = f^{-1}(t)$$

39. $\log_4 64 = 3$

41. $e^1 = e$

43. $\log_{10} 1000 = 3$ because $10^3 = 1000$.

45. $\log_3 \frac{1}{9} = -2$ because $3^{-2} = \frac{1}{9}$.

47. $\ln e^7 = 7 \ln e = 7$

49. $\ln 1 = 0$

51. (a) $f(1) = \log 31 = 0$

(b) $f(27) = \log_3 27 = 3$

(c) $f(0.5) = \log_3 0.5 = \frac{\log 0.5}{\log 3} \approx -0.631$

53. (a) $f(e) = \ln 3 = 1$

(b) $f\left(\frac{1}{3}\right) = \ln \frac{1}{3} \approx -1.099$

(c) $f(10) = \ln 10 \approx 2.303$

55. (a) $g(-2) = \ln e^{3(-2)} = -6$

(b) $g(0) = \ln e^{3(0)} = 0$

(c) $g(7.5) = \ln e^{3(7.5)} = \ln e^{22.5} = 22.5$

57.

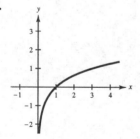

Table of values:

x	1	3
y	0	1

59.

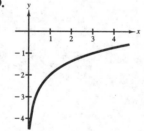

Table of values:

x	1	3
y	-2	-1

61.

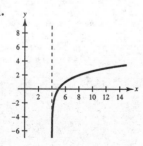

Table of values:

x	5	6
y	0	1

63.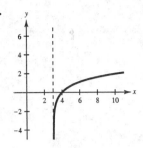

Table of values:

x	4	5
y	0	0.7

65.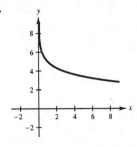

Table of values:

x	1	e
y	5	4

67. $\log_4 9 = \dfrac{\log 9}{\log 4} \approx 1.585$

69. $\log_{12} 200 = \dfrac{\log 200}{\log 12} \approx 2.132$

71. $\log_5 18 = \log_5 3^2 + \log_5 2$

$= 2 \log_5 3 + \log 2$

$\approx 2(0.6826) + 0.43068$

≈ 1.79588

73. $\log_5 \frac{1}{2} = \log_5 1 - \log_5 2$

$\approx 0 - (0.43068)$

≈ -0.43068

75. $\log_5 (12)^{2/3} = \frac{2}{3}[2 \log_5 2 + \log_5 3]$

$\approx \frac{2}{3}[2(0.43068) + 0.6826]$

≈ 1.02931

77. $\log_4 6x^4 = \log_4 6 + 4 \log_4 x$

79. $\log_5 \sqrt{x+2} = \dfrac{1}{2} \log_5(x+2)$

81. $\ln \dfrac{x+2}{x-2} = \ln(x+2) - \ln(x-2)$

83. $\ln\left[\sqrt{2x}(x+3)^5 \right] = \ln \sqrt{2x} + \ln(x+3)^5$

$= \ln(2x)^{1/2} + 5\ln(x+3)$

$= \dfrac{1}{2}[\ln 2 + \ln x] + 5\ln(x+3)$

85. $-\dfrac{2}{3} \ln 3y = \ln(3y)^{-2/3} = \ln\left(\dfrac{1}{3y}\right)^{2/3}$

87. $\log_8 16x + \log_8 2x^2 = \log_8(16x \cdot 2x^2)$

$= \log_8(32x^3)$

89. $-2(\ln 2x - \ln 3) = \ln\left(\dfrac{2x}{3}\right)^{-2}$

$= \ln\left(\dfrac{3}{2x}\right)^2 = \ln \dfrac{9}{4x^2}, \; x > 0$

91. $4[\log_2 k - \log_2(k-t)] = 4\left[\log_2\left(\dfrac{k}{k-t}\right) \right]$

$= \log_2\left(\dfrac{k}{k-t}\right)^4, \; t < k$

93. $3 \ln x + 4 \ln y + \ln z = \ln x^3 + \ln y^4 + \ln z$

$= \ln x^3 y^4 z, \; x > 0, \; y > 0, \; z > 0$

95. False

$\log_2 4x = \log_2 4 + \log_2 x$

$= 2 + \log_2 x$

97. True

$\log_{10} 10^{2x} = 2x \log_{10} 10 = 2x$

99. True

$\log_4 \dfrac{16}{x} = \log_4 16 - \log_4 x$

$= 2 - \log_4 x$

101. $2^x = 64$

$2^x = 2^6$

$x = 6$

103. $4^{x-3} = \frac{1}{16}$

$4^{x-3} = 4^{-2}$

$x - 3 = -2$

$x = 1$

105. $\log_3 x = 5$

$3^{\log_3 x} = 3^5$

$x = 243$

107. $\log_2 2x = \log_2 100$

$2x = 100$

$x = 50$

109. $\log_3(2x + 1) = 2$

$3^{\log_3(2x+1)} = 3^2$

$2x + 1 = 9$

$2x = 8$

$x = 4$

111. $3^x = 500$

$\log_3 3^x = \log_3 500$

$x = \frac{\log 500}{\log 3}$

$x \approx 5.66$

113. $\ln x = 7.25$

$e^{\ln x} = e^{7.25}$

$x = e^{7.25}$

$x \approx 1408.10$

115. $2e^{0.5x} = 45$

$e^{0.5x} = 22.5$

$\ln e^{0.5x} = \ln 22.5$

$0.5x = \ln 22.5$

$x = 2 \ln 22.5$

$x \approx 6.23$

117. $12(1 - 4^x) = 18$

$1 - 4^x = \frac{18}{12}$

$-4^x = \frac{3}{2} - 1$

$-4^x = \frac{1}{2}$

$4^x = -\frac{1}{2}$

No solution; there is no power that will raise 4 to $-\frac{1}{2}$.

119. $\log_{10} 2x = 1.5$

$2x = 10^{1.5}$

$x = \frac{10^{1.5}}{2} \approx 15.81$

121. $\frac{1}{3} \log_2 x + 5 = 7$

$\frac{1}{3} \log_2 x = 2$

$\log_2 x = 6$

$2^{\log_2 x} = 2^6$

$x = 2^6 = 64$

123. $\log_2 x + \log_2 3 = 3$

$\log_2 x(3) = 3$

$2^{\log_2 3x} = 2^3$

$3x = 8$

$x = \frac{8}{3} \approx 2.67$

125. $A = P\left(1 + \frac{r}{n}\right)^{nt}$

$410.90 = 250\left(1 + \frac{r}{4}\right)^{4(10)}$

$1.6436 = \left(1 + \frac{r}{4}\right)^{40}$

$(1.6436)^{1/40} = 1 + \frac{r}{4}$

$1.0124997 = 1 + \frac{r}{4}$

$0.0124997 = \frac{r}{4}$

$0.0499 = r$

$5\% \approx r$

127. $A = P\left(1 + \frac{r}{n}\right)^{nt}$

$15399.30 = 5000\left(1 + \frac{r}{365}\right)^{365(15)}$

$3.07986 = \left(1 + \frac{r}{365}\right)^{5475}$

$(3.07986)^{1/5475} = 1 + \frac{r}{365}$

$1.000205479 = 1 + \frac{r}{365}$

$0.000205479 = \frac{r}{365}$

$0.074999 = r$

$7.5\% \approx r$

129.
$$A = Pe^{rt}$$
$$24{,}666.97 = 1500e^{r(40)}$$
$$16.44464667 = e^{40r}$$
$$\ln 16.4464667 = \ln e^{40r}$$
$$\ln 16.4464667 = 40r$$
$$\frac{\ln 16.4464667}{40} = r \approx 7\%$$

131. $A = P\left(1 + \dfrac{r}{n}\right)^{nt}$
$$A = 1000\left(1 + \frac{0.055}{365}\right)^{365(1)}$$
$$A = \$1056.54$$
$$\text{Effective yield} = \frac{56.54}{1000} = 0.0565 \approx 5.65\%$$

133. $A = P\left(1 + \dfrac{r}{n}\right)^{nt}$
$$A = 1000\left(1 + \frac{0.075}{4}\right)^{4(1)}$$
$$A = \$1077.14$$
$$\text{Effective yield} = \frac{77.14}{1000} - 0.07714 \approx 7.71\%$$

135. $A = Pe^{rt}$
$$A = 1000e^{0.075(1)}$$
$$A = \$1077.88$$
$$\text{Effective yield} = \frac{77.88}{1000} = 0.07788 \approx 7.79\%$$

137.
$$y = Ce^{kt}$$
$$3.5 = Ce^{k(0)}$$
$$3.5 = C$$

$$1.75 = 3.5e^{k(1620)}$$
$$0.5 = e^{1620k}$$
$$\ln 0.5 = \ln e^{1620k}$$
$$\ln 0.5 = 1620k$$
$$\frac{\ln 0.5}{1620} = k$$
$$-0.00043 \approx k$$

$$y = 3.5e^{-0.00043(1000)}$$
$$y \approx 2.282 \text{ grams}$$

139.
$$y = Ce^{kt}$$
$$0.5C = Ce^{k(5730)}$$
$$0.5 = e^{k(5730)}$$
$$\ln 0.5 = \ln e^{5730k}$$
$$\ln 0.5 = 5730k$$
$$\frac{\ln 0.5}{5730} = k$$
$$-0.00012 \approx k$$

$$2.6 = Ce^{-0.00012(1000)}$$
$$2.6 = Ce^{-0.12}$$
$$\frac{2.6}{e^{-0.12}} = C$$
$$2.934 \text{ grams} \approx C$$

141. $y = Ce^{kt}$
$$5 = Ce^{k(0)}$$
$$5 = C$$

$$2.5 = 5e^{k(24{,}360)}$$
$$0.5 = e^{24{,}360k}$$
$$\ln 0.5 = \ln e^{24{,}360k}$$
$$\ln 0.5 = 24{,}360k$$
$$\frac{\ln 0.5}{24{,}360} = k$$
$$-0.000028 \approx k$$

$$y = 5e^{-0.000028(1000)}$$
$$y \approx 4.860 \text{ grams}$$

143.
$$30.00 = 24.95(1.05)^t$$

$$\frac{30.00}{24.95} = 1.05^t$$

$$\log_{1.05} \frac{30.00}{24.95} = \log_{1.05} 1.05^t$$

$$\frac{\log \frac{30.00}{24.95}}{\log 1.05} = t$$

$$3.8 \text{ years} \approx t$$

145.
$$A = Pe^{rt}$$

$$1500 = 750e^{0.055t}$$

$$2 = e^{0.055t}$$

$$\ln 2 = \ln e^{0.055t}$$

$$\ln 2 = 0.055t$$

$$\frac{\ln 2}{0.055} = t \approx 12.6 \text{ years}$$

147.
$$B = 10 \log_{10}\left(\frac{I}{10^{-16}}\right)$$

$$125 = 10 \log_{10}\left(\frac{I}{10^{-16}}\right)$$

$$12.5 = \log_{10}\left(\frac{I}{10^{-16}}\right)$$

$$10^{12.5} = 10^{\log_{10}(I/10^{-16})}$$

$$10^{12.5} = \frac{I}{10^{-16}}$$

$$10^{12.5}(10^{-16}) = I$$

$$10^{-3.5} = I$$

$$= 3.16 \times 10^{-4} \text{ watts}$$
per square centimeter

149. *Keystrokes:*

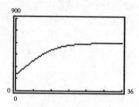

The limiting size of the population in this habitat is 600.

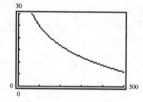

151. (a) *Keystrokes:*

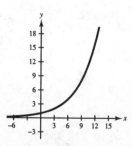

(b) $V = 14.3$ cubic feet per minute per person

Trace to $x = 250$

Chapter Test for Chapter 9

1. (a) $f(-1) = 54\left(\frac{2}{3}\right)^{-1}$
$= 54\left(\frac{3}{2}\right)$
$= 81$

(b) $f(0) = 54\left(\frac{2}{3}\right)^0$
$= 54$

(c) $f\left(\frac{1}{2}\right) = 54\left(\frac{2}{3}\right)^{1/2}$
≈ 44.09

(d) $f(2) = 54\left(\frac{2}{3}\right)^2$
$= 54\left(\frac{4}{7}\right)$
$= 24$

2.

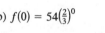

3. (a) $f \circ g = f(g(x)) = f(x^2 + 1) = 3(x^2 + 1) - 4$
$= 3x^2 + 3 - 4$
$= 3x^2 - 1$

Domain: $(-\infty, \infty)$

(b) $g \circ f = g(f(x)) = g(3x - 4) = (3x - 4)^2 + 1$
$= 9x^2 - 24x + 16 + 1$
$= 9x^2 - 24x + 17$

Domain: $(-\infty, \infty)$

4. $f(x) = 5x + 6$ $\qquad$ $x = 5y + 6$ $\qquad$ $\dfrac{x-6}{5} = y$ $\qquad$ $f^{-1}(x) = \dfrac{1}{5}(x-6)$

$\quad\; y = 5x + 6$ $\qquad$ $x - 6 = 5y$

5. $f(g(x)) = f(-2x + 6)$

$\qquad\qquad = -\dfrac{1}{2}(-2x + 6) + 3$

$\qquad\qquad = x - 3 + 3$

$\qquad\qquad = x$

$\quad g(f(x)) = g\left(-\dfrac{1}{2}x + 3\right)$

$\qquad\qquad = -2\left(-\dfrac{1}{2}x + 3\right) + 6$

$\qquad\qquad = x - 6 + 6$

$\qquad\qquad = x$

6. f and g are inverse functions.

7. $\log_4 \dfrac{5x^2}{\sqrt{y}} = \log_4 5 + 2\log_4 x - \dfrac{1}{2}\log_4 y$

8. $\ln x - \ln y = \ln \dfrac{x}{y^4}, \; y > 0$

9. $\log_5(5^3 \cdot 6) = 3\log_5 5 + \log_5 6$

$\qquad\qquad\quad = 3 + \log_5 6$

10. $\log_4 x = 3$

$\quad\; 4^{\log_4 x} = 4^3$

$\qquad\quad\; x = 64$

11. $\qquad 10^{3y} = 832$

$\quad \log 10^{3y} = \log 832$

$\qquad\quad\; 3y = \log 832$

$\qquad\qquad y = \dfrac{\log 832}{3}$

$\qquad\qquad y \approx 0.973$

12. $400e^{0.08t} = 1200$

$\qquad\; e^{0.08t} = 3$

$\quad \ln e^{0.08t} = \ln 3$

$\qquad\; 0.08t = \ln 3$

$\qquad\qquad t = \dfrac{\ln 3}{0.08}$

$\qquad\qquad t \approx 13.733$

13. $3\ln(2x - 3) = 10$

$\qquad \ln(2x - 3) = \dfrac{10}{3}$

$\qquad\; e^{\ln(2x-3)} = e^{10/3}$

$\qquad\quad 2x - 3 = e^{10/3}$

$\qquad\qquad\quad x = \dfrac{e^{10/3} + 3}{2}$

$\qquad\qquad\quad x \approx 15.516$

14. $8(2 - 3^x) = -56$

$\qquad 2 - 3^x = -7$

$\qquad\quad -3^x = -9$

$\qquad\qquad 3^x = 9$

$\qquad\qquad 3^x = 3^2$

$\qquad\; \text{so } x = 2$

15. $\log_2 x + \log_2 4 = 5$

$\qquad \log_2 x(4) = 5$

$\qquad\; 2^{\log_2 4x} = 2^5$

$\qquad\qquad 4x = 32$

$\qquad\qquad\; x = 8$

16. $\ln x - \ln 2 = 4$

$\qquad \ln \dfrac{x}{2} = 4$

$\qquad e^{\ln(x/2)} = e^4$

$\qquad\quad \dfrac{x}{2} = e^4$

$\qquad\quad\; x = 2e^4$

$\qquad\quad\; x \approx 109.196$

17. $30(e^x + 9) = 300$

$\qquad e^x + 9 = 10$

$\qquad\qquad e^x = 1$

$\qquad\qquad e^x = e^0$

$\qquad\; \text{so } x = 0$

18. (a) $A = 2000\left(1 + \dfrac{0.07}{4}\right)^{4(20)}$

$= \$8012.78$

(b) $A = 2000e^{0.07(20)}$

$= \$8110.40$

19. $100,000 = P\left(1 + \dfrac{0.09}{4}\right)^{4(25)}$

$\dfrac{100,000}{(1.0225)^{100}} = P$

$\$10,806.08 = P$

20. $1006.88 = 500e^{r(10)}$

$2.01376 = e^{10r}$

$\ln 2.01376 = \ln e^{10r}$

$\ln 2.01376 = 10r$

$\dfrac{\ln 2.01376}{10} = r$

$0.07 \approx r$

$7\% \approx r$

21. $y = Ce^{kt}$

$18,000 = Ce^{k(0)}$

$18,000 = C$

$14,000 = 18,000e^{k(1)}$

$\dfrac{14,000}{18,000} = e^{k}$

$\ln \dfrac{14}{18} = \ln e^{k}$

$\ln \dfrac{14}{18} = k$

$-0.2513144 = k$

$y = 18,000^{-0.2513144(3)}$

$= \$8469.14$

22. $p(0) = \dfrac{2400}{1 + 3e^{-0/4}} = 600$

23. $p(4) = \dfrac{2400}{1 + 3e^{-4/4}} \approx 1141$

24. $1200 = \dfrac{2400}{1 + 3e^{-t/4}}$

$1 + 3e^{-t/4} = \dfrac{2400}{1200}$

$3e^{-t/4} = 1$

$e^{-t/4} = \dfrac{1}{3}$

$\ln e^{-t/4} = \ln \dfrac{1}{3}$

$-\dfrac{t}{4} = \ln \dfrac{1}{3}$

$t = -4 \ln \dfrac{1}{3} \approx 4.4 \text{ years}$

Cumulative Test For Chapters 7–9

1. V varies directly as the square root of x and inversely as y.

$$V = \frac{k\sqrt{x}}{y}$$

2. $v = kt^2$

$-64 = k(2)^2$

$-16 = k$

3. $d = ks^2$

$50 = k(25)^2$

$\dfrac{50}{625} = k$

$\dfrac{2}{25} = k$

$d = \dfrac{2}{25}(40)^2$

$d = 128$ feet

4. $N = \dfrac{k}{t + 1}$ $N = \dfrac{300}{5 + 1}$

$300 = \dfrac{k}{0 + 1}$ $N = 50$ prey

$300 = k$

5. $5x + 2y > 10$ or $y > -\dfrac{5}{2}x + 5$

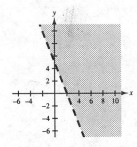

6. $m = \dfrac{2 - 0}{0 - (-1)} = \dfrac{2}{1} = 2$

$y - 2 = 2(x - 0)$

$y - 2 = 2x$

$\quad y = 2x + 2$

$\quad y \ge 2x + 2$

7. $y = a(x - h)^2 + k$ $y = \frac{2}{3}(x - 3)^2 - 2$

$4 = a(0 - 3)^2 - 2$

$4 = a(9) - 2$

$6 = 9a$

$\dfrac{6}{9} = a$

$\dfrac{2}{3} = a$

8. $x^2 + y^2 = 8$

center $= (0, 0)$ $r = \sqrt{8} \approx 2.8$

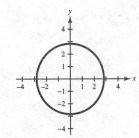

9. $x^2 + 2y = 0$

$2y = -x^2$

$y = -\dfrac{x^2}{2}$

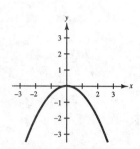

10. $\dfrac{x^2}{1} + \dfrac{y^2}{4} = 1$

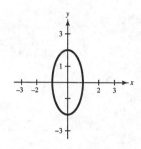

11. $\dfrac{x^2}{1} + \dfrac{y^2}{4} = 1$

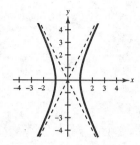

12. $x^2 + y^2 = 25$ equation at circular arch

$y = \sqrt{25 - x^2}$

$y = \sqrt{25 - 16}$

$\quad = \sqrt{9} = 3$

Maximum height of truck: $8 + 3 = 11$ feet

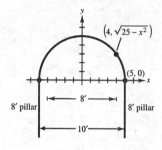

13. $y = \dfrac{4}{x - 2}$

y-intercept: $y = \dfrac{4}{0 - 2} = -2$

x-intercept: $0 = \dfrac{4}{x - 2}$

$\qquad\qquad\quad 0 = 4$ none

vertical asymptote: $x - 2 = 0$

$\qquad\qquad\qquad\qquad x = 2$

horizontal asymptote: $y = 0$ since the degree of the numerator is less than the degree of the denominator

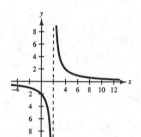

14. $y = \dfrac{4x^2}{x^2 + 1}$

y-intercept: $y = \dfrac{4(0)^2}{0 + 1} = 0$

x-intercept: $0 = \dfrac{4x^2}{x^2 + 1}$

$\qquad\qquad\quad 0 = 4x^2$

$\qquad\qquad\quad 0 = x$

vertical asymptote: $x + 1 \neq 0$ none

horizontal asymptote: $y = 4$ since the degrees are equal and the leading coefficient of the numerator is 4 and the leading coefficient of the denominator is 1.

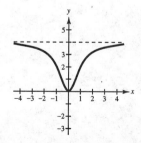

15. vertical asymptote: $x = 3$

horizontal asymptote: $y = 2$

$$f(x) = \frac{2x}{x - 3}$$

16. $\overline{C}(x) = \dfrac{10x + 13}{x}$

horizontal asymptote is $y = 10$ since the degrees are equal and the leading coefficient of the numerator is 10 and the leading coefficient of the denominator is 1. As x increases, the average cost approaches \$10.

17. $x - y = 1$

$2x + y = 5$

$x - y = 1$ $\qquad$ $2x + y = 5$

$-y = -x + 1$ $\qquad$ $y = -2x + 5$

$y = x - 1$

$(2, 1)$

Keystrokes:

y_1 [Y=] [X,T,θ] [−] 1 [ENTER]

y_2 [(−)] 2 [X,T,θ] [+] 5 [GRAPH]

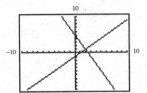

18. $4x + 2y = 8$

$x - 5y = 13$

$x = 5y + 13$ $\qquad$ $22y = -44$

$4(5y + 13) + 2y = 8$ $\qquad$ $y = -2$

$20y + 52 + 2y = 8$ $\qquad$ $x = 5(-2) + 13$

$= 3$

$(3, -2)$

19. $4x - 3y + 2z = -2$

$-2x + y + z = 1$

$x - 2y - 6z = -12$

$x - 2y - 6z = -12$ $\qquad$ $x - 2y - 6z = -12$

$4x - 3y + 2z = -2$ $\qquad$ $y + \dfrac{26}{5}z = \dfrac{46}{5}$

$-2x + y + z = 1$

$\qquad\qquad\qquad\qquad$ $\dfrac{23}{5}z = \dfrac{23}{5}$

$x - 2y - 6z = -12$

$5y + 26z = 46$ $\qquad$ $x - 2y - 6z = -12$

$-3y - 11z = -23$ $\qquad$ $y + \dfrac{26}{5}z = \dfrac{46}{5}$

$x - 2y - 6z = -12$ $\qquad\qquad$ $z = 1$

$y + \dfrac{26}{5}z = \dfrac{46}{5}$

$-3y - 11z = -23$ $\qquad$ $y + \dfrac{26}{5} = \dfrac{46}{5}$

$\qquad\qquad\qquad\qquad$ $y = \dfrac{20}{5} = 4$

$x - 2(4) - 6(1) = -12$

$x - 8 - 6 = -12$

$x = 2$ $\quad$ $(2, 4, 1)$

20. $2x - y = 4$

$3x + y = -5$

$$D = \begin{vmatrix} 2 & -1 \\ 3 & 1 \end{vmatrix} = (2) - (-3) = 5$$

$$x = \frac{\begin{vmatrix} 4 & -1 \\ -5 & 1 \end{vmatrix}}{5} = -\frac{1}{5}$$

$$x = \frac{\begin{vmatrix} 2 & 4 \\ 3 & -5 \end{vmatrix}}{5} = -\frac{22}{5}$$

$$\left(-\frac{1}{5}, -\frac{22}{5}\right)$$

21.
$$x + 5y \qquad = 29$$
$$2x \qquad - 3z = 4$$
$$-4y + z = -26$$

$$\begin{bmatrix} 1 & 5 & 0 & \vdots & 29 \\ 2 & 0 & -3 & \vdots & 4 \\ 0 & -4 & 1 & \vdots & -26 \end{bmatrix}$$

$$-2R_1 + R_2 \begin{bmatrix} 1 & 5 & 0 & \vdots & 29 \\ 0 & -10 & -3 & \vdots & -54 \\ 0 & -4 & 1 & \vdots & -26 \end{bmatrix}$$

$$-\tfrac{1}{10}R_2 \begin{bmatrix} 1 & 5 & 0 & \vdots & 29 \\ 0 & 1 & \tfrac{3}{10} & \vdots & \tfrac{27}{5} \\ 0 & -4 & 1 & \vdots & -26 \end{bmatrix}$$

$$4R_2 + R_3 \begin{bmatrix} 1 & 5 & 0 & \vdots & 29 \\ 0 & 1 & \tfrac{3}{10} & \vdots & \tfrac{27}{5} \\ 0 & 0 & \tfrac{11}{5} & \vdots & -\tfrac{22}{5} \end{bmatrix}$$

$$\tfrac{5}{11}R_3 \begin{bmatrix} 1 & 5 & 0 & \vdots & 29 \\ 0 & 1 & \tfrac{3}{10} & \vdots & \tfrac{27}{5} \\ 0 & 0 & 1 & \vdots & -2 \end{bmatrix}$$

$$z = -2 \qquad y + \tfrac{3}{10}(-2) = \tfrac{27}{5}$$
$$y - \tfrac{3}{5} = \tfrac{27}{5}$$
$$y = \tfrac{30}{5}$$
$$y = 6$$

$$x + 5(6) = 29$$
$$x + 30 = 29$$
$$x = -1$$

$$(-1, 6, -2)$$

22. $(x_1, y_1) = (-1, 1)$

$(x_2, y_2) = (2, 2)$

$(x_3, y_3) = (1, -2)$

$$\begin{vmatrix} x_1 & y_1 & 1 \\ x_2 & y_2 & 1 \\ x_3 & y_3 & 1 \end{vmatrix} = \begin{vmatrix} -1 & 1 & 1 \\ 2 & 2 & 1 \\ 1 & -2 & 1 \end{vmatrix}$$

$$= -1\begin{vmatrix} 2 & 1 \\ -2 & 1 \end{vmatrix} - 1\begin{vmatrix} 2 & 1 \\ 1 & 1 \end{vmatrix} + 1\begin{vmatrix} 2 & 2 \\ 1 & -2 \end{vmatrix}$$

$$= -1(2 + 2) - 1(2 - 1) + 1(-4 - 2)$$

$$= -4 - 1 - 6$$

$$= -11$$

$$\text{Area} = -\tfrac{1}{2}(-11) = \tfrac{11}{2}$$

23.
$$4x - 8y = -3$$
$$2x + Ky = 16$$

if $K = -4$ system is inconsistent

$$4x - 8y = -3$$
$$(-2)2x - 4y = 16(-2)$$

$$4x - 8y = -3$$
$$\underline{-4x + 8y = -32}$$
$$0 \neq -35$$

24. $g(x) = \log_3(x - 1)$

25. $\log_4 \tfrac{1}{16} = -2$ because $4^{-2} = \tfrac{1}{16}$

26.

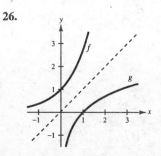

f and g are inverse functions, so the graphs are reflections in the line $y = x$.

27. $3(\log_2 x + \log_2 y) - \log_2 z = \log_2(xy)^3 - \log_2 z$

$$= \log_2 \frac{(xy)^3}{z}$$

28. $\ln \dfrac{5x}{(x+1)^2} = \ln 5 + \ln x - \ln(x+1)^2$

$$= \ln 5 + \ln x - 2\ln(x+1)$$

29. (a) $\log_x\left(\dfrac{1}{9}\right) = -2$

$$x^{\log_x(\frac{1}{9})} = x^{-2}$$

$$\frac{1}{9} = x^{-2}$$

$$\frac{1}{9} = \frac{1}{x^2}$$

$$9 = x^2$$

$$3 = x$$

(b) $4\ln x = 10$

$$\ln x = \frac{10}{4}$$

$$\ln x = \frac{5}{2}$$

$$e^{\ln x} = e^{\frac{5}{2}}$$

$$x = e^{\frac{5}{2}}$$

$$x \approx 12.18$$

(c) $500(1.08)^t = 2000$

$$1.08^t = \frac{2000}{500}$$

$$1.08^t = 4$$

$$\log_{1.08} 1.08^t = \log_{1.08} 4$$

$$t = \frac{\log 4}{\log 1.08}$$

$$t \approx 18.01$$

(d) $3(1 + e^{2x}) = 20$

$$1 + e^{2x} = \frac{20}{3}$$

$$e^{2x} = \frac{17}{3}$$

$$\ln e^{2x} = \ln \frac{17}{3}$$

$$2x = \ln \frac{17}{3}$$

$$x = \frac{\ln \frac{17}{3}}{2}$$

$$x \approx 0.87$$

30. $C(t) = P(1.035)^t$

$C(5) = 24.95(1.035)^5$

$C(5) = \$29.63$

31. $A = Pe^{rt}$

$A = 1000e^{0.08(1)}$

$A = \$1083.29$

effective yield $= \dfrac{83.29}{1000}$

$= 0.08329$

$= 8.329\%$

32. $A = Pe^{rt}$

$4000 = 1000e^{0.09t}$

$4 = e^{0.09t}$

$\ln 4 = \ln e^{0.09t}$

$\ln 4 = 0.09t$

$\dfrac{\ln 4}{0.09} = t$

15.40 years $= t$

CHAPTER 10
Sequences, Series, and Probability

CHAPTER 10
Sequences, Series, and Probability

Section 10.1   Sequences and Series

Solutions to Odd-Numbered Exercises

1. $a_1 = 2(1) = 2$

$a_2 = 2(2) = 4$

$a_3 = 2(3) = 6$

$a_4 = 2(4) = 8$

$a_5 = 2(5) = 10$

$2, 4, 6, 8, 10, \ldots, 2n, \ldots$

3. $a_1 = (-1)^1 \cdot 2(1) = -2$

$a_2 = (-1)^2 \cdot 2(2) = 4$

$a_3 = (-1)^3 \cdot 2(3) = -6$

$a_4 = (-1)^4 \cdot 2(4) = 8$

$a_5 = (-1)^5 \cdot 2(5) = -10$

$-2, 4, -6, 8, -10, \ldots, (-1)^n 2n, \ldots$

5. $a_1 = \left(\dfrac{1}{2}\right)^1 = \dfrac{1}{2}$

$a_2 = \left(\dfrac{1}{2}\right)^2 = \dfrac{1}{4}$

$a_3 = \left(\dfrac{1}{2}\right)^3 = \dfrac{1}{8}$

$a_4 = \left(\dfrac{1}{2}\right)^4 = \dfrac{1}{16}$

$a_1 = \left(\dfrac{1}{2}\right)^5 = \dfrac{1}{32}$

$\dfrac{1}{2}, \dfrac{1}{4}, \dfrac{1}{8}, \dfrac{1}{16}, \dfrac{1}{32}, \ldots, \left(\dfrac{1}{2}\right)^n, \ldots$

7. $a_1 = \left(-\dfrac{1}{2}\right)^2 = \dfrac{1}{4}$

$a_2 = \left(-\dfrac{1}{2}\right)^3 = -\dfrac{1}{8}$

$a_3 = \left(-\dfrac{1}{2}\right)^4 = \dfrac{1}{16}$

$a_4 = \left(-\dfrac{1}{2}\right)^5 = -\dfrac{1}{32}$

$a_5 = \left(-\dfrac{1}{2}\right)^6 = \dfrac{1}{64}$

$\dfrac{1}{4}, \dfrac{1}{8}, -\dfrac{1}{16}, \dfrac{1}{32}, -\dfrac{1}{64}, \ldots, \left(-\dfrac{1}{2}\right)^{n+1}, \ldots$

9. $a_1 = (-0.2)^{1-1} = (-0.2)^0 = 1$

$a_2 = (-0.2)^{2-1} = (-0.2)^1 = -0.2$

$a_3 = (-0.2)^{3-1} = (-0.2)^2 = 0.04$

$a_4 = (-0.2)^{4-1} = (-0.2)^3 = -0.008$

$a_5 = (-0.2)^{5-1} = (-0.2)^4 = 0.0016$

11. $a_1 = \dfrac{1}{1+1} = \dfrac{1}{2}$

$a_2 = \dfrac{1}{2+1} = \dfrac{1}{3}$

$a_3 = \dfrac{1}{3+1} = \dfrac{1}{4}$

$a_4 = \dfrac{1}{4+1} = \dfrac{1}{5}$

$a_5 = \dfrac{1}{5+1} = \dfrac{1}{6}$

$\dfrac{1}{2}, \dfrac{1}{3}, \dfrac{1}{4}, \dfrac{1}{5}, \dfrac{1}{6}, \ldots, \dfrac{1}{n+1}, \ldots$

13. $a_1 = \dfrac{2(1)}{3(1) + 2} = \dfrac{2}{5}$

$a_2 = \dfrac{2(2)}{3(2) + 2} = \dfrac{4}{8} = \dfrac{1}{2}$

$a_3 = \dfrac{2(3)}{3(3) + 2} = \dfrac{6}{11}$

$a_4 = \dfrac{2(4)}{3(4) + 2} = \dfrac{8}{14} = \dfrac{4}{7}$

$a_5 = \dfrac{2(5)}{3(5) + 2} = \dfrac{10}{17}$

$\dfrac{2}{5}, \dfrac{1}{2}, \dfrac{6}{11}, \dfrac{10}{17}, \ldots, \dfrac{2n}{3n + 2}, \ldots$

15. $a_1 = \dfrac{(-1)^1}{1^2} = -1$

$a_2 = \dfrac{(-1)^2}{2^2} = \dfrac{1}{4}$

$a_3 = \dfrac{(-1)^3}{3^2} = -\dfrac{1}{9}$

$a_4 = \dfrac{(-1)^4}{4^2} = \dfrac{1}{16}$

$a_5 = \dfrac{(-1)^5}{5^2} = -\dfrac{1}{25}$

$-1, \dfrac{1}{4}, -\dfrac{1}{9}, \dfrac{1}{16}, -\dfrac{1}{25}, \ldots, \dfrac{(-1)^n}{n^2}, \ldots$

17. $a_1 = 5 - \dfrac{1}{2^1} = \dfrac{9}{2}$

$a_2 = 5 - \dfrac{1}{2^2} = \dfrac{19}{4}$

$a_3 = 5 - \dfrac{1}{2^3} = \dfrac{39}{8}$

$a_4 = 5 - \dfrac{1}{2^4} = \dfrac{79}{16}$

$a_5 = 5 - \dfrac{1}{2^5} = \dfrac{159}{32}$

$\dfrac{9}{2}, \dfrac{19}{4}, \dfrac{39}{8}, \dfrac{79}{16}, \dfrac{159}{32}, \ldots, 5 - \dfrac{1}{2^n}, \ldots$

19. $a_1 = \dfrac{(1 + 1)!}{1!} = \dfrac{2!}{1!} = \dfrac{2 \cdot 1}{1} = 2$

$a_2 = \dfrac{(2 + 1)!}{2!} = \dfrac{3!}{2!} = \dfrac{3 \cdot 2!}{2!} = 3$

$a_3 = \dfrac{(3 + 1)!}{3!} = \dfrac{4!}{3!} = \dfrac{4 \cdot 3!}{3!} = 4$

$a_4 = \dfrac{(4 + 1)!}{4!} = \dfrac{5!}{4!} = \dfrac{5 \cdot 4!}{4!} = 5$

$a_5 = \dfrac{(5 + 1)!}{5!} = \dfrac{6!}{5!} = \dfrac{6 \cdot 5!}{5!} = 6$

21. $a_1 = \dfrac{2 + (-2)^1}{1!} = 0$

$a_2 = \dfrac{2 + (-2)^2}{2!} = \dfrac{6}{2 \cdot 1} = 3$

$a_3 = \dfrac{2 + (-2)^3}{3!} = \dfrac{-6}{3 \cdot 2 \cdot 1} = -1$

$a_4 = \dfrac{2 + (-2)^4}{4!} = \dfrac{18}{4 \cdot 3 \cdot 2 \cdot 1} = \dfrac{3}{4}$

$a_5 = \dfrac{2 + (-2)^5}{5!} = \dfrac{-30}{5 \cdot 4 \cdot 3 \cdot 2 \cdot 1} = \dfrac{-1}{4}$

23. $a_{15} = (-1)^{15}[5(15) - 3]$

$= -1[72]$

$= -72$

25. $a_8 = \dfrac{8^2 - 2}{(8 - 1)!} = \dfrac{62}{7!} = \dfrac{62}{7 \cdot 6 \cdot 5 \cdot 4 \cdot 3 \cdot 2 \cdot 1} = \dfrac{31}{2520}$

27. $\dfrac{5!}{4!} = \dfrac{5 \cdot 4 \cdot 3 \cdot 2 \cdot 1}{4 \cdot 3 \cdot 2 \cdot 1} = 5$

29. $\dfrac{10!}{12!} = \dfrac{10!}{12 \cdot 11 \cdot 10!} = \dfrac{1}{132}$

31. $\dfrac{25!}{20!\, 5!} = \dfrac{25 \cdot 24 \cdot 23 \cdot 22 \cdot 21 \cdot 20!}{20!\, 5!}$

$= \dfrac{25 \cdot 24 \cdot 23 \cdot 22 \cdot 21}{5 \cdot 4 \cdot 3 \cdot 2 \cdot 1} = 5 \cdot 6 \cdot 23 \cdot 11 \cdot 7$

$= 53130$

33. $\dfrac{n!}{(n+1)!} = \dfrac{n \cdot 1}{(n+1)n \cdot 1} = \dfrac{1}{n+1}$ **35.** $\dfrac{(n+1)!}{(n-1)!} = \dfrac{(n+1)n(n-1)!}{(n-1)!}$
$= (n+1)n$

37. $\dfrac{(2n)!}{(2n-1)!} = \dfrac{(2n)(2n-1)!}{(2n-1)!} = 2n$

39. (c)   **41.** (b)

43. *Keystrokes* (calculator in sequence and dot mode):

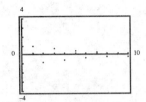

45. *Keystrokes* (calculator in sequence and dot mode):

Y= .5 *n* TRACE

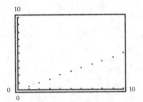

47. *Keystrokes* (calculator in sequence and dot mode):

Y= 3 − ((4 ÷ *n*)) TRACE

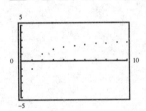

49. *n*: 1 2 3 4 5
Terms: 3 6 9 12 15

Apparent pattern: Each term is three times *n*.

$a_n = 3n$

51. *n*: 1 2 3 4 5

Terms: 1 4 7 10 13

Apparent pattern: Each term is three times *n* minus two.

$a_n = 3n - 2$

53. *n*: 1 2 3 4 5

Terms: 0 3 8 15 24

Apparent pattern: Each term is the square of *n* minus one.

$a_n = n^2 - 1$

55. *n*: 1 2 3 4 5

Terms: 2 −4 6 −8 10

Apparent pattern: The terms have alternating signs with those in the even position being negative. Each term is double *n*.

$a_n = (-1)^{n+1}2n$

57. *n*: 1 2 3 4 5

Terms: $\dfrac{2}{3}$ $\dfrac{3}{4}$ $\dfrac{4}{5}$ $\dfrac{5}{6}$ $\dfrac{6}{7}$

Apparent pattern: The numerator is 1 more than *n* and the denominator is 2 more than *n*.

$a_n = \dfrac{n+1}{n+2}$

59. *n*: 1 2 3 4

Terms: $\dfrac{1}{2}$ $-\dfrac{1}{4}$ $\dfrac{1}{8}$ $-\dfrac{1}{16}$

Apparent pattern: The numerator is 1 and each denominator is two to the nth power. The terms have alternating signs with those in the even position being negative.

$a_n = \dfrac{(-1)^{n+1}}{2^n}$

61. *n*: 1 2 3 4

Terms: 1 $\dfrac{1}{2}$ $\dfrac{1}{4}$ $\dfrac{1}{8}$

Apparent pattern: The numerator is 1 and the denominator is two to the $n - 1$ power.

$a_n = \dfrac{1}{2^{n-1}}$

63.

n:	1	2	3	4	5
Terms:	$1 + \frac{1}{1}$	$1 + \frac{1}{2}$	$1 + \frac{1}{3}$	$1 + \frac{1}{4}$	$1 + \frac{1}{5}$

Apparent pattern: The sum of one and $\frac{1}{n}$.

$$a_n = 1 + \frac{1}{n}$$

65.

n:	1	2	3	4	5
Terms:	1	$\frac{1}{2}$	$\frac{1}{6}$	$\frac{1}{24}$	$\frac{1}{120}$

Apparent pattern: The numerator is one and the denominator is n factorial.

$$a_n = \frac{1}{n!}$$

67. $\displaystyle\sum_{k=1}^{6} 3k = 3(1) + 3(2) + 3(3) + 3(4) + 3(5) + 3(6)$

$= 3 + 6 + 9 + 12 + 15 + 18$

$= 63$

69. $\displaystyle\sum_{i=0}^{6} (2i + 5) = [2(0) + 5] + [2(1) + 5] + [2(2) + 5] + [2(3) + 5] + [2(4) + 5] + [2(5) + 5] + [2(6) + 5]$

$= 5 + 7 + 9 + 11 + 13 + 15 + 17$

$= 77$

71. $\displaystyle\sum_{j=3}^{7} (6j - 10) = (6 \cdot 3 - 10) + (6 \cdot 4 - 10) + (6 \cdot 5 - 10) + (6 \cdot 6 - 10) + (6 \cdot 7 - 10)$

$= (18 - 10) + (24 - 10) + (30 - 10) + (36 - 10) + (42 - 10)$

$= 8 + 14 + 20 + 26 + 32$

$= 100$

73. $\displaystyle\sum_{j=1}^{5} \frac{(-1)^{j+1}}{j^2} = \frac{(-1)^{1+1}}{1^2} + \frac{(-1)^{2+1}}{2^2} + \frac{(-1)^{3+1}}{3^2} + \frac{(-1)^{4+1}}{4^2} + \frac{(-1)^{5+1}}{5^2}$

$= 1 - \frac{1}{4} + \frac{1}{9} - \frac{1}{16} + \frac{1}{25}$

$= \frac{3600}{3600} - \frac{900}{3600} + \frac{400}{3600} - \frac{225}{3600} + \frac{144}{3600}$

$= \frac{3019}{3600}$

75. $\displaystyle\sum_{m=2}^{6} \frac{2m}{2(m - 1)} = \frac{2(2)}{2(2 - 1)} + \frac{2(3)}{2(3 - 1)} + \frac{2(4)}{2(4 - 1)} + \frac{2(5)}{2(5 - 1)} + \frac{2(6)}{2(6 - 1)}$

$= \frac{4}{2} + \frac{6}{4} + \frac{8}{6} + \frac{10}{8} + \frac{12}{10}$

$= 2 + \frac{3}{2} + \frac{4}{3} + \frac{5}{4} + \frac{6}{5}$

$= \frac{437}{60} \approx 7.283$

77. $\displaystyle\sum_{k=1}^{6} (-8) = (-8) + (-8) + (-8) + (-8) + (-8) + (-8) = -48$

79.
$$\sum_{i=1}^{8}\left(\frac{1}{i}-\frac{1}{i+1}\right)=\left[\frac{1}{1}-\frac{1}{1+1}\right]+\left[\frac{1}{2}-\frac{1}{2+1}\right]+\left[\frac{1}{3}-\frac{1}{3+1}\right]+\left[\frac{1}{4}-\frac{1}{4+1}\right]+\left[\frac{1}{5}-\frac{1}{5+1}\right]+\left[\frac{1}{6}-\frac{1}{6+1}\right]+$$

$$\left[\frac{1}{7}-\frac{1}{7+1}\right]+\left[\frac{1}{8}-\frac{1}{8+1}\right]$$

$$=1+\left(-\frac{1}{2}+\frac{1}{2}\right)+\left(-\frac{1}{3}+\frac{1}{3}\right)+\left(-\frac{1}{4}+\frac{1}{4}\right)+\left(-\frac{1}{5}+\frac{1}{5}\right)+\left(-\frac{1}{6}+\frac{1}{6}\right)+\left(-\frac{1}{7}+\frac{1}{7}\right)+\left(-\frac{1}{8}+\frac{1}{8}\right)-\frac{1}{9}$$

$$=1-\frac{1}{9}=\frac{8}{9}$$

81. $\displaystyle\sum_{n=0}^{5}\left(-\frac{1}{3}\right)^{n}=\left(-\frac{1}{3}\right)^{0}+\left(-\frac{1}{3}\right)^{1}+\left(-\frac{1}{3}\right)^{2}+\left(-\frac{1}{3}\right)^{3}+\left(-\frac{1}{3}\right)^{4}+\left(-\frac{1}{3}\right)^{5}$

$$=1+\left(-\frac{1}{3}\right)+\frac{1}{9}+\left(-\frac{1}{27}\right)+\frac{1}{81}+\left(-\frac{1}{243}\right)$$

$$=\frac{243-81+27-9+3-1}{243}$$

$$=\frac{182}{243}$$

83. *Keystrokes*:

[LIST] [MATH 5] [LIST] [OPS 5] 3 [X,T,θ] [x^2] [,] [X,T,θ] [,] 1 [,] 6 [,] 1 [ ] [ )] [ENTER]

$$\sum_{n=1}^{6}3n^{2}=273$$

85. *Keystrokes*:

[LIST] [MATH 5] [LIST] [OPS 5] [X,T,θ] [MATH] [PRB 4] [−] [X,T,θ] [,] [X,T,θ] [,] 2 [,] 6 [,] 1 [ )] [ENTER]

$$\sum_{j=2}^{6}(j!-j)=852$$

87. *Keystrokes*:

[LIST] [MATH 5] [LIST] [OPS 5] [X,T,θ] 6 [÷] [MATH] [PRB 4] [,] [X,T,θ] [,] 0 [,] 4 [,] 1 [ )] [ENTER]

$$\sum_{j=0}^{4}\frac{6}{j!}=16.25$$

89. *Keystrokes*:

[LIST] [MATH 5] [LIST] [OPS 5] [LN] [X,T,θ] [,] [X,T,θ] [,] 0 [,] 6 [,] 1 [ )] [ENTER]

$$\sum_{k=1}^{6}\ln k=6.5793$$

91. $\displaystyle\sum_{k=1}^{5}k$

93. $\displaystyle\sum_{k=1}^{5}2k$

95. $\displaystyle\sum_{k=1}^{10}\frac{1}{2k}$

97. $\displaystyle\sum_{k=1}^{20}\frac{1}{k^{2}}$

99. $\displaystyle\sum_{k=0}^{9}\frac{1}{(-3)^{k}}$

101. $\displaystyle\sum_{k=1}^{20}\frac{4}{k+3}$

103. $\displaystyle\sum_{k=1}^{11}\frac{k}{k+1}$

105. $\displaystyle\sum_{k=1}^{20}\frac{2k}{k+3}$

107. $\sum_{k=0}^{6} k!$

109. $\bar{x} = \dfrac{3 + 7 + 2 + 1 + 5}{5}$

$= \dfrac{18}{5} = 3.6$

111. $\bar{x} = \dfrac{0.5 + 0.8 + 1.1 + 0.8 + 0.7 + 0.7 + 1.0}{7}$

$= \dfrac{5.6}{7} = 0.8$

113. (a) $A_1 = 500(1 + 0.07)^1 = \$535.00$

$A_2 = 500(1 + 0.07)^2 = \$572.45$

$A_3 = 500(1 + 0.07)^3 = \$612.52$

$A_4 = 500(1 + 0.07)^4 = \$655.40$

$A_5 = 500(1 + 0.07)^5 = \$701.28$

$A_6 = 500(1 + 0.07)^6 = \$750.37$

$A_7 = 500(1 + 0.07)^7 = \$802.89$

$A_8 = 500(1 + 0.07)^8 = \$859.09$

(b) $A_{40} = 500(1 + 0.07)^{40} = \$7487.23$

(c) *Keystrokes* (calculator in sequence and dot mode):

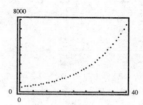

(d) Yes. Investment earning compound interest increases at an increasing rate.

115. $a_5 = \dfrac{180(5 - 2)}{5} = 108°$

$a_6 = \dfrac{180(6 - 2)}{6} = 120°$

$a_5 + 2a_6 = 108° + 240° = 348° < 360°$

117. $d_7 = \dfrac{180(7 - 6)}{7} = 25.7°$

$d_8 = \dfrac{180(8 - 6)}{8} = 45°$

$d_9 = \dfrac{180(9 - 6)}{9} = 60°$

$d_{10} = \dfrac{180(10 - 6)}{10} = 72°$

$d_{11} = \dfrac{180(11 - 6)}{11} = 81.8°$

119. An infinite sequence has an unlimited number of terms such as $a_n = 3n$.

121. The nth term of a sequence is $a_n = (-1)^n n$. When n is odd, the terms are negative.

123. True. $\sum_{k=1}^{4} 3k = 3 \sum_{k=1}^{4} k.$

$\sum_{k=1}^{4} 3k = 30 = 3 \sum_{k=1}^{4} k = 3(10)$

Section 10.2   Arithmetic Sequences

1. $d = 3$

$5 - 2 = 3, \; 8 - 5 = 3, \; 11 - 8 = 3$

3. $d = -6$

$94 - 100 = -6, \; 88 - 94 = -6, \; 82 - 88 = -6$

5. $d = -12$

$-2 - 10 = -12,\ -14 - {}^-2 = -12,$

$-26 - {}^-14 = -12,\ -38 - {}^-26 = -12$

7. $d = \frac{2}{3}$

$\frac{5}{3} - 1 = \frac{2}{3},\ \frac{7}{3} - \frac{5}{3} = \frac{2}{3},\ 3 - \frac{7}{3} = \frac{2}{3}$

9. $d = -\frac{5}{4}$

$\frac{9}{4} - \frac{7}{2} = -\frac{5}{4},\ 1 - \frac{9}{4} = -\frac{5}{4},\ -\frac{1}{4} - 1 = -\frac{5}{4}$

11. The sequence is arithmetic.

$d = 2$

$4 - 2 = 2,\ 6 - 4 = 2,\ 8 - 6 = 2$

13. arithmetic; $d = -2$

$8 - 10 = -2,\ 6 - 8 = -2,\ 4 - 6 = -2,\ 2 - 4 = -2$

15. The sequence is arithmetic.

$d = -16$

$16 - 32 = -16,\ 0 - 16 = -16,\ -16 - 0 = -16$

17. The sequence is arithmetic.

$d = 0.8$

$4 - 3.2 = 0.8,\ 4.8 - 4 = 0.8,\ 5.6 - 4.8 = 0.8$

19. The sequence is arithmetic.

$d = \frac{3}{2}$

$\frac{7}{2} - 2 = \frac{3}{2},\ 5 - \frac{7}{2} = \frac{3}{2},\ \frac{13}{2} - 5 = \frac{3}{2}$

21. The sequence is not arithmetic.

$\frac{2}{3} - \frac{1}{3} = \frac{1}{3}$

$\frac{4}{3} - \frac{2}{3} = \frac{2}{3}$

The difference is NOT the same.

23. The sequence is not arithmetic.

$\sqrt{2} - 1 = \sqrt{2} - 1 \approx .41$

$\sqrt{3} - \sqrt{2} = \sqrt{3} - \sqrt{2} \approx .31$

The difference is NOT the same.

25. The sequence is not arithmetic.

$\ln 8 - \ln 4 = \ln 8 - \ln 4 \approx .69$

$\ln 12 - \ln 8 = \ln 12 - \ln 8 \approx .41$

The difference is NOT the same.

27. $a_1 = 3(1) + 4 = 7$

$a_2 = 3(2) + 4 = 10$

$a_3 = 3(3) + 4 = 13$

$a_4 = 3(4) + 4 = 16$

$a_5 = 3(5) + 4 = 19$

29. $a_1 = -2(1) + 8 = 6$

$a_2 = -2(2) + 8 = 4$

$a_3 = -2(3) + 8 = 2$

$a_4 = -2(4) + 8 = 0$

$a_5 = -2(5) + 8 = -2$

31. $a_1 = \frac{5}{2}(1) - 1 = \frac{3}{2}$

$a_2 = \frac{5}{2}(2) - 1 = 4$

$a_3 = \frac{5}{2}(3) - 1 = \frac{13}{2}$

$a_4 = \frac{5}{2}(4) - 1 = 9$

$a_5 = \frac{5}{2}(5) - 1 = \frac{23}{2}$

33. $a_1 = \frac{3}{5}(1) + 1 = \frac{8}{5}$

$a_2 = \frac{3}{5}(2) + 1 = \frac{11}{5}$

$a_3 = \frac{3}{5}(3) + 1 = \frac{14}{5}$

$a_4 = \frac{3}{5}(4) + 1 = \frac{17}{5}$

$a_5 = \frac{3}{5}(5) + 1 = \frac{20}{5} = 4$

35. $a_1 = -\frac{1}{4}(1 - 1) + 4 = 4$

$a_2 = -\frac{1}{4}(2 - 1) + 4 = \frac{15}{4}$

$a_3 = -\frac{1}{4}(3 - 1) + 4 = \frac{7}{2}$

$a_4 = -\frac{1}{4}(4 - 1) + 4 = \frac{13}{4}$

$a_5 = -\frac{1}{4}(5 - 1) + 4 = 3$

37. $a_n = a_1 + (n - 1)d$

$a_n = 3 + (n - 1)\frac{1}{2}$

$a_n = 3 + \frac{1}{2}n - \frac{1}{2}$

$a_n = \frac{1}{2}n + \frac{5}{2}$

39. $a_n = a_1 + (n - 1)d$

$a_n = 1000 + (n - 1)(-25)$

$a_n = 1000 - 25n + 25$

$a_n = -25n + 1025$

41. $a_n = a_1 + (n-1)d$

$20 = a_1 + (3-1)(-4)$ so $a_n = 28 + (n-1)(-4)$

$20 = a_1 - 8$ $a_n = 28 - 4n + 4$

$28 = a_1$ $a_n = -4n + 32$

43. $a_n = a_1 + (n-1)d$

$a_n = 3 + (n-1)\frac{3}{2}$

$a_n = 3 + \frac{3}{2}n - \frac{3}{2}$

$a_n = \frac{3}{2}n + \frac{3}{2}$

45. $a_n = a_1 + (n-1)d$

$15 = 5 + (5-1)d$ so $a_n = 5 + (n-1)\frac{5}{2}$

$15 = 5 + 4d$ $a_n = 5 + \frac{5}{2}n - \frac{5}{2}$

$10 = 4d$ $a_n = \frac{5}{2}n + \frac{5}{2}$

$\frac{5}{2} = \frac{10}{4} = d$

47. $a_n = a_1 + (n-1)d$

$16 = a_1 + (3-1)4$

$8 = a_1$

$a_n = 8 + (n-1)(4)$

$a_n = 4n + 4$

49. $a_n = a_1 + (n-1)d$

$30 = 50 + (3-1)d$

$-20 = 2d$

$-10 = d$

$a_n = 50 + (n-1)(-10)$

$a_n = -10n + 60$

51. $d = \dfrac{8-10}{4} = -\dfrac{1}{2}$

$a_n = a_1 + (n-1)d$

$10 = a_1 + (2-1)\left(-\dfrac{1}{2}\right)$

$10 = a_1 - \dfrac{1}{2}$

$\dfrac{21}{2} = a_1$

$a_n = \dfrac{21}{2} + (n-1)\left(-\dfrac{1}{2}\right)$

$a_n = \dfrac{21}{2} - \dfrac{1}{2}n + \dfrac{1}{2}$

$a_n = -\dfrac{1}{2}n + 11$

53. $d = \dfrac{0.30 - 0.35}{1} = -0.05$

$a_n = a_1 + (n-1)d$

$a_n = 0.35 + (n-1)(-0.05)$

$a_n = 0.35 - 0.05n + 0.05$

$a_n = -0.05n + 0.40$

55. $a_n = a_1 + (n-1)d$

$a_1 = 25$ and $d = 3$

$a_2 = 25 + (2-1)(3) = 28$

$a_2 = 25 + (3-1)(3) = 31$

$a_2 = 25 + (4-1)(3) = 34$

$a_2 = 25 + (5-1)(3) = 37$

57. $a_n = a_1 + (n-1)d$

$a_1 = 9$

$a_2 = a_{1+1} = a_1 - 3 = 9 - 3 = 6$

$a_3 = a_{2+1} = a_2 - 3 = 6 - 3 = 3$

$a_4 = a_{3+1} = a_3 - 3 = 3 - 3 = 0$

$a_5 = a_{4+1} = a_4 - 3 = 0 - 3 = -3$

59. $a_n = a_1 + (n-1)d$

$a_1 = -10$

$a_2 = a_{1+1} = a_1 + 6 = -10 + 6 = -4$

$a_3 = a_{2+1} = a_2 + 6 = -4 + 6 = 2$

$a_4 = a_{3+1} = a_3 + 6 = 2 + 6 = 8$

$a_5 = a_{4+1} = a_4 + 6 = 8 + 6 = 14$

61. $a_n = a_1 + (n-1)d$

$a_1 = 100$ and $d = -20$

$a_2 = 100 + (2-1)(-20) = 80$

$a_3 = 100 + (3-1)(-20) = 60$

$a_4 = 100 + (4-1)(-20) = 40$

$a_5 = 100 + (5-1)(-20) = 20$

63. $\displaystyle\sum_{k=1}^{20} k = 20\left(\dfrac{1+20}{2}\right)$

$= 210$

65. $\displaystyle\sum_{k=1}^{50} (k+3) = 50\left(\dfrac{4+53}{2}\right)$

$= 1425$

67. $\displaystyle\sum_{k=1}^{10} (5k-2) = 10\left(\dfrac{3+48}{2}\right)$

$= 255$

69. $\displaystyle\sum_{n=1}^{500} \frac{n}{2} = 500\left(\frac{\frac{1}{2} + 250}{2}\right)$

$= 62,625$

71. $\displaystyle\sum_{n=1}^{30} \left(\frac{1}{3}n - 4\right) = 30\left(\frac{-\frac{11}{3} + 6}{2}\right)$

$= 35$

73. $\displaystyle\sum_{n=1}^{12} (7n - 2) = 12\left(\frac{5 + 82}{2}\right)$

$= 522$

75. $\displaystyle\sum_{n=1}^{25} (6n - 4) = 25\left(\frac{2 + 146}{2}\right)$

$= 1850$

77. $\displaystyle\sum_{n=1}^{8} (225 - 25n) = 8\left(\frac{200 + 25}{2}\right)$

$= 900$

79. $\displaystyle\sum_{n=1}^{50} (12n - 62) = 50\left(\frac{-50 + 538}{2}\right)$

$= 12,200$

81. $\displaystyle\sum_{n=1}^{12} (3.5n - 2.5) = 12\left(\frac{1 + 39.5}{2}\right)$

$= 243$

83. $\displaystyle\sum_{n=1}^{10} (0.4n + 0.1) = 10\left(\frac{0.5 + 4.1}{2}\right)$

$= 23$

85. (b)

87. (e)

89. (c)

91. *Keystrokes* (calculator in sequence and dot mode):

$\boxed{Y=}$ $\boxed{(-)}$ 2 $\boxed{n}$ $\boxed{+}$ 21 $\boxed{\text{TRACE}}$

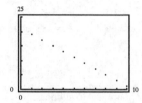

93. *Keystrokes* (calculator in sequence and dot mode):

$\boxed{Y=}$ .6 $\boxed{n}$ $\boxed{+}$ 1.5 $\boxed{\text{TRACE}}$

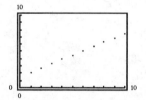

95. *Keystrokes* (calculator in sequence and dot mode):

$\boxed{Y=}$ 2.5 $\boxed{n}$ $\boxed{-}$ 8 $\boxed{\text{TRACE}}$

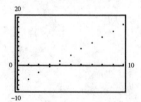

97. *Keystrokes:*

$\boxed{\text{LIST}}$ $\boxed{\text{MATH 5}}$ $\boxed{\text{LIST}}$ $\boxed{\text{OPS 5}}$ 750 $\boxed{-}$ 30 $\boxed{\text{X,T,}\theta}$ $\boxed{,}$ $\boxed{\text{X,T,}\theta}$ $\boxed{,}$ 1 $\boxed{,}$ 25 $\boxed{,}$ 1 $\boxed{)}$ $\boxed{\text{ENTER}}$

$\displaystyle\sum_{j=1}^{25} (750 - 30j) = 9000$

99. *Keystrokes:*

$\boxed{\text{LIST}}$ $\boxed{\text{MATH 5}}$ $\boxed{\text{LIST}}$ $\boxed{\text{OPS 5}}$ 300 $\boxed{-}$ 8 $\boxed{\text{X,T,}\theta}$ $\boxed{\div}$ 3 $\boxed{,}$ $\boxed{\text{X,T,}\theta}$ $\boxed{,}$ 1 $\boxed{,}$ 60 $\boxed{,}$ 1 $\boxed{)}$ $\boxed{\text{ENTER}}$

$\displaystyle\sum_{i=1}^{60} \left(300 - \frac{8}{3}i\right) = 13,120$

101. *Keystrokes:*

$\boxed{\text{LIST}}$ $\boxed{\text{MATH 5}}$ $\boxed{\text{LIST}}$ $\boxed{\text{OPS 5}}$ 2.15 $\boxed{\text{X,T,}\theta}$ $\boxed{+}$ 5.4 $\boxed{,}$ $\boxed{\text{X,T,}\theta}$ $\boxed{,}$ 1 $\boxed{,}$ 50 $\boxed{,}$ 1 $\boxed{)}$ $\boxed{\text{ENTER}}$

$\displaystyle\sum_{n=1}^{50} (2.15n + 5.4) = 3011.25$

103. $\displaystyle\sum_{n=1}^{75} = 75\left(\dfrac{1+75}{2}\right) = 2850$

105. $\displaystyle\sum_{n=1}^{50} 2n = 50\left(\dfrac{2+100}{2}\right) = 2550$

107. 36,000, 38,000, 40,000, 42,000, 44,000, 46,000

Total salary $= 6\left(\dfrac{36,000+46,000}{2}\right) = \$246,000$

109. Sequence $= 20, 21, 22, \ldots \quad n = 20 \quad d = 1$

$a_n = a_1 + (n-1)d \qquad \displaystyle\sum_{n=1}^{20}(19+n) = 20\left(\dfrac{20+39}{2}\right)$

$a_n = 20 + (n-1)1 \qquad\qquad\qquad = 590 \text{ seats}$

$a_n = 19 + n$

$\dfrac{\text{Total cost}}{\text{Total seats}} = \text{Cost per ticket}$

$\dfrac{15,000}{590} = 25.43$

Charge \$25.43 to make at least \$15,000

111. Sequence $= 93, 89, 85, 81, \ldots$

$\displaystyle\sum_{n=1}^{8}(97-4n) = 8\left(\dfrac{93+65}{2}\right)$

$\qquad\qquad\qquad = 632 \text{ bales}$

113. Sequence $= 1, 2, 3, 4, \ldots$

$a_n = a_1 + (n-1)d \qquad \displaystyle\sum_{n=1}^{12} n = 12\left(\dfrac{1+12}{2}\right)$

$a_n = 1 + (n-1)(1) \qquad\qquad = 78 \text{ chimes}$

$a_n = 1 + n - 1$

$a_n = n$

3 chimes each hour $\times$ 12 hours $=$ 36 chimes

Total chimes $= 78 + 36 = 114$ chimes

115. Sequence $= 16, 48, 80, \ldots \quad n = 8 \quad d = 32$

$a_n = a_1 + (n-1)d \qquad\qquad a_n = 16 + (n-1)32$

$a_n = 16 + (8-1)32 \qquad\qquad = 16 + 32n - 32$

$a_n = 16 + 224 \qquad\qquad a_n = 32n - 16$

$a_n = 240$

$\displaystyle\sum_{n=1}^{8}(32n-16) = 8\left(\dfrac{16+240}{2}\right)$

$\qquad\qquad\qquad = 1024 \text{ feet}$

117. (a) $1 + 3 = 4$

$1 + 3 + 5 = 9$

$1 + 3 + 5 + 7 = 16$

$1 + 3 + 5 + 7 + 9 = 25$

$1 + 3 + 5 + 7 + 9 + 11 = 36$

(b) The sums of positive odd integers yield perfect squares.

$1 + 3 + 5 + 7 + 9 + 11 + 13 = 49$

(c) $\displaystyle\sum_{k=1}^{n}[1 + (k-1)2] = n\left(\dfrac{1+(2n-1)}{2}\right)$

$\qquad\qquad\qquad = n\left(\dfrac{2n}{2}\right) = n^2$

119. $a_n = a_1 + (n-1)d$

$d = 15 - 12 = 3$

$12 = a_1 + (2-1)3$

$9 = a_1$

121. A recursion formula gives the relationship between the terms a_{n+1} and a_n.

123. Sequence $= 100, 101, 102, \ldots, 200$

$\displaystyle\sum_{n=100}^{200} n = 101\left(\dfrac{100+200}{2}\right)$

$\qquad\qquad = 15,150$

(*Note:* $a_n = a_1 + (n-1)d$

$a_n = 100 + (n-1)1$

$a_n = n + 99$ if n begins at 1.

To start at 100, use n.)

Section 10.3   Geometric Sequences and Series

1. $r = 3$ since

$$\frac{6}{2} = 3, \quad \frac{18}{6} = 3, \quad \frac{54}{18} = 3$$

3. $r = -3$ since

$$\frac{-3}{1} = -3, \quad \frac{9}{-3} = -3, \quad \frac{-27}{9} = -3$$

5. $r = -\dfrac{1}{2}$ since

$$\frac{-6}{12} = -\frac{1}{2}, \quad \frac{3}{-6} = -\frac{1}{2}, \quad \frac{-\frac{3}{2}}{3} = -\frac{1}{2}$$

7. $r = -\dfrac{3}{2}$ since

$$\frac{-\frac{3}{2}}{1} = -\frac{3}{2}, \quad \frac{\frac{9}{4}}{-\frac{3}{2}} = -\frac{3}{2}, \quad \frac{-\frac{27}{8}}{\frac{9}{4}} = -\frac{3}{2}$$

9. $r = \pi$ since

$$\frac{\pi}{1} = \pi, \quad \frac{\pi^2}{\pi} = \pi, \quad \frac{\pi^3}{\pi} = \pi$$

11. $r = 1.06$ since

$$\frac{500(1.06)^2}{500(1.06)} = 1.06, \quad \frac{500(1.06)^3}{500(1.06)^2} = 1.06$$

13. The sequence is geometric.

$r = \dfrac{1}{2}$ since

$$\frac{32}{64} = \frac{1}{2}, \quad \frac{16}{32} = \frac{1}{2}, \quad \frac{8}{16} = \frac{1}{2}$$

15. The sequence is not geometric, because

$\frac{15}{10} = \frac{3}{2}$ and $\frac{20}{15} = \frac{4}{3}$

17. The sequence is geometric.

$r = 2$ since $\dfrac{10}{5} = 2, \quad \dfrac{20}{10} = 2, \quad \dfrac{40}{20} = 2$

19. The sequence is not geometric, because

$\frac{8}{1} = 8$ and $\frac{27}{8} = \frac{27}{8}$

21. The sequence is geometric.

$r = -\dfrac{2}{3}$ since

$$\frac{-\frac{2}{3}}{1} = -\frac{2}{3}, \quad \frac{\frac{4}{9}}{-\frac{2}{3}} = -\frac{2}{3}, \quad \frac{-\frac{8}{27}}{\frac{4}{9}} = -\frac{2}{3}$$

23. The sequence is geometric.

$r = (1 + 0.02)$ since

$$\frac{10(1 + 0.02)^2}{10(1 + 0.02)} = (1 + 0.02), \quad \frac{10(1 + 0.02)^3}{10(1 + 0.02)^2} = (1 + 0.02)$$

25. $a_n = a_1 r^{n-1}$

$a_n = 4(2)^{n-1}$

$a_1 = 4(2)^{1-1} = 4$

$a_2 = 4(2)^{2-1} = 8$

$a_3 = 4(2)^{3-1} = 16$

$a_4 = 4(2)^{4-1} = 32$

$a_5 = 4(2)^{5-1} = 64$

27. $a_n = a_1 r^{n-1}$

$a_n = 6\left(\dfrac{1}{3}\right)^{n-1}$

$a_1 = 6\left(\dfrac{1}{3}\right)^{1-1} = 6$

$a_2 = 6\left(\dfrac{1}{3}\right)^{2-1} = 2$

$a_3 = 6\left(\dfrac{1}{3}\right)^{3-1} = \dfrac{2}{3}$

$a_4 = 6\left(\dfrac{1}{3}\right)^{4-1} = \dfrac{2}{9}$

$a_5 = 6\left(\dfrac{1}{3}\right)^{5-1} = \dfrac{2}{27}$

29. $a_n = a_1 r^{n-1}$

$a_n = 1\left(-\dfrac{1}{2}\right)^{n-1}$

$a_1 = 1\left(-\dfrac{1}{2}\right)^{1-1} = 1$

$a_2 = 1\left(-\dfrac{1}{2}\right)^{2-1} = -\dfrac{1}{2}$

$a_3 = 1\left(-\dfrac{1}{2}\right)^{3-1} = \dfrac{1}{4}$

$a_4 = 1\left(-\dfrac{1}{2}\right)^{4-1} = -\dfrac{1}{8}$

$a_5 = 1\left(-\dfrac{1}{2}\right)^{5-1} = \dfrac{1}{16}$

31. $a_n = a_1 r^{n-1}$

$a_n = 4\left(-\dfrac{1}{2}\right)^{n-1}$

$a_1 = 4\left(-\dfrac{1}{2}\right)^{1-1} = 4$

$a_2 = 4\left(-\dfrac{1}{2}\right)^{2-1} = -2$

$a_3 = 4\left(-\dfrac{1}{2}\right)^{3-1} = 1$

$a_4 = 4\left(-\dfrac{1}{2}\right)^{4-1} = -\dfrac{1}{2}$

$a_5 = 4\left(-\dfrac{1}{2}\right)^{5-1} = \dfrac{1}{4}$

33. $a_n = a_1 r^{n-1}$

$a_n = 1000(1.01)^{n-1}$

$a_1 = 1000(1.01)^{1-1} = 1000$

$a_2 = 1000(1.01)^{2-1} = 1010$

$a_3 = 1000(1.01)^{3-1} = 1020.1$

$a_4 = 1000(1.01)^{4-1} = 1030.301$

$a_5 = 1000(1.01)^{5-1} = 1040.604$

35. $a_n = a_1 r^{n-1}$

$a_n = 4000\left(\dfrac{1}{1.01}\right)^{n-1}$

$a_1 = 4000\left(\dfrac{1}{1.01}\right)^{1-1} = 4000\left(\dfrac{1}{1.01}\right)^{0} = 4000(1) = 4000$

$a_2 = 4000\left(\dfrac{1}{1.01}\right)^{2-1} = 4000\left(\dfrac{1}{1.01}\right)^{1} \approx 3960.40$

$a_3 = 4000\left(\dfrac{1}{1.01}\right)^{3-1} = 4000\left(\dfrac{1}{1.01}\right)^{2} \approx 3921.18$

$a_4 = 4000\left(\dfrac{1}{1.01}\right)^{4-1} = 4000\left(\dfrac{1}{1.01}\right)^{3} \approx 3882.36$

$a_5 = 4000\left(\dfrac{1}{1.01}\right)^{5-1} = 4000\left(\dfrac{1}{1.01}\right)^{4} \approx 3843.92$

37. $a_n = a_1 r^{n-1}$

$a_n = 10\left(\dfrac{3}{5}\right)^{n-1}$

$a_1 = 10\left(\dfrac{3}{5}\right)^{1-1} = 10\left(\dfrac{3}{5}\right)^{0} = 10(1) = 10$

$a_2 = 10\left(\dfrac{3}{5}\right)^{2-1} = 10\left(\dfrac{3}{5}\right)^{1} = 6$

$a_3 = 10\left(\dfrac{3}{5}\right)^{3-1} = 10\left(\dfrac{3}{5}\right)^{2} = 10\left(\dfrac{9}{25}\right) = \dfrac{18}{5}$

$a_4 = 10\left(\dfrac{3}{5}\right)^{4-1} = 10\left(\dfrac{3}{5}\right)^{3} = 10\left(\dfrac{27}{125}\right) = \dfrac{54}{25}$

$a_5 = 10\left(\dfrac{3}{5}\right)^{5-1} = 10\left(\dfrac{3}{5}\right)^{4} = 10\left(\dfrac{81}{625}\right) = \dfrac{162}{125}$

39. $a_n = a_1 r^{n-1}$

$a_{10} = 6\left(\dfrac{1}{2}\right)^{10-1} = \dfrac{3}{256}$

41. $a_n = a_1 r^{n-1}$

$a_{10} = 3(\sqrt{2})^{10-1} = 48\sqrt{2}$

43. $a_n = a_1 r^{n-1}$

$a_{12} = 200(1.2)^{12-1}$

$a_{12} \approx 1486.02$

45. $a_n = a_1 r^{n-1}$

$a_{10} \approx 120\left(-\dfrac{1}{3}\right)^{10-1}$

$a_{10} \approx -0.0061$

47. $a_n = a_1 r^{n-1}$

$a_5 = 4\left(\dfrac{3}{4}\right)^{5-1} = \dfrac{81}{64}$

49. $a_n = a_1 r^{n-1}$

$a_6 = 1\left(\pm\dfrac{3}{2}\right)^{6-1} = \pm\dfrac{243}{32}$

51. $r = \dfrac{a_3}{a_2} = \dfrac{16}{12} = \dfrac{4}{3}$

$a_n = a_1 r^{n-1}$

$12 = a_1\left(\dfrac{4}{3}\right)^{2-1}$

$12 = a_1\left(\dfrac{4}{3}\right)$

$9 = a_1$

$a_n = 9\left(\dfrac{4}{3}\right)^{n-1}$

$a_4 = 9\left(\dfrac{4}{3}\right)^{4-1}$

$a_4 = 9\left(\dfrac{4}{3}\right)^{3} = 9\left(\dfrac{64}{27}\right) = \dfrac{64}{3}$

53. $a_n = a_1 r^{n-1}$

$a_n = 2(3)^{n-1}$

55. $a_n = a_1 r^{n-1}$

$a_n = 1(2)^{n-1}$

57. $a_n = a_1 r^{n-1}$

$a_n = 1\left(-\dfrac{1}{5}\right)^{n-1}$

59. $a_n = a_1 r^{n-1}$

$a_n = 4\left(-\dfrac{1}{2}\right)^{n-1}$

61. $a_n = a_1 r^{n-1}$

$a_n = 8\left(\dfrac{1}{4}\right)^{n-1}$

63. $r = \dfrac{a_2}{a_1} = \dfrac{\frac{21}{2}}{14} = \dfrac{3}{4}$

$a_n = a r^{n-1}$

$a_n = 14\left(\dfrac{3}{4}\right)^{n-1}$

65. $4r = -6$

$r = -\dfrac{6}{4} = -\dfrac{3}{2}$

$a_n = a_1 r^{n-1}$

$a_n = 4\left(-\dfrac{3}{2}\right)^{n-1}$

67. (b)

69. (a)

71. $\displaystyle\sum_{i=1}^{10} 2^{i-1} = 1\left(\dfrac{2^{10}-1}{2-1}\right) = \dfrac{1024-1}{1} = 1023$

73. $\displaystyle\sum_{i=1}^{12} 3\left(\dfrac{3}{2}\right)^{i-1} = 3\left(\dfrac{\left(\frac{3}{2}\right)^{12}-1}{\frac{3}{2}-1}\right) = 3\left(\dfrac{128.74634}{0.5}\right) \approx 772.48$

75. $\displaystyle\sum_{i=1}^{15} 3\left(-\dfrac{1}{3}\right)^{i-1} = 3\left(\dfrac{\left(-\frac{1}{3}\right)^{15}-1}{-\frac{1}{3}-1}\right)$

$= 3\left(\dfrac{-1.0000001}{-1.3333333}\right)$

≈ 2.25

77. $\displaystyle\sum_{i=1}^{12} 4(-2)^{i-1} = 4\left(\dfrac{(-2)^{12}-1}{-2-1}\right)$

$= 4\left(\dfrac{4095}{-3}\right)$

$= -5460$

79. $\displaystyle\sum_{i=1}^{8} 6(0.1)^{i-1} = 6\left(\dfrac{(0.1)^8-1}{0.1-1}\right)$

$= 6\left(\dfrac{-.99\overline{9}}{-.9}\right)$

$= 6(1.\overline{1})$

≈ 6.67

81. $\displaystyle\sum_{i=1}^{10} 1(-3)^{i-1} = \left(\dfrac{(-3)^{10}-1}{-3-1}\right)$

$= -14{,}762$

83. $\displaystyle\sum_{i=1}^{15} 8\left(\dfrac{1}{2}\right)^{i-1} = 8\left(\dfrac{\left(\frac{1}{2}\right)^{15}-1}{\frac{1}{2}-1}\right)$

≈ 16

85. $\displaystyle\sum_{i=1}^{8} 4(3)^{i-1} = 4\left(\dfrac{3^8-1}{3-1}\right)$

$= 4\left(\dfrac{6560}{2}\right)$

$= 13{,}120$

87. $\displaystyle\sum_{i=1}^{12} 60\left(-\dfrac{1}{4}\right)^{i-1} = 60\left(\dfrac{\left(-\frac{1}{4}\right)^{12}-1}{\left(-\frac{1}{4}\right)-1}\right)$

$\approx 60\left(\dfrac{-1.000}{-1.25}\right)$

≈ 48

89. $\displaystyle\sum_{i=1}^{20} 30(1.06)^{i-1} = 30\left(\dfrac{1.06^{20}-1}{1.06-1}\right)$

≈ 1103.57

91. $\displaystyle\sum_{i=1}^{18} 500(1.04)^{i-1} = 500\left(\dfrac{1.04^{18}-1}{1.04-1}\right)$

$= 500\left(\dfrac{1.025816515}{0.04}\right)$

$\approx 12{,}822.71$

93. $\displaystyle\sum_{n=0}^{\infty} \left(\dfrac{1}{2}\right)^n = \dfrac{1}{1-\frac{1}{2}} = \dfrac{1}{\frac{1}{2}} = 2$

95. $\displaystyle\sum_{n=0}^{\infty} \left(-\dfrac{1}{2}\right)^n = \dfrac{1}{1-\left(\frac{1}{2}\right)}$

$= \dfrac{1}{\frac{3}{2}}$

$= \dfrac{2}{3}$

97. $\displaystyle\sum_{n=0}^{\infty} 2\left(-\dfrac{2}{3}\right)^n = \dfrac{2}{1-\left(-\frac{2}{3}\right)}$

$= \dfrac{2}{\frac{5}{3}}$

$= \dfrac{6}{5}$

99. $\displaystyle\sum_{n=0}^{\infty} 8\left(\dfrac{3}{4}\right)^n = \dfrac{8}{1-\frac{3}{4}}$

$= \dfrac{8}{\frac{1}{4}}$

$= 32$

101. $a_n = 20(-0.6)^{n-1}$

Keystrokes (calculator in sequence and dot mode):

$\boxed{Y=}$ 20 $\boxed{(}$ $\boxed{(-)}$ 0.6 $\boxed{)}$ $\boxed{\wedge}$ $\boxed{(}$ $\boxed{n}$ $\boxed{-}$ 1 $\boxed{)}$ $\boxed{TRACE}$

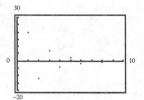

103. $a_n = 15(0.6)^{n-1}$

Keystrokes (calculator in sequence and dot mode):

$\boxed{Y=}$ 15 $\boxed{(}$ 0.6 $\boxed{)}$ $\boxed{\wedge}$ $\boxed{(}$ $\boxed{n}$ $\boxed{-}$ 1 $\boxed{)}$ $\boxed{TRACE}$

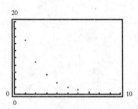

105. $a_0 = 250,000$

$a_1 = 250,000(0.75)$

$a_2 = 250,000(0.75)^2$

$a_3 = 250,000(0.75)^3$

$a_4 = 250,000(0.75)^4$

(a) $a_n = 250,000(0.75)^n$

(b) $a_5 = 250,000(0.75)^5 = \$59,326.17$

(c) the first year

107. Total salary $= \sum_{n=1}^{40} 30,000(1.05)^n$

$= 30,000\left(\dfrac{1.05^{40}-1}{1.05-1}\right)$

$= \$3,623,993.23$

109. $A = P\left(1 + \dfrac{r}{n}\right)^{nt}$

$a_{120} = 100\left(1 + \dfrac{0.09}{12}\right)^{12(10)} = 100(1.0075)^{120}$

$a_1 = 100(1.0075)^1$

balance $= [100(1.0075)]\left[\dfrac{1.0075^{120}-1}{1.0075-1}\right] \approx \$19,496.56$

111. $A = P\left(1 + \dfrac{r}{n}\right)^{nt}$

$a_{480} = 30\left(1 + \dfrac{0.08}{12}\right)^{12(40)} = 30\left(\dfrac{151}{150}\right)^{480}$

$a_1 = 30\left(\dfrac{151}{150}\right)^1$

balance $= \left[30\left(\dfrac{151}{150}\right)\right]\left[\dfrac{\left(\frac{151}{150}\right)^{480}-1}{\left(\frac{151}{150}\right)-1}\right] \approx \$105,428.44$

113. $A = P\left(1 + \dfrac{r}{n}\right)^{nt}$

$a_{360} = 75\left(1 + \dfrac{0.06}{12}\right)^{12(30)} = 75(1.005)^{360}$

$a_1 = 75(1.005)^1$

balance $= [75(1.005)]\left[\dfrac{1.005^{360}-1}{1.005-1}\right] \approx \$75,715.32$

115. $a_n = 0.01(2)^{n-1}$

(a) Total income $= \sum_{n=1}^{29} 0.01(2)^{n-1}$

$= 0.01\left[\dfrac{2^{29}-1}{2-1}\right]$

$\approx \$5,368,709.11$

(b) Total income $= \sum_{n=1}^{30} 0.01(2)^{n-1}$

$= 0.01\left[\dfrac{2^{30}-1}{2-1}\right]$

$\approx \$10,737,418.23$

117. (a) $P = (0.999)^n$

(b) $P = (0.999)^{365}$

$= .694069887$

$\approx 69.4\%$

(c) *Keystrokes* (calculator in sequence and dot mode):

$\boxed{Y=}\ .999\ \boxed{\wedge}\ \boxed{n}\ \boxed{TRACE}$

700 days

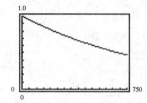

119. $a_1 = 6^2 = 36$

$a_2 = (3\sqrt{2})^2 = 18$

$r = \dfrac{a_2}{a_1} = \dfrac{18}{36} = \dfrac{1}{2}$

$a_n = 36\left(\dfrac{1}{2}\right)^{n-1}$

Total area $= \displaystyle\sum_{n=1}^{6} 36\left(\dfrac{1}{2}\right)^{n-1} = 36\left(\dfrac{\left(\frac{1}{2}\right)^6 - 1}{\frac{1}{2} - 1}\right)$

$= 70.875$ square inches

121. $\displaystyle\sum_{i=1}^{10} 2(100)(0.75)^n = 2(100)(0.75)\left[\dfrac{0.75^{10} - 1}{0.75 - 1}\right]$

$= 150(3.774745941)$

≈ 566.21

Total distance $= 100 + \displaystyle\sum_{i=1}^{10} 2(100)(0.75)^n$

$= 100 + 566.21$

$= 666.21$ feet

123. (a) Sequence $= 2,\ 4,\ 8,\ 16, \ldots$

$a_n = 2^n$

(b) Total ancestors $= \displaystyle\sum_{i=1}^{66} 2^n$

$= 2\left(\dfrac{2^{66} - 1}{2 - 1}\right)$

$= 1.4757 \times 10^{20}$

(c) It is likely that you have had no common ancestors in the last 2000 years.

125. The general formula for the nth term of a geometric sequence is $a_n = a_1 r^{n-1}$

127. An example of a geometric sequence whose terms alternate in sign is $a_n = \left(-\frac{2}{3}\right)^{n-1}$.

129. An increasing annuity is an investment plan where equal deposits are made in an account at equal time intervals.

Mid-Chapter Quiz for Chapter 10

1. $a_1 = 32\left(\dfrac{1}{4}\right)^{1-1} = 32$

$a_2 = 32\left(\dfrac{1}{4}\right)^{2-1} = 8$

$a_3 = 32\left(\dfrac{1}{4}\right)^{3-1} = 2$

$a_4 = 32\left(\dfrac{1}{4}\right)^{4-1} = \dfrac{1}{2}$

$a_5 = 32\left(\dfrac{1}{4}\right)^{5-1} = \dfrac{1}{8}$

2. $a_1 = \dfrac{(-3)^1 \cdot 1}{1 + 4} = -\dfrac{3}{5}$

$a_2 = \dfrac{(-3)^2 \cdot 2}{2 + 4} = 3$

$a_3 = \dfrac{(-3)^3 \cdot 3}{3 + 4} = -\dfrac{81}{7}$

$a_4 = \dfrac{(-3)^4 \cdot 4}{4 + 4} = \dfrac{81}{2}$

$a_5 = \dfrac{(-3)^5 \cdot 5}{5 + 4} = -135$

3. $\displaystyle\sum_{k=1}^{4} 10k = 4\left(\dfrac{10 + 40}{2}\right) = 100$

4. $\displaystyle\sum_{i=1}^{10} 4 = 10\left(\dfrac{4 + 4}{2}\right) = 40$

5. $\sum_{j=1}^{5}\frac{60}{j+1} = \frac{60}{2} + \frac{60}{3} + \frac{60}{4} + \frac{60}{5} + \frac{60}{6}$

$= 30 + 20 + 15 + 12 + 10$

$= 87$

6. $\sum_{n=1}^{8}8\left(-\frac{1}{2}\right) = 8(-4) = -32$

7. $\sum_{k=1}^{20}\frac{2}{3k}$

8. $\sum_{k=1}^{25}\frac{(-1)^{k-1}}{k^3}$

9. $d = \frac{1}{2}$

10. $d = -6$

11. $r = \frac{6}{2} = 3$

12. $r = \frac{1}{2}$

13. $a_n = a_1 + (n-1)d$ $\qquad a_n = 20 + (n-1)(-3)$

$11 = 20 + (4-1)d$ $\qquad a_n = 20 - 3n + 3$

$-9 = 3d$ $\qquad\qquad\quad a_n = -3n + 23$

$-3 = d$

14. $a_n = a_1r^{n-1}$

$a_n = 32\left(-\frac{1}{4}\right)^{n-1}$

15. $\sum_{n=1}^{50}(3n+5) = 50\left(\frac{8+155}{2}\right)$

$= 4075$

16. $\sum_{n=1}^{300}\frac{n}{5} = 300\left(\frac{\frac{1}{5}+60}{2}\right)$

$= 9030$

17. $\sum_{i=1}^{8}9\left(\frac{2}{3}\right)^{i-1} = 9\left(\frac{\left(\frac{2}{3}\right)^8 - 1}{\frac{2}{3} - 1}\right)$

$= 9\left(\frac{\frac{256}{6561} - 1}{-\frac{1}{3}}\right)$

$= 9\left(\frac{-.96098}{-.33\overline{3}}\right)$

≈ 25.947

18. $\sum_{j=1}^{20}500(1.06)^{j-1} = 500\left(\frac{1.06^{20} - 1}{1.06 - 1}\right)$

$= 500\left(\frac{2.2071}{.06}\right)$

$\approx 18{,}392.796$

19. $\sum_{i=0}^{\infty}3\left(\frac{2}{3}\right)^i = 3\left(\frac{1}{1-\frac{2}{3}}\right)$

$= 3(3) = 9$

20. $\sum_{i=0}^{\infty}\frac{4}{5}\left(\frac{1}{4}\right)^i$

$= \frac{4}{5}\left(\frac{1}{1-\frac{1}{4}}\right)$

$= \frac{4}{5}\left(\frac{4}{3}\right) = \frac{16}{15}$

21. Geometric sequence with $a_1 = 625$ and $r = -.4$.

$a_n = a_1r^{n-1}$

$a_n = 625(-.4)^{n-1}$

$a_{12} = 625(-.4)^{12-1}$

≈ -0.026

22. $a_n = 10\left(\frac{1}{2}\right)^{n-1} \Rightarrow$ upper graph

$b_n = 10\left(-\frac{1}{2}\right)^{n-1} \Rightarrow$ lower graph

23. Sequence $= 25.75,\ 23.5,\ 21.25,\ 19, \ldots$

arithmetic with $a_1 = 25.75$, $d = -2.25$

$a_n = 25.75 + (n-1)(-2.25)$

$a_n = 25.75 + (10-1)(-2.25)$

$a_{10} = 5.5°$

24. $b_n = \ln a_n$ is arithmetic.

Section 10.4   The Binomial Theorem

1. $_6C_4 = {_6C_2} = \dfrac{6 \cdot 5}{2 \cdot 1} = 15$

3. $_{10}C_5 = \dfrac{10 \cdot 9 \cdot 8 \cdot 7 \cdot 6}{5 \cdot 4 \cdot 3 \cdot 2 \cdot 1} = 252$

5. $_{20}C_{20} = 1$

7. $_{18}C_{18} = 1$

9. $_{50}C_{48} = {_{50}C_2} = \dfrac{50 \cdot 49}{2 \cdot 1} = 1225$

11. $_{25}C_4 = \dfrac{25 \cdot 24 \cdot 23 \cdot 22}{4 \cdot 3 \cdot 2 \cdot 1} = 12{,}650$

13. *Keystrokes:*

30 [MATH] [PRB 3] 6 [ENTER] $_{30}C_6 = 593{,}775$

15. *Keystrokes:*

12 [MATH] [PRB 3] 7 [ENTER] $_{12}C_7 = 792$

17. *Keystrokes:*

52 [MATH] [PRB 3] 5 [ENTER] $_{52}C_5 = 2{,}598{,}960$

19. *Keystrokes:*

200 [MATH] [PRB 3] 195 [ENTER] $_{200}C_{195} = 2{,}535{,}650{,}040$

21. *Keystrokes:*

25 [MATH] [PRB 3] 12 [ENTER] $_{25}C_{12} = 5{,}200{,}300$

23. $_6C_2 = 15$

Row 6: 1 6 15 20 15 6 1

entry 2

25. $_7C_3 = 35$

Row 7: 1 7 21 35 35 21 7 1

entry 3

27. $_8C_4 = 70$

Row 8: 1 8 28 56 70 56 28 8 1

entry 4

29. $(a + 2)^3 = (1)a^3 + (3)a^2(2) + (3)a(2^2) + 1(2^3)$

$= a^3 + 6a^2 + 12a + 8$

31. $(x + y)^8 = 1x^8 + 8x^7y + 28x^6y^2 + 56x^5y^3 + 70x^4y^4 + 56x^3y^5 + 28x^2y^6 + 8xy^7 + 1y^8$

33. $(2x - 1)^5 = 1(2x)^5 + 5(2x)^4(-1) + 10(2x)^3(-1)^2 + 10(2x)^2(-1)^3 + 5(2x)(-1)^4 + (-1)^5$

$= 32x^5 - 80x^4 + 80x^3 - 40x^2 + 10x - 1$

35. $(2y + z)^6 = (1)(2y)^6 + 6(2y)^5z + 15(2y)^4z^2 + 20(2y)^3z^3 + 15(2y)^2z^4 + 6(2y)z^5 + 1z^6$

$= 64y^6 + 192y^5z + 240y^4z^2 + 160y^3z^3 + 60y^2z^4 + 12yz^5 + z^6$

37. $(x^2 + 2)^4 = 1(x^2)^4 + 4(x^2)^3(2) + 6(x^2)^2(2)^2 + 4(x^2)(2)^3 + 1(2)^4$

$= x^8 + 8x^6 + 24x^4 + 32x^2 + 16$

39. $(x + 3)^6 = 1x^6 + 6x^5(3) + 15x^4(3)^2 + 20x^3(3)^3 + 15x^2(3)^4 + 6x(3)^5 + 1(3)^6$

$= x^6 + 18x^5 + 135x^4 + 540x^3 + 1215x^2 + 1458x + 729$

41. $(x - 4)^6 = (1)x^6 - (6)x^5(4) + (15)x^4(4^2) - (20)x^3(4^3) + (15)x^2(4^4) - (6)x(4^5) + (1)4^6$

$= x^6 - 24x^5 + 240x^4 - 1280x^3 + 3840x^2 - 6144x + 4096$

43. $(x + y)^4 = 1x^4 + 4x^3y + 6x^2y^2 + 4xy^3 + 1y^4$

45. $(u - 2v)^3 = 1u^3 - 3u^2(2v) + 3u(2v)^2 - 1(2v)^3$

$= u^3 - 6u^2v + 12uv - 8v^3$

47. $(3a + 2b)^4 = 1(3a)^4 + 4(3a)^3(2b) + 6(3a)^2(2b)^2 + 4(3a)(2b)^3 + 1(2b)^4$

$\qquad = 81a^4 + 216a^3b + 216a^2b^2 + 96ab^3 + 16b^4$

49. $(2x^2 - y)^5 = 1(2x^2)^5 + 5(2x^2)^4(-y) + 10(2x^2)^3(-y)^2 + 10(2x^2)^2(-y)^3 + 5(2x^2)(-y)^4 + 1(-y)^5$

$\qquad = 32x^{10} - 80x^8y + 80x^6y^2 - 40x^4y^3 + 10x^2y^4 - y^5$

51. ${}_nC_r x^{n-r}y^r$

$n = 10, \quad n - r = 7, \quad r = 3, \quad x = x, \quad y = 1$

${}_{10}C_3 x^7 1^3$

${}_{10}C_3 = \dfrac{10 \cdot 9 \cdot 8}{3 \cdot 2 \cdot 1} = 120$

53. ${}_nC_r x^{n-r}y^r$

$n = 15, \quad n - r = 4, \quad r = 11, \quad x = x, \quad y = (-y)$

${}_{15}C_{11} x^4 (-y)^{11} = -{}_{15}C_{11} x^4 y^{11}$

$-{}_{15}C_{11} = -{}_{15}C_4 = -\dfrac{15 \cdot 14 \cdot 13 \cdot 12}{4 \cdot 3 \cdot 2 \cdot 1} = -1365$

55. ${}_nC_r x^{n-r}y^r$

$n = 12, \quad n - r = 3, \quad r = 9, \quad x = 2x, \quad y = y$

${}_{12}C_9 (2x)^3 y^9$

${}_{12}C_9 = {}_{12}C_3 = \dfrac{12 \cdot 11 \cdot 10}{3 \cdot 2 \cdot 1} = 220$

$(2)^3 {}_{12}C_9 = 8(220) = 1760$

57. ${}_nC_r x^{n-r}y^r$

$n = 4, \quad n - r = 2, \quad r = 2, \quad x = x^2, \quad y = (-3)$

${}_4C_2 (x^2)^2 (-3)^2$

${}_4C_2 = \dfrac{4 \cdot 3}{(2 \cdot 1)} = 6$

$(-3)^2 {}_4C_2 = 9(6) = 54$

59. ${}_nC_r x^{n-r}y^r$

$n = 8, \quad n - r = 4, \quad r = 4, \quad x = \sqrt{x}, \quad y = 1$

${}_8C_4 (\sqrt{x})^4 (1)$

${}_8C_4 = \dfrac{8 \cdot 7 \cdot 6 \cdot 5}{4 \cdot 3 \cdot 2 \cdot 1} = 70$

61. $(1.02)^8 = (1 + 0.02)^8$

$\qquad = (1)^8 + 8(1)^7(0.02) + 28(1)^6(0.02)^2 + 56(1)^5(0.02)^3 + \cdots$

$\qquad \approx 1 + 0.16 + 0.0112 + 0.000448$

$\qquad \approx 1.172$

63. $(2.99)^{12} = (3 - 0.01)^{12}$

$\qquad = 1(3)^{12} - 12(3)^{11}(0.01) + 66(3)^{10}(0.01)^2 - 220(3)^9(0.01)^3 + 495(3)^8(0.01)^4 - 792(3)^7(0.01)^5 + \cdots$

$\qquad \approx 531{,}441 - 21{,}257.64 + 389.7234 - 4.33026 + 0.03247695 - 0.0001732104$

$\qquad \approx 510{,}568.785$

65. $\left(\dfrac{1}{2} + \dfrac{1}{2}\right)^5 = 1\left(\dfrac{1}{2}\right)^5 + 5\left(\dfrac{1}{2}\right)^4\left(\dfrac{1}{2}\right) + 10\left(\dfrac{1}{2}\right)^3\left(\dfrac{1}{2}\right)^2 + 10\left(\dfrac{1}{2}\right)^2\left(\dfrac{1}{2}\right)^3 + 5\left(\dfrac{1}{2}\right)\left(\dfrac{1}{2}\right)^4 + 1\left(\dfrac{1}{2}\right)^5$

$\qquad = \dfrac{1}{32} + \dfrac{5}{32} + \dfrac{10}{32} + \dfrac{10}{32} + \dfrac{5}{32} + \dfrac{1}{32}$

67. $\left(\dfrac{1}{4} + \dfrac{3}{4}\right)^4 = 1\left(\dfrac{1}{4}\right)^4 + 4\left(\dfrac{1}{4}\right)^3\left(\dfrac{3}{4}\right) + 6\left(\dfrac{1}{4}\right)^2\left(\dfrac{3}{4}\right)^2 + 4\left(\dfrac{1}{4}\right)\left(\dfrac{3}{4}\right)^3 + 1\left(\dfrac{3}{4}\right)^4$

$\qquad = \dfrac{1}{256} + \dfrac{12}{256} + \dfrac{54}{256} + \dfrac{108}{256} + \dfrac{81}{256}$

69. The difference between consecutive entries increases by 1.
2, 3, 4, 5

71. There are $n + 1$ terms in the expansion of $(x + y)^n$.

73. The signs in the expansion of $(x + y)^n$ are all positive.
The signs in the expansion of $(x - y)^n$ alternate.

75. $_nC_r = {_nC_{n-r}}$

Section 10.5   Counting Principles

1. $\{0, 2, 4, 6, 8\}$ 5 ways

3.

First number	Second number
1	9
2	8
3	7
4	6
5	5
6	4
7	3
8	2
9	1

9 ways

5.

First number	Second number
1	9
2	8
3	7
4	6
6	4
7	3
8	2
9	1

8 ways

7. $\{1, 3, 5, 7, 9, 11, 13, 15, 17, 19\}$ 10 ways

9. $\{2, 3, 5, 7, 11, 13, 17, 19\}$ 8 ways

11. $\{3, 6, 9, 12, 15, 18\}$ 6 ways

13.

First number	Second number
1	7
2	6
3	5
4	4
5	3
6	2
7	1

7 ways

15.

First number	Second number
1	7
2	6
3	5
5	3
6	2
7	1

6 ways

17. $3 \cdot 2 = 6$ ways

19. label = letter   number
$\qquad\qquad 26 \quad \cdot \quad 10 \quad = 260$ labels

21. plate = digit   digit   digit   digit   letter   letter
$\qquad\qquad 10 \quad \cdot 10 \quad \cdot 10 \quad \cdot 10 \quad \cdot 26 \quad \cdot 26 \quad = 6{,}760{,}000$ plates

23. (a) $9 \cdot 10 \cdot 10 = 900$ numbers   (b) $10 \cdot 9 \cdot 8 = 720$ numbers   (c) $4 \cdot 10 \cdot 10 = 400$ numbers

25. $3 \cdot 3 \cdot 2 \cdot 1 = 18$ ways   **27.** $3 \cdot 2 \cdot 1 \cdot 5 \cdot 4 \cdot 3 \cdot 2 \cdot 1 = 720$ ways

29. A, B, C, D; A, B, D, C; A, C, B, D; A, C, D, B; A, D, B, C; A, D, C, B;

B, A, C, D; B, A, D, C; B, C, A, D; B, C, D, A; B, D, A, C; B, D, C, A;

C, A, B, D; C, A, D, B; C, B, A, D; C, B, D, A; C, D, A, B; C, D, B, A;

D, A, B, C; D, A, C, B; D, B, A, C; D, B, C, A; D, C, A, B; D, C, B, A

31.
AB	BA
AC	CA
AD	DA
BC	CB
BD	DB
CD	DC

33. $6! = 6 \cdot 5 \cdot 4 \cdot 3 \cdot 2 \cdot 1 = 720$ ways

35. $40 \cdot 40 \cdot 40 = 64{,}000$ ways   **37.** $8! = 40{,}320$ ways   **39.** $_{10}P_4 = 10 \cdot 9 \cdot 8 \cdot 7 = 5040$

41. $_6C_2 = \dfrac{6!}{4! \, 2!} = \dfrac{6 \cdot 5}{2 \cdot 1} = 15$ subsets

{A, B}, {A, C}, {A, D}, {A, E}, {A, F}, {B, C},
{B, D}, {B, E}, {B, F}, {C, D}, {C, E}, {C, F},
{D, E}, {D, F}, {E, F}

43. $_{20}C_3 = \dfrac{20!}{17! \, 3!} = \dfrac{20 \cdot 19 \cdot 18}{3 \cdot 2 \cdot 1} = 1140$ ways

45. $_9C_4 = \dfrac{9!}{5! \, 4!} = \dfrac{9 \cdot 8 \cdot 7 \cdot 6}{4 \cdot 3 \cdot 2 \cdot 1}$
$= 126$ ways

47. $_{12}C_9 = \dfrac{12!}{3! \, 9!} = \dfrac{12 \cdot 11 \cdot 10}{3 \cdot 2 \cdot 1}$
$= 220$ ways

49. $_{15}C_5 = \dfrac{15!}{5! \, 10!}$
$= 3003$ ways

51. (a) $_6C_4 = \dfrac{6!}{2! \, 4!} = \dfrac{6 \cdot 5}{2 \cdot 1}$
$= 15$ ways

(b) $_4C_2 = \dfrac{4!}{2! \, 2!} = \dfrac{4 \cdot 3}{2 \cdot 1} = 6$

$_2C_2 = \dfrac{2!}{0! \, 2!} = 1$

$_4C_2 \cdot {_2C_2} = 6 \cdot 1$
$= 6$ ways

53. (a) $_8C_4 = \dfrac{8!}{4! \, 4!} = \dfrac{8 \cdot 7 \cdot 6 \cdot 5}{4 \cdot 3 \cdot 2 \cdot 1} = 70$

(b) $_2C_1 \cdot {_2C_1} \cdot {_2C_1} \cdot {_2C_1} = 2 \cdot 2 \cdot 2 \cdot 2 = 16$

55. $_7C_2 = \dfrac{7!}{5! \, 2!} = \dfrac{7 \cdot 6}{2 \cdot 1} = 21$

57. Diagonals of Hexagon $= {_6C_4} - {_6C_1} = 9$

59. Diagonals of Decagon $= {_{10}C_8} - {_{10}C_1} = 35$

61. The Fundamental Counting Principle: Let E_1 and E_2 be two events that can occur in m_1 ways and m_2 ways, respectively. The number of ways the two events can occur is $m_1 \cdot m_2$.

63. Permutation: The ordering of five students for a picture.

Combination: The selection of three students from a group of five students for a class project.

Section 10.6   Probability

1. {a, b, c, d, e, f, g, h, i, j, k, l, m, n, o, p, q, r, s, t, u, v, w, x, y, z}

number of outcomes = 26

3. {AB, AC, AD, AE, BC, BD, BE, CD, CE, DE}

number of outcomes = 10

5. {ABC, ACB, BAC, BCA, CAB, CBA}

7. {WWW, WWL, WLW, WLL, LWW, LWL, LLW, LLL}

9. $1 - 0.35 = 0.65$

11. $P(E) = 1 - p = 1 - 0.82 = 0.18$

13. $P(E) = \frac{n(E)}{n(S)} = \frac{3}{8}$

15. $P(E) = \frac{n(E)}{n(S)} = \frac{7}{8}$

17. $P(E) = \frac{n(E)}{n(S)} = \frac{26}{52} = \frac{1}{2}$

19. $P(E) = \frac{n(E)}{n(S)} = \frac{12}{52} = \frac{3}{13}$

21. $P(E) = \frac{n(E)}{n(S)} = \frac{1}{6}$

23. $P(E) = \frac{n(E)}{n(S)} = \frac{5}{6}$

25. $P(E) = 1 - \frac{n(F)}{n(S)} = 1 - \frac{1}{10} = \frac{9}{10}$

(*F* is event that person does have type *B*.)

27. $P(E) = \frac{n(E)}{n(S)} = \frac{24.3}{100} = 0.243$

29. $P(E) = \frac{n(E)}{n(S)} = \frac{60.9}{100} = 0.609$

31. (a) $P(E) = \frac{n(E)}{n(S)} = \frac{1}{5}$

(b) $P(E) = \frac{n(E)}{n(S)} = \frac{1}{3}$

(c) $P(E) = \frac{n(E)}{n(S)} = 1$

33. (a) $P(\text{candidate } A \text{ or candidate } B) = 0.5 + 0.3 = 0.8$

(b) $P(\text{Candidate } 3) = 1 - 0.5 - 0.3 = 0.2$

35. $P(E) = \frac{n(E)}{n(S)} = \frac{70}{325} = \frac{14}{65}$

37. (a) $P(E) = \frac{n(E)}{n(S)} = \frac{57,510,000}{196,950,000} = \frac{1917}{6565}$

(b) $P(E) = \frac{n(E)}{n(S)} = \frac{139,440,000}{196,950,000} = \frac{4648}{6565}$

39. $P(E) = \frac{n(E)}{n(S)} = \frac{45^2}{60^2} = \frac{2025}{3600} = 0.5625$

(*E* is the probability that they do not meet.)

$1 - P(E) = 1 - 0.5625 = 0.4375$

41. (a)

	Female	
	X	X
X	XX	XX
Y	XY	XY

(Male on left side; Female on top)

Probability of a girl $= \frac{2}{4} = \frac{1}{2}$

Probability of a boy $= \frac{2}{4} = \frac{1}{2}$

(b) Because the probabilities are the same, it is equally likely that a newborn will be a boy or a girl.

43. $P(E) = \dfrac{n(E)}{n(S)} = \dfrac{1}{1 \cdot 4 \cdot 3 \cdot 2 \cdot 1} = \dfrac{1}{24}$

45. $P(E) = \dfrac{n(E)}{n(S)} = \dfrac{1}{10 \cdot 10 \cdot 10 \cdot 10 \cdot 10} = \dfrac{1}{100,000}$

47. $P(E) = \dfrac{n(E)}{n(S)} = \dfrac{1}{{}_{10}C_8} = \dfrac{1}{45}$

49. $P(E) = \dfrac{n(E)}{n(S)} = \dfrac{1}{{}_{10}C_2} = \dfrac{1}{\frac{10}{8!\,2!}} = \dfrac{1}{\frac{10 \cdot 9}{2 \cdot 1}} = \dfrac{1}{45}$

51. $P(E) = \dfrac{n(E)}{n(S)} = \dfrac{{}_4C_4}{{}_{10}C_4} = \dfrac{1}{\frac{10!}{6!\,4!}} = \dfrac{1}{\frac{10 \cdot 9 \cdot 8 \cdot 7}{4 \cdot 3 \cdot 2 \cdot 1}} = \dfrac{1}{210}$

53. $P(E) = \dfrac{n(E)}{n(S)} = \dfrac{{}_{13}C_5}{{}_{52}C_5} = \dfrac{\frac{13!}{8!\,5!}}{\frac{52!}{47!\,5!}} = \dfrac{\frac{13 \cdot 12 \cdot 11 \cdot 10 \cdot 9}{5 \cdot 4 \cdot 3 \cdot 2 \cdot 1}}{\frac{52 \cdot 51 \cdot 50 \cdot 49 \cdot 48}{5 \cdot 4 \cdot 3 \cdot 2 \cdot 1}} = \dfrac{13 \cdot 11 \cdot 9}{52 \cdot 51 \cdot 5 \cdot 49 \cdot 4} = \dfrac{11 \cdot 3}{4 \cdot 17 \cdot 5 \cdot 49 \cdot 4} = \dfrac{33}{66,640}$

55. (d) $8 \cdot 5 \cdot 3 = 120$

(e) The drawing will be done without replacement since each person receives only one gift.

(f) (a) $P(E) = \dfrac{n(E)}{n(S)} = \dfrac{1}{150}$

(b) $P(E) = \dfrac{n(E)}{n(S)} = \dfrac{1}{105}$

57. The probability that the event does not occur is $1 - \frac{3}{4} = \frac{1}{4}$.

59. Over an extended period, it will rain 40% of the time under the given weather conditions.

Review Exercises for Chapter 10

1. $a_1 = 3(1) + 5 = 8$

$a_2 = 3(2) + 5 = 11$

$a_3 = 3(3) + 5 = 14$

$a_4 = 3(4) + 5 = 17$

$a_5 = 3(5) + 5 = 20$

3. $a_1 = \dfrac{1}{2^1} + \dfrac{1}{2} = 1$

$a_2 = \dfrac{1}{2^2} + \dfrac{1}{2} = \dfrac{3}{4}$

$a_3 = \dfrac{1}{2^3} + \dfrac{1}{2} = \dfrac{1}{8} + \dfrac{4}{8} = \dfrac{5}{8}$

$a_4 = \dfrac{1}{2^4} + \dfrac{1}{2} = \dfrac{1}{16} + \dfrac{8}{16} = \dfrac{9}{16}$

$a_5 = \dfrac{1}{2^5} + \dfrac{1}{2} = \dfrac{1}{32} + \dfrac{16}{32} = \dfrac{17}{32}$

5. $a_n = 2n - 1$

7. $a_n = \dfrac{n}{(n + 1)^2}$

9. (a)

11. (b)

13. (d)

15. $\displaystyle\sum_{k=1}^{4} 7 = 7 + 7 + 7 + 7 = 28$

17. $\displaystyle\sum_{n=1}^{4} \left(\frac{1}{n} - \frac{1}{n+1}\right) = \frac{1}{2} + \frac{1}{6} + \frac{1}{12} + \frac{1}{20} = \frac{30 + 10 + 5 + 3}{60} = \frac{48}{60} = \frac{4}{5}$

19. $\displaystyle\sum_{n=1}^{4} (5n - 3)$

21. $\displaystyle\sum_{n=1}^{6} \frac{1}{3n}$

23. $d = -2.5$

25. $a_1 = 132 - 5(1) = 127$
$a_2 = 132 - 5(2) = 122$
$a_3 = 132 - 5(3) = 117$
$a_4 = 132 - 5(4) = 112$
$a_5 = 132 - 5(5) = 107$

27. $a_1 = \frac{3}{4}(1) + \frac{1}{2} = \frac{5}{4}$
$a_2 = \frac{3}{4}(2) + \frac{1}{2} = 2$
$a_3 = \frac{3}{4}(3) + \frac{1}{2} = \frac{11}{4}$
$a_4 = \frac{3}{4}(4) + \frac{1}{2} = \frac{7}{2}$
$a_5 = \frac{3}{4}(5) + \frac{1}{2} = \frac{17}{4}$

29. $a_1 = 5$
$a_2 = 5 + 3 = 8$
$a_3 = 8 + 3 = 11$
$a_4 = 11 + 3 = 14$
$a_5 = 14 + 3 = 17$

31. $a_1 = 80$
$a_2 = 80 - \frac{5}{2} = \frac{160}{2} - \frac{5}{2} = \frac{155}{2}$
$a_3 = \frac{155}{2} - \frac{5}{2} = \frac{150}{2} = 75$
$a_4 = \frac{150}{2} - \frac{5}{2} = \frac{145}{2}$
$a_5 = \frac{145}{2} - \frac{5}{2} = \frac{140}{2} = 70$

33. $a_n = dn + c$
$10 = 4(1) + c$
$6 = c$
$a_n = 4n + 6$

35. $a_n = dn + c$
$1000 = -50(1) + c$
$1050 = c$
$a_n = -50n + 1050$

37. $\displaystyle\sum_{k=1}^{12} (7k - 5) = 12\left(\frac{2 + 79}{2}\right) = 486$

39. $\displaystyle\sum_{j=1}^{100} \frac{j}{4} = 100\left(\frac{\frac{1}{4} + 25}{2}\right) = 1262.5$

41. *Keystrokes:*

[LIST] [MATH 5] [LIST] [OPS 5] 1.25 [X,T,θ] [+] 4 [,] [X,T,θ] [,] 1 [,] 60 [,] 1 [)] [ENTER]

$\displaystyle\sum_{i=1}^{60} (125i + 4) = 2527.5$

43. $r = \frac{3}{2}$

45. $a_n = a_1 r^{n-1}$
$a_n = 10(3)^{n-1}$
$a_1 = 10(3)^{1-1} = 10$
$a_2 = 10(3)^{2-1} = 30$
$a_3 = 10(3)^{3-1} = 90$
$a_4 = 10(3)^{4-1} = 270$
$a_5 = 10(3)^{5-1} = 810$

47. $a_n = a_1 r^{n-1}$

$a_n = 100\left(-\frac{1}{2}\right)^{n-1}$

$a_1 = 100\left(-\frac{1}{2}\right)^{1-1} = 100$

$a_2 = 100\left(-\frac{1}{2}\right)^{2-1} = -50$

$a_3 = 100\left(-\frac{1}{2}\right)^{3-1} = 25$

$a_4 = 100\left(-\frac{1}{2}\right)^{4-1} = -12.5$

$a_5 = 100\left(-\frac{1}{2}\right)^{5-1} = 6.25$

49. $a_1 = 3$

$a_2 = 2(3) = 6$

$a_3 = 2(6) = 12$

$a_4 = 2(12) = 24$

$a_5 = 2(24) = 48$

51. $a_n = a_1 r^{n-1}$

$a_n = 1\left(-\frac{2}{3}\right)^{n-1}$

53. $a_n = a_1 r^{n-1}$

$a_n = 24(2)^{n-1}$

55. $a_n = a_1 r^{n-1}$

$a_n = 12\left(-\frac{1}{2}\right)^{n-1}$

57. $\displaystyle\sum_{n=1}^{12} 2^n = 2\left(\frac{2^{12}-1}{2-1}\right) = 8190$

59. $\displaystyle\sum_{k=1}^{8} 5\left(-\frac{3}{4}\right)^k = -\frac{15}{4}\left(\frac{\left(-\frac{3}{4}\right)^8 - 1}{-\frac{3}{4} - 1}\right) \approx -1.928$

61. $\displaystyle\sum_{i=1}^{8} (1.25)^{i-1} = 1\left(\frac{1.25^8 - 1}{1.25 - 1}\right) \approx 19.842$

63. $\displaystyle\sum_{n=1}^{120} 500(1.01)^n = 505\left(\frac{1.01^{120} - 1}{1.01 - 1}\right) \approx 116{,}169.54$

65. $\displaystyle\sum_{i=1}^{\infty} \left(\frac{7}{8}\right)^{i-1} = \frac{1}{1 - \frac{7}{8}} = \frac{1}{\frac{1}{8}} = 8$

67. $\displaystyle\sum_{k=1}^{\infty} 4\left(\frac{2}{3}\right)^{k-1} = \frac{4}{1 - \frac{2}{3}} = \frac{4}{\frac{1}{3}} = 12$

69. *Keystrokes:*

$\boxed{\text{LIST}}$ $\boxed{\text{MATH 5}}$ $\boxed{\text{LIST}}$ $\boxed{\text{OPS 5}}$ 50 $\boxed{(}$ 1.2 $\boxed{)}$ $\boxed{\wedge}$ $\boxed{(}$ $\boxed{\text{X,T,}\theta}$ $\boxed{-}$ 1 $\boxed{)}$ $\boxed{,}$ $\boxed{\text{X,T,}\theta}$ $\boxed{,}$ 1 $\boxed{,}$ 50 $\boxed{,}$ 1 $\boxed{)}$ $\boxed{\text{ENTER}}$

$\displaystyle\sum_{k=1}^{50} 50(1.2)^{k-1} \approx 2.275 \times 10^6$

71. $_8C_3 = \dfrac{8!}{3!\,5!} = \dfrac{8 \cdot 7 \cdot 6 \cdot 5!}{3 \cdot 2 \cdot 5!} = 56$

73. $_{12}C_0 = 1$

75. *Keystrokes:*

40 $\boxed{\text{MATH}}$ $\boxed{\text{PRB 3}}$ 4 $\boxed{\text{ENTER}}$ $_{40}C_4 = 91{,}390$

77. *Keystrokes:*

25 $\boxed{\text{MATH}}$ $\boxed{\text{PRB 3}}$ 6 $\boxed{\text{ENTER}}$ $_{25}C_6 = 177{,}100$

79. $(x + 1)^{10} = 1x^{10} + 10x^9(1) + 45x^8(1)^2 + 120x^7(1)^3 + 210x^6(1)^4 + 252x^5(1)^5 + 210x^4(1)^6 + 120x^3(1)^7 + 45x^2(1)^8$

$\qquad + 10x(1)^9 + 1(1)^{10}$

$\qquad = x^{10} + 10x^9 + 45x^8 + 120x^7 + 210x^6 + 252x^5 + 210x^4 + 120x^3 + 45x^2 + 10x + 1$

81. $(3x - 2y)^4 = 1(3x)^4 + 4(3x)^3(-2y) + 6(3x)^2(-2y)^2 + 4(3x)(-2y)^3 + (-2y)^4$

$\qquad = 81x^4 - 216x^3y + 216x^2y^2 - 96xy^3 + 16y^4$

83. $(u^2 + v^3)^9 = 1(u^2)^9 + 9(u^2)^8(v^3) + 36(u^2)^7(v^3)^2 + 84(u^2)^6(v^3)^3 + 126(u^2)^5(v^3)^4 + 126(u^2)^4(v^3)^5 + 84(u^2)^3(v^3)^6 + 36(u^2)^2(v^3)^7$

$\qquad + 9(u^2)(v^3)^8 + (v^3)^9$

$\qquad = u^{18} + 9u^{16}v^3 + 36u^{14}v^6 + 84u^{12}v^9 + 126u^{10}v^{12} + 126u^8v^{15} + 84u^6v^{18} + 36u^4v^{21} + 9u^2v^{24} + v^{27}$

85. $_nC_r x^{n-r} y^r$

$\quad n = 10, \quad n - r = 5, \quad r = 5, \quad x = 3, \quad y = (-3)$

$\quad _{10}C_5 = 252 \cdot (-3)^5 = -61{,}236$

87. $_nC_r x^{n-r} y^r$

$\quad n = 7, \quad r = 3, \quad n - r = 4, \quad x = x, \quad y = (2y)$

$\quad _7C_3(2)^3 = 35 \cdot 8 = 280$

89. $\displaystyle\sum_{n=1}^{50} 4n = 50\left(\frac{4 + 200}{2}\right) = 5100$

91. $\displaystyle\sum_{n=1}^{12} (3n + 19) = 12\left(\frac{22 + 55}{2}\right) = 462$

93. (a) $a_n = 85{,}000(1.012)^n$

$\quad$ (b) $a_{50} = 85{,}000(1.012)^{50}$

$\qquad\qquad \approx 154{,}328$

95. $2 \cdot 2 \cdot 2 = 8$

97. $_{15}C_5 = \dfrac{15 \cdot 14 \cdot 13 \cdot 12 \cdot 11}{5 \cdot 4 \cdot 3 \cdot 2 \cdot 1}$

$\qquad\qquad = 3003$

99. $P(E) = \dfrac{n(E)}{n(S)} = \dfrac{2}{6} = \dfrac{1}{3}$

101. $P(E) = \dfrac{n(E)}{n(S)} = \dfrac{1}{4 \cdot 3 \cdot 2 \cdot 1} = \dfrac{1}{24}$

103. $P(E) = \dfrac{n(E)}{n(S)} = \dfrac{_{74}C_8}{_{84}C_8} \approx 0.346$

Chapter Test for Chapter 10

1. $a_n = \left(-\frac{2}{3}\right)^{n-1}$

$\quad a_1 = \left(-\frac{2}{3}\right)^{1-1} = 1$

$\quad a_2 = \left(-\frac{2}{3}\right)^{2-1} = -\frac{2}{3}$

$\quad a_3 = \left(-\frac{2}{3}\right)^{3-1} = \frac{4}{9}$

$\quad a_4 = \left(-\frac{2}{3}\right)^{4-1} = -\frac{8}{27}$

$\quad a_5 = \left(-\frac{2}{3}\right)^{5-1} = \frac{16}{81}$

2. $\displaystyle\sum_{j=0}^{4} (3j + 1) = 1 + 4 + 7 + 10 + 13 = 35$

3. $\displaystyle\sum_{n=1}^{5} (3 - 4n) = 5\left(\frac{-1 + -17}{2}\right) = -45$

4. $\displaystyle\sum_{n=1}^{12} \frac{2}{3n + 1}$

5. $a_n = a_1 + (n - 1)d$

$\quad a_n = 12 + (n - 1)4$

$\qquad = 12 + 4n - 4 = 4n + 8$

$\quad a_1 = 4(1) + 8 = 12$

$\quad a_2 = 4(2) + 8 = 16$

$\quad a_3 = 4(3) + 8 = 20$

$\quad a_4 = 4(4) + 8 = 24$

$\quad a_5 = 4(5) + 8 = 28$

6. $a_n = a_1 + (n - 1)d$

$\quad a_n = 5000 + (n - 1)(-100)$

$\quad a_n = 5000 - 100n + 100$

$\quad a_n = -100n + 5100$

7. $\displaystyle\sum_{n=1}^{50} = 50\left(\frac{3 + 150}{2}\right) = 3825$

8. $r = -\dfrac{3}{2}$

9. $a_n = a_1 r^{n-1}$

$\quad a_n = 4\left(\dfrac{1}{2}\right)^{n-1}$

10. $\displaystyle\sum_{n=1}^{8} 2(2^n) = 4\left(\frac{2^8 - 1}{2 - 1}\right) = 1020$

11. $\displaystyle\sum_{n=1}^{10} 3\left(\frac{1}{2}\right)^n = \frac{3}{2}\left(\frac{\frac{1}{2}^{10}-1}{\frac{1}{2}-1}\right) = \frac{3069}{1024}$

12. $\displaystyle\sum_{i=1}^{\infty}\left(\frac{1}{2}\right)^i = \frac{\frac{1}{2}}{1-\frac{1}{2}} = \frac{\frac{1}{2}}{\frac{1}{2}} = 1$

13. $\displaystyle\sum_{i=1}^{\infty} 4\left(\frac{2}{3}\right)^{i-1} = \frac{4}{1-\frac{2}{3}} = \frac{4}{\frac{1}{3}} = 12$

14. $A = P\left(1 + \dfrac{r}{n}\right)^{nt}$

$$a_{300} = \left(1 + \frac{0.08}{12}\right)^{12(25)} = 50(1.0066667)^{300}$$

$$a_1 = 50(1.0066667)^1$$

$$\text{balance} = [50(1.0066667)^1]\left[\frac{1.0066667^{300} - 1}{1.0066667 - 1}\right] = \$47{,}868.64$$

15. $_{20}C_3 = \dfrac{20 \cdot 19 \cdot 18}{3 \cdot 2 \cdot 1} = 1140$

16. $(x - 2)^5 = 1(x^5) - 5x^4(2) + 10x^3(2)^2 - 10x^2(2)^3 + 5x(2)^4 - 1(2)^5$
$$= x^5 - 10x^4 + 40x^3 - 80x^2 + 80x - 32$$

17. The coefficient of x^3y^5 in expansion of $(x + y)^8$ is 56, since $_8C_3 = 56$.

18. plates = letter   digit   digit   digit
$$= 26 \ \cdot \ 10 \ \cdot \ 10 \ \cdot \ 10 \ = 26{,}000 \text{ plates}$$

19. $_{25}C_4 = \dfrac{25!}{4!\,21!} = \dfrac{25 \cdot 24 \cdot 23 \cdot 22}{4 \cdot 3 \cdot 2 \cdot 1} = 12{,}650$

20. $1 - 0.75 = 0.25$

21. $P(E) = \dfrac{n(E)}{n(S)} = \dfrac{6}{52} = \dfrac{3}{26}$

22. $P(E) = \dfrac{n(E)}{n(S)} = \dfrac{1}{_4C_2} = \dfrac{1}{\dfrac{4!}{2!\,2!}} = \dfrac{1}{\dfrac{4 \cdot 3}{2 \cdot 1}} = \dfrac{1}{6}$

APPENDICES

Appendix A   Introduction to Graphing Utilities

Solutions to Odd-Numbered Exercises

1. *Keystrokes:*

$\boxed{Y=}$ $\boxed{(-)}$ 3 $\boxed{X,T,\theta}$ $\boxed{GRAPH}$

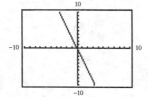

3. *Keystrokes:*

$\boxed{Y=}$ $\boxed{(}$ 3 $\boxed{\div}$ 4 $\boxed{)}$ $\boxed{X,T,\theta}$ $\boxed{-}$ 6 $\boxed{GRAPH}$

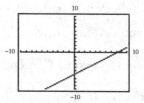

5. *Keystrokes:*

$\boxed{Y=}$ $\boxed{(}$ 1 $\boxed{\div}$ 2 $\boxed{)}$ $\boxed{X,T,\theta}$ $\boxed{x^2}$ $\boxed{GRAPH}$

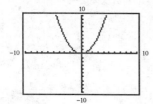

7. *Keystrokes:*

$\boxed{Y=}$ $\boxed{X,T,\theta}$ $\boxed{x^2}$ $\boxed{-}$ 4 $\boxed{X,T,\theta}$ $\boxed{+}$ 2 $\boxed{GRAPH}$

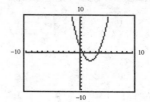

9. *Keystrokes:*

$\boxed{Y=}$ $\boxed{ABS}$ $\boxed{(}$ $\boxed{X,T,\theta}$ $\boxed{-}$ 3 $\boxed{)}$ $\boxed{GRAPH}$

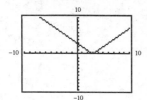

11. *Keystrokes:*

$\boxed{Y=}$ $\boxed{ABS}$ $\boxed{(}$ $\boxed{X,T,\theta}$ $\boxed{x^2}$ $\boxed{-}$ 4 $\boxed{)}$ $\boxed{GRAPH}$

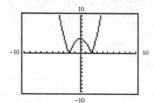

13. *Keystrokes:*

$\boxed{Y=}$ 27 $\boxed{X,T,\theta}$ $\boxed{+}$ 100 $\boxed{GRAPH}$

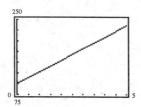

15. *Keystrokes:*

$\boxed{Y=}$ 0.001 $\boxed{X,T,\theta}$ $\boxed{x^2}$ $\boxed{+}$ 0.5 $\boxed{X,T,\theta}$ $\boxed{GRAPH}$

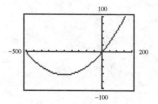

17. *Keystrokes:*

$\boxed{Y=}$ 15 $\boxed{+}$ $\boxed{ABS}$ $\boxed{(}$ $\boxed{X,T,\theta}$ $\boxed{-}$ 12 $\boxed{)}$ $\boxed{GRAPH}$

Xmin = 4
Xmax = 20
Xscl = 1
Ymin = 14
Ymax = 22
Yscl = 1

19. *Keystrokes:*

$\boxed{Y=}$ $\boxed{(-)}$ 15 $\boxed{+}$ $\boxed{ABS}$ $\boxed{(}$ $\boxed{X,T,\theta}$ $\boxed{+}$ 12 $\boxed{)}$ $\boxed{GRAPH}$

$$\begin{array}{l} \text{Xmin} = -20 \\ \text{Xmax} = -4 \\ \text{Xscl} = 1 \\ \text{Ymin} = -16 \\ \text{Ymax} = -8 \\ \text{Yscl} = 1 \end{array}$$

21. *Keystrokes:*

y_1 $\boxed{Y=}$ 2 $\boxed{X,T,\theta}$ $\boxed{+}$ $\boxed{(}$ $\boxed{X,T,\theta}$ $\boxed{+}$ 1 $\boxed{)}$ $\boxed{ENTER}$

y_2 $\boxed{(}$ 2 $\boxed{X,T,\theta}$ $\boxed{+}$ $\boxed{X,T,\theta}$ $\boxed{)}$ $\boxed{+}$ 1 $\boxed{GRAPH}$

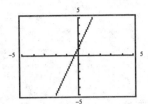

Associative Property of Addition

23. *Keystrokes:*

y_1 $\boxed{Y=}$ 2 $\boxed{(}$ 1 $\boxed{\div}$ 2 $\boxed{)}$ $\boxed{ENTER}$

y_2 1 $\boxed{GRAPH}$

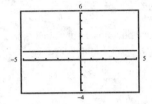

Multiplicative Inverse Property

25. *Keystrokes:*

$\boxed{Y=}$ 9 $\boxed{-}$ $\boxed{X,T,\theta}$ $\boxed{x^2}$ $\boxed{GRAPH}$

Trace to x-intercepts: $(-3, 0)$ and $(3, 0)$

Trace to y-intercept: $(0, 9)$

27. *Keystrokes:*

$\boxed{Y=}$ 6 $\boxed{-}$ $\boxed{ABS}$ $\boxed{(}$ $\boxed{X,T,\theta}$ $\boxed{+}$ 2 $\boxed{)}$ $\boxed{GRAPH}$

Trace to x-intercepts: $(-8, 0)$ and $(4, 0)$

Trace to y-intercept: $(0, 4)$

29. *Keystrokes:*

$\boxed{Y=}$ 2 $\boxed{X,T,\theta}$ $\boxed{-}$ 5 $\boxed{GRAPH}$

Trace to x-intercept: $\left(\frac{5}{2}, 0\right)$

Trace to y-intercept: $(0, -5)$

31. *Keystrokes:*

$\boxed{Y=}$ $\boxed{X,T,\theta}$ $\boxed{x^2}$ $\boxed{+}$ 1.5 $\boxed{X,T,\theta}$ $\boxed{-}$ 1 $\boxed{GRAPH}$

Trace to x-intercepts: $(-2, 0)$ and $\left(\frac{1}{2}, 0\right)$

Trace to y-intercept: $(0, -1)$

33. *Keystrokes:*

y_1 $\boxed{Y=}$ $\boxed{(-)}$ 4 $\boxed{ENTER}$

y_2 $\boxed{(-)}$ $\boxed{ABS}$ $\boxed{X,T,\theta}$ $\boxed{GRAPH}$

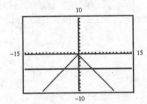

Triangle

35. *Keystrokes:*

y_1 $\boxed{Y=}$ $\boxed{ABS}$ $\boxed{X,T,\theta}$ $\boxed{-}$ 8 $\boxed{ENTER}$

y_2 $\boxed{(-)}$ $\boxed{ABS}$ $\boxed{X,T,\theta}$ $\boxed{+}$ 8 $\boxed{GRAPH}$

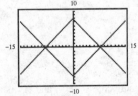

Square

37. *Keystrokes:*

y_1 $\boxed{Y=}$ 0.07 $\boxed{X,T,\theta}$ $\boxed{x^2}$ $\boxed{+}$ 1.06 $\boxed{X,T,\theta}$ $\boxed{+}$ 88.97 $\boxed{ENTER}$

y_2 0.02 $\boxed{X,T,\theta}$ $\boxed{x^2}$ $\boxed{-}$ 0.23 $\boxed{X,T,\theta}$ $\boxed{+}$ 10.70 $\boxed{GRAPH}$

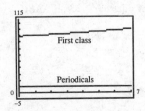

Appendix B   Further Concepts in Geometry

Appendix B.1   Exploring Congruence and Similarity

1. Answers will vary.

3.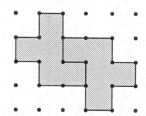

5. Two figures are similar if they have the same shape. Figures (a) and (b) are similar.

7.

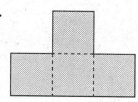

9. The grid contains 7 congruent triangles with 2-unit sides.

11. No. All the triangles in the grid are equilteral triangles, and all of these triangles have the same shape. Therefore all the triangles in the grid are similar to each other.

13. False. For example, the two squares shown below are similar, but they are not congruent.

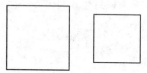

15. True. Any two squares have the same shape, so any two squares are similar.

17. The ray from P through Q is matched with notation (d).

19. The length of the segment between P and Q is matched with notation (b).

21. $\angle ZXW$ and $\angle WXZ$ are names for the same angle.

$\angle ZXY$ and $\angle YXZ$ are names for the same angle.

$\angle YXW$ and $\angle WXY$ are names for the same angle.

$\angle ZXY$ and $\angle YXW$ are adjacent angles.

23. (b) $m\angle WXY \approx 30°$

25. (d) Equiangular

A triangle with angle measures of 60°, 60°, and 60° is an equiangular triangle because all the angles are the same size.

27. (f) Right

A triangle with angle measures of 30°, 60°, and 90° is a right triangle because it contains a right angle.

29. (c) Obtuse

A triangle with angle measures of 20°, 145°, and 15° is an obtuse triangle because it contains an obtuse angle.

31. The three points of congruent sides are

$\overline{LM} \cong \overline{NO}, \overline{MP} \cong \overline{NQ},$ and $\overline{LP} \cong \overline{OQ}.$

33. If $\triangle ABC \cong \triangle TUV$, then $m\angle C = m\angle V.$

35. If $\triangle LMN \cong \triangle TUV$, then $\overline{LN} \cong \overline{TV}.$

37.

	Scalene	Isosceles	Equilateral
Acute	Yes	Yes	Yes
Obtuse	Yes	Yes	No
Right	Yes	Yes	No

(Not possible)

(Not possible)

39. $AC = BC$

   $2x + 6 = 12$

   $2x = 6$

   $x = 3$

   $BC = 12$

   $AC = 2(3) = 6 + 6 = 12$

   $AB = 4x = 4(3) = 12.$

Therefore, all three sides of the triangle are of length 12. Yes, the triangle is equilateral.

41. $AC = BC$

   $2x = 4x - 6$

   $-2x = -6$

   $x = 3$

   $AC = 2x = 2(3) = 6$

   $BC = 4x - 6 = 4(3) - 6 = 12 - 6 = 6$

   $AB = x + 3 = 3 + 3 = 6.$

Therefore, all three sides of the triangles are of length 6. Yes, the triangle is equilateral.

43. $\dfrac{1/8 \text{ inch}}{1 \text{ foot}} = \dfrac{1/(8 \cdot 12) \text{ foot}}{1 \text{ foot}} = \dfrac{1/96 \text{ foot}}{1 \text{ foot}} = \dfrac{1}{96}$

$\dfrac{1}{96} \cdot 1200 = 12.5$

The scale drawing would be 12.5 feet by 12.5 feet. No, such a large drawing does not seem reasonable.

45. If V is located at either $(3, 1)$ or $(3, 5)$, then $\triangle PQR \cong \triangle TUV$.

47. Form a tetrahedron, a three-dimensional figure with four congruent triangular faces.

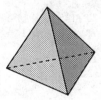

Appendix B.2   Angles

1. Answers will vary.

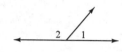

3. Answers will vary.

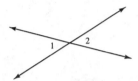

5. Answers will vary.

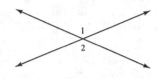

7. ∠*AOC* and ∠*COD* are adjacent, congruent, supplementary angles.

9. ∠*BOC* and ∠*COE* are adjacent, supplementary angles.

11. ∠*BOC* and ∠*COF* are adjacent, complementary angles.

13. False.

$m\angle 3 = 30° \implies m\angle 1 = 150° \implies m\angle 4 = 30°.$

15. False.

For example,
$m\angle 3 = 30° \implies m\angle 1 = 150° \implies m\angle 2 = 150°,$ and thus $\angle 2 \neq \angle 3.$

17. True.

19. $x = 110°$ because vertical angles are congruent.

21. $(2x - 5°) + 75° = 180°$ because two angles that form a linear pair are supplementary.

$$2x - 5° + 75° = 180°$$
$$2x + 70° = 180°$$
$$2x = 110°$$
$$x = \frac{110°}{2}$$
$$x = 55°$$

23. $3x + 20° = 5x - 50°$ because vertical angles are congruent.

$$3x - 5x + 20° = -50°$$
$$-2x + 20° = -50°$$
$$-2x = -70°$$
$$x = \frac{-70°}{-2}$$
$$x = 35°$$

25. Answer (c)

$m\angle PSQ + m\angle QST = 180°$ because two angles that form a linear pair are supplementary.

$$m\angle PSQ + 110° = 180°$$
$$m\angle PSQ = 70°$$

$m\angle PSQ + m\angle P + m\angle Q = 180°$ because the sum of the measures of the interior angles of a triangle is 180°.

$$70° + 40° + m\angle Q = 180°$$
$$110° + m\angle Q = 180°$$
$$m\angle Q = 70°$$

27. ∠3 and ∠5 are alternate interior angles because they lie between *l* and *m* and on opposite sides of *t*.

∠4 and ∠6 are alternate interior angles because they lie between *l* and *m* and on opposite sides of *t*.

29. ∠3 and ∠6 are corresponding interior angles because they lie between *l* and *m* and on the same side of *t*.

∠4 and ∠5 are corresponding interior angles because they lie between *l* and *m* and on the same side of *t*.

31. $m\angle 1 + 70° = 180°$ because two angles that form a linear pair are supplementary.

$m\angle 1 = 110°$

$m\angle 2 = m\angle 1$ by the Alternate Exterior Angle Theorem

$m\angle 2 = 110°$

33. $m\angle 2 + 110° = 180°$ because two angles that form a linear pair are supplementary.

$m\angle 2 = 70°$

$m\angle 1 = m\angle 2$ by the Alternate Interior Angles Theorem

$m\angle 1 = 70°$

Alternate approach for angle 1:

$m\angle 1 + 110° = 180°$ by Consecutive Interior Angles Theorem

$m\angle 1 = 70°$

35. $a = 4a - 90°$ because corresponding angles are congruent.

$-3a = 90°$

$a = \dfrac{-90°}{-3}$

$a = 30°$

$60° - b = 2b$ because corresponding angles are congruent.

$60° = 3b$

$\dfrac{60°}{3} = b$

$20° = b$

37. ∠2, ∠5, and ∠7 are the interior angles of the triangle.

(These are the original three angles of the triangle.)

39. *Step 1:* $m\angle 1 + 110° = 180°$ because two angles that form a linear pair are supplementary.

$m\angle 1 = 70°$

Step 2: $m\angle 3 + 110° = 180°$ because two angles that form a linear pair are supplementary.

$m\angle 3 = 70°$

Step 3: $m\angle 2 = 110°$ because vertical angles are congruent.

Step 4: $m\angle 7 + 155° = 180°$ because two angles that form a linear pair are supplementary.

$m\angle 7 = 25°$

Step 5: $m\angle 8 = 155°$ because vertical angles are congruent.

—**CONTINUED**—

39. —CONTINUED—

Step 6: $m\angle 5 + m\angle 7 + m\angle 2 = 180°$ because the sum of the measures of the interior angles of a triangle is 180°.

$$m\angle 5 + 25° + 110° = 180°$$
$$m\angle 5 + 135° = 180°$$
$$m\angle 5 = 45°$$

Step 7: $m\angle 4 + m\angle 5 = 180°$ because two angles that form a linear pair are supplementary.

$$m\angle 4 + 45° = 180°$$
$$m\angle 4 = 135°$$

Step 8: $m\angle 6 = 135°$ because vertical angles are congruent.

41. $m\angle B = 35°$ because corresponding angles of congruent triangles are congruent.

43. $m\angle D + m\angle E + m\angle F = 180°$
$$105° + 35° + m\angle F = 180°$$
$$140° + m\angle F = 180°$$
$$m\angle F = 40°$$

45. True.

The sum of the measures of three angles of a triangle is 180°.

The sum of the measures of the two 60° angles is 120°.

Therefore, the measure of the third angle is $180° - 120° = 60°$.

Thus, the triangle has three 60° angles, so the triangle is equiangular.

47. *Step 1:* $m\angle 1 + 60° + 90° = 180°$ because the sum of the measures of three angles of a triangle is 180°.

$$m\angle 1 + 150° = 180°$$
$$m\angle 1 = 30°$$

Step 2: $m\angle 2 = 60°$ because vertical angles are congruent.

Step 3: $m\angle 3 + 60° + 70° = 180°$ because the sum of the measurers of the three angles of a triangle is 180°.

$$m\angle 3 + 130° = 180°$$
$$m\angle 3 = 50°$$

Step 4: $m\angle 6 + 70° + 55° = 180°$ because the three angles combine to form a straight angle.

$$m\angle 6 + 125° = 180°$$
$$m\angle 6 = 55°$$

Step 5: $m\angle 7 = 55°$ because vertical angles are congruent.

Step 6: $m\angle 8 + 55° = 180°$ because two angles that form a linear pair are supplementary.

$$m\angle 8 = 125°$$

Step 7: $m\angle 4 + 55° + 90° = 180°$ because the sum of the measures of the three angles of a triangle is 180°.

$$m\angle 4 + 145° = 180°$$
$$m\angle 4 = 35°$$

Step 8: $m\angle 5 + 90° = 180°$ becaused two angles that form a linear pair are supplementary.

$$m\angle 5 = 90°$$

Step 9: $m\angle 9 + 90° + 55° = 180°$ because the sum of the measures of three angles of a triangle is 180°.

$$m\angle 9 + 145° = 180°$$
$$m\angle 9 = 35°$$

49.

$m\angle A + m\angle B + m\angle C = 180°$ because the sum of the measures of the three interior angles of a triangle is 180°.

$$13° + m\angle B + 90° = 180°$$

$$m\angle B + 103° = 180°$$

$$m\angle B = 77°$$

51.

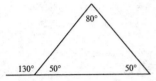

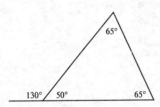

53. The sum of the measures of the three interior angles of a triangle is 180°.

$$x + (x + 30°) + (x + 60°) = 180°$$

$$x + x + 30° + x + 60° = 180°$$

$$3x + 90° = 180°$$

$$3x = 90°$$

$$x = 30°$$

$$x + 30° = 30° + 30° = 60°$$

$$x + 60° = 30° + 60° = 90°$$

The measures of the three interior angles are 30°, 60°, and 90°.

55. The sum of the measures of the three interior angles of a triangle is 180°.

$(3x + 2°) + (5x - 1°) + (6x + 11°) = 180°$ $3x + 2° = 3(12°) + 2° = 38°$

$3x + 2° + 5x - 1° + 6x + 11° = 180°$ $5x - 1° = 5(12°) - 1° = 59°$

$14x + 12° = 180°$ $6x + 11° = 6(12°) + 11° = 83°$

$$14x = 168°$$

$$x = 12°$$

The measures of the three interior angles are 38°, 59°, and 83°.

Appendix C   Further Concepts in Statistics

1. Organize scores by ordering the numbers.
Let the leaves represent the units digits.
Let the stems represent the tens digits.

Stems	Leaves
7	0 5 5 5 7 7 8 8 8
8	1 1 1 1 2 3 4 5 5 5 5 7 8 9 9 9
9	0 2 8
10	0 0

3. Organize scores by ordering the numbers.
Let the leaves represent the units digits.
Let the stems represent the tens digits.

Stems	Leaves
5	2 5 9
6	2 3 6 6 7
7	0 1 2 3 4 7 8 8 9
8	0 1 3 4 5 7 9
9	0 0 2 3 3 3 5 6 8 9
10	0 0

5. Frequency Distribution

Interval	Tally
[15, 22)	ЖЖ |||
[22, 29)	ЖЖ	
[29, 36)	ЖЖ
[36, 43)	||||
[43, 50)	ЖЖ ||

Histogram

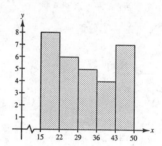

7.

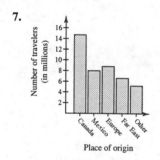

9. 1985: 165 million tons

1995: 210 million tons

11. Total waste and recycled waste increased every year.

13. Total waste equals the sum of the other three quantities.

15.

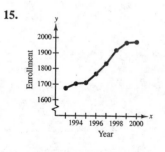

17.

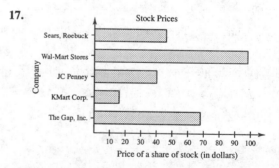

19.

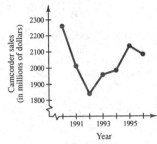

21. x and y have a positive correlation because as x increases y also increases.

23. Yes, it appears that players with more hits tend to have more runs batted in.

25. Negative correlation, because as the age of the car increases the value of the car decreases.

27. Positive correlation, because as the age of a tree increases the height also increases.

29.

[Scatter plot: Pressure, P (in lb/ft^2) vs Altitude, A (in thousands of ft)]

31. The air pressure at 42,500 feet is approximately 2.45 pounds per square inch.

33.

[Scatter plot: Yield (in bushels) vs Units of fertilizer]

Use graphing utility by entering data in 2 lists with [STAT PLOT] graph.

35. Use graphing utility to find regression line [STAT] [CALC4] [Lin Reg($ax + b$)].

(a) $y = 57.49 + 1.43x$

(b) 71.8

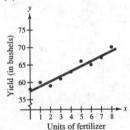

37.

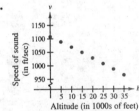

Use graphing utility by entering data in 2 lists with [STAT PLOT] graph.

39. Use graphing utility to find regression line [STAT] [CALC4] [Lin Reg($ax + b$)].

(a) $v = 1117.3 - 4.1h$

(b) 1006.6

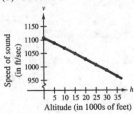

41. $y = -2.179x + 22.964$

[Graph]

Use graphing utility by entering data in 2 lists with [STAT PLOT] graph. Find regression line with [STAT] [CALC4].

43. $y = 2.378x + 23.546$

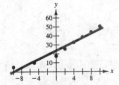

Use graphing utility by entering data in 2 lists with [STAT PLOT] graph. Find regression line with [STAT] [CALC4].

45. (a) $y = 11.1 + 0.28t$ 12.78

(b)

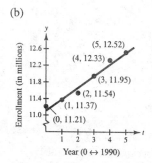

(c) $r \approx 0.987$

Use graphing utility by entering data in 2 lists with $\boxed{\text{STAT PLOT}}$ graph. Find regression line with $\boxed{\text{STAT}}$ $\boxed{\text{CALC4}}$.

47. Mean: $\dfrac{5 + 12 + 7 + 14 + 8 + 9 + 7}{7} = 8.86$

Median: 14 12 9 8 7 7 5 = 8
$\uparrow$
Middle score

Mode: 7 occurs twice = 7

49. Mean: $\dfrac{5 + 12 + 7 + 24 + 8 + 9 + 7}{7} = 10.29$

Median: 24 12 9 8 7 7 5 = 8
$\uparrow$
Middle score

Mode: 7 occurs twice = 7

51. (a) $(67.92 + 59.84 + 52 + 52.50 + 57.99 + 65.35 + 81.76 + 74.98 + 87.82 + 83.18 + 65.35 + 57) \div 12 = \$67.14$

(b) Median: 87.82
83.18
81.76
74.98
67.92
65.35
65.35 $\Big]$ average of 2 middle bills = \$65.35
59.84
57.99
57.00
52.50
52.00

53. (a) Mean: $\dfrac{0 \cdot 1 + 1 \cdot 24 + 2 \cdot 45 + 3 \cdot 54 + 4 \cdot 50 + 5 \cdot 19 + 6 \cdot 7}{200} \approx 3.07$

(b) Median: List all the data. Find the average of the two 100th scores = 3

(c) Mode: 3 occurs 54 times

55. Answers vary. One possibility: {4, 4, 10}

57. (a) $(99 + 64 + 80 + 77 + 59 + 72 + 87 + 79 + 92 + 88 + 90 +$
$42 + 20 + 89 + 42 + 100 + 98 + 84 + 78 + 91) \div 20 = 76.55$

(b) Median: list the scores from highest to lowest
100, 99, 98, 92, 91, 90, 89, 88, 87, 84, 80, 79, 78, 77, 72, 64, 59, 42, 42, 20
Find the average of the two tenth scores: 84 and 80 = 82

(c) Mode: 42 occurs twice
The median gives the most representative description since more of the test scores are in the 80's.

Appendix D   Introduction to Logic

Appendix D.1   Statements and Truth Tables

1. Statement, because only one truth value can be assigned.

3. Open statement, because a specific figure is needed to assign a truth value.

5. Open statement, because a value of x is needed to assign a truth value.

7. Open statement, because values of x and y are needed to assign a truth value.

9. Nonstatement, because no truth value can be assigned.

11. Open statement, because a specific place is needed to assign a truth value.

13. (a) $2^2 - 5(2) + 6 \overset{?}{=} 0$

$$4 - 10 + 6 = 0$$

$$0 = 0 \text{ True}$$

(b) $(-2)^2 - 5(-2) + 6 \overset{?}{=} 0$

$$4 + 10 + 6 = 0$$

$$20 \neq 0 \text{ False}$$

15. (a) $(-2)^2 \overset{?}{\leq} 4$

$$4 \leq 4 \text{ True}$$

(b) $0^2 \overset{?}{\leq} 4$

$$0 \leq 4 \text{ True}$$

17. (a) $4 - |0| \overset{?}{=} 2$

$$4 \neq 2 \text{ False}$$

(b) $4 - |1| \overset{?}{=} 2$

$$3 \neq 2 \text{ False}$$

19. (a) $\dfrac{-4}{-4} \overset{?}{=} 1$

$$1 = 1 \text{ True}$$

(b) $\qquad \dfrac{0}{0} \overset{?}{=} 1$

Undefined $\neq 1$ False

21. (a) $\sim p$: The sun is not shining.

(b) $\sim q$: It is not hot.

(c) $p \wedge q$: The sun is shining and it is hot.

(d) $p \vee q$: The sun is shining or it is hot.

23. (a) $\sim p$: Lions are not mammals.

(b) $\sim q$: Lions are not carnivorous.

(c) $p \wedge q$: Lions are mammals and lions are carnivores.

(d) $p \vee q$: Lions are mammals or lions are carnivorous.

25. (a) $\sim p \wedge q$: The sun is not shining and it is hot.

(b) $\sim p \vee q$: The sun is not shining or it is hot.

(c) $p \wedge \sim q$: The sun is shining and it is not hot.

(d) $p \vee \sim q$: The sun is shining or it is not hot.

27. (a) $\sim p \wedge q$: Lions are not mammals and lions are carnivorous.

(b) $\sim p \vee q$: Lions are not mammals or lions are carnivorous.

(c) $p \wedge \sim q$: Lions are mammals and lions are not carnivorous.

(d) $p \vee \sim q$: Lions are mammals or lions are not carnivorous.

29. p: It is four o'clock.

q: It is time to go home.

$p \wedge \sim q$

31. p: It is four o'clock.

q: It is time to go home.

$\sim p \vee q$

33. p: The dog has fleas.

q: The dog is scratching.

$\sim p \vee \sim q$

35. p: The dog has fleas.

q: The dog is scratching.

$\sim p \wedge q$

37. The bus is blue.

39. x is not equal to 4.

41. The earth is flat.

43.

p	q	~p	~p ∧ q
T	T	F	F
T	F	F	F
F	T	T	T
F	F	T	F

45.

p	q	~p	~q	~p ∨ ~q
T	T	F	F	F
T	F	F	T	T
F	T	T	F	T
F	F	T	T	T

47.

p	q	~q	p ∨ ~q
T	T	F	T
T	F	T	T
F	T	F	F
F	F	T	T

49.

p	q	~p	~q	~p ∧ q	p ∨ ~q
T	T	F	F	F	T
T	F	F	T	F	T
F	T	T	F	T	F
F	F	T	T	F	T

not identical
not logically equivalent

51.

p	q	~p	~q	p ∨ ~q	~(p ∨ ~q)	~p ∧ q
T	T	F	F	T	F	F
T	F	F	T	T	F	F
F	T	T	F	F	T	T
F	F	T	T	T	F	F

identical
logically equivalent

53.

p	q	~p	~q	p ∧ ~q	~p ∨ q	~(~p ∨ q)
T	T	F	F	F	T	F
T	F	F	T	T	F	T
F	T	T	F	F	T	F
F	F	T	T	F	T	F

identical
logically equivalent

55. Let p = The house is red.

q = It is made of wood.

(a)   = p ∧ ~q

(b) p ∨ ~q

p	q	~q	p ∧ ~q	p ∨ ~q
T	T	F	F	T
T	F	T	T	T
F	T	F	F	F
F	F	T	T	T

not identical
not logically equivalent

57. Let p = The house is white.

q = It is blue.

(a) ~(p ∨ q)

(b) ~p ∧ ~q

p	q	p ∨ q	~(p ∨ q)	~p	~q	~p ∧ ~q
T	T	T	F	F	F	F
T	F	T	F	F	T	F
F	T	T	F	T	F	F
F	F	F	T	T	T	T

identical
logically equivalent

59.

p	~p	~p ∧ p
T	F	F
T	F	F
F	T	F
F	T	F

not a tautology

61.

p	$\sim p$	$\sim(\sim p)$	$\sim(\sim p) \vee \sim p$
T	F	T	T
T	F	T	T
F	T	F	T
F	T	F	T

a tautology

63.

p	q	$\sim p$	$\sim q$	$p \wedge q$	$\sim(p \wedge q)$	$\sim p \vee \sim q$
T	T	F	F	T	F	F
T	F	F	T	F	T	T
F	T	T	F	F	T	T
F	F	T	T	F	T	T

identical
logically equivalent

Appendix D.2   Implications, Quantifiers, and Venn Diagrams

1. (a) $p \rightarrow q$:   If the engine is running,
then the engine is wasting gasoline.

(b) $q \rightarrow p$:   If the engine is wasting gasoline,
then the engine is running.

(c) $\sim q \rightarrow \sim p$:   If the engine is not wasting gasoline,
then the engine is not running.

(d) $p \rightarrow \sim q$:   If the engine is running, then the
engine is not wasting gasoline.

3. (a) $p \rightarrow q$:   If the integer is even,
then it is divisible by 2.

(b) $q \rightarrow p$:   If it is divisible by 2,
then the integer is even.

(c) $\sim q \rightarrow \sim p$:   If if it is not divisible by 2,
then the integer is not even.

(d) $p \rightarrow \sim q$:   If the integer is even,
then it is not divisible by 2.

5. Let p = The economy is expanding.

q = Interest rates are low.

$q \rightarrow p$

7. Let p = The economy is expanding.

q = Interest rates are low.

$p \rightarrow q$

9. Let p = The economy is expanding.

q = Interest rates are low.

$p \rightarrow q$

11.

Hypothesis	Conclusion	Implication
T	T	T

13.

Hypothesis	Conclusion	Implication
F	T	T

15.

Hypothesis	Conclusion	Implication
T	F	F

17.

Hypothesis	Conclusion	Implication
F	T	T

19.

Hypothesis	Conclusion	Implication
T	T	T

21. Converse:
If you can see the eclipse, then the sky is clear.

Inverse:
If the sky is not clear, then you cannot see the eclipse.

Contrapositive:
If you cannot see the eclipse, then the sky is not clear.

23. Converse:
If the deficit increases, then taxes were raised.

Inverse:
If taxes are not raised, then the deficit will not increase.

Contrapositive:
If the deficit does not increase, then taxes were not raised.

25. Converse:
It is necessary to apply for the
visa to have a birth certificate.

Inverse:
It is not necessary to have a birth
certificate to not apply for the visa.

Contrapositive:
It is not necessary to apply for the
visa to not have a birth certificate.

27. Negation:
Paul is not a junior
and not a senior.

29. Negation:
If the temperature increases,
then the metal rod will not expand.

31. Negation:
We will go to the ocean and the
weather forecast is not good.

33. Negation: No students are in extracurricular activities.

35. Negation: Some contact sports are not dangerous.

37. Negation: Some children are allowed at the concert.

39. Negation: None of the $20 bills are counterfeit.

41.

p	q	$\sim q$	$p \rightarrow \sim q$	$\sim(p \rightarrow \sim q)$
T	T	F	F	T
T	F	T	T	F
F	T	F	T	F
F	F	T	T	F

43.

p	q	$q \rightarrow p$	$\sim(q \rightarrow p)$	$\sim(q \rightarrow p) \wedge q$
T	T	T	F	F
T	F	T	F	F
F	T	F	T	T
F	F	T	F	F

45.

p	q	$(p \vee q)$	$\sim p$	$(p \vee q) \wedge (\sim p)$	$[(p \vee q) \wedge (\sim p)] \rightarrow q$
T	T	T	F	F	T
T	F	T	F	F	T
F	T	T	T	T	T
F	F	F	T	F	T

47.

p	q	$\sim p$	$\sim q$	$p \rightarrow \sim q$	$\sim q \rightarrow p$	$p \leftrightarrow \sim q$	$(p \leftrightarrow \sim q) \rightarrow \sim p$
T	T	F	F	F	T	F	T
T	F	F	T	T	T	T	F
F	T	T	F	T	T	T	T
F	F	T	T	T	F	F	T

49.

p	q	$q \rightarrow p$	$\sim p$	$\sim q$	$\sim p \rightarrow \sim q$
T	T	T	F	F	T
T	F	T	F	T	T
F	T	F	T	F	F
F	F	T	T	T	T

⎣_____⎦
identical

51.

p	q	$p \rightarrow q$	$\sim(p \rightarrow q)$	$\sim q$	$p \wedge \sim q$
T	T	T	F	F	F
T	F	F	T	T	T
F	T	T	F	F	F
F	F	T	F	T	F

⎣_____⎦
identical

53.

p	q	$p \to q$	$\sim q$	$(p \to q) \vee \sim q$	$\sim p$	$p \vee \sim p$
T	T	T	F	T	F	T
T	F	F	T	T	F	T
F	T	T	F	T	T	T
F	F	T	T	T	T	T

identical

55.

p	q	$\sim p$	$\sim p \wedge q$	$p \to (\sim p \wedge q)$
T	T	F	F	F
T	F	F	F	F
F	T	T	T	T
F	F	T	F	T

identical

57. Let p = A number is divisible by 6.

q = It is divisible by 2.

Statement is $p \to q$

p	q	$p \to q$	$\sim p$	$\sim q$	$\sim q \to \sim p$
T	T	T	F	F	T
T	F	F	F	T	F
F	T	T	T	F	T
F	F	T	T	T	T

identical

(c) If a number is not divisible by 2, then it is not divisible by 6.

$\sim q \to \sim p$

$p \to q \equiv \sim q \to \sim p$

59. (a) Some citizens over the age of 18 have the right to vote is *not* logically equivalent to above statement.

61. Let A = people who are happy

B = college students

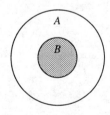

63. Let A = people who are happy

B = college students

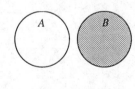

65. Let A = people who are happy

B = college students

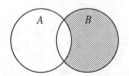

67. Let A = people who are happy

B = college students

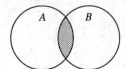

69. Let A = people who are happy

B = college students

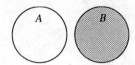

71. (a) Statement does not follow.

(b) Statement follows.

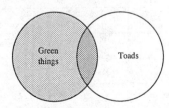

73. (a) Statement does not follow.

(b) Statement does not follow.

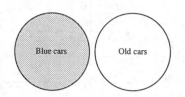

Appendix D.3   Logical Arguments

1.

p	q	$\sim p$	$\sim q$	$p\rightarrow\sim q$	$(p\rightarrow\sim q)\wedge q$
T	T	F	F	F	F
T	F	F	T	T	F
F	T	T	F	T	T
F	F	T	T	T	F

$[(p\rightarrow\sim q)\wedge q]\rightarrow\sim p$
T
T
T
T

3.

p	q	$\sim p$	$p\vee q$	$(p\vee q)\wedge\sim p$
T	T	F	T	F
T	F	F	T	F
F	T	T	T	T
F	F	T	F	F

$[(p\vee q)\wedge\sim p]\rightarrow q$
T
T
T
T

5.

p	q	$\sim p$	$\sim q$	$\sim p\rightarrow q$	$(\sim p\rightarrow q)\wedge p$
T	T	F	F	T	T
T	F	F	T	T	T
F	T	T	F	T	F
F	F	T	T	F	F

$[(\sim p\rightarrow q)\wedge p]\rightarrow\sim q$
F
T
T
T

7.

p	q	$p\vee q$	$(p\vee q)\wedge q$	$[(p\vee q)\wedge q]\rightarrow p$
T	T	T	T	T
T	F	T	F	T
F	T	T	T	F
F	F	F	F	T

9. Let: p = taxes are increased

q = businesses will leave the state

Premise #1: $p\rightarrow q$

Premise #2: p

Conclusion: q

p	q	$p\rightarrow q$	$(p\rightarrow q)\wedge p$	$(p\rightarrow q)\wedge p\rightarrow q$
T	T	T	T	T
T	F	F	F	T
F	T	T	F	T
F	F	T	F	T

Argument is valid.

11. Let: p = taxes are increased

      q = businesses will leave the state

Premise #1: $p \rightarrow q$

Premise #2: q

Conclusion: p

p	q	$p \rightarrow q$	$(p \rightarrow q) \wedge q$	$(p \rightarrow q) \wedge q \rightarrow p$
T	T	T	T	T
T	F	F	F	T
F	T	T	T	F
F	F	T	F	T

Argument is invalid.

13. Let: p = doors are locked

      q = car was not stolen

Premise #1: $p \rightarrow q$

Premise #2: $\sim q$

Conclusion: $\sim p$

p	q	$p \rightarrow q$	$\sim p$	$\sim q$	$(p \rightarrow q) \wedge \sim q$	$(p \rightarrow q) \wedge \sim q \rightarrow \sim p$
T	T	T	F	F	F	T
T	F	F	F	T	F	T
F	T	T	T	F	F	T
F	F	T	T	T	T	T

Argument is valid.

15.

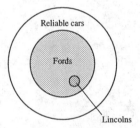

Argument is valid.

17.

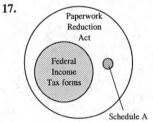

Argument is invalid.

19. Let: p = Eric is at the store.

      q = He is at the handball court.

Premise #1: $p \vee q$

Premise #2: $\sim p$

Conclusion: q

p	q	$\sim p$	$p \vee q$	$(p \vee q) \wedge \sim p$	$(p \vee q) \wedge \sim p \rightarrow q$
T	T	F	T	F	T
T	F	F	T	F	T
F	T	T	T	T	T
F	F	T	F	F	T

Argument is valid.

21. Let: p = It is a diamond.

q = It sparkles in the sunlight.

p	q	$p \wedge q$	$\sim(p \wedge q)$	$\sim(p \wedge q) \wedge q$	$\sim(p \wedge q) \wedge q \rightarrow p$
T	T	T	F	F	T
T	F	F	T	F	T
F	T	F	T	T	F
F	F	F	T	F	T

Argument is invalid.

Premise #1: $\sim(p \wedge q)$

Premise #2: q

Conclusion: p

23. Let: p = 7 is a prime number

q = 7 does not divide evenly into 21

Premise #1: $p \rightarrow q$

Premise #2: $\sim q$

So conclusion must be $\sim p$ or 7 is not a prime number which is (b).

25. Let: p = Economy improves

q = Interest rates lowered

Premise #1: $p \rightarrow q$

Premise #2: $\sim q$

So conclusion must be $\sim p$ or the economy does not improve which is (c).

27. Let: p = Smokestack emissions must be reduced

q = Acid rain will continue as an environmental problem

Premise #1: $p \vee q$

Premise #2: $\sim p$

So conclusion must be q or acid rain will continue as an environmental problem which is (b).

29. Let: p = Rodney studies

q = He will make good grades

r = He will get a good job

Premise #1: $p \rightarrow q$

Premise #2: $q \rightarrow r$

Conclusion: $p \rightarrow r$ Law of Transitivity

$\sim r$: If Rodney doesn't get a good job

$\sim p$: He didn't study

So by the Law of Contraposition the answer is (c).

31. Let A = All numbers divisible by 5

B = All numbers divisible by 10

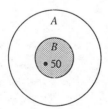

Argument is valid.

33. Let A = People eligible to vote

B = People under the age of 18

C = College students

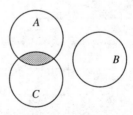

Argument is invalid.

35. Let p represent the statement "Sue drives to work," let q represent "Sue will stop at the grocery store," and let r represent "Sue will buy milk."

First write:

Premise #1: $p \rightarrow q$

Premise #2: $q \rightarrow r$

Premise #3: p

Reorder the premises:

Premise #3: p

Premise #1: $p \rightarrow q$

Premise #2: $q \rightarrow r$

Conclusion: r

Then we can conclude r. That is, "Sue will buy milk."

37. Let p represent "This is a good product," let q represent "We will buy it," and let r represent "the product was made by XYZ Corporation."

First write:

Premise #1: $p \rightarrow \sim q$

Premise #2: $r \vee \sim q$

Premise #3: $\sim r$

Note that $p \rightarrow q \equiv q \rightarrow \sim p$, and reorder the premises:

Premise #2: $r \vee \sim q$

Premise #3: $\sim r$

(Conclusion from Premise #2, Premise #3: $\sim q$)

Premise #1: $\sim q \rightarrow \sim p$

Conclusion: $\sim p$

Then we can conclude $\sim p$. That is, "It is not a good product."